1969

Concepts

of

CALCULUS II

An Undergraduate Title in Harper's Modern Mathematics Series

I. N. Herstein and Gian-Carlo Rota, Editors

Concepts
of
CALCULUS II

A. H. LIGHTSTONE

Queen's University

Kingston, Canada

HARPER & ROW, Publishers New York and London

Contents

II *Three-Dimensional Analytic Geometry*

III *Calculus*

IV   *Differential Equations*

Preface

Just as *Concepts of Calculus I* is concerned primarily with the calculus of functions with one argument, so this book is concerned primarily with the calculus of functions with several arguments. Again, considerable effort is devoted to clarifying the underlying ideas of the subject so that the student will not blindly manipulate symbols, but rather will understand the meaning of the mathematical expressions he formulates.

This work is divided into four parts. Part I presents basic ideas of linear algebra beginning with an introduction to the axiomatic method. In Chapter 2 matrices are introduced via linear systems of equations. The mapping *determinant* is presented and its properties are developed. With experience at handling the rows and columns of a matrix, it is natural to regard these objects as *mathematical* objects; so, in Chapter 3, the algebra of ordered *n*-tuples is developed. This is vector algebra; here, then, some elementary *vector space* theory is presented. Applications to linear systems of equations are considered; this brings out the power of vector space theory. Some matrix algebra is developed, and linear operators and characteristic vectors are touched on lightly.

In Part II, the ideas of Hilbert are used to construct three-dimensional Euclidean space. The basic geometric objects—point, line, plane, and distance between points—are easily defined in terms of the vector space $\mathcal{V}_3(\mathcal{R})$. Here, the student has an opportunity to master the ideas of the preceding chapters by actually using vectors in a simple and meaningful situation.

Once ordered *n*-tuples and their algebra have been well-digested, it is time to consider the calculus of functions with several arguments. First, we consider functions with two arguments and develop a systematic method of obtaining names for elementary functions. Following the pattern of volume I, the limit concept is introduced for sequences. The usual metamathematical argument is used to prove that each elementary function is continuous. The problem of defining the tangent plane to a surface at a point on the surface is used to introduce partial derivatives. The fact that $F_{12} = F_{21}$ whenever F is elementary, is established by a metamathematical argument. These ideas are extended, in detail, to the case of functions with three arguments. Directional derivatives are developed in the process of demonstrating the existence of a tangent plane to a surface under certain conditions. The usual "max-min" problems are treated, and the gradient of a function is introduced. The basic theory is then presented from the vector viewpoint. In Chapter 7 the fundamental properties of continuous functions are established, and the notion of a *simple* region is introduced. This prepares the way for a discussion of volume and the double integral. A technique for evaluating double integrals is carefully presented, and some applications of the double integral are included. The theory is repeated when the triple integral is presented.

Part IV is an introduction to the study of differential equations. Chapter 8 considers first-order differential equations, Chapter 9 treats second-order differential equations, and Chapter 10 is confined to linear differential equations. In Chapter 10 the algebraic approach is exploited by developing the notion of an *operator;* the power of this approach is amply illustrated. Power series methods are the subject of Chapter 11; here Legendre polynomials are studied and their connection with the problem of approximating a function by a polynomial is emphasized; it is shown that a certain linear combination of Legendre polynomials is the best possible polynomial approximation of given degree to a given function. The mathematics is developed in a form suitable for computation by an automatic digital computer. To pound home the fact that a Legendre approximation to a function is the best possible approximation, computer-produced tables are presented that compare a Legendre approximation to the function *sin* with the Maclaurin approximation to *sin* of the same degree. A digital computer is also used to study the gamma function and the Bessel functions J_0 and J_1. Extensive use is made of computers throughout Chapter 12, which is devoted to numerical methods of solving first-order differential equations. An algebraic-analytic technique is presented for obtaining quadrature formulas. Starting methods and continuing methods are discussed and illustrated by computer-produced tables. The Runge-Kutta method is presented, and Milne's predictor-corrector method is developed and illustrated. An improved predictor-corrector method is developed on the basis of the highly accurate quadrature formulas produced by the algebraic-analytic technique of Section 12.2. This method is shown to be an improvement over Milne's method by comparing computer-produced tables. To complete the discussion of methods of solving differential equations, Chapter 13 develops the theory of the Laplace transform and illustrates the connection with differential equations.

In connection with the numerical solution of differential equations, there are two appendixes that present an accurate starting method and a self-starting continuing method.

For the sake of completeness, Fortran programs precede the computer-produced tables that appear throughout this book. These programs in fact were used to direct an automatic digital computer to produce the tables involved. Though it is the resulting tables that concern us, a student who has some knowledge of programming may well find these programs of interest. In any case, it is clear that mathematics or science students will benefit from an early acquaintance with an automatic digital computer.

Portions of chapter 1 of this book are taken from chapter 3 of *Symbolic Logic and the Real Number System* by A. H. Lightstone (Harper & Row, 1965). The material in *Symbolic Logic and the Real Number System* grew out of material first presented in *The Axiomatic Method: An Introduction to Mathematical Logic* by A. H. Lightstone, © 1964, Prentice-Hall, Inc., Englewood Cliffs, New Jersey. The author is grateful to the publishers for permission to use this material once again.

A. H. LIGHTSTONE

January, 1966

PART

I

Linear Algebra

Chapter 1 The Axiomatic Method and Abstract Algebra

1.1 Algebraic Systems

The axiomatic method in mathematics goes back to the days of the Greek geometers who regarded mathematics as the supreme achievement of the human mind. Since Euclid's *Elements* is still in vogue, we can only marvel at this triumph of Greek civilization. In recent years, however, there has been a tremendous explosion in mathematical activity which has led to an unprecedented increase in mathematical knowledge. In particular, work at the foundations of mathematics has resulted in the emergence of *sets* as basic mathematical objects. This has led to a refinement of Euclid's method itself; this refinement centers around the concept of an *algebraic system*. Essentially this is a matter of setting out the kinds of objects that are involved in a particular mathematical investigation. For example, in the study of geometry we are concerned with a set of objects called *points* and with certain relations on this set. In the study of a number system we deal with a set of objects called *numbers*, two binary operations on this set called *addition* and *multiplication*, the binary relation *less than*, and possibly the special numbers 0 and 1.

Generally speaking, a mathematical investigation involves a nonempty set, say A, possibly certain operations on A, possibly certain relations on A, and possibly certain special members of A. In any event there is at least one operation or relation on A. Thus the ingredients of a mathematical investigation are found in the following list: a set, operations or relations on the set, and specified members of the set. It is convenient to use an ordered n-tuple to display the particular ingredients required for a specific mathematical investigation. The first term of this ordered n-tuple is the set A referred to above, and the remaining terms are the operations on A, the relations on A, and the special members of A that are involved. Let us give a name to this very special type of ordered n-tuple; we shall call it an *algebraic system*. Furthermore, we shall call the first term of an algebraic system the *basic set* or the *universal set* of the algebraic system.

For example, the ordered pair $(S, \circ)$, where $S = \{a, b\}$ and $\circ = \{(a, a, b), (a, b, a),$ $(b, a, a), (b, b, b)\}$, is an algebraic system; the basic set of this algebraic system is $\{a, b\}$, and its second term, $\circ$, is a binary operation on $\{a, b\}$. Notice that b possesses the following properties: $x \circ b = x$ whenever $x \in S$; moreover, given any member of S, say x, there is a member of S, say y, such that $x \circ y = b$. If we wish to draw attention to the algebraic properties of b, we do so by presenting the algebraic system $(S, \circ, b)$; in this way b is displayed as a component part of the algebraic system.

3

As another example of an algebraic system, we present the natural number system $(N, +, \cdot, <, 1)$; here, N is the set of all natural numbers, $+$ and $\cdot$ are binary operations on N (namely, addition and multiplication), "$<$" denotes the relation *less than* on N, and $1 \in N$.

The preceding discussion is made precise by the following definition.

DEFINITION 1.1.1. Any ordered n-tuple whose first term is a nonempty set, say A, and whose remaining terms are operations on A, relations on A, or specific members of A is called an *algebraic system*—provided that there is at least one operation or relation on A.

For example, consider the ordered 4-tuple $(B, ?, !, 0)$, where $B = \{0, 1\}, ? = \{(0, 0, 0),$ $(0, 1, 1), (1, 0, 1), (1, 1, 0)\}$, and $! = \{(0, 0, 0), (0, 1, 0), (1, 0, 0), (1, 1, 0)\}$. The first term of this ordered 4-tuple is a nonempty set; the second term, $?$, is a binary operation on B; the third term is also a binary operation on B; and the fourth term is a member of B. Therefore this ordered 4-tuple is an algebraic system; furthermore, the basic set of this algebraic system is $\{0, 1\}$. Let us prove that $t ? 0 = t$ whenever $t \in B$. Since $B = \{0, 1\}$, we must prove that $0 ? 0 = 0$ and $1 ? 0 = 1$. Examining the binary operation $?$, we see that this is so; therefore $t ? 0 = t$ whenever $t \in B$. On the other hand, we note that $(1 ! 1) ? 1 \neq 1 ? 1$ since $(1 ! 1) ? 1 = 0 ? 1 = 1$, whereas $1 ? 1 = 0$. It follows from this observation that the proposition "$(t ! t) ? t = t ? t$ whenever $t \in B$" is false.

As another example, consider the ordered pair (S, R), where $S = \{a, b, c, d\}$ and $R = \{(a, b), (a, c), (a, d), (b, c), (b, d), (c, d)\}$. This is an algebraic system since R is a binary relation on S, a nonempty set. Let us demonstrate that given any member of S, say x, there is a member of S, say y, such that xRy or yRx. Since $S = \{a, b, c, d\}$, we must establish each of the following:

(i) There is a member of S, say y, such that aRy or yRa.

(ii) There is a member of S, say y, such that bRy or yRb.

(iii) There is a member of S, say y, such that cRy or yRc.

(iv) There is a member of S, say y, such that dRy or yRd.

But $(a, b) \in R$, i.e., aRb; therefore aRb or bRa. This establishes (i). Also, $(b, c) \in R$, i.e., bRc; therefore bRc or cRb. This establishes (ii). Since bRc, it follows that "cRb or bRc" is true; this establishes (iii). Finally, we note that $(b, d) \in R$, i.e., bRd; therefore dRb or bRd. This establishes (iv). We conclude that given any member of S, say x, there is a member of S, say y, such that xRy or yRx.

The concept of an algebraic system is based on the elementary concepts of set theory. In the remaining sections of this chapter we shall see how algebraic systems are used as building blocks in constructing mathematical concepts.

E X E R C I S E S

1. Show that the following propositions are true in the algebraic system $(S, \circ)$ of the text.
   a. $x \circ y = y \circ x$ whenever $x \in S$ and $y \in S$.
   b. $x \circ y = b$ if $x = y$, whereas $x \circ y = a$ if $x \neq y$, whenever $x \in S$ and $y \in S$.
   c. $a \circ (y \circ z) = (a \circ y) \circ z$ whenever $y \in S$ and $z \in S$.
   d. $b \circ (y \circ z) = (b \circ y) \circ z$ whenever $y \in S$ and $z \in S$.
   e. $x \circ (y \circ z) = (x \circ y) \circ z$ whenever $x \in S$, $y \in S$, and $z \in S$.

2. In the algebraic system $(B, ?, !, 0)$ of the text, show the following.
   a. $1 ? (1 ! 0) = 1$.
   b. $(0 ! 1) ? (1 ? 1) = (0 ? 1) ! (1 ! 1)$.
   c. $[(1 ? 0) ? 1] ? 1 = (0 ! 0) ? (0 ? 1)$.
   d. $(0 ! 1) ! (0 ! 0) \neq (1 ? 0) ? (1 ? 1)$.
   e. $x ? y = y ? x$ whenever $x \in B$ and $y \in B$.
   f. $x ! y = 0$ whenever $x \in B$ and $y \in B$.
   g. $x ? (y ! z) = x$ whenever $x \in B$ and $y \in B$.
   h. Given any member of B, say x, there is a member of B, say y, such that $x ? y = 0$.
   i. Given any member of B, say x, there is a *unique* member of B, say y, such that $x ? y = 0$.
   j. It is false that there is a member of B, say y, such that for each member of B, say x, $x ? y = 0$.
   k. $0 ? (y ? z) = (0 ? y) ? z$ whenever $y \in B$ and $z \in B$.
   l. $1 ? (y ? z) = (1 ? y) ? z$ whenever $y \in B$ and $z \in B$.
   m. $x ? (y ? z) = (x ? y) ? z$ whenever $x \in B$, $y \in B$, and $z \in B$.
   n. Given any members of B, say x and y, not necessarily distinct, there is a member of B, say z, such that $x ? z = y$.

3. Consider the algebraic system $(\{a, b, c\}, +, \circ)$, where

$$+ = \{(a, a, b), (a, b, c), (a, c, a), (b, a, a), (b, b, c)\ (b, c, b), (c, a, a), (c, b, b), (c, c, c)\}$$

and $\circ = \{(a, a, a), (a, b, b), (a, c, c), (b, a, a), (b, b, b), (b, c, c), (c, a, a), (c, b, b), (c, c, c)\}$.

Calculate the following.
   a. $a + b$.
   b. $a + (b + a)$.
   c. $(b + c) + (a + b)$.
   d. $(a + b) \circ c$.
   i. $[(a + b) \circ (b + c)] + [(a + b) \circ (a + (b \circ c))]$.

   e. $(a \circ c) + b$.
   f. $a + (b \circ c)$.
   g. $[a + (b \circ c)] \circ b$.
   h. $b \circ (c \circ b)$.

4. Referring to the algebraic system $(\{a, b, c\}, +, \circ)$ of Exercise 3, which of the following propositions are true? In the following, $S = \{a, b, c\}$.
   a. $x \circ y = y$ whenever $x \in S$ and $y \in S$.
   b. $x \circ (y + z) = (x \circ y) + (x \circ z)$ whenever $x \in S$, $y \in S$, and $z \in S$.
   c. $x + y = y + x$ whenever $x \in S$ and $y \in S$.
   d. $x \circ y = y \circ x$ whenever $x \in S$ and $y \in S$.
   e. Given any member of S, say x, there is a member of S, say y, such that $x \circ y = y \circ x$.
   f. Given any member of S, say x, there is a *unique* member of S, say y, such that $x \circ y = y \circ x$.
   g. Given any member of S, say x, there is a member of S, say y, such that $x + y = y + x$.
   h. Given any member of S, say x, there is a *unique* member of S, say y, such that $x + y = y + x$.
   i. There is a member of S, say x, such that $x + y = y + x$ whenever $y \in S$.

j. There is a *unique* member of S, say x, such that $x + y = y + x$ whenever $y \in S$.
k. $x + (y + z) = (x + y) + z$ whenever $x \in S$, $y \in S$, and $z \in S$.
l. $x \circ (y \circ z) = (x \circ y) \circ z$ whenever $x \in S$, $y \in S$, and $z \in S$.
m. $x + (y \circ z) = (x + y) \circ z$ whenever $x \in S$, $y \in S$, and $z \in S$.
n. $x \circ (y + z) = (x \circ y) + z$ whenever $x \in S$, $y \in S$, and $z \in S$.
o. $x + (y \circ z) = (x + y) \circ (x + z)$ whenever $x \in S$, $y \in S$, and $z \in S$.

5. Show that $(\mathscr{P}S, \cup, \cap, \subset, \varnothing)$ is an algebraic system whenever S is a set.

6. Show that $(\mathscr{P}S, \dot{-}, \varnothing)$ is an algebraic system whenever S is a set.

7. Which is more important, the nature of the members of the basic set of an algebraic system or the operations and relations of the algebraic system?

1.2   The Axiomatic Method

Let's play a game! The game is called "Find the Algebraic System", and its object is to construct an algebraic system, given certain hints about the desired algebraic system. For example, find an algebraic system, say (S, R), given that R is a binary relation on S, and given that:

(i) there is a member of S, say x, and there is a member of S, say y, such that $x \neq y$;
(ii) there is a member of S, say x, and there is a member of S, say y, such that $z = x$ or $z = y$ whenever $z \in S$;
(iii) xRy iff $x \neq y$ whenever $x \in S$ and $y \in S$.

Examining these hints, we see that there are at least two members in S, since that is the meaning of (i). Furthermore, there are at most two members in S, since that is what (ii) asserts. We conclude that S has *exactly* two members. Suppose the members of S are a and b; so $S = \{a, b\}$. From (iii) it follows that $R = \{(a, b), (b, a)\}$. We have found the desired algebraic system, namely $(\{a, b\}, \{(a, b), (b, a)\})$. Of course, if c and d are any two objects, then the algebraic system $(\{c, d\}, \{(c, d), (d, c)\})$ also meets the given conditions.

Next, let us find an algebraic system of the form (S, R), given that R is a binary relation on S, and given that:

(i) there is a member of S, say x, and there is a member of S, say y, such that $x \neq y$;
(ii) there is a member of S, say x, and there is a member of S, say y, such that $z = x$ or $z = y$ whenever $z \in S$;
(iii) xRy whenever x and y are distinct members of S.

Here, (i) and (ii) are as in the previous example, whereas the third proposition given above has been altered. Again, S has exactly two members, say a and b. However, we cannot be as definite about R as in the preceding case. There are four possibilities: $R = \{(a, b), (b, a)\}$ as before, or $R = \{(a, b), (b, a), (a, a)\}$, or $R = \{(a, b), (b, a), (b, b)\}$, or $R = \{(a, b), (b, a), (a, a), (b, b)\}$. Thus the given hints lead us to four algebraic systems:

I $(\{a, b\}, \{(a, b), (b, a)\})$, $(\{a, b\}, \{(a, b), (b, a), (a, a)\})$,

$(\{a, b\}, \{(a, b), (b, a), (b, b)\})$ $(\{a, b\}, \{(a, b), (b, a), (a, a), (b, b)\})$.

(In a sense which we shall make clear later, two of these algebraic systems are essentially the same.)

Actually there are many algebraic systems which meet the given conditions. For example, let c and d be distinct objects; then the algebraic systems

II $(\{c, d\}, \{(c, d), (d, c)\}),$ $(\{c, d\}, \{(c, d), (d, c), (c, c)\})$

$$(\{c, d\}, \{(c, d), (d, c), (d, d)\}), \quad (\{c, d\}, \{(c, d), (d, c), (c, c), (d, d)\})$$

also meet the given conditions. However, each of these algebraic systems can be constructed from the corresponding algebraic system listed in I by merely replacing "a" by "c" and replacing "b" by "d" throughout the algebraic system. In this sense the algebraic systems of I characterize all the algebraic systems that meet the given conditions.

The two illustrations given above show that it is sometimes possible to characterize a given collection of algebraic systems *of the same type* by first specifying the type and then listing certain propositions which are true in each of the algebraic systems. By the *type* of an algebraic system, we mean the general shape of the algebraic system, i.e., the kinds of things that are terms of the algebraic system.

The famous philosopher and logician Bertrand Russell has said that "mathematics may be defined as the subject in which we never know what we are talking about, nor whether what we are saying is true". Of course, this was a tongue-in-cheek statement and was intended to be amusing; nevertheless, Russell has pointed out most clearly the essentials of the axiomatic method. Since the power of mathematics lies in the generality of its results, we deliberately avoid spelling out precisely the objects and operations or relations being investigated. Rather, we describe the *type* of algebraic system being studied—by first stating that it involves a unary operation, or two binary operations, or a binary relation, or one special member of the basic set, as the case may be, and then listing certain propositions which are true for the algebraic system. The propositions are called *axioms* or *postulates*. On the basis of the given information, it is sometimes possible to establish that certain propositions are true about each of the algebraic systems so characterized. Such propositions are called *theorems*. Thus we do not really know what we are talking about, nor do we know if our theorems are really true. However, should we encounter an algebraic system of the specified type, one in which each of the given postulates is true, then we can assert that each of our theorems is true for this algebraic system. In this way, the sum total of knowledge has been increased.

Notice there are two aspects to the axiomatic method. (1) A class of algebraic systems is described by stating the type of algebraic system in the class and then listing certain propositions which are true for each algebraic systems of the class. (2) Certain propositions are demonstrated to be true for each algebraic system of the class; these propositions are called theorems. In general, a theorem is established by considering any algebraic system in the class (without specifying which one) and showing, by any means at hand, that the given proposition is true for that algebraic system.

To illustrate the axiomatic method, let us investigate the class of algebraic systems of the type $(S, \circ)$, where $\circ$ is a binary operation on S, for which the following propositions are true.

POSTULATES.   1. $x \circ x = x$ whenever $x \in S$.
  2. $x \circ (y \circ z) = (x \circ y) \circ z$ whenever $x \in S$, $y \in S$, and $z \in S$.
For example, the algebraic systems $(\{1\}, \{(1, 1, 1)\})$, $(\{0, 1\}, \{(0, 0, 0), (0, 1, 0), (1, 0, 1), (1, 1, 1)\})$, and $(\{0, 1\}, \{(0, 0, 0), (0, 1, 1), (1, 0, 0), (1, 1, 1)\})$ are members of this class.

We now demonstrate the manner in which a theorem is established.

THEOREM 1.2.1. $x \circ (x \circ y) = x \circ y$ whenever $x \in S$ and $y \in S$.

Proof: Let $(S, \circ)$ be any algebraic system of our family; we wish to show that $x \circ (x \circ y) = x \circ y$ whenever $x \in S$ and $y \in S$. But

$$x \circ (x \circ y) = (x \circ x) \circ y \qquad \text{by Postulate 2}$$

$$= x \circ y \qquad \text{by Postulate 1.}$$

We conclude that each algebraic system of our class possesses the stated property.

It should now be clear that though we do not know the precise objects we are talking about, we do know the *type* of algebraic system being discussed; and though we do not know if the theorems are true, we do know that they are true about each algebraic system of the specified type for which the postulates are true.

It is worth noting that the postulates characterizing a particular family of algebraic systems need not be propositions of the type that we have considered so far (which refer to *members* of the basic set of an algebraic system in the family). For example, consider the famous Peano Postulates which characterize Peano systems, the basis of the natural number system. An algebraic system of the type $(N, ', 1)$, where $'$ is a unary operation on N and $1 \in N$, is said to be a *Peano system* iff

(i) $x' \neq 1$ whenever $x \in N$;

(ii) $x = y$ if $x' = y'$, whenever $x \in N$ and $y \in N$;

(iii) $S = N$ if $S \subset N$ and if $1 \in S$ and if $x' \in S$ whenever $x \in S$.

Here, (i) and (ii) refer to the members of N, the basic set of the algebraic system, whereas (iii) refers to subsets of N. In words, (iii) asserts that no *proper* subset of N has the property that 1 is a member of the subset and x' is a member of the subset whenever x is a member. Thus (iii) is a proposition of a different type from (i) and (ii).

In the subsequent pages of this chapter we shall consider the axiomatic method against the background of modern algebra, since this important branch of mathematics serves well to illustrate the axiomatic approach. Here, we briefly consider the axiomatic method as applied to geometry. The concept of a *projective plane*, for example, can be characterized as follows. By a projective plane we mean any ordered triple, say (Σ, Λ, I), where Σ is a nonempty set whose members are called *points* and are denoted by capital letters, Λ is a nonempty set whose members are called *lines* and are denoted by small letters, and I

is a binary relation on $\Sigma \cup \Lambda$ called the *incidence* relation, such that

(1) *PIl* iff *lIP* whenever *P* is a point and *l* is a line,
(2) corresponding to distinct points *P* and *Q* there is a unique line *l* such that *PIl* and *QIl*,
(3) corresponding to distinct lines *p* and *q* there is a unique point *L* such that *pIL* and *qIL*,
(4) there exist four points such that each line is incident with at most two of the four points.

Clearly, the ordered triple (Σ, Λ, I) is not an algebraic system. However, it is possible to represent (Σ, Λ, I) by an algebraic system, namely $(\Sigma \cup \Lambda, \Sigma, \Lambda, I)$. The basic set of this algebraic system is $\Sigma \cup \Lambda$, Σ is a unary relation on $\Sigma \cup \Lambda$, Λ is a unary relation on $\Sigma \cup \Lambda$, and *I* is a binary relation on $\Sigma \cup \Lambda$. Moreover, it is easy to translate the projective-plane postulates given above into this language; e.g., (1) becomes

$$xIy \text{ iff } yIx \text{ whenever } \Sigma(x) \text{ and } \Lambda(y).$$

Thus our analysis of the axiomatic method in terms of algebraic systems applies also to the study of geometry.

E X E R C I S E S

1. Consider the class of all algebraic systems of the type $(S, {}')$, where ${}'$ is a unary operation on S, such that

    (i) $x' \neq x$ whenever $x \in S$,

    (ii) $(x')' = x$ whenever $x \in S$.

    a. Prove that S cannot have an odd number of members.
    b. Present an algebraic system in the class.
2. Consider the class of all algebraic systems of the type $(S, \circ)$, where $\circ$ is a binary operation on S, such that $x \circ y = x$ whenever $x \in S$ and $y \in S$.
    a. Demonstrate that $x \circ x = x$ whenever $x \in S$.
    b. Demonstrate that $x \circ (y \circ z) = (x \circ y) \circ z$ whenever $x \in S$, $y \in S$, and $z \in S$.
    c. Prove that given any member of S, say x, and given any member of S, say y, there is a member of S, say z, such that $x \circ y = z$.
    d. Present an algebraic system in the class.
3. Consider the class of algebraic systems of the type (S, R), where R is a binary relation on S, such that

    (i) $x \neq y$ whenever xRy,

    (ii) xRz whenever xRy and yRz.

    a. Prove that xRx is false whenever $x \in S$.
    b. Prove that xRy is false or yRx is false whenever $x \in S$ and $y \in S$.
    c. Present an algebraic system in the class.

4. Consider the class of all algebraic systems of the type $(S, \circ, R)$, where $\circ$ is a binary operation on S and R is a binary relation on S, such that

(i) $x \circ y = y \circ x$ whenever $x \in S$ and $y \in S$,

(ii) $x \circ x = x$ whenever $x \in S$,

(iii) $xR(x \circ y)$ whenever $x \in S$ and $y \in S$.

a. Prove that $yR(x \circ y)$ whenever $x \in S$ and $y \in S$.
b. Prove that xRx whenever $x \in S$.
c. Present an algebraic system in the class.

5. By an *affine plane* we mean an ordered triple (Σ, Λ, I), where Σ is a nonempty set whose members are called *points* and are denoted by capital letters, Λ is a nonempty set whose members are called *lines* and are denoted by small letters, and I is a binary relation on $\Sigma \cup \Lambda$ called the *incidence relation*, such that

(1) any two points are incident with exactly one line;
(2) given a line and a point which are not incident, there is exactly one line incident with the given point and parallel to the given line (*note*: p and q are said to be *parallel* iff no point is incident with both p and q);
(3) there are four points such that each line is incident with at most two of the four points.

Show that the concept of an affine plane can be expressed in terms of algebraic systems, and that the postulates are propositions which refer only to the members of the basic set of an algebraic system in the class.

6. The mathematical system (M, d), where M is a nonempty set and d is a mapping of $M \times M$ into R, the set of all real numbers, is said to be a *metric space* iff

(i) $d(x, y) = 0$ iff $x = y$,

(ii) $d(x, y) = d(y, x)$ whenever $x \in M$ and $y \in M$,

(iii) $d(x, z) \le d(x, y) + d(y, z)$ whenever $x \in M$, $y \in M$, and $z \in M$.

a. Prove that $(R \times R, d)$ is a metric space, where $d(x, y) = [(x_1 - y_1)^2 + (x_2 - y_2)^2]^{1/2}$ whenever $x = (x_1, x_2)$ and $y = (y_1, y_2)$.
b. Prove that (R, d) is a metric space, where

$$d(x, y) = \begin{cases} 0 \text{ if } x = y \\ 1 \text{ if } x \neq y. \end{cases}$$

c. Given that (M, d) is a metric space, prove that $d(x, y) \ge 0$ whenever $x \in M$ and $y \in M$.
d. Prove that (M, d) is a metric space iff

(i) $d(x, y) = 0$ iff $x = y$,

(ii) $d(x, z) \le d(x, y) + d(z, y)$ whenever $x \in M$, $y \in M$, and $z \in M$.

1.3 Semigroups

We now introduce the notion of a *semigroup*.

> DEFINITION 1.3.1.   Any algebraic system of the type $(S, \circ)$, where $\circ$ is a binary operation on S such that $\circ$ is associative, is said to be a semigroup.

Thus the one postulate for a semigroup is

$$x \circ (y \circ z) = (x \circ y) \circ z \text{ whenever } x \in S, y \in S, \text{ and } z \in S.$$

The simplest example of a semigroup is the algebraic system $(\{a\}, \{(a, a, a)\})$; this example is considered to be simple because the basic set of the algebraic system has few members.

Of course, there are many examples of semigroups. The algebraic system $(N, +)$ is a semigroup, where the first term is the set of all natural numbers and where the second term is the usual operation of addition on the natural numbers; taking multiplication in place of addition, we obtain another semigroup. Similarly, $(I, +)$ and $(I, \cdot)$, where "I" denotes the set of all integers, are semigroups.

It is desirable to develop an intuition about algebraic systems and in particular to regard algebraic systems as mathematical objects. In order to build up a feeling of this kind, let us now characterize all semigroups in which the basic set has exactly two members. To this end we first consider all distinct algebraic systems $(\{a, b\}, \circ)$, where $\circ$ is a binary operation on $\{a, b\}$. It is helpful to develop an efficient method of denoting a binary operation on $\{a, b\}$: let us agree to represent the binary operation $\{(a, a, c), (a, b, d), (b, a, e), (b, b, f)\}$ by the array

$$\begin{pmatrix} c & d \\ e & f \end{pmatrix},$$

which is the main body of the table for this binary operation. For example, $\{(a, a, b), (a, b, a), (b, a, a), (b, b, b)\}$ will be denoted by

$$\begin{pmatrix} b & a \\ a & b \end{pmatrix}.$$

This agreement will enable us to avoid considerable writing.

It turns out that there are only ten distinct algebraic systems of the form $(\{a, b\}, \circ)$, where $\circ$ is a binary operation on $\{a, b\}$. The binary operations of these ten algebraic systems are as follows:

1. $\begin{pmatrix} a & a \\ a & a \end{pmatrix}$. 2. $\begin{pmatrix} a & a \\ a & b \end{pmatrix}$. 3. $\begin{pmatrix} a & a \\ b & a \end{pmatrix}$. 4. $\begin{pmatrix} a & b \\ a & a \end{pmatrix}$. 5. $\begin{pmatrix} b & a \\ a & a \end{pmatrix}$.

6. $\begin{pmatrix} b & a \\ a & b \end{pmatrix}$. 7. $\begin{pmatrix} a & a \\ b & b \end{pmatrix}$. 8. $\begin{pmatrix} a & b \\ a & b \end{pmatrix}$. 9. $\begin{pmatrix} b & a \\ b & a \end{pmatrix}$. 10. $\begin{pmatrix} b & b \\ a & a \end{pmatrix}$.

In naming ten binary operations on $\{a, b\}$, we have in effect named ten algebraic systems. For example, using the second binary operation listed above, we obtain the algebraic system $(\{a, b\}, \{(a, a, a), (a, b, a), (b, a, a), (b, b, b)\})$. Let us show that this algebraic system is a semigroup. Denoting the binary operation of this algebraic system by "$\circ$", we see by inspection that $a \circ x = a$ whenever $x \in \{a, b\}$; also, $b \circ x = x$ whenever $x \in \{a, b\}$. We can now prove that $x \circ (y \circ z) = (x \circ y) \circ z$ whenever $x \in \{a, b\}$, $y \in \{a, b\}$, and $z \in \{a, b\}$. Simplifying, we must prove that $a \circ (y \circ z) = (a \circ y) \circ z$ and $b \circ (y \circ z) = (b \circ y) \circ z$ whenever $y \in \{a, b\}$ and $z \in \{a, b\}$. But $a \circ x = a$ whenever $x \in \{a, b\}$; therefore $a \circ (y \circ z) = a$ and $(a \circ y) \circ z = a \circ z = a$ whenever $y \in \{a, b\}$ and $z \in \{a, b\}$. Again, $b \circ x = x$ whenever $x \in \{a, b\}$; therefore $b \circ (y \circ z) = y \circ z$ and $(b \circ y) \circ z = y \circ z$ whenever $y \in \{a, b\}$ and $z \in \{a, b\}$. We conclude that the associative law is true in this algebraic system.

Five of the algebraic systems listed above are, in fact, semigroups; the remaining five algebraic systems are not semigroups. The results are listed as follows:

1. Semigroup.   2. Semigroup.   3. No.   4. No.   5. No.

6. Semigroup.   7. Semigroup.   8. Semigroup.   9. No.   10. No.

For example, let us demonstrate that the third algebraic system listed here, namely $(\{a, b\}, \{(a, a, a), (a, b, a), (b, a, b), (b, b, a)\})$, is not a semigroup: denoting the binary operation of this algebraic system by "?", we note that $b ? (b ? b) = b ? a = b$, whereas $(b ? b) ? b = a ? b = a$. It follows that the associative law is not true in this algebraic system; hence this is not a semigroup.

We turn now to the observation that there are really only ten essentially different algebraic systems consisting of a basic set with exactly two members and a binary operation. At first sight, it appears there are sixteen distinct algebraic systems possessing the stated form. For example, the algebraic system with binary operation

$$\begin{pmatrix} a & b \\ b & a \end{pmatrix}$$

appears to have been left out. Now, this algebraic system is essentially the same as $(\{c, d\}, \{(c, c, c), (c, d, d), (d, c, d), (d, d, c)\})$; we claim that this algebraic system is represented in our list. To see this, consider the sixth algebraic system in the above list, namely $(\{a, b\}, \{(a, a, b), (a, b, a), (b, a, a), (b, b, b)\})$, and consider the one–one mapping of $\{a, b\}$ onto $\{c, d\}$ which associates d with a and associates c with b. Under this mapping the sixth algebraic system of our list becomes $(\{d, c\}, \{(d, d, c), (d, c, d), (c, d, d), (c, c, c)\})$, the algebraic system which apparently had been omitted from the list. Following a similar procedure, it is easy to show that the remaining five algebraic systems which appear to have been omitted are, in fact, represented in the above list.

In this section we have discussed the important notion of two algebraic systems which are essentially the same, i.e. which have the property that one of the algebraic systems can be constructed from the other by applying a suitably chosen one–one mapping to the given algebraic system. The technical term used in this connection is the word *isomorphic*. Before formalizing this important concept, we must clarify what we mean by applying a mapping to an algebraic system.

Let S be the basic set of $\mathscr{S}$ and let μ be any mapping of S into some set; then "$\mu\mathscr{S}$" denotes the algebraic system obtained from $\mathscr{S}$ by replacing each instance in $\mathscr{S}$ of a member of S, say x, by μx. For example, let $\mu 0 = a$ and $\mu 1 = b$; then

$\mu(\{0, 1\}, \{(0, 0, 0), (0, 1, 1), (1, 0, 1), (1, 1, 0)\}, 0)$

$$= (\{a, b\}, \{(a, a, a), (a, b, b), (b, a, b), (b, b, a)\}, a).$$

DEFINITION 1.3.2. $\mathscr{S}$ is said to be isomorphic to $\mathscr{T}$ (in symbols, $\mathscr{S} \cong \mathscr{T}$) iff there exists a one–one mapping of the basic set of $\mathscr{S}$ onto the basic set of $\mathscr{T}$, say μ, such that $\mu\mathscr{S} = \mathscr{T}$.

For example

$(\{0, 1\}, \{(0, 0, 0), (0, 1, 1), (1, 0, 1), (1, 1, 0)\}, 0)$

$$\cong (\{a, b\}, \{(a, a, a), (a, b, b), (b, a, b), (b, b, a)\}, a).$$

Clearly, $\cong$ is a binary relation on algebraic systems. It is easy to prove that $\cong$ is an equivalence relation on the set of all algebraic systems. For this reason we regard isomorphic algebraic systems as equal—from the algebraic point of view.

E X E R C I S E S

1. Present a semigroup whose basic set has exactly three members.

2. a. Prove that the algebraic systems numbered 1, 6, 7, and 8 on page 11 are semigroups.
   b. Prove that the algebraic systems numbered 4, 5, 9, and 10 on page 11 are not semigroups.

3. a. List the operations of the six algebraic systems that apparently are not included in the list of the text.
   b. Demonstrate that each of these algebraic systems is, in fact, represented in the list.

4. Show that $(\mathscr{P}S, \cup)$, where S is a set, is a semigroup.

5. Show that $(\mathscr{P}S, \cap)$, where S is a set, is a semigroup.

6. Show that $(I, \circ)$ is not a semigroup, where "I" denotes the set of all integers and $\circ = \{(a, b, c) \mid a \in I, b \in I, \text{ and } c = a - b\}$.

7. Show that $(I, ?)$ is not a semigroup, where "I" denotes the set of all integers and $? = \{(a, b, c) \mid a \in I, b \in I, \text{ and } c = a(a + b)\}$.

8. Show that $(I, \circ)$ is a semigroup, where "I" denotes the set of all integers and $\circ = \{(a, b, c) \mid a \in I, b \in I, \text{ and } c = 3 + a + b\}$.

9. Consider the algebraic system $(\{a, b\}, \{(a, a, b), (a, b, a), (b, a, a), (b, b, a)\})$. Denoting the binary operation of this algebraic system by "$\circ$", prove the following.
   a. $a \circ x \neq x$ whenever $x \in \{a, b\}$.
   b. $b \circ = a\ x$ whenever $x \in \{a, b\}$.

10. Consider the algebraic system ($\{a, b\}$, ?), where ? $= \{(a, a, b), (a, b, a), (b, a, a), (b, b, b)\}$. Prove the following.

    a. $a \,?\, x \neq x$ whenever $x \in \{a, b\}$.
    b. $b \,?\, x = x$ whenever $x \in \{a, b\}$.
    c. There is a member of $\{a, b\}$, say y, such that $y \,?\, x \neq x$ whenever $x \in \{a, b\}$.
    d. There is a member of $\{a, b\}$, say y, such that $y \,?\, x = x$ whenever $x \in \{a, b\}$.
    e. There is a member of $\{a, b\}$, say x, such that $y \,?\, y = x$ whenever $y \in \{a, b\}$.
    f. There is a member of $\{a, b\}$, say x, such that $y \,?\, y \neq x$ whenever $y \in \{a, b\}$.
    g. Given any member of $\{a, b\}$, say x, there is a member of $\{a, b\}$, say y, such that $x \,?\, y = y$.

11. Present a semigroup, say $(S, \circ)$, such that $\circ$ is not a mapping of $S \times S$ onto S.

1.4 Groups

In this section we shall apply the axiomatic method to the study of a significant mathematical concept—the notion of a group.

First, we shall develop some terminology. Let $(S, \circ)$ be any algebraic system such that $\circ$ is a binary operation on S. A member of S, say e, is said to be a *right identity* iff $x \circ e = x$ whenever $x \in S$; e is said to be a *left identity* iff $e \circ x = x$ whenever $x \in S$. Furthermore, a member of S, say e, is said to be an *identity* iff e is both a right identity and a left identity. Moreover, in case e is a right or left identity, y is said to be a *right inverse* of x and x is said to be a *left inverse* of y iff $x \circ y = e$.

Let us define the term *group*.

> **DEFINITION 1.4.1.** An algebraic system, say $(S, \circ, e)$, where $\circ$ is a binary operation on S and $e \in S$, is said to be a *group* iff
>
>   (i) $x \circ (y \circ z) = (x \circ y) \circ z$ whenever $x \in S$, $y \in S$, and $z \in S$;
>   (ii) $x \circ e = x$ whenever $x \in S$;
>   (iii) given any member of S, say x, there is a member of S, say y, such that $x \circ y = e$.

In other words, $(S, \circ, e)$ is a group iff $\circ$ is associative, e is a right identity, and each member of S possesses a right inverse with respect to e.

For example, $(I, +, 0)$ is a group, where I is the set of all integers; $(S, \cdot, 1)$ is a group, where S is the set of all nonzero rational numbers; and $(\mathscr{P}S, \div, \varnothing)$ is a group, where S is a set.

Propositions (i), (ii), and (iii) in Definition 1.4.1 are called the *group postulates*. Let us apply the axiomatic method to establish the truth for any group of certain other propositions. Let $(S, \circ, e)$ be any group; the following theorems refer to this algebraic system.

> **THEOREM 1.4.1.** $e \circ e = e$.

Proof: Since $(S, \circ, e)$ is a group, $x \circ e = x$ whenever $x \in S$. But $e \in S$; therefore $e \circ e = e$. This establishes our result.

We now prove that if y is a right inverse of x with respect to e, then y is a left inverse of x.

THEOREM 1.4.2.   If x and y are members of S such that $x \circ y = e$, then $y \circ x = e$.

Proof: Suppose that $x \circ y = e$. By (iii), there is a member of S, say c, such that $y \circ c = e$. Therefore

$$
\begin{aligned}
y \circ x &= (y \circ x) \circ e && \text{by (ii)} \\
&= (y \circ x) \circ (y \circ c) && \text{since } y \circ c = e \\
&= [(y \circ x) \circ y] \circ c && \text{by (i)} \\
&= [y \circ (x \circ y)] \circ c && \text{by (i)} \\
&= (y \circ e) \circ c && \text{since } x \circ y = e \\
&= y \circ c && \text{by (ii)} \\
&= e.
\end{aligned}
$$

This establishes Theorem 1.4.2.

Next, we show that each member of S possesses a *left* inverse with respect to e.

COROLLARY 1.4.1.   Given any member of S, say x, there is a member of S, say y, such that $y \circ x = e$.

Proof: Consider Theorem 1.4.2 and (iii).

We now establish a *cancellation law*.

THEOREM 1.4.3. $x = y$ whenever $x \circ z = y \circ z$.

Proof: Suppose that x, y, and z are members of S such that $x \circ z = y \circ z$. By (iii), there is a member of S, say a, such that $z \circ a = e$. Now, $(x \circ z) \circ a = (y \circ z) \circ a$ since $x \circ z = y \circ z$. Therefore,

$$
\begin{aligned}
(x \circ z) \circ a &= x \circ (z \circ a) && \text{by (i)} \\
&= x \circ e && \text{since } z \circ a = e \\
&= x && \text{by (ii).}
\end{aligned}
$$

Moreover,
$$
\begin{aligned}
(y \circ z) \circ a &= y \circ (z \circ a) && \text{by (i)} \\
&= y \circ e && \text{since } z \circ a = e \\
&= y && \text{by (ii).}
\end{aligned}
$$

Hence $x = y$. This establishes Theorem 1.4.3.

Next, we prove that e is a *left identity*.

THEOREM 1.4.4. $e \circ x = x$ whenever $x \in S$.

Proof: Suppose $x \in S$; by (iii), there is a member of S, say a, such that $x \circ a = e$. Therefore

$$e \circ x = (x \circ a) \circ x = x \circ (a \circ x) \qquad \text{by (i)}$$

$$= x \circ e \qquad \text{by Th. 1.4.2}$$

$$= x \qquad \text{by (ii).}$$

This establishes our result.

We now establish another *cancellation law.*

THEOREM 1.4.5. $x = y$ whenever $z \circ x = z \circ y$.

Proof: The proof is similar to the proof of Theorem 1.4.3; use Corollary 1.4.1 in place of (iii), and use Theorem 1.4.4 in place of (ii).

We now prove that each member of the basic set of a group possesses a *unique* right inverse.

THEOREM 1.4.6. Given any member of S, say x, there is a unique member of S, say y, such that $x \circ y = e$.

Proof: Suppose $x \in S$; we know that x possesses a right inverse; assume that x possesses two right inverses, say a and b. Then $x \circ a = x \circ b = e$. By (i), $b \circ (x \circ a) = (b \circ x) \circ a$. Now,

$$b \circ (x \circ a) = b \circ e = b \qquad \text{by } (ii).$$

Moreover,
$$(b \circ x) \circ a = e \circ a \qquad \text{by Th. 1.4.2}$$

$$= a \qquad \text{by Th. 1.4.4.}$$

Hence $a = b$. This contradiction establishes Theorem 1.4.6.

COROLLARY 1.4.2. Given any member of S, say x, there is a *unique* member of S, say y, such that $x \circ y = y \circ x = e$.

Proof: Apply Theorem 1.4.2.

Since each member of S has a unique inverse, we may speak of *the* inverse of a member of S. It is useful to introduce a unary operation on S which associates the inverse of x with x whenever $x \in S$. In case the group operation is denoted by " $\circ$ " or " $\cdot$ ", the inverse of x is denoted by " x^{-1} "; in case the group operation is denoted by " $+$ ", the inverse of x is denoted by " $-x$ ".

It turns out that a group possesses just one right identity and just one left identity. Indeed, it is easy to prove the following theorem.

THEOREM 1.4.7.   There is a unique member of S, say y, such that $x \circ y = x$ whenever $x \in S$; furthermore, there is a unique member of S, say z, such that $z \circ x = x$ whenever $x \in S$.

Moreover, we can prove the next theorem.

THEOREM 1.4.8.   There is a unique member of S, say y, such that $x \circ y = x$ and $y \circ x = x$ whenever $x \in S$.

Proof: These theorems are easy to prove; the proofs are left as exercises.

In view of Theorem 1.4.8, we may speak of *the* identity of a group. In case the binary operation of a group is denoted by "$+$", it is convenient to denote the identity of the group by "0". Accordingly, let $(S, +, 0)$ be any group. The following theorems refer to this algebraic system and are easily established. Remember that "$-x$" denotes the unique inverse of x, so that $x + -x = 0$ whenever $x \in S$.

THEOREM 1.4.9. $-(-x) = x$ whenever $x \in S$.

THEOREM 1.4.10. $-(x + y) = -y + -x$ whenever $x \in S$ and $y \in S$.

The operations $+$ and $-$ give rise to a binary operation on S which associates $x + -y$ with the ordered pair (x, y); this binary operation is usually denoted by "$-$". Of course, it is possible to confuse the binary operation $-$ with the unary operation $-$; however, it is generally clear from the context whether a unary or a binary operation is under discussion.

DEFINITION 1.4.2. $x - y = x + -y$ whenever $x \in S$ and $y \in S$.

To illustrate this definition, consider the group $(\{0, 1, 2\}, +, 0)$, where $+$ is given by the following table:

+	0	1	2
0	0	1	2
1	1	2	0
2	2	0	1

Here, the unary operation $-$ is

$$- = \{(0, 0), (1, 2), (2, 1)\},$$

whereas the binary operation $-$ has the following table:

$-$	0	1	2
0	0	2	1
1	1	0	2
2	2	1	0

The following theorems are easy to establish and their proofs are left as exercises.

THEOREM 1.4.11. $x - x = 0$ whenever $x \in S$.

THEOREM 1.4.12. $x - 0 = x$ whenever $x \in S$.

THEOREM 1.4.13. $(x + y) - y = x$ whenever $x \in S$ and $y \in S$.

THEOREM 1.4.14. $-(x - y) = y - x$ whenever $x \in S$ and $y \in S$.

THEOREM 1.4.15. $x - (y - z) = (x + z) - y$ whenever $x \in S$, $y \in S$, and $z \in S$.

THEOREM 1.4.16. $x + (y - z) = (x + y) - z$ whenever $x \in S$, $y \in S$, and $z \in S$.

THEOREM 1.4.17. $x - (y + z) = (x - z) - y$ whenever $x \in S$, $y \in S$, and $z \in S$.

EXERCISES

1. Show that the algebraic system $(\{0, 1\}, +, 0)$ is a group, where $+$ is given by the following table:

$+$	0	1
0	0	1
1	1	0

2. Show that the algebraic system $(\{0, 1, 2\}, +, 0)$ is a group, where $+$ is given by the following table:

$+$	0	1	2
0	0	1	2
1	1	2	0
2	2	0	1

3. Prove that an ordered triple, say $(S, \circ, e)$, is a group iff

(i) $(S, \circ)$ is a semigroup,

(ii) e is a right identity,

(iii) each member of S possesses a right inverse with respect to e.

4. Let $(S, +, 0)$ be any group. Prove the following.
   a. Given any members of S, say x and z, there is a *unique* member of S, say y, such that $x + y = z$.
   b. Given any members of S, say y and z, there is a *unique* member of S, say x, such that $x + y = z$.

5. A group, say $(S, \circ, e)$, is said to be *abelian* or *commutative* iff $\circ$ is commutative; i.e., $x \circ y = y \circ x$ whenever $x \in S$ and $y \in S$. Present an example of an abelian group; present an example of a group which is not abelian.

6. Show that $(\mathscr{P}S, \dot{-}, \varnothing)$ is an abelian group, where S is a set.

7. The ordered pair $(S, \circ)$ is said to be a *quasigroup* iff S is a nonempty set and $\circ$ is a binary operation on S such that (i) given any members of S, say x and z, there is a *unique* member of S, say y, such that $x \circ y = z$; (ii) given any members of S, say y and z, there is a *unique* member of S, say x, such that $x \circ y = z$.
   a. Characterize the notion of a quasigroup in terms of statements about the table for $\circ$.
   b. Show that the algebraic system $(I, -)$ is a quasigroup, where I is the set of all integers and "$-$" denotes the binary operation of subtraction.
   c. Show that the algebraic system $(I, -, 0)$ is *not* a group.
   d. Show that the algebraic system $(I, \circ)$ is *not* a quasigroup, where I is the set of all integers and $x \circ y = |x - y|$ whenever $x \in I$ and $y \in I$.

8. The ordered triple $(S, \circ, e)$ is said to be a *loop* iff $(S, \circ)$ is a quasigroup and e is an identity (i.e., $x \circ e = e \circ x = x$ whenever $x \in S$).
   a. Characterize the notion of a loop in terms of statements about the table for $\circ$.
   b. Prove that all groups are loops.
   c. Show that $(\{0, 1, 2, 3\}, +, 0)$ is a loop, where the table for $+$ is as follows:

+	0	1	2	3
0	0	1	2	3
1	1	0	3	2
2	2	3	0	1
3	3	2	1	0

   d. Show that the algebraic system of **c** is a group.

9. Present a loop whose basic set has five members and is *not* a group.

10. Let $(S, \circ)$ be a quasigroup such that $x \circ (y \circ z) = (x \circ y) \circ z$ whenever $x \in S$, $y \in S$, and $z \in S$. Show the following.
   a. $x = y$ whenever $x \circ z = y \circ z$.
   b. $x = y$ whenever $z \circ x = z \circ y$.
   c. Given any member of S, say x, there is a *unique* member of S, say y, such that $x \circ y = x$ and $y \circ x = x$.

d. There is a *unique* member of S, say z, such that $x \circ z = z \circ x = x$ whenever $x \in S$.

e. $(S, \circ, e)$ is a group, where e is the *unique* member of S such that $x \circ e = e \circ x = x$ whenever $x \in S$.

11. Let $(S, \circ, e)$ be any group and let a be any member of S. The expression "a^n", where n is any integer, is defined as follows: $a^1 = a$ and $a^{n+1} = a^n \circ a$ whenever n is a positive integer; moreover, $a^0 = e$ and $a^{-n} = (a^{-1})^n$ whenever n is a positive integer. Prove the following.

a. $a^n \circ a^m = a^{n+m}$ whenever n and m are integers.

b. $a^n \circ a^m = a^m \circ a^n$ whenever n and m are integers.

c. $(a^n)^m = a^{n \cdot m}$ whenever n and m are integers.

12. Let $(S, \circ, e)$ and $(S', \circ', e')$ be groups such that $S' \subset S$ and $\circ' \subset \circ$; then $(S', \circ', e')$ is said to be a *subgroup* of $(S, \circ, e)$. Prove that $e' = e$.

13. Given that $(S, \circ, e)$ is a group, $S' \subset S$, and $\circ' \subset \circ$, prove that $(S', \circ', e)$ is a subgroup of $(S, \circ, e)$ iff

(i) $\circ'$ is a binary operation on S',

(ii) $x^{-1} \in S'$ whenever $x \in S'$.

14. Let $(S, \circ, e)$ be a group and let $a \in S$; prove that $(S', \circ', e)$ is a subgroup of $(S, \circ, e)$, where $S' = \{a^n \mid n \text{ is an integer}\}$ and $\circ'$ is $\circ$ restricted to S'. Prove that $(S', \circ', e)$ is an abelian group.

15. Let $(G, \circ, e)$ be a group whose basic set is finite, and let S be the basic set of a subgroup of $(G, \circ, e)$. Let $a \in G$; then $\{x \circ a \mid x \in S\}$ is denoted by "Sa" and is said to be a *right coset* of S in G. Similarly, $\{a \circ x \mid x \in S\}$ is denoted by "aS" and is said to be a *left coset* of S in G.

a. Prove that $Sa = Sb$ or else $Sa \cap Sb = \varnothing$ whenever $a \in G$ and $b \in G$.

b. Prove that $\{Sa \mid a \in G\}$ is a partition of G.

16. Let $(S', \circ', e)$ be a subgroup of $(S, \circ, e)$, where S is a finite set with m members and S' has n members. Prove that m is a multiple of n.

17. Let $(G, +, 0)$ be any group. Prove that $(M, \circ, \varphi)$ is a group, where M is the set of all mappings of G into G, "$\mu \circ \nu$" denotes the mapping that associates $\mu(t) + \nu(t)$ with t whenever $t \in G$, and $\varphi = \{(t, 0) \mid t \in G\}$. Show that $\circ$ is commutative iff $+$ is commutative.

18. Let $(G, +, 0)$ be any group, and let M be the mapping of G into G which associates $-a$ with a whenever $a \in G$. Prove that M is a one–one mapping of G onto G.

1.5 More Examples of Groups

We now present two methods for producing groups: the first method that we shall discuss produces abelian groups, whereas the second method results in groups for which the commutative law fails, i.e. nonabelian groups.

Consider a circle whose circumference has been divided into three equal parts by means of three points labeled "0", "1", and "2" (see Figure 1.5.1). Suppose that a pointer is pivoted at the center of the circle so that it is free to point at any one of the three numbers on the circumference. Let us use this device to construct an algebraic system which is, in fact, an abelian group. The basic set of our algebraic system is $\{0, 1, 2\}$. We introduce $+$, a binary operation on $\{0, 1, 2\}$, as follows. Let x and y be any members of $\{0, 1, 2\}$; then $x + y$ is found by first setting the pointer at the number x and then turning the pointer clockwise through y parts; the number the pointer stops at is defined to be $x + y$. Finally, we display 0, a member of our basic set. Thus the algebraic system we have constructed by using the above device is ($\{0, 1, 2\}, +, 0$). We want to show that (1) + is associative, (2) 0 is a right identity, (3) each member of the basic set has a right inverse, and (4) + is commutative.

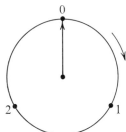

First, we shall demonstrate that + is commutative. To this purpose, we observe that the procedure of setting the pointer at a number, say x, can be broken down into two parts: (1) set the pointer at 0 and (2) move the pointer clockwise through x parts. This means that $x + y$ can be found by first setting the pointer at 0, then moving the pointer clockwise through x parts, and finally moving the pointer clockwise through y parts— where x and y are any members of $\{0, 1, 2\}$. Now, $y + x$ is found by setting the pointer at 0, moving the pointer clockwise through y parts, and then moving the pointer clockwise through

Figure 1.5.1

x parts. Thus in both cases the pointer is moved through x parts and through y parts (the pointer does not care about the *order* in which the movements are performed); therefore $x + y = y + x$ whenever x and y are members of $\{0, 1, 2\}$. This establishes that + is commutative.

Next, we shall establish that + is associative. Let x, y, and z be any members of $\{0, 1, 2\}$; we want to show that $x + (y + z) = (x + y) + z$. But $x + (y + z) = (y + z) + x$, since + is commutative. So $x + (y + z)$ is the number obtained by setting the pointer at 0, then moving it clockwise through y parts, then through z parts (so that the pointer now points at the number $y + z$), and finally through x parts. On the other hand, $(x + y) + z$ is the number obtained by setting the pointer at 0, then moving the pointer clockwise through x parts, then through y parts (so that the pointer now points at the number $x + y$), and finally through z parts. Notice that in each case the pointer was moved through the sum of x, y, and z parts, so that the pointer came to rest at the same number in both cases. This establishes that $x + (y + z) = (x + y) + z$ whenever $x \in \{0, 1, 2\}$, $y \in \{0, 1, 2\}$, and $z \in \{0, 1, 2\}$.

We now consider the proposition: "$x + 0 = x$ whenever $x \in \{0, 1, 2\}$". Of course, this is true here, since setting the pointer at a number and then moving the pointer through no parts leaves the pointer where it was.

Finally, we prove that each member of $\{0, 1, 2\}$ possesses a right inverse. To see this, note that $0 + 0 = 0$, $1 + 2 = 0$, and $2 + 1 = 0$. This completes our demonstration that the ordered triple ($\{0, 1, 2\}, +, 0$) is an abelian group.

The binary operation +, discussed above, is actually of mathematical interest; this operation is called *addition modulo three*. We should notice that by dividing the circumference of a circle into n equal parts, where n is any natural number, we can construct an abelian group by defining a binary operation +, as above, on the basic set $\{0, 1, \cdots, n - 1\}$ and displaying 0 as the third term of the algebraic system.

We now present another method of generating a group, a method which produces nonabelian groups. Let M be the set of all mappings of $\{1, 2, 3\}$ onto $\{1, 2, 3\}$; then M has six members as follows:

$$\{(1, 1), (2, 2), (3, 3)\}, \quad \{(1, 1), (2, 3), (3, 2)\}, \quad \{(1, 2), (2, 1), (3, 3)\},$$
$$\{(1, 2), (2, 3), (3, 1)\}, \quad \{(1, 3), (2, 1), (3, 2)\}, \quad \{(1, 3), (2, 2), (3, 1)\}.$$

The set M is to be the basic set of our algebraic system. Next, let us construct a binary operation on M, which we shall denote by "$\circ$". Let μ and v be any members of M; then "$\mu \circ v$" denotes the mapping of $\{1, 2, 3\}$ onto $\{1, 2, 3\}$ which associates $\mu(v(x))$ with x whenever $x \in \{1, 2, 3\}$. For example,

$$\{(1, 2), (2, 1), (3, 3)\} \circ \{(1, 3), (2, 2), (3, 1)\} = \{(1, 3), (2, 1), (3, 2)\}.$$

It is easily seen that if μ and v are any mappings of $\{1, 2, 3\}$ onto $\{1, 2, 3\}$, then $\mu \circ v$ is also a mapping of $\{1, 2, 3\}$ onto $\{1, 2, 3\}$. Finally, for the third term of our ordered triple we take the identity mapping $\{(1, 1), (2, 2), (3, 3)\}$, which we shall denote by "φ". Thus our algebraic system is $(M, \circ, \varphi)$.

Let us show that the binary operation $\circ$ is associative. Let λ, μ, and v be any members of M, and let $x \in \{1, 2, 3\}$; then

$$[\lambda \circ (\mu \circ v)](x) = \lambda[(\mu \circ v)(x)] = \lambda(\mu(v(x)))$$

and

$$[(\lambda \circ \mu) \circ v](x) = [\lambda \circ \mu](v(x)) = \lambda(\mu(v(x))).$$

Therefore $\lambda \circ (\mu \circ v) = (\lambda \circ \mu) \circ v$. This demonstrates that $\circ$ is associative.

Clearly, $\mu \circ \varphi = \mu$ whenever $\mu \in M$; therefore φ is a right identity of our algebraic system.

Moreover, $\{(1, a), (2, b), (3, c)\} \circ \{(a, 1), (b, 2), (c, 3)\} = \{(1, 1), (2, 2), (3, 3)\}$ provided that $\{a, b, c\} = \{1, 2, 3\}$. This proves that each member of M possesses a right inverse.

We conclude that the algebraic system $(M, \circ, \varphi)$ is a group.

We claim that this is a nonabelian group. We must show that there are members of the basic set, say μ and v, such that $\mu \circ v \neq v \circ \mu$. But

$$\{(1, 2), (2, 1), (3, 3)\} \circ \{(1, 3), (2, 2), (3, 1)\} = \{(1, 3), (2, 1), (3, 2)\}$$

and

$$\{(1, 3), (2, 2), (3, 1)\} \circ \{(1, 2), (2, 1), (3, 3)\} = \{(1, 2), (2, 3), (3, 1)\}.$$

Thus

$$\{(1, 2), (2, 1), (3, 3)\} \circ \{(1, 3), (2, 2), (3, 1)\}$$
$$\neq \{(1, 3), (2, 2), (3, 1)\} \circ \{(1, 2), (2, 1), (3, 3)\}.$$

Here, we obtained a group by considering the set of all one–one mappings of $\{1, 2, 3\}$ onto $\{1, 2, 3\}$. It is not difficult to see that we will obtain a nonabelian group by using $\{1, 2, \cdots, n\}$, where n is any natural number greater than 2, in place of $\{1, 2, 3\}$.

In Section 2.2 we shall make some use of the ideas of this section. Accordingly, it is worthwhile to introduce certain suitable terms. In particular we shall call each member of the basic set of our group a *permutation*.

DEFINITION 1.5.1.   Let S be any nonempty set; then each one–one mapping of S onto S is said to be a *permutation* of S.

The permutation $\{(1, a_1), (2, a_2), \cdots, (n, a_n)\}$ is frequently denoted by the expression

$$\begin{pmatrix} 1 & 2 & \cdots & n \\ a_1 & a_2 & \cdots & a_n \end{pmatrix}.$$

We shall now develop other ways of denoting permutations. To this purpose we introduce the notion of a *cycle*.

DEFINITION 1.5.2.   Let μ be any permutation of $\{1, 2, \cdots, n\}$; then μ is said to be a *cycle* iff there is an ordered t-tuple $(a_1, a_2, \cdots, a_t)$ such that $\mu(a_1) = a_2$, $\mu(a_2) = a_3, \cdots, \mu(a_{t-1}) = a_t$, and $\mu(a_t) = a_1$, whereas $\mu(b) = b$ whenever $b \in \{1, 2, \cdots, n\} - \{a_1, a_2, \cdots, a_t\}$. This permutation is denoted by "$(a_1 \ a_2 \ \cdots \ a_t)$".
For example, the permutation $\{(1, 3), (2, 1), (3, 2)\}$ is a cycle and is denoted by "$(1 \ 3 \ 2)$".
Two cycles $(a_1 \ a_2 \ \cdots \ a_s)$ and $(b_1 \ b_2 \ \cdots \ b_t)$ are said to be *disjoint* iff the sets $\{a_1, a_2, \cdots, a_s\}$ and $\{b_1, b_2, \cdots, b_t\}$ are disjoint.
The following theorem indicates why we are interested in cycles.

THEOREM 1.5.1.   Each permutation of a finite set either is a cycle or is the product of a finite number of disjoint cycles.

Proof: There is no loss of generality in considering the set $\{1, 2, \cdots, n\}$, where n is a natural number. Let μ be any permutation of $\{1, 2, \cdots, n\}$. We proceed as follows. First, we form the cycle $(1 \ a_1 \ a_2 \ \cdots \ a_s)$, where $a_1 = \mu(1)$, $a_2 = \mu(a_1)$, $\cdots$, $a_s = \mu(a_{s-1})$, and $\mu(a_s) = 1$. If $s = n - 1$, then $\mu = (1 \ a_1 \ a_2 \ \cdots \ a_s)$, and we have finished. If $s < n - 1$, then we choose any member of $\{1, 2, \cdots, n\} - \{1, a_1, a_2, \cdots, a_s\}$, say b, and form a cycle which begins with b. Continuing in this way, we obtain a finite number of disjoint cycles whose product is μ. To illustrate our procedure, we point out that

$$\begin{pmatrix} 1 \ 2 \ 3 \ 4 \ 5 \ 6 \\ 5 \ 2 \ 6 \ 1 \ 4 \ 3 \end{pmatrix} = (1 \ 5 \ 4) \circ (2) \circ (3 \ 6).$$

Any cycle of length 2 is said to be a *transposition*.

DEFINITION 1.5.3.   Each cycle of the form $(a \ b)$, where $a \neq b$, is called a *transposition*.

For example, the permutation $\{(1, 4), (2, 2), (3, 3), (4, 1)\}$ is a transposition, namely $(1 \ 4)$.
We point out that each finite cycle with length more than 2 is the product of a finite number of transpositions.

THEOREM 1.5.2.   Let s be any natural number greater than 2; then

$$(a_1 \ a_2 \ \cdots \ a_s) = (a_1 \ a_s) \circ (a_1 \ a_{s-1}) \circ (a_1 \ a_{s-2}) \circ \cdots \circ (a_1 \ a_3) \circ (a_1 \ a_2).$$

Proof: The proof is obvious.

COROLLARY 1.5.1.   Each permutation of a finite set with more than two members is the product of a finite number of transpositions.

Proof: Use Theorems 1.5.1 and 1.5.2.

E X E R C I S E S

1. Exhibit the table for the binary operation called *addition modulo three*.

2. Exhibit the table for the operation of the group based on dividing the circumference of a circle into four equal parts (this operation is called *addition modulo four*).

3. Present an abelian group whose basic set has five members.

4. Let the set of all integers from 0 to 9 inclusive be the basic set of an algebraic system whose second term is the binary operation $+$ based on dividing the circumference of a circle into five equal parts (i.e., $x + y$ is calculated by setting the pointer at 0, then moving it clockwise through x parts, and then through y parts), and whose third term is 0.

a. Display the table for the binary operation.
b. Is the operation associative?
c. Is the operation commutative?
d. Is it true that $x + 5 = x$ whenever x is a member of the basic set?
e. Is this algebraic system a group?
f. Is this algebraic system a loop?

5. Prove that if n is any natural number greater than 2, there is a nonabelian group whose basic set has $n!$ members.

6. Present a nonabelian group whose basic set has 24 members.

7. a. Let n be any natural number and let "$\oplus$" denote the binary operation on the set of all natural numbers based on dividing the circumference of a circle into n equal parts (i.e., $x \oplus y$ is computed by setting the pointer at 0, then moving it clockwise through x parts, and then through y parts). This operation is called *addition modulo n*. Given that x and y are any natural numbers, show that $x \oplus y = r$, where q is a natural number such that $nq \leq x + y < n(q + 1)$ and $x + y = nq + r$ (i.e., r is the remainder on dividing $x + y$ by n).

(*Note:* The proposition "$x \oplus y = r$" is given by writing "$x + y \equiv r \pmod{n}$".)

b. Let n be any natural number and let "$\circ$" denote the binary operation on the set of all nonnegative integers such that $x \circ y = r$, where r is the remainder on dividing $x \cdot y$ by n; more precisely, $x \circ y = r$ iff there is a natural number q such that $n \cdot q \leq x \cdot y < n \cdot (q + 1)$ and $x \cdot y = n \cdot q + r$. The operation $\circ$ is called *multiplication modulo n*.

(i) Display the table for $\circ$, given that $n = 3$.
(ii) Display the table for $\circ$, given that $n = 4$.

(*Note:* The proposition "$x \circ y = r$" is given by writing "$x \cdot y \equiv r \pmod{n}$".)

8. A group, say $(S, \circ, e)$, is said to be *cyclic* iff there is a member of S, say a, such that $S = \{a^n \mid n \text{ is an integer}\}$; moreover, a is said to *generate* the group.

a. Show that the group $(I, +, 0)$, where I is the set of all integers and $+$ is the usual operation of addition, is cyclic and is generated by 1.

b. Prove that for each positive integer k the group $(\{0, 1, 2, \cdots, k - 1\}, +, 0)$ is cyclic with generator 1, where "$+$" denotes addition modulo k.

9. Show that the permutation group whose basic set consists of all permutations of $\{1, 2, 3, 4\}$ is nonabelian.

10. Express the permutation $\begin{pmatrix} 1\,2\,3\,4\,5 \\ 3\,5\,4\,1\,2 \end{pmatrix}$ as a product of cycles.

11. Express the permutation $\begin{pmatrix} 1\,2\,3\,4\,5\,6\,7 \\ 5\,4\,2\,3\,1\,7\,6 \end{pmatrix}$ as a product of cycles.

12. Let n be any natural number; prove that the identity permutation $\begin{pmatrix} 1\,2\,\cdots\,n \\ 1\,2\,\quad n \end{pmatrix}$ is *not* the product of an odd number of transpositions of $\{1, 2, \cdots, n\}$.

1.6   Rings: Integral Domains

In this section we shall see how the concept of a group can be used to build up, or describe, more complex mathematical systems.

DEFINITION 1.6.1.   An ordered 4-tuple, say $(R, +, \cdot, 0)$, is said to be a *ring* iff

(i) $(R, +, 0)$ is an abelian group;

(ii) $(R, \cdot)$ is a semigroup;

(iii) $x \cdot (y + z) = x \cdot y + x \cdot z$ whenever $x \in R, y \in R$, and $z \in R$;

(iv) $(y + z) \cdot x = y \cdot x + z \cdot x$ whenever $x \in R, y \in R$, and $z \in R$.

Propositions (iii) and (iv) are called *distributive laws*.

Recalling the definitions of a group and a semigroup, we easily establish the following theorem.

THEOREM 1.6.1.   An algebraic system, say $(R, +, \cdot, 0)$, where $+$ and $\cdot$ are binary operations on R and $0 \in R$, is a ring iff
(a) $x + (y + z) = (x + y) + z$ whenever $x \in R, y \in R$, and $z \in R$;
(b) $x + 0 = x$ whenever $x \in R$;
(c) given any member of R, say x, there is a member of R, say y, such that $x + y = 0$;
(d) $x + y = y + x$ whenever $x \in R$ and $y \in R$;
(e) $x \cdot (y \cdot z) = (x \cdot y) \cdot z$ whenever $x \in R, y \in R$, and $z \in R$;
(f) $x \cdot (y + z) = x \cdot y + x \cdot z$ whenever $x \in R, y \in R$, and $z \in R$;
(g) $(y + z) \cdot x = y \cdot x + z \cdot x$ whenever $x \in R, y \in R$, and $z \in R$.

For example, the ordered 4-tuple $(I, +, \cdot, 0)$ is a ring, where I is the set of all integers, and "$+$" and "$\cdot$" denote addition and multiplication. Again, the algebraic system $(\mathscr{P}S, \doteq, \cap, \varnothing)$, where S is a set, is a ring; this is easy to see in view of the properties of the *symmetric difference* and *intersection*.

As another example of a ring, we present the algebraic system $(\{0, 1, 2, 3\}, +, \cdot, 0)$, where the binary operations $+$ and $\cdot$ are given by the following tables:

+	0	1	2	3
0	0	1	2	3
1	1	2	3	0
2	2	3	0	1
3	3	0	1	2

$\cdot$	0	1	2	3
0	0	0	0	0
1	0	1	2	3
2	0	2	0	2
3	0	3	2	1

Here, $+$ represents *addition modulo four*, and $\cdot$ represents *multiplication modulo four*. In view of the results contained in Section 1.5, it is clear that $(\{0, 1, 2, 3\}, +, 0)$ is an abelian group. The remaining ring postulates are easily established by first observing that can be expressed in terms of $+$, as follows. If x is any member of $\{0, 1, 2, 3\}$, then

(1) $0 \cdot x = 0$,

(2) $1 \cdot x = x$,

(3) $2 \cdot x = x + x$,

(4) $3 \cdot x = (x + x) + x$.

These statements are easily verified by examining the tables for $+$ and $\cdot$. Moreover, from the table for $\cdot$ we see that this operation is commutative. We can now establish the distributive laws. Since $\cdot$ is commutative, it is enough to demonstrate one distributive law, say (f) in Theorem 1.6.1. Simplifying, we must show that if y and z are any members of $\{0, 1, 2, 3\}$, then $0 \cdot (y + z) = 0 \cdot y + 0 \cdot z$, $1 \cdot (y + z) = 1 \cdot y + 1 \cdot z$, $2 \cdot (y + z) = 2 \cdot y + 2 \cdot z$, and $3 \cdot (y + z) = 3 \cdot y + 3 \cdot z$. The truth of these propositions follows from (1), (2), (3), and (4) above and the fact that $+$ is asociative and commutative. This verifies our distributive law.

Finally, we must establish (e), which states that $\cdot$ is associative. Simplifying, we must prove that if y and z are any members of $\{0, 1, 2, 3\}$, then $0 \cdot (y \cdot z) = (0 \cdot y) \cdot z$, $1 \cdot (y \cdot z) = (1 \cdot y) \cdot z$, $2 \cdot (y \cdot z) = (2 \cdot y) \cdot z$, $3 \cdot (y \cdot z) = (3 \cdot y) \cdot z$. Again, these propositions can be verified by applying (1), (2), (3), and (4) above and the distributive laws. This completes our demonstration that the algebraic system $(\{0, 1, 2, 3\}, +, \cdot, 0)$ is a ring.

We now establish two theorems about rings. Let $(R, +, \cdot, 0)$ be any ring; the following two theorems refer to this algebraic system.

THEOREM 1.6.2. $0 \cdot x = 0$ whenever $x \in R$.
Proof: Let $x \in R$; then

$$0 \cdot x = (0 + 0) \cdot x \qquad \text{since } 0 + 0 = 0$$
$$= 0 \cdot x + 0 \cdot x \qquad \text{by (iv)}.$$

Let $y = -(0 \cdot x)$; then

$$0 = 0 \cdot x + y = (0 \cdot x + 0 \cdot x) + y,$$

$$= 0 \cdot x + (0 \cdot x + y) \qquad \text{since } + \text{ is associative}$$

$$= 0 \cdot x + 0$$

$$= 0 \cdot x.$$

This establishes Theorem 1.6.2.

THEOREM 1.6.3. $-(x \cdot y) = (-x) \cdot y$ whenever $x \in R$ and $y \in R$.

Proof: Let x and y be any members of R. Now,

$$x \cdot y + (-x) \cdot y = (x + -x) \cdot y \qquad \text{by (iv)}$$

$$= 0 \cdot y \qquad \text{since "} -x \text{" denotes the inverse of } x$$

$$= 0 \qquad \text{by Th. 1.6.2.}$$

Thus $(-x) \cdot y$ is the inverse of $x \cdot y$. This establishes Theorem 1.6.3.

If $(R, +, \cdot, 0)$ is a ring such that $\cdot$ is commutative, then this algebraic system is said to be a *commutative ring.*

Now suppose that $(R, +, \cdot, 0)$ is a ring with the following property: there is a member of R, say e, such that $x \cdot e = x$ and $e \cdot x = x$ whenever $x \in R$. Then e is said to be an *identity*; moreover, the algebraic system $(R, +, \cdot, 0)$ is called a *ring with identity.*

THEOREM 1.6.4.   Each ring has at most one identity.

Proof: We indicate a proof, leaving the details as an exercise. Suppose that a particular ring has two identities; this will quickly lead you to a contradiction.

To illustrate the notions that we have just introduced, we note that the ring $(\mathscr{P}S, \dot{-}, \cap, \varnothing)$ is a commutative ring with identity; here, the identity is S. Considering the ring $(\{0, 1, 2, 3\}, +, \cdot, 0)$ given above, we see that this ring is commutative and has an identity namely 1.

A commutative ring with identity, say $(R, +, \cdot, 0)$, is said to be an *integral domain* iff 0 has no proper divisors, i.e., iff $x = 0$ or $y = 0$ whenever $x \cdot y = 0$.

The prime example of an integral domain is the ring of integers $(I, +, \cdot, 0)$. Another example is the ring $(\{0, 1\}, +, \cdot, 0)$, where $+$ and $\cdot$ are given as follows:

+	0	1		$\cdot$	0	1
0	0	1		0	0	0
1	1	0		1	0	1

Notice that $(\{0, 1, 2, 3\}, +, \cdot, 0)$ is *not* an integral domain since $2 \cdot 2 = 0$; thus 2 is a divisor of 0. Moreover, the ring $(\mathscr{P}\{1, 2\}, \dot{-}, \cap, \varnothing)$ is *not* an integral domain since $\{1\} \cap \{2\} = \varnothing$.

We now establish one theorem about integral domains.

THEOREM 1.6.5. Let $(R, +, \cdot, 0)$ be any integral domain, and let x, y, and z be any members of R such that $z \neq 0$ and $x \cdot z = y \cdot z$; then $x = y$.

Proof: Since $x \cdot z = y \cdot z$, it follows that $-(x \cdot z) = -(y \cdot z)$; but the inverse of $y \cdot z$ is $(-y) \cdot z$, by Theorem 1.6.3. Therefore

$$x \cdot z + (-y) \cdot z = 0;$$

so
$$(x + -y) \cdot z = 0 \qquad \text{by (iv).}$$

Since $z \neq 0$, by assumption, and 0 has no proper divisors, it follows that $x + -y = 0$. Therefore $(x + -y) + y = 0 + y = y$; hence $x = y$. This establishes Theorem 1.6.5.

It is sometimes convenient to display the identity of an integral domain; thus we shall say that $(R, +, \cdot, 0, 1)$ is an integral domain provided that $(R, +, \cdot, 0)$ is an integral domain with identity 1.

E X E R C I S E S

1. Let $(R, +, \cdot, 0)$ be any ring. Prove that $x \cdot 0 = 0$ whenever $x \in R$.

2. a. Present a ring whose basic set has exactly five members.
   b. Is your solution to part **a** also an integral domain?

3. Present a ring which is *not* commutative.

4. Present a ring which has no identity.

5. Show that $(R, +, \cdot, 0)$ is a ring, where $R = \{0, 1, 2, 3, 4\}$ and " $+$ " and " $\cdot$ " represent *addition modulo five* and *multiplication modulo five*, respectively.

6. Show that the algebraic system $(\{0\}, \{(0, 0, 0)\}, \{(0, 0, 0)\}, 0, 0)$ is an integral domain.

7. Let $(R, +, \cdot, 0, 1)$ be any integral domain. Prove the following.
   a. $-x = (-1) \cdot x$ whenever $x \in R$.
   b. $-1 \cdot -1 = 1$.
   c. $(-x) \cdot (-y) = x \cdot y$ whenever $x \in R$ and $y \in R$.

8. Prove that the algebraic system $(\{0, 1, 2, \cdots, k - 1\}, +, \cdot, 0, 1)$, where " $+$ " and " $\cdot$ " represent *addition modulo k* and *multiplication modulo k*, respectively, is an integral domain iff k is prime.

9. Let $(S, +, \cdot, 0, 1)$ be any integral domain; by the *characteristic* of a, where a is any nonzero member of S, we mean the smallest natural number k such that $0 = a + a + \cdots + a(k \ a\text{'s})$. In case $0 \neq a + a + \cdots + a(k \ a\text{'s})$ for each natural number k, we say that the characteristic of a is zero.
   a. Prove that any two nonzero members of S have the same characteristic.
      (*Hint:* Consider the characteristic of 1.)
   b. Let k be the characteristic of 1, and suppose that $k \neq 0$. Prove that k is prime.

10. Let $(R, +, \cdot, 0)$ be any ring and let S be any subset of R such that (i) $(S, +', 0)$ is a group where $+'$ is $+$ restricted to S; (ii) $x \cdot y \in S$ and $y \cdot x \in S$ whenever $x \in S$ and $y \in R$. Then S is said to be an *ideal* of the given ring.

    a. List the ideals of the ring $(\{0, 1, 2, 3, 4, 5\}, +, \cdot, 0)$, where "$+$" and "$\cdot$" represent *addition modulo six* and *multiplication modulo six*, respectively.

    b. Show that for each integer k, $\{a \cdot k \mid a \in I\}$, the set of all multiples of k, is an ideal of the ring of integers $(I, +, \cdot, 0)$.

    c. Prove that the only ideals of the ring of integers are those given by part **b**.

11. Given that $(R, +, \cdot, 0)$ is a ring with identity 1 and that each nonzero member of R possesses a multiplicative inverse, prove that the only ideals of this ring are R and $\{0\}$.

1.7   Fields; Ordered Fields

We now introduce the notion of a *field*.

DEFINITION 1.7.1.   An ordered 5-tuple, say $(S, +, \cdot, 0, 1)$, is said to be a *field* iff

    (i) $(S, +, \cdot, 0, 1)$ is an integral domain,

    (ii) each nonzero member of S possesses a multiplicative inverse,

    (iii) $0 \neq 1$.

For example, the algebraic system $(Rt, +, \cdot, 0/1, 1/1)$ is a field, where Rt is the set of all rational numbers, $+$ and $\cdot$ are the operations of addition and multiplication, respectively, and $0/1$ and $1/1$ are the rational numbers zero and one.

Also, the algebraic system $(\{0, 1\}, +, \cdot, 0, 1)$ is a field, where the binary operations $+$ and $\cdot$ are given by the following tables:

$+$	0	1		$\cdot$	0	1
0	0	1		0	0	0
1	1	0		1	0	1

Again, $(\{0, 1, 2\}, +, \cdot, 0, 1)$ is a field, where $+$ and $\cdot$ are given by the following tables:

$+$	0	1	2		$\cdot$	0	1	2
0	0	1	2		0	0	0	0
1	1	2	0		1	0	1	2
2	2	0	1		2	0	2	1

Since there are nine postulates for an integral domain, we see that there are eleven postulates for a field. However, it is easy to show that the integral domain postulate "0 has no proper divisors" follows from the other field postulates. Thus we have the following theorem, which displays the necessary field postulates in detail.

THEOREM 1.7.1.   An algebraic system, say $(S, +, \cdot, 0, 1)$, where $+$ and $\cdot$ are binary operations on S and $0 \in S$ and $1 \in S$, is a field iff

(1) $x + (y + z) = (x + y) + z$ whenever $x \in S$, $y \in S$, and $z \in S$;
(2) $x + 0 = x$ whenever $x \in S$;
(3) given any member of S, say x, there is a member of S, say y, such that $x + y = 0$;
(4) $x + y = y + x$ whenever $x \in S$ and $y \in S$;
(5) $x \cdot (y \cdot z) = (x \cdot y) \cdot z$ whenever $x \in S$, $y \in S$, and $z \in S$;
(6) $x \cdot 1 = x$ whenever $x \in S$;
(7) given any nonzero member of S, say x, there is a member of S, say y, such that $x \cdot y = 1$;
(8) $x \cdot y = y \cdot x$ whenever $x \in S$ and $y \in S$;
(9) $x \cdot (y + z) = x \cdot y + x \cdot z$ whenever $x \in S$, $y \in S$, and $z \in S$;
(10) $0 \neq 1$.

Next, we introduce the notion of an *ordered field*.

DEFINITION 1.7.2.   An ordered 6-tuple, say $(S, +, \cdot, <, 0, 1)$, is said to be an *ordered field* iff

(a) $(S, +, \cdot, 0, 1)$ is a field,

(b) $<$ is an order relation on S,

(c) $x + z < y + z$ whenever $x < y$ and $z \in S$,

(d) $x \cdot z < y \cdot z$ whenever $x < y$ and $0 < z$.

We note that the postulates for an ordered field are (1)–(10) inclusive, and the following:

(11) $x < z$ whenever $x < y$ and $y < z$;

(12) if $x \in S$, then exactly one of the following is true: $x = 0$, $0 < x$, $x < 0$;

(13) $x + z < y + z$ whenever $x < y$ and $z \in S$;

(14) $x \cdot z < y \cdot z$ whenever $x < y$ and $0 < z$.

For example, the algebraic system $(Rt, +, \cdot, <, 0/1, 1/1)$ is an ordered field, where Rt is the set of all rational numbers and $+, \cdot, <, 0/1, 1/1$ are interpreted in the usual way.

Notice that there is no ordered field whose basic set is finite; this is a consequence of postulates (10), (11), (12), and (13).

We now establish some theorems about ordered fields. Let $(S, +, \cdot, <, 0, 1)$ be any ordered field; the following theorems refer to this algebraic system.

THEOREM 1.7.2. $0 < -x$ whenever $x < 0$.

Proof: Assume $x < 0$. By (12), exactly one of the following is true: $-x = 0$, $0 < -x$, $-x < 0$. If $-x = 0$, then $x + -x = x + 0 = x$, i.e., $x = 0$; this is impossible by (12) since we are assuming that $x < 0$. If $-x < 0$, then $-x + x < 0 + x$ by (13), i.e., $0 < x$; again, this is impossible by (12). We conclude, again by (12), that $0 < -x$. This establishes Theorem 1.7.2.

THEOREM 1.7.3 $0 < 1$.

Proof: From (10), $0 \neq 1$; therefore, by (12), either $0 < 1$ or $1 < 0$. Suppose $1 < 0$; then, by Theorem 1.7.2, $0 < -1$. But $1 < 0$; hence, by (14), $1 \cdot -1 < 0 \cdot -1$, i.e., $-1 < 0$. Thus $0 < -1$ and $-1 < 0$; this contradicts (12). We conclude that $0 < 1$.

THEOREM 1.7.4. $0 < x \cdot x$ whenever $x \neq 0$.

Proof: Let x be any nonzero member of S; then, by (12), $x < 0$ or else $0 < x$. If $x < 0$, then, by Theorem 1.7.2, $0 < -x$; hence, by (14), $0 \cdot -x < -x \cdot -x$. But, by Theorem 1.6.2, $0 \cdot -x = 0$, and, by Exercise 7c, Section 1.6, $-x \cdot -x = x \cdot x$; hence $0 < x \cdot x$. If $0 < x$, then, by (14), $0 \cdot x < x \cdot x$; hence, by Theorem 1.6.2, $0 < x \cdot x$. This establishes Theorem 1.7.4.

Finally, we wish to say what is meant by a *complete ordered field*. Consider any ordered field, say $(S, +, \cdot, <, 0, 1)$. Suppose that K is any nonempty subset of S and that b is a member of S, not necessarily in K, such that $x < b$ or $x = b$ whenever $x \in K$; then we call b an *upper bound of K*. Now, suppose that L is an upper bound of K such that $L < b$ or $L = b$ whenever b is an upper bound of K; then we call L a *least upper bound of K*. A word of warning about language: it is customary to say "K possesses an upper bound" when we mean "an upper bound of K exists"; similarly, we say "K possesses a least upper bound" when we mean "a least upper bound of K exists". Do not interpret "K *possesses* an upper bound" as meaning that an upper bound of K is a *member* of K.

To illustrate these concepts, consider again the system of rational numbers $(Rt, +, \cdot, <, 0/1, 1/1)$, which is an ordered field. The set of all negative rational numbers, namely $\{x \mid x \in Rt \text{ and } x < 0/1\}$, possesses many upper bounds—in fact, each rational number not in the set is an upper bound of the set. Furthermore, $0/1$ is a least upper bound of this set.

Now we can say what is meant by a *complete ordered field*.

DEFINITION 1.7.3.   Let $(S, +, \cdot, <, 0, 1)$ be any ordered field; then this algebraic system is said to be a *complete ordered field* iff each nonempty subset of S which possesses an upper bound also possesses a least upper bound.

It is easy to show that the system of rational numbers is *not* a complete ordered field; on the other hand, the system of real numbers *is* a complete ordered field. Furthermore, there is essentially just one complete ordered field; i.e., any two complete ordered fields are isomorphic.

E X E R C I S E S

1. Show that the algebraic system $(\{0, 1, 2, 3, 4\}, +, \cdot, 0, 1)$ is a field, where the binary operations $+$ and $\cdot$ are given by the following tables:

+	0	1	2	3	4
0	0	1	2	3	4
1	1	2	3	4	0
2	2	3	4	0	1
3	3	4	0	1	2
4	4	0	1	2	3

$\cdot$	0	1	2	3	4
0	0	0	0	0	0
1	0	1	2	3	4
2	0	2	4	1	3
3	0	3	1	4	2
4	0	4	3	2	1

2. List the field postulates implied by Definition 1.7.1.

3. Prove Theorem 1.7.1.

4. Let $(S, +, \cdot, <, 0, 1)$ be any ordered field. Prove that $-x < 0$ whenever $0 < x$.

5. Let $(S, +, \cdot, <, 0, 1)$ be any ordered field. Prove that $-x < 0$ iff $0 < x$.

6. Let $(S, +, \cdot, <, 0, 1)$ be any ordered field. Given that x and y are any members of S, prove that exactly one of the following is true: $x = y$, $x < y$, $y < x$.

7. Show that $(\{0, 1\}, +, \cdot, <, 0, 1)$ is *not* an ordered field, given that

$$+ = \{(0, 0, 0), (0, 1, 1), (1, 0, 1), (1, 1, 0)\},$$

$$\cdot = \{(0, 0, 0), (0, 1, 0), (1, 0, 0), (1, 1, 1)\},$$

$$< = \{(0, 1)\}.$$

Which postulate is false here?

8. Present an example of an algebraic system for which each of the postulates of an ordered field is true, with the exception of (14).

9. Prove that $x < y$ iff $-y < -x$ whenever x and y are members of S, where $(S, +, \cdot, <, 0, 1)$ is an ordered field.

10. Let $(S, +, \cdot, <, 0, 1)$ be any ordered field. Prove that $y \cdot z < x \cdot z$ whenever $x < y$ and $z < 0$.

11. Let $(S, +, \cdot, <, 0, 1)$ be any ordered field. Prove that $x + z < y + w$ whenever $x < y$ and $z < w$,

12. Let $(S, +, \cdot, <, 0, 1)$ be any ordered field. Prove that $x \cdot z < y \cdot w$ whenever $x < y$, $z < w$, $0 < x$, and $0 < z$.

13. Let $(S, +, \cdot, 0, 1)$ be any field. Prove that given any nonzero member of S, say x, and any member of S, say y, there is a *unique* member of S, say z, such that $x \cdot z = y$.

14. Let $(S, +, \cdot, <, 0, 1)$ be any ordered field, and suppose that K is a nonempty subset of S. Show that K does not possess *two* least upper bounds.

15. Suppose that $(S, +, \cdot, <, 0, 1)$ is an ordered field, K is a nonempty subset of S, and $b \in S$. Then b is called a *lower bound of K* iff $b < x$ or $b = x$ whenever $x \in K$; furthermore, G is called a *greatest lower bound of K* iff G is a lower bound of K and $b < G$ or $b = G$ whenever

b is a lower bound of K. Assuming that $(S, +, \cdot, <, 0, 1)$ is complete, prove that each non-empty subset of S which possesses a lower bound also possesses a greatest lower bound. (*Hint:* Consider $\{x \mid -x \in K\}$.)

16. Prove that the ordered field $(S, +, \cdot, <, 0, 1)$ is complete iff each nonempty subset of S which possesses a lower bound also possesses a greatest lower bound.

17. Prove that any two complete ordered fields are isomorphic.

18. Prove that the algebraic system $(\{0, 1, 2, \cdots, k-1\}, +, \cdot, 0, 1)$, where "$+$" and "$\cdot$" represent *addition modulo k* and *multiplication modulo k*, respectively, is a field iff k is prime.

1.8 Vector Spaces

We now come to the concept of a vector space; we shall use this notion in the following chapters. Notice the use of algebraic systems in the following definition.

DEFINITION 1.8.1.   An ordered triple, say $(\mathscr{F}, \mathscr{V}, \circ)$, where $\mathscr{F} = (F, +, \cdot, 0, 1)$ and $\mathscr{V} = (V, +, \mathbf{0})$, is said to be a *vector space* iff

(i) $\mathscr{F}$ is a field;

(ii) $\mathscr{V}$ is an abelian group;

(iii) $\circ$ is a mapping of $F \times V$ into V;

(iv) $a \circ (x + y) = a \circ x + a \circ y$ whenever $a \in F$, $x \in V$, and $y \in V$;

(v) $(a + b) \circ x = a \circ x + b \circ x$ whenever $a \in F$, $b \in F$, and $x \in V$;

(vi) $(a \cdot b) \circ x = a \circ (b \circ x)$ whenever $a \in F$, $b \in F$, and $x \in V$;

(vii) $1 \circ x = x$ whenever $x \in V$.

The members of V are called *vectors* and the members of F are called *scalars*. The mapping $\circ$ is called *scalar multiplication*. It is customary to denote $a \circ x$, where a is a scalar and x is a vector, by writing "ax"; indeed, $a \cdot b$ is customarily denoted by "ab", where a and b are scalars. One relies on the context to distinguish between field multiplication and scalar multiplication.

We now present some vector spaces.

EXAMPLE 1.   Let $\mathscr{F}$ be the real number field $(R, +, \cdot, 0, 1)$, let V be the set of all ordered n-tuples of real numbers, let $(a_1, a_2, \cdots, a_n) + (b_1, b_2, \cdots, b_n) = (a_1 + b_1, a_2 + b_2, \cdots, a_n + b_n)$ whenever $(a_1, a_2, \cdots, a_n)$ and $(b_1, b_2, \cdots, b_n)$ are ordered n-tuples of real numbers, let $\mathbf{0} = (0, 0, \cdots, 0)$, and let $c \circ (a_1, a_2, \cdots, a_n) = (ca_1, ca_2, \cdots, ca_n)$ whenever c is a real number and $(a_1, a_2, \cdots, a_n)$ is an ordered n-tuple of real numbers.

EXAMPLE 2.   Let $(F, +, \cdot, 0, 1)$ be any field, let $V = F \times F$, let $(a, b) + (c, d) = (a + c, b + d)$ whenever $(a, b) \in V$ and $(c, d) \in V$, let $\mathbf{0} = (0, 0)$, and let $c \circ (a, b) = (c \cdot a, c \cdot b)$ whenever $c \in F$ and $(a, b) \in V$.

EXAMPLE 3. Let $(F, +, \cdot, 0, 1)$ be any field, let V be the set of all mappings of $\{0, 1\}$ into F, let $f + g = \{(0, f(0) + g(0)), (1, f(1) + g(1))\}$ whenever $f \in V$ and $g \in V$, let $\mathbf{0} = \{(0, 0), (1, 0)\}$, and let $c \circ f = \{(0, c \cdot f(0)), (1, c \cdot f(1))\}$ whenever $c \in F$ and $f \in V$.

EXAMPLE 4. Let $(F, +, \cdot, 0, 1)$ be any field, let V be the set of all mappings of F into F, let $f + g = \{(t, f(t) + g(t)) \mid t \in F\}$ whenever $f \in V$ and $g \in V$, let $\mathbf{0} = \{(t, 0) \mid t \in F\}$, and let $c \circ f = \{(t, c \cdot f(t)) \mid t \in F\}$ whenever $c \in F$ and $f \in V$.

EXAMPLE 5. Let $\mathscr{R}$ be the real number field, let V be the set of all continuous functions with domain $[0, 1]$, let $f + g = \{(a, b) \mid b = f(a) + g(a)\}$ whenever $f \in V$ and $g \in V$, let $\mathbf{0} = \{(a, 0) \mid a \in [0, 1]\}$, and let $c \circ f = \{(a, b) \mid b = c \cdot f(a)\}$ whenever $c \in R$ and $f \in V$.

We now establish some theorems about vector spaces. Let $(\mathscr{F}, \mathscr{V}, \circ)$ be any vector space where $\mathscr{F} = (F, +, \cdot, 0, 1)$ and $\mathscr{V} = (V, +, \mathbf{0})$; the following theorems refer to this mathematical system.

THEOREM 1.8.1. $0 \circ x = \mathbf{0}$ whenever $x \in V$.

Proof: Let $x \in V$; by (v), $(0 + 0) \circ x = 0 \circ x + 0 \circ x$. By (i), $0 + 0 = 0$, so $0 \circ x = 0 \circ x + 0 \circ x$. Hence, by (ii), $0 \circ x = \mathbf{0}$. This establishes Theorem 1.8.1.

THEOREM 1.8.2. $(-1) \circ x = -x$ whenever $x \in V$.

Proof: Let $x \in V$; by (v), $(1 + -1) \circ x = 1 \circ x + (-1) \circ x$. By (i), $(1 + -1) = 0$; by (vii), $1 \circ x = x$. Therefore $0 \circ x = x + (-1) \circ x$. Hence, by Theorem 1.8.1, $x + (-1) \circ x = \mathbf{0}$. This means that $(-1) \circ x$ is the inverse of x, i.e., $(-1) \circ x = -x$. This establishes Theorem 1.8.2.

THEOREM 1.8.3. $a \circ \mathbf{0} = \mathbf{0}$ whenever $a \in F$.

Proof: Apply (iv); the details are left as an exercise.

We now introduce the concept of a *subsystem* of a vector space.

DEFINITION 1.8.2. Let $(\mathscr{F}, \mathscr{V}, \circ)$ be any vector space, and suppose that W is any nonempty subset of V such that

(i) $x + y \in W$ whenever $x \in W$ and $y \in W$,

(ii) $a \circ x \in W$ whenever $a \in F$ and $x \in W$;

then the mathematical structure $(\mathscr{F}, \mathscr{W}, \circ \mid F \times W)$ is said to be a *subsystem* of $(\mathscr{F}, \mathscr{V}, \circ)$, where $\mathscr{W} = (W, + \mid W \times W, \mathbf{0})$.

Note: "$\circ \mid S$" denotes $\circ$ restricted to S.

THEOREM 1.8.4. $(\mathcal{F}, \mathcal{W}, \circ \,|\, F \times W)$ is a vector space.

Proof: First, we must show that $(W, + \,|\, W \times W, \mathbf{0})$ is an abelian group; next, we must show that the remaining conditions of Definition 1.8.1 have been met. The details are left as an exercise.

Since vector addition is associative, we are entitled to suppress parentheses when summing three vectors; thus for $x + (y + z) = (x + y) + z$ there is no ambiguity in writing "$x + y + z$". Also, consider the expression "$x + y + z + w$", where x, y, z, and w are vectors. To make sense of this expression, we insert parentheses in all possible ways. It is easy to see that no matter how we insert parentheses, we obtain the same vector: e.g., $(x + y) + z + w = x + (y + z + w) = (x + y + z) + w = x + (y + z) + w$. (Notice our use of the preceding result, which enables us to add three vectors without inserting parentheses.) For this reason, we agree to suppress parentheses and write "$x + y + z + w$". It is easy to generalize this convention—indeed, let n be any natural number and let $x_1, x_2, \cdots, x_n$ be any vectors; then there is no ambiguity in writing "$x_1 + x_2 + \cdots + x_n$". No matter how we insert parentheses in this expression, we end up with the same vector.

We now introduce the notion of a *linear combination*.

DEFINITION 1.8.3. Let $x_1, x_2, \cdots, x_n$ be any vectors and let $a_1, a_2, \cdots, a_n$ be any scalars; then the vector $a_1 x_1 + a_2 x_2 + \cdots + a_n x_n$ is said to be a *linear combination* of the vectors $x_1, x_2, \cdots, x_n$.

THEOREM 1.8.5. Let $(\mathcal{F}, \mathcal{V}, \circ)$ be any vector space and suppose $\{x_1, x_2, \cdots, x_n\} \subset V$. Let W be the set of all linear combinations of $x_1, x_2, \cdots, x_n$; then $(\mathcal{F}, \mathcal{W}, \circ \,|\, F \times W)$ is a subsystem of $(\mathcal{F}, \mathcal{V}, \circ)$, where $\mathcal{W} = (W, + \,|\, W \times W, \mathbf{0})$.

Proof: The details are left as an exercise.

DEFINITION 1.8.4. The vectors $x_1, x_2, \cdots, x_n$ are said to be *linearly dependent* iff there are scalars $a_1, a_2, \cdots, a_n$, not all zero, such that $a_1 x_1 + a_2 x_2 + \cdots + a_n x_n = \mathbf{0}$.

DEFINITION 1.8.5. The vectors $x_1, x_2, \cdots, x_n$ are said to be *linearly independent* iff they are not linearly dependent.

Considering the vector space of Example 2, we note that the vectors $(1, 0)$ and $(-1, 0)$ are linearly dependent since $1 \circ (1, 0) + 1 \circ (-1, 0) = (0, 0) = \mathbf{0}$. In this same vector space the vectors $(1, 0)$ and $(0, 1)$ are linearly independent. To see this, let a and b be scalars such that $a \circ (1, 0) + b \circ (0, 1) = \mathbf{0}$; then $(a, b) = \mathbf{0}$, i.e., $a = 0$ and $b = 0$.

DEFINITION 1.8.6. The *dimension* of a vector space is the largest nonnegative integer t such that there are t linearly independent vectors in the vector space; if there is no such number, the vector space is said to have *infinite* dimension.

Notice that the vector space of Example 2 has dimension 2 since any three or more vectors of this vector space are linearly dependent.

We come, now, to the notion of a *basis* for a vector space.

DEFINITION 1.8.7.   Let $(\mathscr{F}, \mathscr{V}, \circ)$ be any finite-dimensional vector space; then $\{x_1, x_2, \cdots, x_n\}$ is said to be a *basis* for $(\mathscr{F}, \mathscr{V}, \circ)$ iff

(i) V is the set of all linear combinations of $x_1, x_2, \cdots, x_n$;

(ii) $x_1, x_2, \cdots, x_n$ are linearly independent.

For example, $\{(1, 0), (0, 1)\}$ is a basis for the vector space of Example 2; notice that $c \circ (1, 0) + d \circ (0, 1) = (c, d)$ whenever c and d are scalars of the vector space.

E X E R C I S E S

1. Let $\mathscr{F} = (F, +, \cdot, 0, 1)$ be any field. Show that $(\mathscr{F}, \mathscr{V}, \cdot)$ is a vector space where $\mathscr{V} = (F, +, 0)$.

2. **a.** Let $\mathscr{F} = (F, +, \cdot, 0, 1)$ be any field and let n be any natural number. Show that $(\mathscr{F}, \mathscr{V}, \circ)$ is a vector space, where V is the set of all ordered n-tuples of members of F, $(a_1, a_2, \cdots, a_n)$ $+ (b_1, b_2, \cdots, b_n) = (a_1 + b_1, a_2 + b_2, \cdots, a_n + b_n)$ whenever $(a_1, a_2, \cdots, a_n) \in V$ and $(b_1, b_2, \cdots, b_n) \in V$, $\mathbf{0} = (0, 0, \cdots, 0)$, and $c \circ (a_1, a_2, \cdots, a_n) = (c \cdot a_1, c \cdot a_2, \cdots, c \cdot a_n)$ whenever $c \in F$ and $(a_1, a_2, \cdots, a_n) \in V$.
   b. Present n linearly independent vectors of this vector space.
   c. If $t > n$, prove that any t vectors of this vector space are linearly dependent.

3. **a.** Let $\mathscr{F} = (F, +, \cdot, 0, 1)$ be any field and let n be any natural number. Show that $(\mathscr{F}, \mathscr{V}, \circ)$ is a vector space where V is the set of all mappings of $\{1, 2, \cdots, n\}$ into F, $f + g = \{(t, f(t) + g(t)) \mid t \in \{1, 2, \cdots, n\}\}$ whenever $f \in V$ and $g \in V$, $\mathbf{0} = \{(t, 0) \mid t \in \{1, 2, \cdots, n\}\}$, and $c \circ f = \{(t, c \cdot f(t) \mid t \in \{1, 2, \cdots, n\}\}$ whenever $c \in F$ and $f \in V$.
   b. Present n linearly independent vectors of this vector space.
   c. If $t > n$, prove that any t vectors of this vector space are linearly dependent.

4. Given that any t vectors of a vector space are linearly dependent, prove that any $t + n$ vectors of the vector space are linearly dependent, where n is any natural number.

5. Prove Theorem 1.8.3.

6. Prove Theorem 1.8.4.

7. Prove Theorem 1.8.5.

8. Given that a is a nonzero scalar and that x is a vector, prove that $a \circ x = \mathbf{0}$ iff $x = \mathbf{0}$.

9. Prove that $x_1, x_2, \cdots, x_n$ are linearly dependent if $x_1 = x_2$.

10. Show that the vector spaces of Examples 2 and 3 are algebraically the same.

11. Show that the vector spaces of Exercises 2 and 3 are algebraically the same.

12. Let $(\mathscr{F}, \mathscr{V}, \circ)$ be any vector space, let V be the set of all linear combinations of the vectors $x_1, x_2, \cdots, x_t$, and let $y_1, y_2, \cdots, y_m$ be linearly independent vectors of V. Prove that there are $t - m$ of the x's, say $x_{m+1}, x_{m+2}, \cdots, x_t$, such that V is the set of all linear combinations of $y_1, y_2, \cdots, y_m, x_{m+1}, x_{m+2}, \cdots, x_t$.

13. Let $v_1, v_2, \cdots, v_t$ be vectors of a given vector space. Prove that the vectors $x_1, x_2, \cdots, x_{t+1}$ are linearly dependent if each of these vectors is a linear combination of $v_1, v_2, \cdots, v_t$.

14. Let $\{x_1, x_2, \cdots, x_s\}$ be a basis for a vector space and let $\{y_1, y_2, \cdots, y_t\}$ be a basis for the same vector space. Prove that $s = t$.

15. Let $(\mathscr{F}, \mathscr{V}, \circ)$ be a vector space with dimension t. Prove that any set of t linearly independent vectors of this vector space is a basis for the vector space.

16. Prove that a subsystem of a finite-dimensional vector space differs from the vector space iff they have different dimensions.

17. Present an infinite-dimensional vector space.

1.9 Boolean Algebra

The algebraic systems investigated in the preceding three sections are important because of their relationship to the various number systems of mathematics. We turn now to the study of a family of algebraic systems called *Boolean algebras*, an investigation which is largely motivated by the algebra of sets. It is well known that the name of a set can be simplified by applying a strictly algebraic procedure, using seventeen basic laws. Of course, we do not need all seventeen laws, since some of these laws can be established algebraically on the basis of the remaining laws. Furthermore, we do not need all of the operations and relations $\cup, \cap, ', \subset$, since some of these can be defined in terms of the others. Do you see the problem that confronts us? We want to choose certain of the operations and relations $\cup, \cap, ', \subset$ and to list certain of their properties in such a manner that the remaining operations and relations can be defined in terms of the chosen ones, and their properties established.

This problem was investigated by the famous American mathematician, E. V. Huntington, and in 1904 his solution appeared in print (of course, there are other solutions to this problem). He showed that by selecting the binary operations $\cup$ and $\cap$, and the special sets $\varnothing$ and I, only seven basic laws are needed. His basic laws are the following:

LAW 1: $a \cup b = b \cup a$, for each a and b.
LAW 2: $a \cap b = b \cap a$, for each a and b.
LAW 3: $a \cup \varnothing = a$, for each a.
LAW 4: $a \cap I = a$, for each a.
LAW 5: $a \cap (b \cup c) = (a \cap b) \cup (a \cap c)$, for each a, b, and c.
LAW 6: $a \cup (b \cap c) = (a \cup b) \cap (a \cup c)$, for each a, b, and c.
LAW 7: Given a, we can find b such that $a \cup b = I$ and $a \cap b = \varnothing$.

Here, we shall demonstrate that the unary operation $'$ and the binary relation $\subset$ can be defined in terms of $\cup, \cap, \varnothing$, and I, and that each of our seventeen basic laws can be established algebraically by using Huntington's seven laws. To this purpose it is convenient to consider any algebraic system of the type $(B, +, \cdot, 0, 1)$—where B is the basic set of the algebraic system, $+$ and $\cdot$ are binary operations on B, and 0 and 1 are distinct members of B—for which Huntington's seven laws are true; e.g.,

(1) $a + b = b + a$, for each a and b;

(2) $a \cdot b = b \cdot a$, for each a and b;

(3) $a + 0 = a$, for each a;

(4) $a \cdot 1 = a$, for each a;

(5) $a \cdot (b + c) = (a \cdot b) + (a \cdot c)$, for each a, b, and c;

(6) $a + (b \cdot c) = (a + b) \cdot (a + c)$, for each a, b, and c;

(7) given a, we can find b such that $a + b = 1$ and $a \cdot b = 0$.

Such an algebraic system is called a *Boolean algebra*. For example, the algebraic system $(\{0, 1\}, +, \cdot, 0, 1)$, where $+ = \{(0, 0, 0), (0, 1, 1), (1, 0, 1), (1, 1, 1)\}$ and $\cdot = \{(0, 0, 0), (0, 1, 0), (1, 0, 0), (1, 1, 1)\}$ is a Boolean algebra. *Problem:* Demonstrate that Huntington's seven laws are true here!

Of course, the algebraic system $(\mathscr{P}I, \cup, \cap, \varnothing, I)$—where I is a nonempty set, $\cup$ and $\cap$ are the usual operations on sets, and $\varnothing$ is the empty set—is a Boolean algebra, as is easily checked. It is this Boolean algebra that interests us particularly; we want to show that our seventeen basic laws are true here. We accomplish this by proving that these laws are true in *any* Boolean algebra. Suppose, then, that the algebraic system $(B, +, \cdot, 0, 1)$ is a Boolean algebra. Let us prove the following theorems.

THEOREM 1.9.1. $a + a = a$ whenever $a \in B$.

Proof: Suppose $a \in B$; then

$$
\begin{aligned}
a &= a + 0 && \text{by Law 3} \\
&= a + (a \cdot b) && \text{by Law 7, for a certain } b \in B \\
&= (a + a) \cdot (a + b) && \text{by Law 6} \\
&= (a + a) \cdot 1 && \text{by Law 7} \\
&= a + a && \text{by Law 4.}
\end{aligned}
$$

THEOREM 1.9.2. $a \cdot a = a$ whenever $a \in B$.

Proof: The proof parallels the proof of Theorem 1.9.1 and is left as an exercise.

THEOREM 1.9.3. $a + 1 = 1$ whenever $a \in B$.

Proof: Suppose $a \in B$; then

$$
\begin{aligned}
1 &= a + b & &\text{by Law 7, for a certain } b \in B \\
&= a + (b \cdot 1) & &\text{by Law 4} \\
&= (a + b) \cdot (a + 1) & &\text{by Law 6} \\
&= 1 \cdot (a + 1) & &\text{since } a + b = 1 \\
&= (1 \cdot a) + (1 \cdot 1) & &\text{by Law 5} \\
&= (1 \cdot a) + 1 & &\text{by Th. 1.9.2} \\
&= (a \cdot 1) + 1 & &\text{by Law 2} \\
&= a + 1 & &\text{by Law 4.}
\end{aligned}
$$

THEOREM 1.9.4. $a \cdot 0 = 0$ whenever $a \in B$.

Proof: The proof parallels the proof of Theorem 1.9.3 and is left as an exercise.

THEOREM 1.9.5. $a + (a \cdot b) = a$ whenever $a \in B$ and $b \in B$.

Proof: Suppose $a \in B$ and $b \in B$; then

$$
\begin{aligned}
a &= a \cdot 1 & &\text{by Law 4} \\
&= a \cdot (b + 1) & &\text{by Th. 1.9.3} \\
&= a \cdot (1 + b) & &\text{by Law 1} \\
&= (a \cdot 1) + (a \cdot b) & &\text{by Law 5} \\
&= a + (a \cdot b) & &\text{by Law 4.}
\end{aligned}
$$

THEOREM 1.9.6. $a \cdot (a + b) = a$ whenever $a \in B$ and $b \in B$.

Proof: The proof parallels the proof of Theorem 1.9.5 and is left as an exercise.

THEOREM 1.9.7. Let $a, b, c,$ and d be members of B such that $c + d = 1, c \cdot d = 0,$ $c \cdot a = c \cdot b,$ and $d \cdot a = d \cdot b$; then $a = b$.

Proof: Suppose $a, b, c,$ and d are members of B such that $c + d = 1, c \cdot d = 0,$ $c \cdot a = c \cdot b,$ and $d \cdot a = d \cdot b$; then

$$(c \cdot a) + (d \cdot a) = (c \cdot b) + (d \cdot b),$$

and so
$$(c + d) \cdot a = (c + d) \cdot b;$$

i.e.,
$$1 \cdot a = 1 \cdot b;$$

hence $a = b$.

THEOREM 1.9.8. $a + (b + c) = (a + b) + c$ whenever $a \in B$, $b \in B$, and $c \in B$.

Proof: Suppose a, b, and c are any members of B; then, of course, $a + (b + c)$ and $(a + b) + c$ are members of B. Suppose that e is a member of B such that $a + e = 1$ and $a \cdot e = 0$; then

$$
\begin{aligned}
a \cdot [a + (b + c)] &= (a \cdot a) + [a \cdot (b + c)] && \text{by Law 5} \\
&= a + [a \cdot (b + c)] && \text{by Th. 1.9.2} \\
&= a && \text{by Th. 1.9.5,}
\end{aligned}
$$

and

$$
\begin{aligned}
a \cdot [(a + b) + c] &= [a \cdot (a + b)] + (a \cdot c) && \text{by Law 5} \\
&= a + (a \cdot c) && \text{by Th. 1.9.6} \\
&= a && \text{by Th. 1.9.5;}
\end{aligned}
$$

therefore $a \cdot [a + (b + c)] = a \cdot [(a + b) + c]$. Also,

$$
\begin{aligned}
e \cdot [a + (b + c)] &= (e \cdot a) + [e \cdot (b + c)] \\
&= 0 + [e \cdot (b + c)] \\
&= e \cdot (b + c),
\end{aligned}
$$

and

$$
\begin{aligned}
e \cdot [(a + b) + c] &= [e \cdot (a + b)] + (e \cdot c) \\
&= [(e \cdot a) + (e \cdot b)] + (e \cdot c) \\
&= [0 + (e \cdot b)] + (e \cdot c) \\
&= (e \cdot b) + (e \cdot c) \\
&= e \cdot (b + c);
\end{aligned}
$$

therefore $e \cdot [a + (b + c)] = e \cdot [(a + b) + c]$. Thus, by Theorem 1.9.7, $a + (b + c) = (a + b) + c$.

THEOREM 1.9.9. $a \cdot (b \cdot c) = (a \cdot b) \cdot c$ whenever $a \in B$, $b \in B$, and $c \in C$.

Proof: The proof of this theorem is parallel to that of Theorem 1.9.8. This means that you must first state and prove a theorem parallel to Theorem 1.9.7.

THEOREM 1.9.10.   Let a, b, and c be members of B such that $a + b = 1$, $a \cdot b = 0$, $a + c = 1$, and $a \cdot c = 0$; then $b = c$.

Proof: Suppose a, b, and c are members of B such that $a + b = 1$, $a \cdot b = 0$, $a + c = 1$, and $a \cdot c = 0$; then

$$
b = (a + c) \cdot b = (a \cdot b) + (c \cdot b) = 0 + (c \cdot b) = c \cdot b
$$

and

$$
c = (a + b) \cdot c = (a \cdot c) + (b \cdot c) = 0 + (b \cdot c) = b \cdot c = c \cdot b;
$$

hence $b = c$.

In view of Theorem 1.9.10, we know that given a member of B, say a, there is exactly one member of B, say b, such that $a + b = 1$ and $a \cdot b = 0$. For this reason, we introduce a unary operation on B, called $'$, in the following definition.

DEFINITION 1.9.1. $' = \{(a, b) \mid a \in B, b \in B, a + b = 1, \text{ and } a \cdot b = 0\}$.

As usual, if $(a, b) \in '$, then b is denoted by "a'".

THEOREM 1.9.11. $(a')' = a$ whenever $a \in B$.
Proof: Suppose $a \in B$; then $a + a' = 1$ and $a \cdot a' = 0$; therefore $a' + a = 1$ and $a' \cdot a = 0$, and so $(a')' = a$.

THEOREM 1.9.12. $1' = 0$.
Proof: $1 + 0 = 1$ by Law 3, and $1 \cdot 0 = 0 \cdot 1 = 0$ by Law 4; therefore $1' = 0$.

THEOREM 1.9.13. $0' = 1$.
Proof: $0' = (1')' = 1$, by Theorem 1.9.11.

THEOREM 1.9.14. $(a + b)' = a' \cdot b'$ whenever $a \in B$ and $b \in B$.
Proof: Suppose a and b are members of B; then

$$(a + b) + (a' \cdot b') = [(a + b) + a'] \cdot [(a + b) + b'] = 1 \cdot 1 = 1$$

and $(a + b) \cdot (a' \cdot b') = [a \cdot (a' \cdot b')] + [b \cdot (a' \cdot b')] = 0 + 0 = 0;$

therefore $(a + b)' = a' \cdot b'$.

THEOREM 1.9.15. $(a \cdot b)' = a' + b'$ whenever $a \in B$ and $b \in B$.
Proof: Suppose a and b are members of B; then $(a' + b')' = (a')' \cdot (b')' = a \cdot b$, and so $(a \cdot b)' = [(a' + b')']' = a' + b'$.
We now introduce a binary relation on B, denoted by "$\leq$".

DEFINITION 1.9.2. $\leq = \{(a, b) \mid a + b = b\}$.

As usual, the statement "$(a, b) \in \leq$" is denoted by writing "$a \leq b$".
The proofs of the following three theorems are straightforward.

THEOREM 1.9.16. $a \leq a$ whenever $a \in B$.

THEOREM 1.9.17. $a = b$ whenever $a \leq b$ and $b \leq a$.

THEOREM 1.9.18. $a \leq c$ whenever $a \leq b$ and $b \leq c$.

This completes our program of demonstrating that each of our seventeen basic laws can be established algebraically by using Huntington's seven laws.

E X E R C I S E S

1. Show that $(\{0, 1\}, +, \cdot, 1, 0)$ is a Boolean algebra, where
   $+ = \{(0, 0, 0), (0, 1, 0), (1, 0, 0), (1, 1, 1)\}$ and $\cdot = \{(0, 0, 0), (0, 1, 1), (1, 0, 1), (1, 1, 1)\}$.

2. Show that the algebraic system $(\{a, b, c, d\}, +, \cdot, a, b)$ is a Boolean algebra, where the binary operations are defined by the following tables:

+	a	b	c	d
a	a	b	c	d
b	b	b	b	b
c	c	b	c	b
d	d	b	b	d

·	a	b	c	d
a	a	a	a	a
b	a	b	c	d
c	a	c	c	a
d	a	d	a	d

Prove that the following propositions are true in each Boolean algebra $(B, +, \cdot, 0, 1)$.

3. $a + (b \cdot a') = a + b$ whenever $a \in B$ and $b \in B$.
4. $(a \cdot b \cdot c) + (a' + b' + c') = 1$ whenever $a \in B$, $b \in B$, and $c \in B$.
5. $0 \leq a$ and $a \leq 1$ whenever $a \in B$.
6. $c + a \leq c + b$ whenever $a \leq b$ and $c \in B$.
7. $a \leq b$ iff $a \cdot b' = 0$ whenever $a \in B$ and $b \in B$.
8. $a \leq b$ iff $b + a' = 1$ whenever $a \in B$ and $b \in B$.
9. $a \leq b \cdot c$ whenever $a \leq b$ and $a \leq c$.
10. $a \leq b$ iff $b' \leq a'$ whenever $a \in B$ and $b \in B$.
11. $a \leq b$ iff $a \cdot b = a$ whenever $a \in B$ and $b \in B$.
12. If $a \leq b$, then $c \cdot a \leq c \cdot b$ whenever $a \in B$, $b \in B$, and $c \in B$.
13. Construct a Boolean algebra such that the basic set of the algebraic system has exactly eight members.
14. Show that there is no Boolean algebra whose basic set has exactly three members.
15. Show that $(B, ?, !, a, b)$ is a Boolean algebra whenever $(B, !, ?, b, a)$ is a Boolean algebra.
16. Suppose that I is a nonempty set with an even number of members and that I has more than three members. Show that $(B, \cup, \cap, \varnothing, I)$ is *not* a Boolean algebra, where "B" denotes the collection of all subsets of I that have an even number of members, $\cup$ and $\cap$ are the usual operations on sets, and $\varnothing$ is the empty set.

17. Suppose that I is a nonempty set and that B is a collection of subsets of I. Prove that $(B, \cup, \cap, \varnothing, I)$ is a Boolean algebra, where $\cup$ and $\cap$ are the usual operations on sets—provided that $\cup$ and $\cap$ are binary operations on B, $\varnothing \in B$, and $I \in B$.

18. Show that no algebraic system is both a field and a Boolean algebra.

19. a. Show that $(B, +, \cdot, (0, 0), (1, 1))$ is a Boolean algebra, where $B = \{(0, 0), (0, 1), (1, 0), (1, 1)\}$, $(a, b) + (c, d) = (\max\{a, c\}, \max\{b, d\})$, and $(a, b) \cdot (c, d) = (a \cdot c, b \cdot d)$.

b. Construct a Boolean algebra whose basic set has 2^n members, given that n is a natural number.

2

Matrices and the Mapping Determinant

2.1 Linear Systems; Reducing a Matrix

Consider the problem of finding all ordered n-tuples of real numbers, say $(x_1, x_2, \cdots, x_n)$, such that

$$a_{11}x_1 + a_{12}x_2 + \cdots + a_{1n}x_n + b_1 = 0$$
$$a_{21}x_1 + a_{22}x_2 + \cdots + a_{2n}x_n + b_2 = 0$$
$$\vdots$$
$$a_{m1}x_1 + a_{m2}x_2 + \cdots + a_{mn}x_n + b_m = 0,$$

where the a's and b's are given real numbers. Notice that we are faced with m equations in the n unknowns $x_1, x_2, \cdots, x_n$. Our problem is to determine S such that

$$S = \{(c_1, c_2, \cdots, c_n) \,|\, a_{11}c_1 + a_{12}c_2 + \cdots + a_{1n}c_n = -b_1, a_{21}c_1 +$$

$$a_{22}c_2 + \cdots + a_{2n}c_n = -b_2, \cdots, a_{m1}c_1 + a_{m2}c_2 + \cdots + a_{mn}c_n = -b_m\}.$$

The set S is called the *solution set* of the given system of equations.

Notice that the system of equations is an *ordered* set of equations; there is a first equation, a second equation, $\cdots$, and an mth equation.

DEFINITION 2.2.1. Two ordered sets of equations are said to be *equivalent* iff they have the same solution set.

For example, the systems

$$\begin{cases} 3x_1 - x_2 - 1 = 0 \\ 2x_1 + x_2 - 4 = 0 \\ x_1 + 2x_2 - 5 = 0 \end{cases} \quad \text{and} \quad \begin{cases} x_1 - x_2 + 1 = 0 \\ x_1 + x_2 - 3 = 0 \end{cases}$$

are equivalent since each system has solution set $\{(1, 2)\}$. Notice that the systems

$$\begin{cases} x_1 + 2x_2 - x_3 - 2 = 0 \\ x_1 + x_2 - 2x_3 \phantom{{}+ 1} = 0 \\ 2x_1 - x_2 - 2x_3 + 1 = 0 \\ x_1 + x_2 + x_3 - 2 = 0 \end{cases} \quad \text{and} \quad \begin{cases} x_1 - 2x_2 + x_3 - 1 = 0 \\ 2x_1 - 4x_2 + 2x_3 - 3 = 0 \end{cases}$$

are equivalent since each system has solution set $\varnothing$, the empty set.

It is possible to transform a system of equations into an equivalent system whose solution set is easily found. This is achieved as the final result of a series of remarkably simple transformations. The basic question is: How can we obtain an equivalent system from a given system? There are several fundamental transformations, which we shall now consider. First, we observe that the *order* of the equations in the system does not matter; thus, interchanging two equations of the system does not affect the solution set. Therefore, this transformation produces an equivalent system. Second, we can multiply through any equation of the system by a nonzero real number. Let us show that this produces an equivalent system. Consider the systems I and II, where II is obtained from I by multiplying the first equation of I by k, a nonzero real number.

$$\text{I} \quad \begin{cases} a_{11}x_1 + a_{12}x_2 + \cdots + a_{1n}x_n + b_1 = 0 \\ a_{21}x_1 + a_{22}x_2 + \cdots + a_{2n}x_n + b_2 = 0 \\ \qquad\qquad \vdots \\ a_{m1}x_1 + a_{m2}x_2 + \cdots + a_{mn}x_n + b_m = 0. \end{cases}$$

$$\text{II} \quad \begin{cases} ka_{11}x_1 + ka_{12}x_2 + \cdots + ka_{1n}x_n + kb_1 = 0 \\ a_{21}x_1 + a_{22}x_2 + \cdots + a_{2n}x_n + b_2 = 0 \\ \qquad\qquad \vdots \\ a_{m1}x_1 + a_{m2}x_2 + \cdots + a_{mn}x_n + b_m = 0. \end{cases}$$

We shall show that I and II have the same solution set. Let $(c_1, \cdots, c_n)$ be a member of the solution set of II; then

$$ka_{11}c_1 + ka_{12}c_2 + \cdots + ka_{1n}c_n + kb_1 = 0$$
$$a_{21}c_1 + a_{22}c_2 + \cdots + a_{2n}c_n + b_2 = 0$$
$$\vdots$$
$$a_{m1}c_1 + a_{m2}c_2 + \cdots + a_{mn}c_n + b_m = 0.$$

But $k \neq 0$; therefore we can multiply through the first of the above equations by $1/k$, obtaining the equation

$$a_{11}c_1 + a_{12}c_2 + \cdots + a_{1n}c_n + b_1 = 0.$$

It follows immediately that $(c_1, c_2, \cdots, c_n)$ is a member of the solution set of I. This proves that the solution set of II is a subset of the solution set of I. Similarly, it is easy to prove that the solution set of I is a subset of the solution set of II. Thus I and II have the same solution set.

Here is a third way of obtaining an equivalent system from a given system: add one of the equations to another equation. More precisely, replace one equation by the equation obtained by adding another equation to it. Consider

$$\text{III} \quad \begin{cases} (a_{11} + a_{21})x_1 + (a_{12} + a_{22})x_2 + \cdots + (a_{1n} + a_{2n})x_n + b_1 + b_2 = 0 \\ a_{21}x_1 + a_{22}x_2 + \cdots + a_{2n}x_n + b_2 = 0 \\ \quad \vdots \\ a_{m1}x_1 + a_{m2}x_2 + \cdots + a_{mn}x_n + b_m = 0, \end{cases}$$

which has been obtained from I by replacing the first equation of I by the sum of the first and second equations of I. Let us show that I and III have the same solution set. Let $(c_1, c_2, \cdots, c_n)$ be a member of the solution set of III; then

$$(a_{11} + a_{21})c_1 + (a_{12} + a_{22})c_2 + \cdots + (a_{1n} + a_{2n})c_n + b_1 + b_2 = 0$$
$$a_{21}c_1 + a_{22}c_2 + \cdots + a_{2n}c_n + b_2 = 0$$
$$\vdots$$
$$a_{m1}c_1 + a_{m2}c_2 + \cdots + a_{mn}c_n + b_m = 0.$$

Subtracting the second of these equations from the first, we obtain

$$a_{11}c_1 + a_{12}c_2 + \cdots + a_{1n}c_n + b_1 = 0.$$

Hence $(c_1, c_2, \cdots, c_n)$ is a member of the solution set of I. This proves that the solution set of III is a subset of the solution set of I. Similarly, it is easy to prove that the solution set of I is a subset of the solution set of III. Thus I and III are equivalent.

Being lazy, we want to apply our method with a minimum of effort. In particular we shall avoid writing down symbols that are not necessary to our procedure. Since the x's, the plus signs, the 0's, and the equals signs do not vary throughout the system of equations, let us agree not to write down these symbols. This means that we shall represent the system I by writing

$$\begin{array}{ccccc} a_{11} & a_{12} & \cdots & a_{1n} & b_1 \\ a_{21} & a_{22} & \cdots & a_{2n} & b_2 \\ \vdots & & & & \\ a_{m1} & a_{m2} & \cdots & a_{mn} & b_m \end{array}$$

We want to separate the above array of numbers from the rest of the world, so we surround it by parentheses:

$$\begin{pmatrix} a_{11} & a_{12} & \cdots & a_{1n} & b_1 \\ a_{21} & a_{22} & \cdots & a_{2n} & b_2 \\ & & \vdots & & \\ a_{m1} & a_{m2} & \cdots & a_{mn} & b_m \end{pmatrix}.$$

An array of numbers of this sort is called a *matrix*. We shall sometimes want to indicate the number of rows and columns of a given matrix; a matrix which has m rows and n columns is said to be an $m \times n$ matrix. It is easy to recapture the system of equations represented by a matrix. For example, the 3×4 matrix

$$\begin{pmatrix} 1 & 3 & 2 & -1 \\ -1 & 2 & -1 & -4 \\ 2 & 1 & 2 & 3 \end{pmatrix}$$

represents the system of equations

$$x_1 + 3x_2 + 2x_3 - 1 = 0$$

$$-x_1 + 2x_2 - x_3 - 4 = 0$$

$$2x_1 + x_2 + 2x_3 + 3 = 0.$$

Let us solve this system of equations. To assert that two systems are equivalent, we shall insert the symbol "$\sim$" between them. Now,

$$\begin{pmatrix} 1 & 3 & 2 & -1 \\ -1 & 2 & -1 & -4 \\ 2 & 1 & 2 & 3 \end{pmatrix} \sim \begin{pmatrix} 1 & 3 & 2 & -1 \\ 0 & 5 & 1 & -5 \\ 2 & 1 & 2 & 3 \end{pmatrix} \sim \begin{pmatrix} -2 & -6 & -4 & 2 \\ 0 & 5 & 1 & -5 \\ 2 & 1 & 2 & 3 \end{pmatrix}$$

$$\sim \begin{pmatrix} -2 & -6 & -4 & 2 \\ 0 & 5 & 1 & -5 \\ 0 & -5 & -2 & 5 \end{pmatrix} \sim \begin{pmatrix} -2 & -6 & -4 & 2 \\ 0 & 5 & 1 & -5 \\ 0 & 0 & -1 & 0 \end{pmatrix} \sim \begin{pmatrix} -5 & -15 & -10 & 5 \\ 0 & 5 & 1 & -5 \\ 0 & 0 & -1 & 0 \end{pmatrix}$$

$$\sim \begin{pmatrix} -5 & -15 & -10 & 5 \\ 0 & 15 & 3 & -15 \\ 0 & 0 & -1 & 0 \end{pmatrix} \sim \begin{pmatrix} -5 & 0 & -7 & -10 \\ 0 & 15 & 3 & -15 \\ 0 & 0 & -1 & 0 \end{pmatrix} \sim \begin{pmatrix} -5 & 0 & -7 & -10 \\ 0 & 5 & 1 & -5 \\ 0 & 0 & -1 & 0 \end{pmatrix}$$

$$\sim \begin{pmatrix} -5 & 0 & -7 & -10 \\ 0 & 5 & 0 & -5 \\ 0 & 0 & -1 & 0 \end{pmatrix} \sim \begin{pmatrix} -5 & 0 & -7 & -10 \\ 0 & 5 & 0 & -5 \\ 0 & 0 & 7 & 0 \end{pmatrix} \sim \begin{pmatrix} -5 & 0 & 0 & -10 \\ 0 & 5 & 0 & -5 \\ 0 & 0 & 7 & 0 \end{pmatrix}$$

$$\sim \begin{pmatrix} 1 & 0 & 0 & 2 \\ 0 & 5 & 0 & -5 \\ 0 & 0 & 7 & 0 \end{pmatrix} \sim \begin{pmatrix} 1 & 0 & 0 & 2 \\ 0 & 1 & 0 & -1 \\ 0 & 0 & 7 & 0 \end{pmatrix} \sim \begin{pmatrix} 1 & 0 & 0 & 2 \\ 0 & 1 & 0 & -1 \\ 0 & 0 & 1 & 0 \end{pmatrix}.$$

Thus the given system is equivalent to the system

$$x_1 + 2 = 0, \quad x_2 - 1 = 0, \quad x_3 = 0.$$

The solution set of this system is easily found, namely $\{(-2, 1, 0)\}$. We have carefully listed each step in the simplification of the given system so that each transformation is visible.

It is easy to carry out several transformations mentally, indicating on paper the result of three or four transformations. In this way the amount of writing is greatly reduced. Certainly, this requires some practice at handling our basic transformations, but this is all to the good. To illustrate the technique, we simplify the above system of equations once again, this time doing mentally whatever we can:

$$\begin{pmatrix} 1 & 3 & 2 & -1 \\ -1 & 2 & -1 & -4 \\ 2 & 1 & 2 & 3 \end{pmatrix} \sim \begin{pmatrix} 1 & 3 & 2 & -1 \\ 0 & 5 & 1 & -5 \\ 0 & -5 & -2 & 5 \end{pmatrix} \sim \begin{pmatrix} 1 & 3 & 2 & -1 \\ 0 & 5 & 0 & -5 \\ 0 & 0 & -1 & 0 \end{pmatrix}$$

$$\sim \begin{pmatrix} 1 & 0 & 2 & 2 \\ 0 & 1 & 0 & -1 \\ 0 & 0 & 1 & 0 \end{pmatrix} \sim \begin{pmatrix} 1 & 0 & 0 & 2 \\ 0 & 1 & 0 & -1 \\ 0 & 0 & 1 & 0 \end{pmatrix}.$$

The procedure followed in this last example may not be clear. Look at the first column of the second matrix; note that all entries but one are zero. The same is true of the second column of the fourth matrix and also of the third column of the fifth matrix. We have *reduced* the matrix; i.e., we have obtained an equivalent matrix with 1's down the main diagonal and 0's off the main diagonal, with the exception of the entries in the final column.

In general, to reduce the matrix

$$\begin{pmatrix} a_{11} & a_{12} & \cdots & a_{1n} \\ a_{21} & a_{22} & \cdots & a_{2n} \\ & \vdots & & \\ a_{m1} & a_{m2} & \cdots & a_{mn} \end{pmatrix},$$

we operate on the first column so as to produce all 0's but one. This is achieved as follows. If $a_{11} = 0$, we look for an entry in the first column different from 0, and interchange the corresponding row with the first row. Assuming that $a_{11} \neq 0$, we multiply the first row by $-a_{i1}/a_{11}$ and add to the ith row; repeating for each i, where $2 \leq i \leq m$, we obtain a column of 0's except for the entry in the first row. Multiplying the first row through by $1/a_{11}$, we obtain 1 in that position. Having treated the first column in this manner, we transfer our attention to the second column. Supposing that the entry in the second row of this column is not 0, we easily produce 0's throughout the rest of the column. If the entry in the second row is 0, then we interchange the second row with some kth row, $k > 2$, such that the entry in the kth row, second column is not 0, and proceed as above.

EXAMPLE 1. Reduce the matrix

$$\begin{pmatrix} 0 & 1 & 3 & 2 \\ 1 & 3 & -1 & 0 \\ 2 & 1 & 4 & 2 \\ 1 & -7 & 11 & 4 \end{pmatrix}.$$

Solution:

$$\begin{pmatrix} 0 & 1 & 3 & 2 \\ 1 & 3 & -1 & 0 \\ 2 & 1 & 4 & 2 \\ 1 & -7 & 11 & 4 \end{pmatrix} \sim \begin{pmatrix} 1 & 3 & -1 & 0 \\ 0 & 1 & 3 & 2 \\ 0 & -5 & 6 & 2 \\ 0 & -10 & 12 & 4 \end{pmatrix} \sim \begin{pmatrix} 1 & 0 & -10 & -6 \\ 0 & 1 & 3 & 2 \\ 0 & 0 & 21 & 12 \\ 0 & 0 & 0 & 0 \end{pmatrix}$$

$$\sim \begin{pmatrix} 1 & 0 & -10 & -6 \\ 0 & 1 & 3 & 2 \\ 0 & 0 & 1 & \frac{4}{7} \\ 0 & 0 & 0 & 0 \end{pmatrix} \sim \begin{pmatrix} 1 & 0 & 0 & -\frac{2}{7} \\ 0 & 1 & 0 & \frac{2}{7} \\ 0 & 0 & 1 & \frac{4}{7} \\ 0 & 0 & 0 & 0 \end{pmatrix}.$$

EXAMPLE 2. Reduce the matrix

$$\begin{pmatrix} 3 & 1 & -2 & 1 \\ 2 & 2 & -1 & 3 \\ 1 & 0 & 3 & 11 \\ 2 & 1 & 1 & 7 \end{pmatrix}.$$

Solution:

$$\begin{pmatrix} 3 & 1 & -2 & 1 \\ 2 & 2 & -1 & 3 \\ 1 & 0 & 3 & 11 \\ 2 & 1 & 1 & 7 \end{pmatrix} \sim \begin{pmatrix} 1 & 0 & 3 & 11 \\ 0 & 1 & -11 & -32 \\ 0 & 2 & -7 & -19 \\ 0 & 1 & -5 & -15 \end{pmatrix} \sim \begin{pmatrix} 1 & 0 & 3 & 11 \\ 0 & 1 & -11 & -32 \\ 0 & 0 & 15 & 45 \\ 0 & 0 & 6 & 17 \end{pmatrix} \sim \begin{pmatrix} 1 & 0 & 0 & 2 \\ 0 & 1 & 0 & 1 \\ 0 & 0 & 1 & 3 \\ 0 & 0 & 0 & -1 \end{pmatrix}.$$

Question: What can you say about the solution set of the system of equations represented by the matrix of Example 2?

EXAMPLE 3. Solve the system

$$2x_1 - x_2 + 2x_3 + x_4 - 1 = 0$$

$$4x_1 + 2x_2 - x_3 - x_4 - 3 = 0$$

$$x_1 + 3x_2 - 2x_3 - x_4 + 2 = 0$$

$$-x_1 + x_2 + 3x_3 + x_4 + 6 = 0.$$

Solution: We reduce the matrix that represents the given system:

$$
\begin{pmatrix} 2 & -1 & 2 & 1 & -1 \\ 4 & 2 & -1 & -1 & -3 \\ 1 & 3 & -2 & -1 & 2 \\ -1 & 1 & 3 & 1 & 6 \end{pmatrix}
\sim
\begin{pmatrix} 1 & 3 & -2 & -1 & 2 \\ 0 & -7 & 6 & 3 & -5 \\ 0 & -10 & 7 & 3 & -11 \\ 0 & 4 & 1 & 0 & 8 \end{pmatrix}
\sim
\begin{pmatrix} 1 & 3 & -2 & -1 & 2 \\ 0 & 1 & 8 & 3 & 11 \\ 0 & 0 & 87 & 33 & 99 \\ 0 & 0 & -31 & -12 & -36 \end{pmatrix}
$$

$$
\sim
\begin{pmatrix} 1 & 0 & -26 & -10 & -31 \\ 0 & 1 & 8 & 3 & 11 \\ 0 & 0 & -6 & -3 & -9 \\ 0 & 0 & 31 & 12 & 36 \end{pmatrix}
\sim
\begin{pmatrix} 1 & 0 & -26 & -10 & -31 \\ 0 & 1 & 8 & 3 & 11 \\ 0 & 0 & 2 & 1 & 3 \\ 0 & 0 & 1 & -3 & -9 \end{pmatrix}
\sim
\begin{pmatrix} 1 & 0 & 0 & -88 & -265 \\ 0 & 1 & 0 & 27 & 83 \\ 0 & 0 & 1 & -3 & -9 \\ 0 & 0 & 0 & 7 & 21 \end{pmatrix}
$$

$$
\sim
\begin{pmatrix} 1 & 0 & 0 & 0 & -1 \\ 0 & 1 & 0 & 0 & 2 \\ 0 & 0 & 1 & 0 & 0 \\ 0 & 0 & 0 & 1 & 3 \end{pmatrix}.
$$

The reduced matrix represents the system

$$x_1 - 1 = 0, \quad x_2 + 2 = 0, \quad x_3 = 0, \quad x_4 + 3 = 0.$$

The solution set of this system is $\{(1, -2, 0, -3)\}$. Therefore this is the solution set of the given system.

For convenience, we now list the fundamental matrix transformations which produce an equivalent matrix from a given matrix: (1) interchange two rows, (2) multiply each entry of a given row by a nonzero real number, (3) add one row to another row.

E X E R C I S E S

1. Determine the solution set of the system

$$x_1 + 2x_2 + 1 = 0, \quad 2x_1 - x_2 - 3 = 0.$$

2. Determine the solution set of the system

$$x_1 - x_2 + x_3 = 0, \quad x_1 + x_2 - x_3 - 2 = 0, \quad x_1 + x_2 - 3 = 0.$$

3. Determine the solution set of the system

$$x_1 + x_2 - 2x_3 - 5 = 0, \quad x_1 + x_2 - x_3 - 4 = 0, \quad x_1 + x_3 = 0, \quad x_1 + x_3 - 1 = 0.$$

4. Exhibit two members of the solution set of the system

$$x_1 - x_2 + x_3 - 3 = 0, \quad 2x_1 + x_2 - 2x_3 - 2 = 0.$$

5. Exhibit three members of the solution set of the system

$$2x_1 - x_2 + x_3 = 0, \quad x_1 + x_2 - 3x_3 - 2 = 0.$$

6. Show that the following systems are equivalent:

(i) $x_1 + x_2 - 4 = 0, \quad 2x_1 - x_2 + 1 = 0, \quad 3x_1 - 2x_2 + 3 = 0,$

(ii) $2x_1 + x_2 - 5 = 0, \quad x_1 + 3x_2 - 10 = 0.$

7. Show that the following systems are equivalent:

(i) $x_1 - x_2 + x_3 - 6 = 0, \quad 2x_1 + x_2 - x_3 + 3 = 0, \quad x_1 + 2x_2 + 2x_3 - 3 = 0,$

(ii) $3x_1 - x_2 - x_3 - 2 = 0, \quad x_1 + x_2 + x_3 - 2 = 0, \quad 2x_1 + x_2 = 0.$

8. Prove that the binary relation $\sim$ is reflexive, symmetric, and transitive.

9. Prove that the system of equations obtained from a given system by subtracting one of the equations from another equation is equivalent to the given system.

10. By applying the fundamental matrix transformations, prove that

$$\begin{pmatrix} a_{11} & a_{12} & \cdots & a_{1n} \\ a_{21} & a_{22} & \cdots & a_{2n} \\ & \vdots & & \\ a_{m1} & a_{m2} & \cdots & a_{mn} \end{pmatrix} \sim \begin{pmatrix} a_{11} + ka_{21} & a_{12} + ka_{22} & \cdots & a_{1n} + ka_{2n} \\ a_{21} & a_{22} & & a_{2n} \\ & \vdots & & \\ a_{m1} & a_{m2} & & a_{mn} \end{pmatrix}$$

whenever k is a real number.

Reduce the following matrices.

11.
$$\begin{pmatrix} 1 & 1 & -2 & 5 \\ 1 & 1 & -1 & 4 \\ 1 & 0 & 1 & 0 \\ 0 & 1 & 1 & 1 \end{pmatrix}.$$

12.
$$\begin{pmatrix} 1 & 2 & -1 \\ 2 & -1 & 3 \\ 3 & 2 & 1 \\ -1 & -3 & 2 \end{pmatrix}.$$

13.
$$\begin{pmatrix} 3 & -2 & -4 & 2 \\ 1 & 3 & -1 & 1 \\ 2 & 1 & 3 & 7 \\ -1 & 1 & 3 & 1 \\ 2 & 3 & 0 & 4 \end{pmatrix}.$$

14. Solve the system

$$2x_1 + x_2 - x_3 - 2x_4 = 11$$

$$3x_1 - x_2 + x_3 - x_4 = 8$$

$$-x_1 + x_2 - x_3 = -1$$

$$x_1 + x_2 + x_3 + x_4 = -2.$$

2.2   Permutations

In Section 1.5 we considered a group whose basic set consists of all the permutations of a given nonempty set. We now continue the discussion of permutations begun there. In particular, we are interested in the permutations of $\{1, 2, \cdots, n\}$, where n is a natural number. Let $\alpha = \begin{pmatrix} 1 & 2 & \cdots & n \\ a_1 & a_2 & \cdots & a_n \end{pmatrix}$; we want to measure the degree of disarrangement of the n-tuple $(a_1, a_2, \cdots, a_n)$ which is obtained by applying α to each term of the n-tuple $(1, 2, \cdots, n)$. The idea is to measure the disarrangement of each term of $(a_1, a_2, \cdots, a_n)$. To this purpose we introduce the counting function i as follows: $i(a_j)$ is the number of terms of $(a_1, a_2, \cdots, a_n)$ to the right of a_j which are less than a_j. For example, let $\alpha = \begin{pmatrix} 1 & 2 & 3 & 4 & 5 \\ 3 & 5 & 2 & 1 & 4 \end{pmatrix}$; then $i(1) = 0$, $i(2) = 1$, $i(3) = 2$, $i(4) = 0$, and $i(5) = 3$. Now that we can measure the disarrangement of each term of $(a_1, a_2, \cdots, a_n)$, we say that the disarrangement of the n-tuple itself is the sum of the disarrangements of its terms. We shall denote this number by "$\mathscr{I}\alpha$"; i.e., if $\alpha = \begin{pmatrix} 1 & 2 & \cdots & n \\ a_1 & a_2 & \cdots & a_n \end{pmatrix}$, then

$$\mathscr{I}\alpha = \sum_{j=1}^{n} i(a_j).$$

For example,

$$\mathscr{I}\begin{pmatrix} 1 & 2 & 3 & 4 & 5 \\ 3 & 5 & 2 & 1 & 4 \end{pmatrix} = 0 + 1 + 2 + 0 + 3 = 6 \quad \text{and} \quad \mathscr{I}\begin{pmatrix} 1 & 2 & 3 & 4 \\ 2 & 3 & 4 & 1 \end{pmatrix} = 0 + 1 + 1 + 1 = 3.$$

We are particularly interested in whether $\mathscr{I}\alpha$ is even or odd.

THEOREM 2.2.1.   Let n be any natural number and let $\begin{pmatrix} 1 & 2 & \cdots & n \\ a_1 & a_2 & \cdots & a_n \end{pmatrix}$ be any permutation of $\{1, 2, \cdots, n\}$; then $\mathscr{I}\begin{pmatrix} 1 & \cdots & j & j+1 & \cdots & n \\ a_1 & \cdots & a_j & a_{j+1} & \cdots & a_n \end{pmatrix}$ is even iff $\mathscr{I}\begin{pmatrix} 1 & \cdots & j & j+1 & \cdots & n \\ a_1 & \cdots & a_{j+1} & a_j & \cdots & a_n \end{pmatrix}$ is odd.

Proof: The proof is immediate; we have only to examine two cases:
(1) $a_j < a_{j+1}$; then

$$\mathscr{I}\begin{pmatrix} 1 & \cdots & j & j+1 & \cdots & n \\ a_1 & \cdots & a_{j+1} & a_j & \cdots & a_n \end{pmatrix} = 1 + \mathscr{I}\begin{pmatrix} 1 & \cdots & j & j+1 & \cdots & n \\ a_1 & \cdots & a_j & a_{j+1} & \cdots & a_n \end{pmatrix}.$$

(2) $a_{j+1} < a_j$; then

$$\mathscr{I}\begin{pmatrix} 1 & \cdots & j & j+1 & \cdots & n \\ a_1 & \cdots & a_j & a_{j+1} & \cdots & a_n \end{pmatrix} = 1 + \mathscr{I}\begin{pmatrix} 1 & \cdots & j & j+1 & \cdots & n \\ a_1 & \cdots & a_{j+1} & a_j & \cdots & a_n \end{pmatrix}.$$

This completes our proof.

It is easy to generalize Theorem 2.2.1.

THEOREM 2.2.2. Let n be any natural number and let

$$\begin{pmatrix} 1 & \cdots & i & \cdots & j & \cdots & n \\ a_1 & \cdots & a_i & \cdots & a_j & \cdots & a_n \end{pmatrix}$$

be any permutation of $\{1, 2, \cdots, n\}$; then

$$\mathscr{I}\begin{pmatrix} 1 & \cdots & i & \cdots & j & \cdots & n \\ a_1 & \cdots & a_i & \cdots & a_j & \cdots & a_n \end{pmatrix} \text{ is even iff } \mathscr{I}\begin{pmatrix} 1 & \cdots & i & \cdots & j & \cdots & n \\ a_1 & \cdots & a_j & \cdots & a_i & \cdots & a_n \end{pmatrix} \text{ is odd.}$$

Proof: We use mathematical induction on $j - i$. If $j - i = 1$, then we apply Theorem 2.2.1. It is easy to show (by a series of applications of Theorem 2.2.1) that if the result holds whenever $j - i = t$, then the result holds whenever $j - i = t + 1$. So by mathematical induction we have our proof. The details are left as an exercise.

We can use the fact that $\mathscr{I}\alpha$ is either even or odd to classify permutations.

DEFINITION 2.2.1. Let n be any natural number and let α be any permutation of $\{1, 2, \cdots, n\}$. Then α is said to be an *even* permutation if $\mathscr{I}\alpha$ is even, whereas α is said to be an *odd* permutation if $\mathscr{I}\alpha$ is odd.

For example, $\begin{pmatrix} 1 & 2 & 3 & 4 & 5 \\ 3 & 5 & 2 & 1 & 4 \end{pmatrix}$ is an even permutation, whereas $\begin{pmatrix} 1 & 2 & 3 & 4 \\ 2 & 3 & 4 & 1 \end{pmatrix}$ is an odd permutation.

Let us establish some properties of our concept.

THEOREM 2.2.3. Each transposition is an odd permutation.

Proof: Let $(a\ b)$ be a transposition of $\{1, 2, \cdots, n\}$ (see Definition 1.5.3). Now, $(a\ b) = \begin{pmatrix} 1 & \cdots & a & \cdots & b & \cdots & n \\ 1 & \cdots & b & \cdots & a & \cdots & n \end{pmatrix}$, and, by Theorem 2.2.2,

$$\mathscr{I}\begin{pmatrix} 1 & \cdots & a & \cdots & b & \cdots & n \\ 1 & \cdots & a & \cdots & b & \cdots & n \end{pmatrix} \text{ is even iff } \mathscr{I}\begin{pmatrix} 1 & \cdots & a & \cdots & b & \cdots & n \\ 1 & \cdots & b & \cdots & a & \cdots & n \end{pmatrix} \text{ is odd.}$$

Since $\mathscr{I}\varphi$ is even, we see that the transposition $(a\ b)$ is an odd permutation.

THEOREM 2.2.4. Let n be any natural number and let α be any even permutation of $\{1, 2, \cdots, n\}$. Then α is *not* the product of an odd number of transpositions.

Proof: Let α be an even permutation of $\{1, 2, \cdots, n\}$ and suppose that there is an odd number of transpositions, say $\beta_1, \beta_2, \cdots, \beta_{2t+1}$, such that $\alpha = \beta_1 \circ \beta_2 \circ \cdots \circ \beta_{2t+1}$. We shall apply Theorem 2.2.2 repeatedly, sluffing off one transposition each time. Thus

$\beta_1 \circ \beta_2 \circ \cdots \circ \beta_{2t}$ is an odd permutation; therefore $\beta_1 \circ \beta_2 \circ \cdots \circ \beta_{2t-1}$ is an even permutation; $\cdots$; so $\beta_1 \circ \beta_2$ is an odd permutation; thus β_1 is an even permutation. This contradicts Theorem 2.2.3. We conclude that α is not the product of an odd number of transpositions.

THEOREM 2.2.5.   Let n be any natural number and let α be any odd permutation of $\{1, 2, \cdots, n\}$. Then α is not the product of an even number of transpositions.

Proof: Apply the argument of Theorem 2.2.4; the details are left as an exercise.

We point out that Theorems 2.2.4 and 2.2.5 together assert that no permutation can be represented both as the product of an even number of transpositions and as the product of an odd number of transpositions. This result can be established by an alternative argument which uses a little group theory. First, we need a special case of Theorem 2.2.4: the identity permutation $\begin{pmatrix} 1 & 2 & \cdots & n \\ 1 & 2 & \cdots & n \end{pmatrix}$ is not the product of an odd number of transpositions. Next, let α be a permutation of $\{1, 2, \cdots, n\}$ such that $\alpha = \beta_1 \circ \beta_2 \circ \cdots \circ \beta_{2t}$ and $\alpha = \gamma_1 \circ \gamma_2 \circ \cdots \circ \gamma_{2s+1}$, where the β's and γ's are transpositions. Now, α has a unique inverse, namely $\beta_{2t} \circ \cdots \circ \beta_2 \circ \beta_1$ (*note:* the inverse is unique, not its representation as a product of transpositions). Therefore $(\gamma_1 \circ \gamma_2 \circ \cdots \circ \gamma_{2s+1}) \circ (\beta_{2t} \circ \cdots \circ \beta_2 \circ \beta_1)$ is the identity permutation. Thus the identity permutation is the product of an odd number of transpositions. This contradiction gives us our result.

We observe that if $n > 2$ then each permutation of $\{1, 2, \cdots, n\}$ is the product of a finite number of transpositions (see Corollary 1.5.1). Thus we have the following corollaries to Theorems 2.2.4 and 2.2.5.

COROLLARY 2.2.1.   Let n be any natural number greater than 2 and let α be any permutation of $\{1, 2, \cdots, n\}$. Then α is the product of an even number of transpositions iff α is not the product of an odd number of transpositions.

COROLLARY 2.2.2.   Let n be any natural number greater than 2 and let α be any permutation of $\{1, 2, \cdots, n\}$. Then α is an even permutation iff α is the product of an even number of transpositions.

In Section 2.3 we shall make use of *sgn*, a mapping which associates 1 or -1 with each permutation of $\{1, 2, \cdots, n\}$.

DEFINITION 2.2.2.   Let n be any natural number and let α be any permutation of $\{1, 2, \cdots, n\}$; then

$$\text{sgn } \alpha = \begin{cases} 1 & \text{if } \alpha \text{ is an even permutation} \\ -1 & \text{if } \alpha \text{ is an odd permutation.} \end{cases}$$

For example, $\text{sgn}\begin{pmatrix} 1\ 2\ 3\ 4\ 5 \\ 3\ 5\ 2\ 1\ 4 \end{pmatrix} = 1$, whereas $\text{sgn}\begin{pmatrix} 1\ 2\ 3\ 4 \\ 2\ 3\ 4\ 1 \end{pmatrix} = -1$.

We now establish some properties of *sgn* that we shall find useful.

THEOREM 2.2.6.   Let n be any natural number, let α be any permutation of $\{1, 2, \cdots, n\}$, and let β be the inverse of α. Then $\text{sgn } \alpha = \text{sgn } \beta$.

Proof: If $n \leq 2$, the theorem certainly holds. Suppose that $n > 2$. Now, $\alpha \circ \beta$ is the identity permutation; therefore $\alpha \circ \beta$ is an even permutation. Therefore, by Corollary 2.2.2, $\alpha \circ \beta$ is the product of an even number of transpositions. Hence α and β are both even or both odd. This establishes Theorem 2.2.6.

THEOREM 2.2.7.   Let n be any natural number greater than 1, let α be any permutation of $\{1, 2, \cdots, n\}$, and let γ be any transposition. Then $\text{sgn } \alpha = -\text{sgn } \alpha \circ \gamma$.

Proof: Apply Corollary 2.2.2.

It is important that we extend the concepts of this section.

DEFINITION 2.2.3.   Let α be any permutation of a finite set with more than two members; then α is said to be *even* if α is the product of an even number of transpositions, whereas α is said to be *odd* if α is the product of an odd number of transpositions.

This definition takes on added meaning in view of the following theorem.

THEOREM 2.2.8.   Let α be any permutation of a finite set with more than two members. Then α is the product of an even number of transpositions iff α is not the product of an odd number of transpositions.

Proof: The point is that the *names* of the members of the basic set do not matter. We can rename them $1, 2, \cdots, n$. Thus we can apply Corollary 2.2.1.

Next, we extend our mapping *sgn* as follows.

DEFINITION 2.2.4.   Let α be any permutation of a finite set with more than two members; then

$$\text{sgn } \alpha = \begin{cases} 1 \text{ if } \alpha \text{ is an even permutation} \\ -1 \text{ if } \alpha \text{ is an odd permutation.} \end{cases}$$

For example, let $\alpha = \begin{pmatrix} 2\ 5\ 8 \\ 5\ 2\ 8 \end{pmatrix}$; then $\alpha = (2\ 5)$. So α is an odd permutation, and $\text{sgn } \alpha = -1$.

E X E R C I S E S

1. Compute the following.

a. $\mathscr{I}\begin{pmatrix} 1\ 2\ 3\ 4 \\ 2\ 4\ 3\ 1 \end{pmatrix}$.

d. $\mathscr{I}(4\ 1\ 3\ 2)$.

b. $\mathscr{I}\begin{pmatrix} 1\ 2\ 3\ 4\ 5 \\ 3\ 2\ 4\ 5\ 1 \end{pmatrix}$.

e. $\mathscr{I}(2\ 5\ 1) \circ (4\ 3)$.

c. $\mathscr{I}\begin{pmatrix} 1\ 2\ 3\ 4\ 5\ 6 \\ 6\ 1\ 2\ 5\ 3\ 4 \end{pmatrix}$.

2. Prove Theorem 2.2.2.

3. Which of the following are even permutations and which are odd permutations?

a. $\begin{pmatrix} 1\ 2\ 3\ 4 \\ 3\ 2\ 4\ 1 \end{pmatrix}$.

d. $(4\ 2\ 1\ 3)$.

b. $\begin{pmatrix} 1\ 2\ 3\ 4\ 5 \\ 5\ 2\ 1\ 4\ 3 \end{pmatrix}$.

e. $(3\ 1\ 5) \circ (2\ 4)$.

c. $\begin{pmatrix} 1\ 2\ 3\ 4\ 5 \\ 4\ 3\ 5\ 2\ 1 \end{pmatrix}$.

f. $(2\ 6\ 3) \circ (4\ 5)$.

4. Prove Theorem 2.2.5.

5. Let $(a_1\ a_2 \cdots a_s)$ be any permutation of $\{1, 2, \cdots, n\}$. Prove that $(a_1\ a_2 \cdots a_s)$ is an even permutation iff s is odd.

6. Compute each of the following.

a. $\operatorname{sgn}\begin{pmatrix} 1\ 2\ 3\ 4 \\ 4\ 3\ 1\ 2 \end{pmatrix}$.

b. $\operatorname{sgn}(2\ 1\ 4\ 3\ 5)$.

c. $\operatorname{sgn}(3\ 2\ 4\ 1)$.

7. Let α and β be any permutations of $\{1, 2, \cdots, n\}$, where n is a natural number. Show that $\operatorname{sgn} \alpha = -\operatorname{sgn} \beta$ if there is a transposition γ such that $\alpha = \beta \circ \gamma$.

8. Let α be a permutation of $\{1, 2, \cdots, n\}$, say $\begin{pmatrix} 1 & 2 & \cdots & t & \cdots & n \\ t & a_2 & & a_t & & a_n \end{pmatrix}$, and let β be a permutation of $\{1, \cdots, t-1, t+1, \cdots, n\}$, say $\begin{pmatrix} 1 & 2 & \cdots & t-1 & t+1 & \cdots & n \\ a_t & a_2 & & a_{t-1} & a_{t+1} & & a_n \end{pmatrix}$. Prove that $\operatorname{sgn} \alpha = -\operatorname{sgn} \beta$.

2.3 The Mapping Determinant

We shall find that the notion of the *determinant* of a square matrix is useful in carrying out a matrix analysis of a system of equations. Now, *determinant* is a certain mapping of the set of all square matrices into R, the set of all real numbers. The idea, then, is to associate a real number with each square matrix; this real number is said to be the *determinant of the matrix* and is denoted by replacing the parentheses around the matrix by a pair of vertical lines. Now that our notation is established, let us define our mapping; this is our main job. It is natural to classify square matrices according to the number of rows; so we shall begin with 1×1 matrices. This is very simple $|a_{11}| = a_{11}$. Next, we consider 2×2 matrices:

$$\begin{vmatrix} a_{11} & a_{12} \\ a_{21} & a_{22} \end{vmatrix} = a_{11}a_{22} - a_{21}a_{12};$$

and next, 3×3 matrices:

$$\begin{vmatrix} a_{11} & a_{12} & a_{13} \\ a_{21} & a_{22} & a_{23} \\ a_{31} & a_{32} & a_{33} \end{vmatrix} = a_{11}a_{22}a_{33} - a_{11}a_{32}a_{23} + a_{31}a_{12}a_{23} - a_{21}a_{12}a_{33} + a_{21}a_{32}a_{13}$$
$$- a_{31}a_{22}a_{13}$$

Clearly, we cannot continue our definition in this way indefinitely; we must present a rule which will enable us to compute the determinant of any square matrix. Fortunately, such a rule exists. Let n be any natural number and consider any $n \times n$ matrix, say

$$\begin{pmatrix} a_{11} & a_{12} & \cdots & a_{1n} \\ a_{21} & a_{22} & \cdots & a_{2n} \\ & \vdots & & \\ a_{n1} & a_{n2} & \cdots & a_{nn} \end{pmatrix}.$$

The real number which we shall associate with this matrix is the following sum of products, where the summation is taken over all permutations α of $\{1, 2, \cdots, n\}$:

$$\sum_{\alpha} \text{sgn } \alpha \times a_{\alpha(1),1} \times a_{\alpha(2),2} \times \cdots \times a_{\alpha(n),n}.$$

Notice that each term of this sum is a product of n matrix entries; moreover, the n entries are chosen so that each row and column of the matrix is represented exactly once in the term. This is achieved by considering any permutation of $\{1, 2, \cdots, n\}$, say α, and then forming the product $a_{\alpha(1)}, \times a_{\alpha(2),2} \times \cdots \times a_{\alpha(n),n}$. Finally we change the algebraic sign of half of our products by multiplying by sgn α in each case. Thus we have the following definition.

DEFINITION 2.3.1.   Let n be any natural number and let

$$\begin{pmatrix} a_{11} & a_{12} & \cdots & a_{1n} \\ a_{21} & a_{22} & \cdots & a_{2n} \\ & \vdots & & \\ a_{n1} & a_{n2} & \cdots & a_{nn} \end{pmatrix}$$

be any $n \times n$ matrix; then

$$\begin{vmatrix} a_{11} & a_{12} & \cdots & a_{1n} \\ a_{21} & a_{22} & \cdots & a_{2n} \\ \vdots & & & \vdots \\ a_{n1} & a_{n2} & \cdots & a_{nn} \end{vmatrix} = \sum_{\alpha} \operatorname{sgn} \alpha \times a_{\alpha(1),1} \times a_{\alpha(2),2} \times \cdots \times a_{\alpha(n),n}.$$

Note: The summation is over *all* permutations of $\{1, 2, \cdots, n\}$.

We leave as an exercise the verification of the formulas given above for the determinant of a 1×1, 2×2, or 3×3 matrix. Let us illustrate Definition 2.3.1.

EXAMPLE 1. Compute

$$\begin{vmatrix} 2 & 3 & 1 \\ 1 & -4 & -2 \\ -1 & 5 & 7 \end{vmatrix}.$$

Solution: Instead of applying the formula for the determinant of a 3×3 matrix, we shall work directly from Definition 2.3.1. Thus

$$\begin{vmatrix} 2 & 3 & 1 \\ 1 & -4 & -2 \\ -1 & 5 & 7 \end{vmatrix} = \operatorname{sgn}\begin{pmatrix} 1\ 2\ 3 \\ 1\ 2\ 3 \end{pmatrix} \times 2 \times -4 \times 7 + \operatorname{sgn}\begin{pmatrix} 1\ 2\ 3 \\ 1\ 3\ 2 \end{pmatrix} \times 2 \times 5 \times -2$$

$$+ \operatorname{sgn}\begin{pmatrix} 1\ 2\ 3 \\ 2\ 1\ 3 \end{pmatrix} \times 1 \times 3 \times 7 + \operatorname{sgn}\begin{pmatrix} 1\ 2\ 3 \\ 2\ 3\ 1 \end{pmatrix} \times 1 \times 5 \times 1$$

$$+ \operatorname{sgn}\begin{pmatrix} 1\ 2\ 3 \\ 3\ 1\ 2 \end{pmatrix} \times -1 \times 3 \times -2 + \operatorname{sgn}\begin{pmatrix} 1\ 2\ 3 \\ 3\ 2\ 1 \end{pmatrix} \times -1 \times -4 \times 1$$

$$= -56 + 20 - 21 + 5 + 6 - 4$$

$$= -50.$$

THEOREM 2.3.1. Let n be any natural number and let A be the $n \times n$ matrix

$$\begin{pmatrix} 1 & 0 & \cdots & 0 \\ 0 & 1 & \cdots & 0 \\ & \vdots & & \\ 0 & 0 & \cdots & 1 \end{pmatrix},$$

where each entry on the main diagonal is 1 and all other entries are 0. Then $|A| = 1$.

Proof: Apply Definition 2.3.1; the details are left as an exercise.

It is time that we improved our notation for a matrix and for the determinant of a square matrix. Actually, what we need is a method of denoting any $m \times n$ matrix without listing each term of the matrix; yet we want to retain the ability to refer to a particular entry at will. These goals are achieved by the following convention. We shall denote the $m \times n$ matrix whose entry in the ith row and jth column is a_{ij} whenever $1 \leq i \leq m$ and $1 \leq j \leq n$, by writing "(a_{ij})". Of course, this convention does not disclose the dimensions of the matrix, i.e., the m and the n; however, this will not bother us. Next, let us agree to denote the determinant of a square matrix, say (a_{ij}), by writing "$|a_{ij}|$". Clearly, these conventions will enable us to avoid a great deal of writing, and the ideas under discussion will come through more sharply.

Many of the properties of the mapping *determinant* can be deduced directly from Definition 2.3.1 and from the known properties of permutations. At first glance we might wonder whether we can define the determinant of an $n \times n$ matrix, say (a_{ij}), as follows:

$$|a_{ij}| = \sum_\alpha \text{sgn } \alpha \times a_{1,\alpha(1)} \times a_{2,\alpha(2)} \times \cdots \times a_{n,\alpha(n)}.$$

As a matter of fact, this is sometimes taken as the definition of the mapping *determinant*. Under our approach this becomes a theorem.

THEOREM 2.3.2.   Let n be any natural number and let (a_{ij}) be any $n \times n$ matrix; then $|a_{ij}| = \sum_\alpha \text{sgn } \alpha \times a_{1,\alpha(1)} \times a_{2,\alpha(2)} \times \cdots \times a_{n,\alpha(n)}$.

Proof: We must demonstrate that

$$\sum_\alpha \text{sgn } \alpha \times a_{\alpha(1),1} \times \cdots \times a_{\alpha(n),n} = \sum_\alpha \text{sgn } \alpha \times a_{1,\alpha(1)} \times \cdots \times a_{n,\alpha(n)}.$$

First, we point out that each side of this equation possesses $n!$ terms since there are exactly $n!$ permutations of $\{1, 2, \cdots, n\}$. We propose to match each of the $n!$ terms on the left-hand side with an identical term on the right-hand side. Here, the key is the permutation which gives rise to a term on the left-hand side. With each permutation, say α, we shall associate its inverse, say β. Then, by Theorem 2.2.6, sgn α = sgn β. Moreover, since β is the inverse of α, we see that $a_{\alpha(1),1} \times \cdots \times a_{\alpha(n),n} = a_{1,\beta(1)} \times \cdots \times a_{n,\beta(n)}$. [If this is not evident, then consider an example: let $\alpha = \begin{pmatrix} 1\ 2\ 3\ 4\ 5 \\ 3\ 1\ 5\ 2\ 4 \end{pmatrix}$, so $\beta = \begin{pmatrix} 1\ 2\ 3\ 4\ 5 \\ 2\ 4\ 1\ 5\ 3 \end{pmatrix}$;

then $a_{\alpha(1),1} \times a_{\alpha(2),2} \times \cdots \times a_{\alpha(5),5} = a_{3,1} \times a_{1,2} \times a_{5,3} \times a_{2,4} \times a_{4,5}$

and $a_{1,\beta(1)} \times a_{2,\beta(2)} \times \cdots \times a_{5,\beta(5)} = a_{1,2} \times a_{2,4} \times a_{3,1} \times a_{4,5} \times a_{5,3}.$]

Now, the mapping which associates the inverse of a permutation with the permutation is one–one onto; therefore our procedure associates each term on the right-hand side with an identical term on the left-hand side. This establishes Theorem 2.3.2.

We can use Theorem 2.3.2 to establish an important property of our mapping *determinant*. First, we need the notion of the *transpose* of a matrix. This is the matrix obtained from a given matrix by interchanging its rows and columns. A precise definition follows.

DEFINITION 2.3.2.   Let (a_{ij}) be any $m \times n$ matrix; then the transpose of (a_{ij}) is (b_{ij}), where $b_{ij} = a_{ji}$ whenever $1 \le i \le n$ and $1 \le j \le m$. The transpose of a matrix A is denoted by "A^t".

For example, the transpose of $\begin{pmatrix} 2 & -1 & 3 \\ 0 & -2 & 5 \end{pmatrix}$ is $\begin{pmatrix} 2 & 0 \\ -1 & -2 \\ 3 & 5 \end{pmatrix}$.

We shall use Theorem 2.3.2 to prove that the determinant of any square matrix is the determinant of the transpose of the matrix.

THEOREM 2.3.3.   Let A be any square matrix; then $|A| = |A^t|$.

Proof   Let n be any natural number and let (a_{ij}) be any $n \times n$ matrix. Now, $(a_{ij})^t = (b_{ij})$, where $b_{ij} = a_{ji}$ whenever $1 \le i \le n$ and $1 \le j \le n$. Moreover, by Theorem 2.3.2,

$$|b_{ij}| = \sum_{\alpha} \text{sgn } \alpha \times b_{1,\alpha(1)} \times b_{2,\alpha(2)} \times \cdots \times b_{n,\alpha(n)}$$

$$= \sum_{\alpha} \text{sgn } \alpha \times a_{\alpha(1),1} \times a_{\alpha(2),2} \times \cdots \times a_{\alpha(n),n} \qquad \text{by Def. 2.3.2}$$

$$= |a_{ij}|.$$

This establishes Theorem 2.3.3.

This theorem is important because it forms the basis for the Principle of Duality which we shall present in Section 2.4.

Some authors prefer to define the determinant of a square matrix by first stating certain properties possessed by the mapping (e.g., Theorems 2.3.1, 2.4.1, 2.4.10) and then showing that there is a unique mapping which has these properties. This procedure smacks of the axiomatic method; indeed, the selected properties are sometimes called axioms. Admittedly, the axiomatic method is great, but it is not in order to suggest that there is any connection between the axiomatic method and a specific mapping. We point out that the axiomatic method is concerned with mathematical theories.

E X E R C I S E S

Compute each of the following by Applying Definition 2.3.1.

1. $\begin{vmatrix} 1 & 0 & 2 \\ -3 & 1 & 4 \\ 2 & 0 & 5 \end{vmatrix}$.

2. $\begin{vmatrix} 2 & 1 & 4 \\ 0 & 2 & 1 \\ 1 & 0 & -2 \end{vmatrix}$.

3. $\begin{vmatrix} 2 & 1 & 0 & -1 \\ 0 & 2 & 1 & 2 \\ -1 & 1 & 2 & -3 \\ 0 & 3 & -1 & 2 \end{vmatrix}.$

4. $\begin{vmatrix} -1 & 2 & 1 & 0 \\ 2 & 1 & -1 & 1 \\ 3 & 4 & -2 & 0 \\ 1 & 0 & 0 & 1 \end{vmatrix}.$

5. Use Definition 2.3.1 to prove that

$$\begin{vmatrix} a_{11} & a_{12} & a_{13} \\ a_{21} & a_{22} & a_{23} \\ a_{31} & a_{32} & a_{33} \end{vmatrix} = - \begin{vmatrix} a_{11} & a_{12} & a_{13} \\ a_{31} & a_{32} & a_{33} \\ a_{21} & a_{22} & a_{23} \end{vmatrix}.$$

6. Prove that

$$\begin{vmatrix} a_{11} & a_{12} & a_{13} \\ a_{21} & a_{22} & a_{23} \\ a_{31} & a_{32} & a_{33} \end{vmatrix} = \begin{vmatrix} a_{11} & a_{21} & a_{31} \\ a_{12} & a_{22} & a_{32} \\ a_{13} & a_{23} & a_{33} \end{vmatrix}.$$

7. Use Definition 2.3.1 to prove that

$$\begin{vmatrix} ka_{11} & ka_{12} & ka_{13} \\ a_{21} & a_{22} & a_{23} \\ a_{31} & a_{32} & a_{33} \end{vmatrix} = k \begin{vmatrix} a_{11} & a_{12} & a_{13} \\ a_{21} & a_{22} & a_{23} \\ a_{31} & a_{32} & a_{33} \end{vmatrix}$$

whenever $k \in R$.

8. Prove that

$$\begin{vmatrix} a_{11} + a_{21} & a_{12} + a_{22} & a_{13} + a_{23} \\ a_{21} & a_{22} & a_{23} \\ a_{31} & a_{32} & a_{33} \end{vmatrix} = \begin{vmatrix} a_{11} & a_{12} & a_{13} \\ a_{21} & a_{22} & a_{23} \\ a_{31} & a_{32} & a_{33} \end{vmatrix}.$$

9. Prove that

$$\begin{vmatrix} 0 & a_{12} & a_{13} \\ 0 & a_{22} & a_{23} \\ 0 & a_{32} & a_{33} \end{vmatrix} = 0.$$

10. Prove that

$$\begin{vmatrix} 1 & a_{12} & a_{13} \\ 0 & a_{22} & a_{23} \\ 0 & a_{32} & a_{33} \end{vmatrix} = \begin{vmatrix} a_{22} & a_{23} \\ a_{32} & a_{33} \end{vmatrix}.$$

11. Prove that

$$\begin{vmatrix} a_{11} & a_{12} & a_{13} \\ a_{21} & a_{22} & a_{23} \\ a_{31} & a_{32} & a_{33} \end{vmatrix} = a_{11} \begin{vmatrix} a_{22} & a_{23} \\ a_{32} & a_{33} \end{vmatrix} - a_{21} \begin{vmatrix} a_{12} & a_{13} \\ a_{32} & a_{33} \end{vmatrix} + a_{31} \begin{vmatrix} a_{12} & a_{13} \\ a_{22} & a_{23} \end{vmatrix}.$$

12. Prove that

$$\begin{vmatrix} a_{11}+b_1 & a_{12} & a_{13} \\ a_{21}+b_2 & a_{22} & a_{23} \\ a_{31}+b_3 & a_{32} & a_{33} \end{vmatrix} = \begin{vmatrix} a_{11} & a_{12} & a_{13} \\ a_{21} & a_{22} & a_{23} \\ a_{31} & a_{32} & a_{33} \end{vmatrix} + \begin{vmatrix} b_1 & a_{12} & a_{13} \\ b_2 & a_{22} & a_{23} \\ b_3 & a_{32} & a_{33} \end{vmatrix}.$$

13. Prove that the area of the triangle with vertices at (a_1, b_1), (a_2, b_2), (a_3, b_3) is the absolute value of

$$\frac{1}{2}\begin{vmatrix} 1 & a_1 & b_1 \\ 1 & a_2 & b_2 \\ 1 & a_3 & b_3 \end{vmatrix}.$$

14. Use the determinant of a square matrix to compute the area of the triangle with vertices at $(1, 2)$, $(2, 0)$, $(3, 4)$.

15. Use the determinant of a square matrix to compute the area of the triangle with vertices at $(-2, 3)$, $(0, 0)$, $(1, 7)$.

16. Use the determinant of a square matrix to prove that the following points are collinear:

(i) $(-1, 2)$, $(2, 8)$, $(3, 10)$,

(ii) $(3, 0)$, $(-3, -3)$, $(5, 1)$.

17. Prove that the graph of

$$\{(a, b) \mid \begin{vmatrix} 1 & a & b \\ 1 & a_1 & b_1 \\ 1 & a_2 & b_2 \end{vmatrix} = 0\}$$

is the line through the points (a_1, b_1) and (a_2, b_2), provided $a_1 \neq a_2$ or $b_1 \neq b_2$.

18. Prove Theorem 2.3.1.

19. Let n be any natural number and let (a_{ij}) be the $n \times n$ matrix such that

$$a_{ij} = \begin{cases} -1 \text{ if } i = j \\ 0 \text{ if } i \neq j \end{cases}.$$

Prove that $|a_{ij}| = (-1)^n$.

20. Let A be any square matrix whose first and second rows are the same. Use Definition 2.3.1 to prove that $|A| = 0$.

2.4   Properties of the Mapping Determinant

We now state the Principle of Duality referred to in Section 2.3.

PRINCIPLE OF DUALITY. Let P be any proposition about the mapping *determinant* which expresses the value of the mapping in terms of operations on the rows or columns of the matrix involved. Let $\mathscr{D}(P)$ (read "the dual of P") be the proposition obtained from P by interchanging the words *row* and *column* throughout P; then $\mathscr{D}(P)$ is true iff P is true.

Proof: Let P be a true proposition which expresses the number that the mapping *determinant* associates with each square matrix, in terms of operations on the rows or columns of the matrix. Let A be any square matrix; then P asserts that $|A|$ is obtained by carrying out certain operations on the rows of A and certain operations on the columns of A. Symbolically

$$|A| = A(R_1, \cdots, R_s; C_1, \cdots, C_t)$$

where the R_i are row operations and the C_i are column operations, and "$A(R_1, \cdots, R_s; C_1, \cdots, C_t)$" denotes the result of carrying out the specified operations. The point is that the proposition $\mathscr{D}(P)$ is represented symbolically by

$$|A| = A(R_1^*, \cdots, R_s^*; C_1^*, \cdots, C_t^*)$$

where R_i^* is the column operation which corresponds to the row operation R_i, and C_i^* is the row operation which corresponds to the column operation C_i. Since P is a true proposition about any square matrix, in particular it is true about A^t; so

$$|A^t| = A^t(R_1, \cdots, R_s; C_1, \cdots, C_t)$$

Since the rows of A^t are the columns of A, and the columns of A^t are the rows of A, it follows that the given row operations on A^t can be effected by carrying out the corresponding column operations on A, namely $R_1^*, \cdots, R_s^*$; similarly, the column operations on A^t can be effected by carrying out the corresponding row operations on A, namely $C_1^*, \cdots, C_t^*$. So

$$|A^t| = A(R_1^*, \cdots, R_s^*; C_1^*, \cdots, C_t^*).$$

By Theorem 2.3.3, $|A| = |A^t|$; so

$$|A| = A(R_1^*, \cdots, R_s^*; C_1^*, \cdots, C_t^*)$$

Thus, $\mathscr{D}(P)$ provides us with the number that *determinant* associates with the square matrix A. This demonstrates that $\mathscr{D}(P)$ is true whenever P is true. We have established the first part of our theorem; this result can now be used to demonstrate the second part of our theorem. Thus $\mathscr{D}(\mathscr{D}(P))$ is true if $\mathscr{D}(P)$ is true; but $\mathscr{D}(\mathscr{D}(P))$ is P. Therefore P is true if $\mathscr{D}(P)$ is true. We conclude that P is true iff $\mathscr{D}(P)$ is true. This establishes our theorem.

THEOREM 2.4.1.   Let n be any natural number, let A be any $n \times n$ matrix, and let B be a matrix obtained from A by interchanging any two rows of A. Then $|B| = -|A|$.

Proof: Let B be obtained from A by interchanging the first and second rows of A. Then $B = (b_{ij})$, where

$$b_{ij} = \begin{cases} a_{2j} \text{ if } i = 1 \\ a_{1j} \text{ if } i = 2 \\ a_{ij} \text{ otherwise,} \end{cases}$$

i.e., $b_{ij} = a_{\gamma(i),j}$ where $\gamma = (1 \quad 2)$. Then

$$|B| = \sum_{\alpha} \text{sgn } \alpha \times b_{\alpha(1),1} \times b_{\alpha(2),2} \times \cdots \times b_{\alpha(n),n}.$$

Now $(1 \quad 2) \circ (1 \quad 2) \circ \alpha = \alpha$ since $(1 \quad 2) \circ (1 \quad 2) = \varphi$. Accordingly, let $\beta = (1 \quad 2) \circ \alpha$; then $(1 \quad 2) \circ \beta = \alpha$, so $b_{\alpha(t),t} = a_{\beta(t),t}$ for each t. Thus

$$|B| = \sum_{\alpha} \text{sgn } \alpha \times a_{\beta(1),1} \times a_{\beta(2),2} \times \cdots \times a_{\beta(n),n}$$

$$= \sum_{\beta} -\text{sgn } \beta \times a_{\beta(1),1} \times a_{\beta(2),2} \times \cdots \times a_{\beta(n),n}$$

$$= -|a_{ij}| = -|A|.$$

The argument presented here can be applied to the general situation in which *any* two rows of the matrix A are interchanged. This establishes Theorem 2.4.1.

We now illustrate the Principle of Duality.

COROLLARY 2.4.1.   Let n be any natural number, let A be any $n \times n$ matrix, and let B be a matrix obtained from A by interchanging any two columns of A. Then $|B| = -|A|$.

Proof: Observe that Corollary 2.4.1 is the dual of Theorem 2.4.1. Therefore, by the Principle of Duality, our corollary is true.

Next, we introduce a technique for associating a real number with each entry of a square matrix. Let n be any natural number and let (a_{ij}) be any $n \times n$ matrix. First, we shall associate an $n - 1 \times n - 1$ matrix with each entry of (a_{ij}), namely the matrix obtained from (a_{ij}) by deleting the row and column in which the entry occurs. The determinant of the resulting matrix is a real number and is the real number that we shall associate with the entry in question. To be specific, the real number associated with a_{ij} is the determinant of the matrix obtained by deleting the ith row and the jth column of (a_{ij}). This number is said to be the *minor* of a_{ij}.

For example, consider the matrix

$$\begin{pmatrix} 1 & 3 & 2 \\ 2 & 1 & 4 \\ 5 & 2 & 0 \end{pmatrix}.$$

The minor of the entry in the first row and second column is $\begin{vmatrix} 2 & 4 \\ 5 & 0 \end{vmatrix}$, which is -20, whereas

the minor of the entry in the first column and the second row is $\begin{vmatrix} 3 & 2 \\ 2 & 0 \end{vmatrix}$, which is -4. We shall denote the minor of the entry in the ith row and jth column of a matrix by writing "$M_{.j}$".

Related to this idea, we have the notion of the *cofactor* of an entry in a square matrix. By the cofactor of the entry in the *i*th row and *j*th column of a square matrix, we mean the number $(-1)^{i+j} M_{ij}$. This real number is denoted by "A_{ij}". For example, the co-factor of the entry in the first row and second column of the matrix which appears above is $(-1)^3 \begin{vmatrix} 2 & 4 \\ 5 & 0 \end{vmatrix}$, namely 20.

Let us see why minors and cofactors are useful. First, it is convenient to introduce the following terminology. Let *n* be any natural number and let *t* be any natural number which does not exceed *n*; then we shall denote $\{\alpha \mid \alpha$ is a permutation of $\{1, 2, \cdots, n\}$ and $\alpha(1) = t\}$ by writing "αt". Using this notation, we can represent the determinant of an $n \times n$ matrix, say (a_{ij}), as follows:

$$|a_{ij}| = \sum_{\alpha \in \alpha 1} \text{sgn } \alpha \times a_{1,1} \times a_{\alpha(2),2} \times \cdots \times a_{\alpha(n),n}$$

$$+ \sum_{\alpha \in \alpha 2} \text{sgn } \alpha \times a_{2,1} \times a_{\alpha(2),2} \times \cdots \times a_{\alpha(n),n} + \cdots$$

$$+ \sum_{\alpha \in \alpha n} \text{sgn } \alpha \times a_{n,1} \times a_{\alpha(2),2} \times \cdots \times a_{\alpha(n),n}.$$

Consider the following theorem.

THEOREM 2.4.2. Let *n* be any natural number and let (a_{ij}) be any $n \times n$ matrix; then

$$\sum_{\alpha \in \alpha 1} \text{sgn } \alpha \times a_{1,1} \times a_{\alpha(2),2} \times \cdots \times a_{\alpha(n),n} = a_{11} A_{11}.$$

Proof:

$$\sum_{\alpha \in \alpha 1} \text{sgn } \alpha \times a_{1,1} \times a_{\alpha(2),2} \times \cdots \times a_{\alpha(n),n} = a_{1,1} \sum_{\alpha \in \alpha 1} \text{sgn } \beta \times a_{\alpha(2),2} \times \cdots \times a_{\alpha(n),n}$$

where $\beta = \begin{pmatrix} 2 & 3 & \cdots & n \\ \alpha(2) & \alpha(3) & & \alpha(n) \end{pmatrix}$ whenever $\alpha \in \alpha 1$

$$= a_{11} \sum_{\beta} \text{sgn } \beta \times a_{\beta(2),2} \times \cdots \times a_{\beta(n),n}$$

$$= a_{11} M_{11}$$

by Def. 2.3.1

$$= a_{11} A_{11}$$

since $A_{11} = (-1)^2 M_{11} = M_{11}$.

This establishes our result.

We now extend the preceding result.

THEOREM 2.4.3.   Let n be any natural number, and let (a_{ij}) be any $n \times n$ matrix and let t be a natural number which does not exceed n; then $\sum_{\alpha \in \alpha t} \operatorname{sgn} \alpha \times a_{t1} \times a_{\alpha(2),2} \times \cdots \times a_{\alpha(n),n} = a_{t1}A_{t1}$.

Proof: The idea is to interchange the tth row of the given matrix with each of the preceding rows; thus we obtain a matrix (b_{ij}), where

$$b_{ij} = \begin{cases} a_{tj} & \text{if } i = 1 \\ a_{i-1,j} & \text{if } 2 \leq i \leq t \\ a_{ij} & \text{if } i > t. \end{cases}$$

Since we have carried out $t - 1$ interchanges, we have, by Theorem 2.4.1,

(1) $$|b_{ij}| = (-1)^{t-1}|a_{ij}|.$$

Now, we gather together all terms on the left-hand side of (1) which have b_{11} (i.e., the entry in the first row and first column) as a factor. By Theorem 2.4.2, the sum of these terms is the product of b_{11} and the cofactor of b_{11} in the matrix (b_{ij}). By construction, the minor involved is precisely the minor of a_{t1} in the matrix (a_{ij}), namely M_{t1}. Thus our sum is $a_{t1}M_{t1}$. Next, we consider all terms on the right-hand side of (1) which have a_{t1} as a factor. The sum of these terms is $(-1)^{t-1} \sum_{\alpha \in \alpha t} \operatorname{sgn} \alpha \times a_{t1} \times a_{\alpha(2),2} \times \cdots \times a_{\alpha(n),n}$. Now, if our two sums are different, i.e., if there is a matrix (a_{ij}) such that $(-1)^{t-1} \sum_{\alpha \in \alpha t} \operatorname{sgn} \alpha \times a_{t1} \times a_{\alpha(2),2} \times \cdots \times a_{\alpha(n),n} \neq a_{t1}M_{t1}$, then we consider in place of (a_{ij}) the $n \times n$ matrix (c_{ij}), where

$$c_{ij} = \begin{cases} 0 & \text{if } i \neq t \text{ and } j = 1 \\ a_{ij} & \text{otherwise.} \end{cases}$$

Clearly, from (1), $a_{t1}M_{t1} = (-1)^{t-1} \sum_{\alpha \in \alpha t} \operatorname{sgn} \alpha \times a_{t1} \times a_{\alpha(2),2} \times \cdots \times a_{\alpha(n),n}$; this contradiction establishes that our two sums are the same. Thus

$$\sum_{\alpha \in \alpha t} \operatorname{sgn} \alpha \times a_{t1} \times a_{\alpha(2),2} \times \cdots \times a_{\alpha(n),n} = (-1)^{t-1}a_{t1}M_{t1} = a_{t1}A_{t1}.$$

This demonstrates Theorem 2.4.3.

Alternative Proof: We now present another proof of Theorem 2.4.3 which makes direct use of permutations. Let $\gamma = (1 \quad 2) \circ (2 \quad 3) \circ \cdots \circ (t-1 \quad t)$; from elementary group theory, given any permutation of $\{1, \cdots, n\}$, say α, there is a unique permutation β such that $\alpha = \gamma \circ \beta$; of course, $\beta = (t-1 \quad t) \circ (t-2 \quad t-1) \circ \cdots \circ (2 \quad 3) \circ (1 \quad 2) \circ \alpha$. Indeed, the permutation γ induces a one–one mapping of the basic set of the group onto itself. Notice that $\beta(1) = t-1$ iff $\gamma \circ \beta \in \alpha t$.

Next, let (a_{ij}) be any $n \times n$ matrix, and consider the $n \times n$ matrix (b_{ij}) where $b_{ij} = a_{\gamma(i),j}$ whenever $1 \leq i \leq n$ and $1 \leq j \leq n$. Notice that the minor of $b_{1,1}$ in (b_{ij}) is precisely the minor of $a_{t,1}$ in (a_{ij}); moreover, $b_{\beta(i),i} = a_{\gamma \circ \beta(i),i} = a_{\alpha(i),i}$ for each i. Now,

$$\sum_{\alpha \in \alpha t} \text{sgn } \alpha \times a_{\alpha(1),1} \times a_{\alpha(2),2} \times \cdots \times a_{\alpha(n),n}$$

$$= \sum_{\beta \in \alpha[t-1]} \text{sgn } \gamma \circ \beta \times b_{\beta(1),1} \times b_{\beta(2),2} \times \cdots \times b_{\beta(n),n}$$

$$= (-1)^{t-1} b_{t-1,1} \sum_{\beta \in \alpha[t-1]} \text{sgn } \beta \times b_{\beta(2),2} \times \cdots \times b_{\beta(n),n}$$

$$\text{since sgn } \gamma = (-1)^{t-1}$$

$$= (-1)^{t-1} b_{t-1,1} \times \text{minor of } b_{1,1} \text{ in the matrix } (b_{ij})$$

$$= (-1)^{t-1} a_{t,1} \times \text{minor of } a_{t,1} \text{ in the matrix } (a_{ij}) \qquad \text{(by construction)}$$

$$= (-1)^{t-1} a_{t,1} M_{t1}$$

$$= a_{t1} A_{t1}.$$

THEOREM 2.4.4. Let n be any natural number and let (a_{ij}) be any $n \times n$ matrix; then $|a_{ij}| = a_{11}A_{11} + a_{21}A_{21} + \cdots + a_{n1}A_{n1}$.

Proof:

$$|a_{ij}| = \sum_{\alpha \in \alpha 1} \text{sgn } \alpha \times a_{11} \times a_{\alpha(2),2} \times \cdots \times a_{\alpha(n),n} + \cdots$$

$$+ \sum_{\alpha \in \alpha n} \text{sgn } \alpha \times a_{n1} \times a_{\alpha(2),2} \times \cdots \times a_{\alpha(n),n}$$

$$= a_{11}A_{11} + a_{21}A_{21} + \cdots + a_{n1}A_{n1} \qquad \text{by Th. 2.4.3.}$$

COROLLARY 2.4.2. Let n be any natural number and let (a_{ij}) be any $n \times n$ matrix; then $|a_{ij}| = a_{11}A_{11} + a_{12}A_{12} + \cdots + a_{1n}A_{1n}$.

Proof: Apply the Principle of Duality to Theorem 2.4.4; the details are left as an exercise.

Notice that Theorem 2.4.4 reduces the problem of computing the determinant of any $n \times n$ matrix to that of computing the determinants of n $n - 1 \times n - 1$ matrices. Repeating the process, we see that this theorem enables us to compute the determinant of any square matrix by computing the determinants of $n!$ 1×1 matrices. Accordingly, it is possible to define the mapping *determinant* by an inductive definition which utilizes Theorem 2.4.4 and the statement that the determinant of any 1×1 matrix is the entry of the matrix.

We now illustrate Theorem 2.4.4.

EXAMPLE 1. Compute
$$\begin{vmatrix} 2 & 1 & -2 \\ 3 & 1 & 4 \\ 2 & 5 & 1 \end{vmatrix}.$$

Solution: By Theorem 2.4.4,

$$\begin{vmatrix} 2 & 1 & -2 \\ 3 & 1 & 4 \\ 2 & 5 & 1 \end{vmatrix} = 2\begin{vmatrix} 1 & 4 \\ 5 & 1 \end{vmatrix} - 3\begin{vmatrix} 1 & -2 \\ 5 & 1 \end{vmatrix} + 2\begin{vmatrix} 1 & -2 \\ 1 & 4 \end{vmatrix} = 2(-19) - 3(11) + 2(6) = -59.$$

Let us illustrate Corollary 2.4.2.

EXAMPLE 2.   Use Corollary 2.4.2 to compute the determinant of the matrix of Example 1.

Solution: By Corollary 2.4.2,

$$\begin{vmatrix} 2 & 1 & -2 \\ 3 & 1 & 4 \\ 2 & 5 & 1 \end{vmatrix} = 2\begin{vmatrix} 1 & 4 \\ 5 & 1 \end{vmatrix} - 1\begin{vmatrix} 3 & 4 \\ 2 & 1 \end{vmatrix} - 2\begin{vmatrix} 3 & 1 \\ 2 & 5 \end{vmatrix} = 2(-19) - (-5) - 2(13) = -59.$$

We can use Corollary 2.4.1 to generalize Theorem 2.4.4 as follows.

THEOREM 2.4.5.   Let n be any natural number and let r be any natural number which does not exceed n. Then the determinant of any $n \times n$ matrix is the sum of the n terms obtained by multiplying each entry in the rth column of the matrix by its cofactor.

Proof: Let (a_{ij}) be any $n \times n$ matrix and let (b_{ij}) be the matrix obtained from (a_{ij}) by interchanging the rth column with each of the preceding columns. Then, by Corollary 2.4.1, $|a_{ij}| = (-1)^{r-1}|b_{ij}|$. Notice that the minor of each entry in the first column of (b_{ij}) is the minor of the corresponding entry in the rth column of (a_{ij}). Now, the cofactor of each b_{i1} in (b_{ij}) is $(-1)^{i+1}$ times its minor, whereas the cofactor of a_{ir} in (a_{ij}) is $(-1)^{i+r}$ times its minor. Therefore the cofactor of each b_{i1} in (b_{ij}) is $(-1)^{r+1}A_{ir}$, where A_{ir} is the cofactor of a_{ir} in the matrix (a_{ij}). Now we can apply Theorem 2.4.4.:

$$|b_{ij}| = (-1)^{r+1}[b_{11}A_{1r} + b_{21}A_{2r} + \cdots + b_{n1}A_{nr}]$$

$$= (-1)^{r+1}[a_{1r}A_{1r} + a_{2r}A_{2r} + \cdots + a_{nr}A_{nr}].$$

Thus $|a_{ij}| = a_{1r}A_{1r} + a_{2r}A_{2r} + \cdots + a_{nr}A_{nr}$. This completes our proof.

COROLLARY 2.4.3.   Let n be any natural number and let r be any natural number which does not exceed n. Then the determinant of any $n \times n$ matrix is the sum of the n terms obtained by multiplying each entry in the rth row of the matrix by its cofactor.

Proof: Apply the Principle of Duality to Theorem 2.4.5.

THEOREM 2.4.6.   Let n be any natural number, let r be any natural number which does not exceed n, let (a_{ij}) be any $n \times n$ matrix, and let

$$b_{ij} = \begin{cases} ka_{ir} \text{ if } j = r \\ a_{ij} \text{ if } j \neq r. \end{cases}$$

Then $|b_{ij}| = k|a_{ij}|$.

Proof: Expand $|b_{ij}|$ in terms of the entries in the rth column and their cofactors.

COROLLARY 2.4.4.   Let n be any natural number, let r be any natural number which does not exceed n, let (a_{ij}) be any $n \times n$ matrix, and let

$$b_{ij} = \begin{cases} ka_{rj} \text{ if } i = r \\ a_{ij} \text{ if } i \neq r. \end{cases}$$

Then $|b_{ij}| = k|a_{ij}|$.

Proof: Apply the Principle of Duality to Theorem 2.4.6.

The purpose of the following theorems is to demonstrate that our procedure for reducing a matrix can also be used to obtain the determinant of a square matrix.

THEOREM 2.4.7.   The determinant of a square matrix is zero if any two rows of the matrix are the same.

Proof: Let A be any square matrix which has two identical rows. Clearly, the matrix obtained from A by interchanging the identical rows is A itself. Hence, by Theorem 2.4.1, $|A| = -|A|$. Thus $|A| = 0$.

COROLLARY 2.4.5.   The determinant of a square matrix is zero if any two columns of the matrix are the same.

Proof: Apply the Principle of Duality to Theorem 2.4.7.

THEOREM 2.4.8.   Let n be any natural number, let (a_{ij}) be any $n \times n$ matrix, and let r be any natural number which does not exceed n. Let (b_{ij}) and (c_{ij}) be the $n \times n$ matrices defined as follows, where $b_1, b_2, \cdots, b_n$ are real numbers:

$$b_{ij} = \begin{cases} a_{ij} \text{ if } i \neq r \\ a_{rj} + b_j \text{ if } i = r; \end{cases} \qquad c_{ij} = \begin{cases} a_{ij} \text{ if } i \neq r \\ b_j \text{ if } i = r. \end{cases}$$

Then $|b_{ij}| = |a_{ij}| + |c_{ij}|$.

Proof: By Corollary 2.4.3,

$$|b_{ij}| = (a_{r1} + b_1)A_{r1} + (a_{r2} + b_2)A_{r2} + \cdots + (a_{rn} + b_n)A_{rn}$$

$$= [a_{r1}A_{r1} + \cdots + a_{rn}A_{rn}] + [b_1A_{r1} + \cdots + b_nA_{rn}]$$

$$= |a_{ij}| + |c_{ij}| \qquad \text{by Cor. 2.4.3.}$$

This completes our proof.

THEOREM 2.4.9.   Let n be any natural number, let A be any $n \times n$ matrix, and let r be any natural number such that $1 < r \le n$. Let B be the $n \times n$ matrix obtained from A by adding each entry of the first row to the corresponding entry of the rth row. Then $|B| = |A|$.

Proof: Theorems 2.4.8 and 2.4.7.

THEOREM 2.4.10.   Let n be any natural number, let (a_{ij}) be any $n \times n$ matrix, let r be any natural number such that $1 < r \le n$, and let k be any real number. Let (b_{ij}) be the $n \times n$ matrix defined as follows:

$$b_{ij} = \begin{cases} a_{ij} \text{ if } i \ne r \\ a_{rj} + ka_{1j} \text{ if } i = r. \end{cases}$$

Then $|b_{ij}| = |a_{ij}|$.

Proof: By Theorem 2.4.8,

$$|b_{ij}| = |a_{ij}| + |c_{ij}| \qquad \text{where } c_{ij} = \begin{cases} a_{ij} \text{ if } i \ne r \\ ka_{1j} \text{ if } i = r \end{cases}$$

$$= |a_{ij}| + k|d_{ij}| \qquad \text{by Cor. 2.4.4, where } d_{ij} = \begin{cases} a_{ij} \text{ if } i \ne r \\ a_{1j} \text{ if } i = r \end{cases}$$

$$= |a_{ij}| \qquad \text{by Th. 2.4.7.}$$

THEOREM 2.4.11.   Let n be any natural number, let (a_{ij}) be any $n \times n$ matrix, let r and s be two natural numbers which do not exceed n, and let (b_{ij}) be the $n \times n$ matrix defined as follows, where k is any real number:

$$b_{ij} = \begin{cases} a_{ij} \text{ if } i \ne r \\ a_{rj} + ka_{sj} \text{ if } i = r. \end{cases}$$

Then $|b_{ij}| = |a_{ij}|$.

Proof: Theorems 2.4.10 and 2.4.1.

Let us see how to compute the determinant of an $n \times n$ matrix. We shall operate on the first column of the matrix so that all the entries but one will be zero. If each entry in the first column is zero, then the determinant of the matrix is zero, by Theorem 2.4.4, and we have finished. Assume, then, that at least one of these entries is not zero. By interchanging rows suitably (which affects only the algebraic sign of the determinant of our matrix), we can ensure that the entry in the first row and the first column is not zero. Next, we transform the other entries of the first column into zero by applying Theorem 2.4.10 with k suitably chosen. Finally, we reduce the determinant of the given matrix to the determinant of an $n - 1 \times n - 1$ matrix by applying Theorem 2.4.4. We repeat the above procedure until we produce the determinant of a matrix which can be readily computed. An illustration may be helpful.

EXAMPLE 3.   Determine D where

$$
D = \begin{vmatrix}
1 & 2 & 0 & 1 & 2 & -2 \\
2 & 0 & 1 & 2 & 1 & 3 \\
-3 & 3 & 4 & 3 & -1 & 1 \\
0 & -1 & 2 & 2 & -1 & 1 \\
5 & 4 & 3 & 1 & 2 & 0 \\
4 & 2 & 5 & 0 & 0 & 1
\end{vmatrix}.
$$

Solution: Applying our procedure, we see that

$$
D = \begin{vmatrix}
1 & 2 & 0 & 1 & 2 & -2 \\
0 & -4 & 1 & 0 & -3 & 7 \\
0 & 9 & 4 & 6 & 5 & -5 \\
0 & -1 & 2 & 2 & -1 & 1 \\
0 & -6 & 3 & -4 & -8 & 10 \\
0 & -6 & 5 & -4 & -8 & 9
\end{vmatrix}
= \begin{vmatrix}
-4 & 1 & 0 & -3 & 7 \\
9 & 4 & 6 & 5 & -5 \\
-1 & 2 & 2 & -1 & 1 \\
-6 & 3 & -4 & -8 & 10 \\
-6 & 5 & -4 & -8 & 9
\end{vmatrix}
= \begin{vmatrix}
1 & 2 & 2 & -1 & 1 \\
-9 & 4 & 6 & 5 & -5 \\
4 & 1 & 0 & -3 & 7 \\
6 & 3 & -4 & -8 & 10 \\
6 & 5 & -4 & -8 & 9
\end{vmatrix}
$$

$$
= \begin{vmatrix}
1 & 2 & 2 & -1 & 1 \\
0 & 22 & 24 & -4 & 4 \\
0 & -7 & -8 & 1 & 3 \\
0 & -9 & -16 & -2 & 4 \\
0 & -7 & -16 & -2 & 3
\end{vmatrix}
= \begin{vmatrix}
22 & 24 & -4 & 4 \\
-7 & -8 & 1 & 3 \\
-9 & -16 & -2 & 4 \\
-7 & -16 & -2 & 3
\end{vmatrix}
$$

$$
= -8 \begin{vmatrix}
3 & 22 & -4 & 4 \\
-1 & -7 & 1 & 3 \\
-2 & -9 & -2 & 4 \\
-2 & -7 & -2 & 3
\end{vmatrix}
= -8 \begin{vmatrix}
0 & 1 & -1 & 13 \\
-1 & -7 & 1 & 3 \\
0 & 5 & -4 & -2 \\
0 & 2 & 0 & -1
\end{vmatrix}
= -8 \begin{vmatrix}
1 & -1 & 13 \\
5 & -4 & -2 \\
2 & 0 & -1
\end{vmatrix}
$$

$$
= -8 \begin{vmatrix}
1 & -1 & 13 \\
0 & 1 & -67 \\
0 & 2 & -27
\end{vmatrix}
= -8 \begin{vmatrix}
1 & -67 \\
2 & -27
\end{vmatrix}
= -8(-27 + 134) = -856.
$$

The following theorem is a special case of a general expansion theorem known as *Laplace's Expansion Theorem.*

THEOREM 2.4.12.   Let n and m be any natural numbers, let (a_{ij}) be any $n \times n$ matrix, let (b_{ij}) be any $m \times m$ matrix, and let (c_{ij}) be any $m \times n$ matrix. Then

$$
\begin{vmatrix}
a_{11} & a_{12} & \cdots & a_{1n} & 0 & 0 & \cdots & 0 \\
a_{21} & a_{22} & \cdots & a_{2n} & 0 & 0 & \cdots & 0 \\
& & \vdots & & & & & \\
a_{n1} & a_{n2} & \cdots & a_{nn} & 0 & 0 & \cdots & 0 \\
c_{11} & c_{12} & \cdots & c_{1n} & b_{11} & b_{12} & \cdots & b_{1m} \\
c_{21} & c_{22} & \cdots & c_{2n} & b_{21} & b_{22} & \cdots & b_{2m} \\
& & \vdots & & & & & \\
c_{m1} & c_{m2} & \cdots & c_{mn} & b_{m1} & b_{m2} & \cdots & b_{mm}
\end{vmatrix}
$$

$$
=
\begin{vmatrix}
a_{11} & a_{12} & \cdots & a_{1n} \\
a_{21} & a_{22} & \cdots & a_{2n} \\
& \vdots & & \\
a_{n1} & a_{n2} & \cdots & a_{nn}
\end{vmatrix}
\cdot
\begin{vmatrix}
b_{11} & b_{12} & \cdots & b_{1m} \\
b_{21} & b_{22} & \cdots & b_{2m} \\
& \vdots & & \\
b_{m1} & b_{m2} & \cdots & b_{mm}
\end{vmatrix}.
$$

Proof: First, we shall clarify our theorem. Let $A = (a_{ij})$, let $B = (b_{ij})$, let $C = (c_{ij})$, and let "0" denote the $n \times m$ matrix each of whose entries is zero. Then our theorem is

$$
\begin{vmatrix} A & 0 \\ C & B \end{vmatrix} = |A| \cdot |B|.
$$

To prove this theorem, we shall apply mathematical induction on n. This means that we must formulate an appropriate property of natural numbers. First, we fix m (i.e., let m be a particular natural number). Next, we say that a natural number, say t, has the property of the theorem iff $\begin{vmatrix} A & 0 \\ C & B \end{vmatrix} = |A| \cdot |B|$ whenever A is a $t \times t$ matrix, B is an $m \times m$ matrix, and C is an $m \times t$ matrix. Let us show that 1 has the property. Let (a_{11}) be any 1×1 matrix; then

$$
\begin{vmatrix} (a_{11}) & 0 \\ C & B \end{vmatrix} = a_{11}|B| \qquad \text{by Cor. 2.4.2, since } |B| \text{ is the cofactor of } a_{11} \text{ in this matrix}
$$

$$
= |a_{11}| \cdot |B|.
$$

Thus the natural number 1 has the property of the theorem. Next, we assume that k is a natural number which has the property; we shall prove that $k + 1$ has the property.

Let $(a_{ij}) = A$ be any $k + 1 \times k + 1$ matrix. By Corollary 2.4.2 and the induction assumption, we see that

$$
\begin{vmatrix}
a_{11} & a_{12} & \cdots & a_{1,k+1} & \\
a_{21} & a_{22} & \cdots & a_{2,k+1} & \\
& \vdots & & & 0 \\
a_{k+1,1} & a_{k+1,2} & \cdots & a_{k+1,k+1} & \\
& C & & & B
\end{vmatrix}
\begin{aligned}
&= a_{11}A_{11}|B| + a_{12}A_{12}|B| + \cdots + a_{1,k+1}A_{1,k+1}|B| \\
&\quad \text{where } A_{ij} \text{ is the cofactor of } a_{ij} \text{ in the matrix } A \\
&= (a_{11}A_{11} + a_{12}A_{12} + \cdots + a_{1,k+1}A_{1,k+1})|B| \\
&= |A| \cdot |B|.
\end{aligned}
$$

Thus $k + 1$ has the property whenever k has the property. By mathematical induction, then, each natural number has the property. This establishes Theorem 2.4.12.

In Chapter 3 we shall develop an algebra of matrices. There we shall see that if (a_{ij}) and (b_{ij}) are any $n \times n$ matrices, then the $n \times n$ matrix (c_{ij}) is said to be the *product* of (a_{ij}) and (b_{ij}) if $c_{ij} = a_{i1}b_{1j} + a_{i2}b_{2j} + \cdots + a_{in}b_{nj}$ whenever $1 \le i \le n$ and $1 \le j \le n$. With this understanding, the following theorem asserts that the determinant of the product of two $n \times n$ matrices is the product of their determinants.

THEOREM 2.4.13.   Let n be any natural number, let (a_{ij}) and (b_{ij}) be any $n \times n$ matrices, and let $c_{ij} = a_{i1}b_{1j} + a_{i2}b_{2j} + \cdots + a_{in}b_{nj}$ whenever $1 \le i \le n$ and $1 \le j \le n$. Then $|c_{ij}| = |a_{ij}| \cdot |b_{ij}|$.

Proof: By Theorem 2.4.12,

$$
\begin{vmatrix}
a_{11} & a_{12} & \cdots & a_{1n} & 0 & 0 & \cdots & 0 \\
a_{21} & a_{22} & \cdots & a_{2n} & 0 & 0 & \cdots & 0 \\
& \vdots & & & & & & \\
a_{n1} & a_{n2} & \cdots & a_{nn} & 0 & 0 & \cdots & 0 \\
-1 & 0 & \cdots & 0 & b_{11} & b_{12} & \cdots & b_{1n} \\
0 & -1 & \cdots & 0 & b_{21} & b_{22} & \cdots & b_{2n} \\
& \vdots & & & & & & \\
0 & 0 & \cdots & -1 & b_{n1} & b_{n2} & \cdots & b_{nn}
\end{vmatrix}
= |a_{ij}| \cdot |b_{ij}|.
$$

Now consider the matrix on the left-hand side of the equation. By suitable column operations, we can transform the b's into 0's. Multiply the first column by b_{1i} and add to the $n + i$th column, and then divide the first column by b_{1i}, $i = 1, 2, \cdots, n$. This transforms the first row of b's into 0's. Next, multiply the second column by b_{2i} and add to the $n + i$th column, and then divide the second column by b_{2i}, $i = 1, 2 \cdots, n$. This transforms the second row of b's into 0's. We continue this operation until each row of b's is transformed into 0's. Notice that the 0's occupying the upper right-hand corner of the matrix are transformed into c's. Since this process does not change the determinant of the matrix, it follows that

$$\begin{vmatrix} a_{11} & a_{12} & \cdots & a_{1n} & c_{11} & c_{12} & \cdots & c_{1n} \\ a_{21} & a_{22} & \cdots & a_{2n} & c_{21} & c_{22} & \cdots & c_{2n} \\ & & \vdots & & & & & \\ a_{n1} & a_{n2} & \cdots & a_{nn} & c_{n1} & c_{n2} & \cdots & c_{nn} \\ -1 & 0 & \cdots & 0 & 0 & 0 & \cdots & 0 \\ 0 & -1 & \cdots & 0 & 0 & 0 & \cdots & 0 \\ & & \vdots & & & & & \\ 0 & 0 & \cdots & -1 & 0 & 0 & \cdots & 0 \end{vmatrix} = |a_{ij}| \cdot |b_{ij}|.$$

Again, we operate on the left-hand matrix. We want to transform this matrix so that we can obtain its determinant by Theorem 2.4.12. To this purpose we shall carry out the following row operations: interchange the ith and the $n + i$th rows where $i = 1, 2, \cdots, n$. This multiplies the determinant of the matrix by $(-1)^n$; thus

$$(-1)^n \begin{vmatrix} -1 & 0 & \cdots & 0 & 0 & 0 & \cdots & 0 \\ 0 & -1 & \cdots & 0 & 0 & 0 & \cdots & 0 \\ & & \vdots & & & & & \\ 0 & 0 & \cdots & -1 & 0 & 0 & \cdots & 0 \\ a_{11} & a_{12} & \cdots & a_{1n} & c_{11} & c_{12} & \cdots & c_{1n} \\ a_{21} & a_{22} & \cdots & a_{2n} & c_{21} & c_{22} & \cdots & c_{2n} \\ & & \vdots & & & & & \\ a_{n1} & a_{n2} & \cdots & a_{nn} & c_{n1} & c_{n2} & \cdots & c_{nn} \end{vmatrix} = |a_{ij}| \cdot |b_{ij}|.$$

We now use Theorem 2.4.12 to compute the determinant on the left-hand side of this equation. Thus

$$(-1)^n \begin{vmatrix} -1 & 0 & \cdots & 0 \\ 0 & -1 & \cdots & 0 \\ & \vdots & & \\ 0 & 0 & \cdots & -1 \end{vmatrix} \cdot |c_{ij}| = |a_{ij}| \cdot |b_{ij}|.$$

Since

$$\begin{vmatrix} -1 & 0 & \cdots & 0 \\ 0 & -1 & \cdots & 0 \\ & \vdots & & \\ 0 & 0 & \cdots & -1 \end{vmatrix} = (-1)^n,$$

we have our result.

EXERCISES

Compute the following by applying Theorem 2.4.4 or Corollary 2.4.2.

1. $\begin{vmatrix} 2 & 1 & 3 \\ -1 & 2 & 1 \\ 0 & 3 & 4 \end{vmatrix}$.

2. $\begin{vmatrix} 3 & 1 & 5 & 6 \\ 0 & 2 & 4 & 1 \\ -1 & 1 & 3 & 6 \\ 0 & 1 & 5 & 6 \end{vmatrix}$.

3. $\begin{vmatrix} 2 & -1 & 0 & 0 \\ 3 & 1 & 0 & 1 \\ -1 & 2 & 1 & -1 \\ 2 & 1 & 0 & 1 \end{vmatrix}$.

4. $\begin{vmatrix} 3 & 0 & 1 & 0 \\ 2 & 1 & -1 & 1 \\ 4 & 2 & 5 & -2 \\ 3 & 0 & 1 & 2 \end{vmatrix}$.

5. Show directly from Definition 2.3.1 that

$$\begin{vmatrix} a_1 & c_1 & b_1 & d_1 \\ a_2 & c_2 & b_2 & d_2 \\ a_3 & c_3 & b_3 & d_3 \\ a_4 & c_4 & b_4 & d_4 \end{vmatrix} = - \begin{vmatrix} a_1 & b_1 & c_1 & d_1 \\ a_2 & b_2 & c_2 & d_2 \\ a_3 & b_3 & c_3 & d_3 \\ a_4 & b_4 & c_4 & d_4 \end{vmatrix}.$$

6. a. Express Theorem 2.4.4 in terms of operations on the rows or columns of a matrix.
   b. Prove Corollary 2.4.2.

Use any method to compute the following.

7. $\begin{vmatrix} 4 & 3 & 2 \\ 4 & 0 & 1 \\ 4 & 1 & -2 \end{vmatrix}$.

8. $\begin{vmatrix} 3 & 5 & 1 & 3 \\ 0 & 5 & 2 & 0 \\ -1 & 5 & -1 & 1 \\ 2 & 5 & 0 & 2 \end{vmatrix}$.

9. $\begin{vmatrix} 1 & 2 & -3 & 0 \\ -2 & 0 & 1 & 2 \\ 5 & 5 & 5 & 5 \\ -1 & 0 & 1 & 0 \end{vmatrix}$.

10. $\begin{vmatrix} 1 & 2 & -1 & -2 & 0 \\ 1 & 0 & -1 & -2 & 1 \\ 2 & 5 & -2 & 4 & 1 \\ -2 & -4 & 1 & 0 & 0 \\ 1 & 1 & 0 & 0 & 2 \end{vmatrix}$.

11.
$$\begin{vmatrix} 3 & 2 & 10 & -6 \\ 2 & 1 & -1 & 2 \\ 4 & 1 & 0 & -4 \\ 0 & 2 & 2 & 1 \end{vmatrix}.$$

12.
$$\begin{vmatrix} -1 & 4 & 3 & 2 \\ 0 & 1 & 2 & -1 \\ 3 & -2 & 0 & 5 \\ 4 & 1 & -2 & 1 \end{vmatrix}.$$

13.
$$\begin{vmatrix} 1 & 2 & -1 & 0 & 3 \\ 2 & 3 & 2 & 1 & 0 \\ -1 & 0 & 2 & 1 & 1 \\ 2 & 0 & -3 & 2 & -1 \\ 4 & 3 & -1 & 2 & 0 \end{vmatrix}.$$

14.
$$\begin{vmatrix} 2 & 0 & 3 & 1 & 4 & -6 \\ 3 & 2 & 4 & 5 & -1 & -2 \\ 1 & -1 & 0 & 3 & 2 & -2 \\ 2 & 1 & 3 & 1 & -2 & 0 \\ 4 & 1 & 2 & 0 & 3 & -1 \\ -3 & 0 & -2 & 0 & 1 & 1 \end{vmatrix}.$$

15. Let n be any natural number, let (a_{ij}) be any $n \times n$ matrix, let r be any natural number which does not exceed n, let $b_1, b_2, \cdots, b_n$ be any real numbers, and let

$$b_{ij} = \begin{cases} a_{ij} \text{ if } j \neq r \\ a_{ir} + b_i \text{ if } j = r, \end{cases} \qquad c_{ij} = \begin{cases} a_{ij} \text{ if } j \neq r \\ b_i \text{ if } j = r \end{cases}$$

Prove that $|b_{ij}| = |a_{ij}| + |c_{ij}|$.

16. a. Given that A_{ij} is the cofactor of a_{ij} in the $n \times n$ matrix (a_{ij}), prove that $b_1 A_{11} + b_2 A_{21} + \cdots + b_n A_{n1} = |b_{ij}|$, where

$$b_{ij} = \begin{cases} b_i \text{ if } j = 1 \\ a_{ij} \text{ if } j \neq 1. \end{cases}$$

b. Represent $b_1 A_{12} + b_2 A_{22} + \cdots + b_n A_{n2}$ as the determinant of a matrix constructed from the $n \times n$ matrix (a_{ij}).

c. Given that $1 \leq i \leq n$, show that $b_1 A_{1i} + b_2 A_{2i} + \cdots + b_n A_{ni}$ is the determinant of a certain matrix.

d. Given that $1 \leq i \leq n$, show that $b_1 A_{i1} + b_2 A_{i2} + \cdots + b_n A_{in}$ is the determinant of a certain matrix.

17. Let n be any natural number and let (a_{ij}) be any $n \times n$ matrix. Prove the following.

a. $a_{12} A_{11} + a_{22} A_{21} + \cdots + a_{n2} A_{n1} = 0$.

b. $a_{1j} A_{1i} + a_{2j} A_{2i} + \cdots + a_{nj} A_{ni} = 0$ if $i \neq j$.

c. $a_{21} A_{11} + a_{22} A_{12} + \cdots + a_{2n} A_{1n} = 0$.

d. $a_{j1} A_{i1} + a_{j2} A_{i2} + \cdots + a_{jn} A_{in} = 0$ if $i \neq j$.

18. Regarding Theorem 2.4.13, describe how the entries of the matrix (c_{ij}) can be computed in terms of operations on the rows and columns of the matrices (a_{ij}) and (b_{ij}).

19. Compute the following directly and also by applying Theorem 2.4.13.

a.
$$\begin{vmatrix} 1 & 0 & 2 \\ 2 & 1 & 3 \\ -1 & 2 & -2 \end{vmatrix} \cdot \begin{vmatrix} 2 & 1 & -1 \\ 3 & 4 & 0 \\ -2 & -1 & 3 \end{vmatrix}.$$

b.
$$\begin{vmatrix} 1 & 2 & -1 & 0 \\ 1 & 3 & 0 & 1 \\ 2 & 0 & 4 & -2 \\ -1 & 1 & 2 & 1 \end{vmatrix} \cdot \begin{vmatrix} 2 & 1 & 0 & 2 \\ 3 & 4 & -1 & -2 \\ 1 & -2 & -3 & 0 \\ 2 & 1 & -2 & -1 \end{vmatrix}.$$

Chapter 3

Vectors and Linear Systems

3.1 More About Vector Spaces

We have seen that the operations which simplify the determinant of a square matrix involve the rows or columns of the matrix; e.g., we multiply each entry of a column by a nonzero real number k, we add the entries of one column to the corresponding entries of another column, or we interchange two columns of the matrix. Moreover, the corresponding row operations enable us to reduce a matrix to a particularly simple form. For this reason we shall regard each column of a matrix as an object in itself. Having practiced this idea throughout Chapter 2, it is time that we recognize the facts of the situation and admit that the columns of a matrix (or the rows of a matrix) are objects worthy of independent study. All right, each column of a matrix is a mathematical object; the question is "which object?" The simplest answer is this: each column of a matrix is an ordered n-tuple of real numbers, where n is a natural number.

Let us denote the set of all natural numbers by "N" so that we can abbreviate the phrase "n is a natural number" by writing "$n \in N$". It is useful to set up an algebra of n-tuples, where $n \in N$; this means that we shall introduce specific operations on n-tuples. If we do this appropriately, the resulting algebraic system, in conjunction with the real number field, constitutes a vector space. This has been pointed out in Example 1 of Section 1.8. For this reason we shall call any ordered n-tuple a *vector* or *n-vector*. We have already defined vector addition and scalar multiplication in the example to which we have referred. These definitions are worth repeating. Let $(a_1, a_2, \cdots, a_n)$ and $(b_1, b_2, \cdots, b_n)$ be any n-vectors and let k be any real number; then $(a_1, a_2, \cdots, a_n) + (b_1, b_2, \cdots, b_n) = (a_1 + b_1, a_2 + b_2, \cdots, a_n + b_n)$ and $k(a_1, a_2, \cdots, a_n) = (ka_1, ka_2, \cdots, ka_n)$. Notice that these operations are the familiar operations involved in computing the determinant of a square matrix.

We need names for the sets that we have introduced. Let $n \in N$; we shall denote the set of all ordered n-tuples of real numbers by "R_n". Thus R_2 is the set of all ordered pairs of real numbers, and R_3 is the set of all ordered triples of real numbers. Next, consider the algebraic system that we introduced above, namely $(R_n, +, \mathbf{0})$, where $\mathbf{0}$ is the ordered n-tuple $(0, 0, \cdots, 0)$; we shall denote this algebraic system by "$\mathcal{V}_n$". Notice that we are now using the same symbol for vector addition and scalar addition; we shall rely on the context to recognize these operations. We can now formulate a theorem.

78

THEOREM 3.1.1.   Let $\mathscr{R}$ be the real number field and let $n \in N$; then $(\mathscr{R}, \mathscr{V}_n, \circ)$ is a vector space where $\circ$ is the mapping of $R \times R_n$ into R_n defined above.

Proof: Consider Definition 1.8.1. The details are easy and are left as an exercise.

The proof of Theorem 3.1.1 can be simplified by streamlining our notation for vectors. The idea is to denote vectors by Greek letters. For example, let $\alpha = (a_1, a_2, \cdots, a_n)$ and $\beta = (b_1, b_2, \cdots, b_n)$; then $\alpha + \beta = (a_1 + b_1, a_2 + b_2, \cdots, a_n + b_n)$ and $\beta + \alpha = (b_1 + a_1, b_2 + a_2, \cdots, b_n + a_n)$. Thus $\alpha + \beta = \beta + \alpha$ whenever $\alpha \in R_n$ and $\beta \in R_n$.

Since $(\mathscr{R}, \mathscr{V}_n, \circ)$ is a vector space, we shall use the usual terminology of vector spaces introduced in Section 1.8. For example, we shall say that the n-vectors $\alpha_1, \alpha_2, \cdots, \alpha_t$ are *linearly dependent* iff there are real numbers $k_1, k_2, \cdots, k_t$, not all zero, such that $k_1\alpha_1 + k_2\alpha_2 + \cdots + k_t\alpha_t = \mathbf{0}$. Since we propose to use the terminology of Section 1.8 throughout this chapter, it is undoubtedly wise to reread that section before proceeding. To illustrate our terminology, we note that the vectors $(2, 1, -2, 3)$, $(3, -2, 0, 1)$, $(0, 1, 5, 1)$, and $(1, -5, -8, -4)$ are linearly dependent since $1(2, 1, -2, 3) + -1(3, -2, 0, 1) + 2(0, 1, 5, 1) + 1(1, -5, -8, -4) = (0, 0, 0, 0)$. The vectors $(1, 0, 0, 0)$, $(0, 1, 0, 0)$, $(0, 0, 1, 0)$, and $(0, 0, 0, 1)$ are linearly independent since $k_1(1, 0, 0, 0) + k_2(0, 1, 0, 0) + k_3(0, 0, 1, 0) + k_4(0, 0, 0, 1) = (k_1, k_2, k_3, k_4)$ and $(k_1, k_2, k_3, k_4) = \mathbf{0}$ only if $k_1 = k_2 = k_3 = k_4 = 0$. Finally, we point out that the vector $(1, -5, -8, -4)$ is a linear combination of the vectors $(2, 1, -2, 3)$, $(3, -2, 0, 1)$ and $(0, 1, 5, 1)$ since $(1, -5, -8, -4) = -1(2, 1, -2, 3) + 1(3, -2, 0, 1) + -2(0, 1, 5, 1)$.

Consider the following theorem.

THEOREM 3.1.2.   Let $n \in N$ and let $\alpha_1, \alpha_2, \cdots, \alpha_t$ be any n-vectors; then $\alpha_1, \alpha_2, \cdots, \alpha_t$ are linearly dependent iff one of these vectors is a linear combination of the others.

Proof: There are two parts to the proof.

1. Suppose that the given vectors are linearly dependent; then there are real numbers, not all zero, say $k_1, k_2, \cdots, k_t$, such that $k_1\alpha_1 + k_2\alpha_2 + \cdots + k_t\alpha_t = \mathbf{0}$. Since at least one k_i is not zero, there is no loss of generality in assuming that $k_1 \neq 0$; then $k_1\alpha_1 = -k_2\alpha_2 + -k_3\alpha_3 + \cdots + -k_t\alpha_t$. Hence

$$\alpha_1 = \frac{-k_2}{k_1}\alpha_2 + \frac{-k_3}{k_1}\alpha_3 + \cdots + \frac{-k_t}{k_1}\alpha_t.$$

Thus α_1 is a linear combination of the other vectors.

2. Suppose that one of the given vectors, say α_1, is a linear combination of the other vectors. Then there are real numbers $k_2, k_3, \cdots, k_t$ such that $\alpha_1 = k_2\alpha_2 + k_3\alpha_3 + \cdots + k_t\alpha_t$. Therefore $-1\alpha_1 + k_2\alpha_2 + k_3\alpha_3 + \cdots + k_t\alpha_t = \mathbf{0}$. Hence the vectors $\alpha_1, \alpha_2, \cdots, \alpha_t$ are linearly dependent. This establishes Theorem 3.1.2.

In our abstract discussion of vector spaces we introduced the concept of a *subsystem* of a vector space. Here, we shall concentrate on the set of vectors involved in a subsystem; this set is said to be a *subspace* of the vector space involved. First, let us agree to denote the vector space $(\mathscr{R}, \mathscr{V}_n, \circ)$ by "$\mathscr{V}_n(\mathscr{R})$" whenever $n \in N$.

DEFINITION 3.1.1   Let $n \in N$; a nonempty set of n-vectors, say V, is said to be a *subspace* of $\mathscr{V}_n(\mathscr{R})$ iff

(i) $k\alpha \in V$ whenever $\alpha \in V$ and $k \in R$,
(ii) $\alpha + \beta \in V$ whenever $\alpha \in V$ and $\beta \in V$.

For example, $\{(0, 0)\}$ is a subspace of $\mathscr{V}_2(\mathscr{R})$ since $k(0, 0) = (0, 0)$ whenever $k \in R$, and $(0, 0) + (0, 0) = (0, 0)$. Again, it is easily seen that the set of all 2-vectors is a subspace of $\mathscr{V}_2(\mathscr{R})$. Another important example of a subspace is the set of all linear combinations of the n-vectors $\alpha_1, \alpha_2, \cdots, \alpha_t$; we shall say that the given vectors $\alpha_1, \alpha_2, \cdots, \alpha_t$ *span* this subspace. For example, the set of all linear combinations of $(1, 0, 0, 0)$, $(0, 1, 0, 0)$, $(0, 0, 1, 0)$, $(0, 0, 0, 1)$ is the set of all 4-vectors; thus the vectors $(1, 0, 0, 0)$, $(0, 1, 0, 0)$, $(0, 0, 1, 0)$, $(0, 0, 0, 1)$ span R_4.

We now establish the following important result.

STEINITZ REPLACEMENT THEOREM.   Let $n \in N$, let V be the subspace of $\mathscr{V}_n(\mathscr{R})$ spanned by the n-vectors $\alpha_1, \alpha_2, \cdots, \alpha_t$; let $\beta_1, \beta_2, \cdots, \beta_m$ be m linearly independent vectors of V, where $m \le t$. Then there exist $t - m$ α's, say $\alpha_{m+1}, \alpha_{m+2}, \cdots, \alpha_t$, such that $\beta_1, \beta_2, \cdots, \beta_m, \alpha_{m+1}, \alpha_{m+2}, \cdots, \alpha_t$ span V.

Proof: The theorem asserts that we can replace m of the α's by m linearly independent vectors of V and still have a set of vectors which span V, whenever $m \le t$. We shall prove this by mathematical induction over m. Clearly, zero has the property, since we obtain a set which spans V when we replace none of the α's. Now suppose that s has the property, where $s < t$; this means that given any set of s linearly independent vectors of V, there are s of the α's that we can replace by the given vectors and still have a set which spans V. We shall show that $s + 1$ has the property also. Let $\beta_1, \beta_2, \cdots, \beta_{s+1}$ be $s + 1$ linearly independent vectors of V. Then $\beta_1, \beta_2, \cdots, \beta_s$ are linearly independent; therefore, by assumption, there are s α's, say $\alpha_1, \alpha_2, \cdots, \alpha_s$, that we can replace by the β's. Thus $\beta_1, \beta_2, \cdots, \beta_s, \alpha_{s+1}, \cdots, \alpha_t$ span V. This means that each member of V is a linear combination of $\beta_1, \beta_2, \cdots, \beta_s, \alpha_{s+1}, \cdots, \alpha_t$; hence

$$\beta_{s+1} = \sum_1^s k_i \beta_i + \sum_{s+1}^t k_i \alpha_i .$$

At least one of $k_{s+1}, \cdots, k_t$ is not zero; otherwise β_{s+1} is a linear combination of $\beta_1, \beta_2, \cdots, \beta_s$. Suppose $k_{s+1} \ne 0$; then

(1)
$$\alpha_{s+1} = \frac{1}{k_{s+1}} \beta_{s+1} - \sum_1^s \frac{k_i}{k_{s+1}} \beta_i - \sum_{s+2}^t \frac{k_i}{k_{s+1}} \alpha_i .$$

Let us show that $\beta_1, \cdots, \beta_s, \beta_{s+1}, \alpha_{s+2}, \cdots, \alpha_t$ span V. Let $\gamma \in V$; then

$$\gamma = \sum_1^s k_i' \beta_i + \sum_{s+1}^t k_i' \alpha_i = \sum_1^s k_i' \beta_i + \sum_{s+2}^t k_i' \alpha_i + k_{s+1}' \alpha_{s+1}.$$

Thus, by (1), γ is a linear combination of $\beta_1, \cdots, \beta_{s+1}, \alpha_{s+2}, \cdots, \alpha_t$. This proves that $s+1$ has the property if s has the property. Hence, by mathematical induction, each natural number which does not exceed t has the property. This establishes our theorem.

COROLLARY 3.1.1. Let $n \in N$ and let $\beta_1, \beta_2, \cdots, \beta_{t+1}$ be any n-vectors which are linear combinations of $\alpha_1, \alpha_2, \cdots, \alpha_t$; then $\beta_1, \beta_2, \cdots, \beta_{t+1}$ are linearly dependent.

Proof: Let V be the subspace of $\mathscr{V}_n(\mathscr{R})$ spanned by $\alpha_1, \alpha_2, \cdots, \alpha_t$. Assume that $\beta_1, \beta_2, \cdots, \beta_{t+1}$ are linearly independent; then $\beta_1, \beta_2, \cdots, \beta_t$ are linearly independent. Hence, by the Steinitz Replacement Theorem, V is spanned by $\beta_1, \beta_2, \cdots, \beta_t$. But $\beta_{t+1} \in V$; therefore β_{t+1} is a linear combination of $\beta_1, \beta_2, \cdots, \beta_t$. This contradiction proves that $\beta_1, \beta_2, \cdots, \beta_{t+1}$ are linearly dependent.

THEOREM 3.1.3. Let $n \in N$ and let $\beta_1, \beta_2, \cdots, \beta_t$ be any linearly independent n-vectors; then $t \leq n$.

Proof: The subspace R_n is spanned by the n n-vectors $(1, 0, 0, \cdots, 0), (0, 1, 0, \cdots, 0), \cdots, (0, 0, \cdots, 0, 1)$. Therefore each β_i is a linear combination of these vectors. Thus, by Corollary 3.1.1, $t \leq n$.

It is easy to see that a subspace gives rise to a subsystem of the given vector space; it is merely a matter of adjoining the given field and the operation of scalar multiplication restricted suitably (see Definition 1.8.2). Moreover, by Theorem 1.8.4, this subsystem is also a vector space. For this reason it is customary to use the terms *dimension* and *basis* with respect to a subspace. For convenience, we repeat these definitions.

DEFINITION 3.1.2. The *dimension* of a subspace is the largest nonnegative integer t such that there are t linearly independent vectors in the subspace; if there is no such number, then the subspace is said to have *infinite* dimension.

DEFINITION 3.1.3. A set of vectors of a subspace V is said to be a *basis* for V iff (i) the given vectors span V, (ii) the given vectors are linearly independent.

It follows that the dimension of a finite-dimensional subspace is the number of vectors in any basis for the subspace. For example, $\{(1, 0, 0), (0, 1, 0), (0, 0, 1)\}$ is a basis for R_3; thus the subspace R_3 has dimension 3. On the other hand, the subspace $\{(0, 0, 0)\}$, which consists of the zero vector alone, has dimension 0; we point out that this subspace does not have a basis since $\mathbf{0}$ is linearly dependent.

THEOREM 3.1.4. Let V be a subspace with dimension t; then any set of t linearly independent vectors of V is a basis for V.

Proof: Apply the Steinitz Replacement Theorem.

THEOREM 3.1.5.   Let V and V_1 be finite-dimensional subspaces such that $V_1 \subset V$; then $V = V_1$ iff V and V_1 have the same dimension.

Proof: There are two parts to the proof.

1. Suppose that $V = V_1$; then certainly V and V_1 have the same dimension.

2. Suppose that V and V_1 have the same dimension, say t. Let $\{\alpha_1, \alpha_2, \cdots, \alpha_t\}$ be a basis for V_1; then V_1 consists of all linear combinations of $\alpha_1, \alpha_2, \cdots, \alpha_t$. Now, $V_1 \subset V$; therefore, by Theorem 3.1.4, $\{\alpha_1, \alpha_2, \cdots, \alpha_t\}$ is a basis for V. Thus V consists of all linear combinations of $\alpha_1, \alpha_2, \cdots, \alpha_t$. So $V = V_1$. This completes our proof.

To illustrate Theorem 3.1.4, we point out that $\{(a, 0) \mid a \in R\}$ is a subspace with basis $\{(1, 0)\}$; hence, this subspace has dimension 1. On the other hand, $\{(a, b) \mid a \in R$ and $b \in R\}$ is a subspace with basis $\{(1, 0), (0, 1)\}$; hence, this subspace has dimension 2.

The discussion of this chapter has thus far centered around ordered n-tuples of real numbers because of the importance of the vector spaces $(\mathscr{R}, \mathscr{V}_n, \circ)$. The following theorem states that any finite-dimensional vector space which involves the real number field can be represented by a vector space $\mathscr{V}_n(\mathscr{R})$, where $n \in N$.

THEOREM 3.1.6.   Let $n \in N$ and let $(\mathscr{R}, \mathscr{V}, \circ)$ be any vector space of dimension n; then $(\mathscr{R}, \mathscr{V}, \circ) \cong \mathscr{V}_n(\mathscr{R})$.

Proof: Since $(\mathscr{R}, \mathscr{V}, \circ)$ has dimension n, there are n linearly independent members of V, say $\alpha_1, \alpha_2, \cdots, \alpha_n$; which form a basis for V. In particular, each member of V is a linear combination of $\alpha_1, \alpha_2, \cdots, \alpha_n$. Thus, corresponding to each member of V, say α, there is an ordered n-tuple of real numbers, say $(t_1, t_2, \cdots, t_n)$, such that $\alpha = t_1\alpha_1 + t_2\alpha_2 + \cdots + t_n\alpha_n$. Accordingly, we consider the mapping M of V into R_n which associates $(t_1, t_2, \cdots, t_n)$ with α. It is easy to prove that M is actually a one–one mapping of V onto R_n and that the vector space $\mathscr{V}_n(\mathscr{R})$ is the image of the given vector space under M. This completes our proof.

In the following four sections we shall apply our ideas about vectors to the problem of solving a system of linear equations. Also, we shall develop our ideas about matrices by introducing the notion of *rank*. This will put us in a good position to continue our abstract treatment of vector spaces in Section 3.6.

E X E R C I S E S

1. Show that the vectors $(1, 0, 0)$, $(0, 1, 0)$, $(0, 0, 1)$ are linearly independent.
2. Show that the vectors $(k, 0, 0)$, $(0, k, 0)$, $(0, 0, k)$ are linearly independent provided $k \neq 0$.
3. Given that the vectors $\alpha_1, \alpha_2, \cdots, \alpha_t$ are linearly independent, prove that $k\alpha_1, k\alpha_2, \cdots, k\alpha_t$ are linearly independent if $k \neq 0$.
4. Show that the vectors $(1, 2, -3)$, $(2, 0, -1)$, $(7, 6, -11)$ are linearly dependent.
5. Show that the vectors $(3, 0, 1, -1)$, $(2, -1, 0, 1)$, $(1, 1, 1, -2)$ are linearly dependent.

6. Show that $(5, 6, 0)$ is a linear combination of the vectors $(-1, 2, 0)$, $(3, 1, 2)$, $(4, -1, 0)$, $(0, 1, -1)$.

7. Show that $(0, 1, 3, -2)$ is a linear combination of the vectors $(1, 0, 2, -1)$, $(2, -1, 1, 0)$, $(3, -2, 0, -2)$.

8. Show that $\{(0, 0, 0)\}$ is a subspace of $\mathscr{V}_3(\mathscr{R})$.

9. Prove that R_4 is spanned by the vectors $(1, 0, 0, 0)$, $(0, 1, 0, 0)$, $(0, 0, 1, 0)$, $(0, 0, 0, 1)$.

10. Prove that any two bases for a subspace contain the same number of vectors.

11. Prove that $\{(0, 1, 1), (1, 0, 1), (1, 1, 0)\}$ is a basis for R_3.

12. a. Show that $V = \{(0, b) \mid b \in R\}$ is a subspace of $\mathscr{V}_2(\mathscr{R})$.
    b. Find a basis for V.
    c. Compute the dimension of V.

13. a. Show that $V = \{(a, b) \mid (a, b) \in R_2 \text{ and } b = ma\}$ is a subspace of $\mathscr{V}_2(\mathscr{R})$, where m is a given real number.
    b. Find a basis for V.
    c. Compute the dimension of V.

14. a. Show that $V = \{(a, b) \mid (a, b) \in R_2 \text{ and } b = 2a + 5\}$ is *not* a subspace of $\mathscr{V}_2(\mathscr{R})$.
    b. Find a vector, say β, such that $V_1 = \{\alpha + \beta \mid \alpha \in V\}$ is a subspace of $\mathscr{V}_2(\mathscr{R})$.
    c. Compute the dimension of V_1.

15. a. Show that $V = \{(a, b, c) \mid (a, b, c) \in R_3 \text{ and } 2a - b + c = 0\}$ is a subspace of $\mathscr{V}_3(\mathscr{R})$.
    b. Find a basis for V.
    c. Compute the dimension of V.

16. a. Show that $V = \{(a, b, c) \mid (a, b, c) \in R_3 \text{ and } 2a - b + c = 10\}$ is *not* a subspace of $\mathscr{V}_3(\mathscr{R})$.
    b. Find a vector, say β, such that $V_1 = \{\alpha + \beta \mid \alpha \in V\}$ is a subspace of $\mathscr{V}_3(\mathscr{R})$.
    c. Compute the dimension of V_1.

17. a. Show that $V = \{(a, b, c, d) \mid (a, b, c, d) \in R_4 \text{ and } 3a - 2b + 2c - d = 0\}$ is a subspace of $\mathscr{V}_4(\mathscr{R})$.
    b. Find a basis for V.
    c. Compute the dimension of V.

18. a. Show that $V = \{(a, b, c, d) \mid (a, b, c, d) \in R_4 \text{ and } 3a - 2b + 2c - d = 10\}$ is *not* a subspace of $\mathscr{V}_4(\mathscr{R})$.
    b. Find a vector, say β, such that $V_1 = \{\alpha + \beta \mid \alpha \in V\}$ is a subspace of $\mathscr{V}_4(\mathscr{R})$.
    c. Compute the dimension of V_1.

3.2 An Existence Theorem

In this section we shall establish a criterion for the existence of a solution of a system of linear equations. First, we need some terminology. Consider the following system of m equations in n unknowns:

(1)
$$\begin{cases} a_{11}x_1 + a_{12}x_2 + \cdots + a_{1n}x_n + b_1 = 0 \\ a_{21}x_1 + a_{22}x_2 + \cdots + a_{2n}x_n + b_2 = 0 \\ \quad\vdots \\ a_{m1}x_1 + a_{m2}x_2 + \cdots + a_{mn}x_n + b_m = 0. \end{cases}$$

We shall associate two matrices with this system: the first is the matrix of coefficients of the unknowns, namely

$$\begin{pmatrix} a_{11} & a_{12} & \cdots & a_{1n} \\ a_{21} & a_{22} & \cdots & a_{2n} \\ & & \vdots & \\ a_{m1} & a_{m2} & \cdots & a_{mn} \end{pmatrix},$$

which we shall call the *coefficient matrix* of the system (1); the second matrix that we need is the matrix which represents the system (1), namely

$$\begin{pmatrix} a_{11} & a_{12} & \cdots & a_{1n} & b_1 \\ a_{21} & a_{22} & \cdots & a_{2n} & b_2 \\ & & \vdots & & \\ a_{m1} & a_{m2} & \cdots & a_{mn} & b_m \end{pmatrix},$$

which we shall call the *augmented matrix* of the system (1).

We shall find it useful to associate a nonnegative integer with each matrix; this number is said to be the *rank* of the matrix.

DEFINITION 3.2.1.   The *rank* of a matrix is the maximum number of linearly independent column vectors of the matrix.

For example, the matrix

$$\begin{pmatrix} 1 & 0 & 0 & 0 \\ 0 & 0 & 0 & 0 \\ 0 & 1 & 0 & 0 \\ 0 & 0 & 0 & 0 \end{pmatrix}$$

has rank 2 since the first two column vectors of this matrix, namely (1, 0, 0, 0) and (0, 0, 1, 0), are linearly independent, whereas any three column vectors of this matrix are linearly dependent.

We can now formulate a criterion for the existence of a solution of system (1); notice that our criterion involves the ranks of the coefficient matrix and the augmented matrix of (1).

THEOREM 3.2.1.   The system (1) has a solution iff the coefficient matrix and the augmented matrix have the same rank.

Proof: We introduce names for the column vectors of the augmented matrix. Let $\alpha_k = (a_{1k}, a_{2k}, \cdots, a_{mk})$ whenever $1 \le k \le n$, and let $\beta = (b_1, b_2, \cdots, b_m)$; then the system (1) is represented by the single vector equation

(2) $x_1\alpha_1 + x_2\alpha_2 + \cdots + x_n\alpha_n + \beta = 0.$

Notice that (2) possesses a solution for the x_i, $i = 1, 2, \cdots, n$, iff β is a linear combination of $\alpha_1, \alpha_2, \cdots, \alpha_n$. Let V_1 be the subspace of $\mathscr{V}_m(\mathscr{R})$ spanned by the vectors $\alpha_1, \alpha_2, \cdots, \alpha_n$; then the system (1) is solvable iff $\beta \in V_1$. Let V be the subspace of $\mathscr{V}_m(\mathscr{R})$ spanned by the vectors $\alpha_1, \alpha_2, \cdots, \alpha_n, \beta$. There are two possibilities regarding the system (1):

(i) Suppose the system (1) is solvable. Then $\beta \in V_1$; therefore V is spanned by $\alpha_1, \alpha_2, \cdots, \alpha_n$. Hence $V = V_1$. Thus V and V_1 have the same dimension. But the dimension of V_1 is the maximum number of linearly independent vectors among $\alpha_1, \alpha_2, \cdots, \alpha_n$ whereas the dimension of V is the maximum number of linearly independent vectors among $\alpha_1, \alpha_2, \cdots, \alpha_n, \beta$. Thus the coefficient matrix and the augmented matrix have the same rank.

(ii) Suppose the system (1) is not solvable. Then β is not a linear combination of $\alpha_1, \alpha_2, \cdots, \alpha_n$. Therefore $V \neq V_1$; hence dimension $V_1 <$ dimension V. We conclude that the rank of the coefficient matrix is less than the rank of the augmented matrix of system (1). This establishes Theorem 3.2.1.

In order to use the criterion developed in this section, we need a simple method of computing the rank of a matrix. This question is considered in Section 3.4.

E X E R C I S E S

Determine the rank of the following matrices.

1. $\begin{pmatrix} 2 & 1 & 1 \\ 0 & 0 & 1 \\ 0 & 0 & 1 \end{pmatrix}$.

2. $\begin{pmatrix} -1 & -2 & -3 \\ 2 & 4 & 6 \\ 1 & 2 & 3 \end{pmatrix}$.

3. $\begin{pmatrix} 2 & 1 & 1 & 2 \\ 0 & 1 & 0 & 0 \\ 0 & 0 & 0 & 0 \\ 0 & 0 & 1 & 2 \end{pmatrix}$.

4. $\begin{pmatrix} 3 & 0 & 1 & -2 & 4 & 5 \\ 0 & 1 & 2 & 1 & 1 & -2 \\ 0 & 0 & 0 & 0 & 0 & 0 \\ 0 & 0 & 0 & 0 & 0 & 0 \\ 0 & 0 & 0 & 0 & 0 & 0 \end{pmatrix}$.

5. Consider an $m \times n$ matrix whose final t rows consist of 0's only. Prove that the rank of this matrix does not exceed $m - t$.

---

6. Does the following system have a solution?

$$-x_1 - 2x_2 - 3x_3 = -1$$

$$2x_1 + 4x_2 + 6x_3 = 2$$

$$x_1 + 2x_2 + 3x_3 = 0.$$

7. Prove that the system (1) of the text has at least one solution if $b_i = 0$, $i = 1, 2, \cdots, m$.

8. Show that the vector $(b_1, b_2, \cdots, b_n)$ is a linear combination of the vectors $(a_{1i}, a_{2i}, \cdots, a_{ni})$, $i = 1, 2, \cdots, t$, iff the matrices

$$\begin{pmatrix} a_{11} & a_{12} & \cdots & a_{1t} \\ a_{21} & a_{22} & \cdots & a_{2t} \\ & & \vdots & \\ a_{n1} & a_{n2} & \cdots & a_{nt} \end{pmatrix} \quad \text{and} \quad \begin{pmatrix} a_{11} & a_{12} & \cdots & a_{1t} & b_1 \\ a_{21} & a_{22} & \cdots & a_{2t} & b_2 \\ & & \vdots & & \\ a_{n1} & a_{n2} & \cdots & a_{nt} & b_n \end{pmatrix}$$

have the same rank.

9. Show that $(4, -1, 2)$ is a linear combination of $(1, 2, -1)$ and $(2, 1, 0)$. Set up the problem as a linear system.

3.3   Vector Solutions of a Linear System

Consider the following *homogeneous* system of equations:

$$(1) \qquad \begin{cases} a_{11}x_1 + a_{12}x_2 + \cdots + a_{1n}x_n = 0 \\ a_{21}x_1 + a_{22}x_2 + \cdots + a_{2n}x_n = 0 \\ \qquad\qquad \vdots \\ a_{m1}x_1 + a_{m2}x_2 + \cdots + a_{mn}x_n = 0. \end{cases}$$

This system consists of m equations which involve n unknowns. The coefficient matrix of the system is

$$\begin{pmatrix} a_{11} & a_{12} & \cdots & a_{1n} \\ a_{21} & a_{22} & \cdots & a_{2n} \\ & & \vdots & \\ a_{m1} & a_{m2} & \cdots & a_{mn} \end{pmatrix}.$$

Let $\alpha_k = (a_{1k}, a_{2k}, \cdots, a_{mk})$, $k = 1, 2, \cdots, n$; then $\alpha_1, \alpha_2, \cdots, \alpha_n$ are the column vectors of the coefficient matrix. Clearly, the system (1) has a solution iff the vector equation

$$x_1\alpha_1 + x_2\alpha_2 + \cdots + x_n\alpha_n = 0$$

has a solution. Certainly, the system (1) has at least one solution, $x_1 = 0$, $x_2 = 0$, $\cdots$, $x_n = 0$. Given any solution of (1), say $x_1 = t_1$, $x_2 = t_2$, $\cdots$, $x_n = t_n$, consider the associated n-vector $(t_1, t_2, \cdots, t_n)$, which we shall call a *vector solution* of (1).

THEOREM 3.3.1.   The set of all vector solutions of (1) is a subspace of $\mathcal{V}_n(\mathcal{R})$.

Proof: Consider Definition 3.1.1; the details are left as an exercise.

Our problem now is, to find a basis for the set of all vector solutions of (1). Let r be the rank of the coefficient matrix of system (1). We may suppose that α_1, α_2, $\cdots$, α_r are linearly independent; otherwise we renumber the unknowns in (1). It follows that each of the remaining column vectors of the coefficient matrix is a linear combination of the vectors α_1, α_2, $\cdots$, α_r. For example,

$$\alpha_{r+1} = k_1^{(r+1)}\alpha_1 + k_2^{(r+1)}\alpha_2 + \cdots + k_r^{(r+1)}\alpha_r;$$

therefore $k_1^{(r+1)}\alpha_1 + k_2^{(r+1)}\alpha_2 + \cdots + k_r^{(r+1)}\alpha_r - \alpha_{r+1} = \mathbf{0}$.   Hence $(k_1^{(r+1)}, k_2^{(r+1)}, \cdots,$ $k_r^{(r+1)}, -1, 0, 0, \cdots, 0)$ is a vector solution of (1). In this way we construct $n - r$ vector solutions of the system (1), namely β_1, β_2, $\cdots$, β_{n-r}, where

$$\beta_1 = (k_1^{(r+1)}, k_2^{(r+1)}, \cdots, k_r^{(r+1)}, -1, 0, \cdots, 0)$$
$$\beta_2 = (k_1^{(r+2)}, k_2^{(r+2)}, \cdots, k_r^{(r+2)}, 0, -1, 0, \cdots, 0)$$
$$\vdots$$
$$\beta_{n-r} = (k_1^{(n)}, k_2^{(n)}, \cdots, k_r^{(n)}, 0, 0, \cdots, 0, -1).$$

It is clear that β_1, β_2, $\cdots$, β_{n-r} are linearly independent. Let us show that these vectors form a basis for the subspace which consists of all vector solutions of the system (1). We have only to show that β_1, β_2, $\cdots$, β_{n-r} span our subspace. Let $(z_1, z_2, \cdots, z_n) = \zeta$ be any vector solution of the system (1). Consider the vector $\zeta + \sum_{1}^{n-r} z_{r+i}\beta_i$; note that the last $n - r$ terms of this vector vanish, i.e.,

$$\zeta + \sum_{1}^{n-r} z_{r+i}\beta_i = (c_1, c_2, \cdots, c_r, 0, 0, \cdots, 0).$$

But $\zeta + \sum_{1}^{n-r} z_{r+i}\beta_i$ is a member of our subspace since ζ and $\sum_{1}^{n-r} z_{r+i}\beta_i$ are members of the subspace. Therefore $(c_1, c_2, \cdots, c_r, 0, 0, \cdots, 0)$ is a vector solution of (1), i.e.,

$$c_1\alpha_1 + c_2\alpha_2 + \cdots + c_r\alpha_r = \mathbf{0}.$$

Since α_1, α_2, $\cdots$, α_r are linearly independent, it follows that $c_1 = 0$, $c_2 = 0$, $\cdots$, $c_r = 0$. Therefore $\zeta + \sum_{1}^{n-r} z_{r+i}\beta_i = \mathbf{0}$. Hence ζ is a linear combination of β_1, β_2, $\cdots$, β_{n-r}. This proves that $\{\beta_1, \beta_2, \cdots, \beta_{n-r}\}$ is a basis for our subspace. In particular, the subspace of vector solutions of (1) has dimension $n - r$. We have established the following result.

THEOREM 3.3.2.   The subspace of vector solutions of a homogeneous system in n unknowns has dimension $n - r$, where r is the rank of the coefficient matrix of the system.

COROLLARY 3.3.1.   A homogeneous system in n unknowns has a nontrivial solution iff the rank of the coefficient matrix of the system is less than n.

The proof of Theorem 3.3.2 is quite complicated; the following example may clarify the ideas.

EXAMPLE 1.   Find a basis for the subspace of vector solutions of the following homogeneous linear system:

(2)
$$\begin{cases} x_1 + 2x_2 - x_3 + 4x_4 = 0 \\ 2x_1 - x_2 + 3x_3 + 3x_4 = 0 \\ 4x_1 + x_2 + 3x_3 + 9x_4 = 0 \\ x_2 - x_3 + x_4 = 0 \\ 2x_1 + 3x_2 - x_3 + 7x_4 = 0. \end{cases}$$

Solution: The coefficient matrix of this system is

$$\begin{pmatrix} 1 & 2 & -1 & 4 \\ 2 & -1 & 3 & 3 \\ 4 & 1 & 3 & 9 \\ 0 & 1 & -1 & 1 \\ 2 & 3 & -1 & 7 \end{pmatrix}.$$

The column vectors of this matrix are $\alpha_1 = (1, 2, 4, 0, 2)$, $\alpha_2 = (2, -1, 1, 1, 3)$, $\alpha_3 = (-1, 3, 3, -1, -1)$, and $\alpha_4 = (4, 3, 9, 1, 7)$. The rank of the coefficient matrix is 2, since α_1 and α_2 are linearly independent vectors, whereas $\alpha_3 = \alpha_1 - \alpha_2$ and $\alpha_4 = 2\alpha_1 + \alpha_2$. Therefore $\beta_1 = (1, -1, -1, 0)$ and $\beta_2 = (2, 1, 0, -1)$ are vector solutions of the system (2). Furthermore, β_1 and β_2 are linearly independent; indeed, the set $\{\beta_1, \beta_2\}$ is a basis for the vector space of all vector solutions of (2). To see this, let $\zeta = (z_1, z_2, z_3, z_4)$ be any vector solution of (2); consider the vector $\zeta + z_3\beta_1 + z_4\beta_2 = (z_1 + z_3 + 2z_4, z_2 - z_3 + z_4, 0, 0)$. Since this vector is a vector solution of (2), it follows that

$$(z_1 + z_3 + 2z_4)\alpha_1 + (z_2 - z_3 + z_4)\alpha_2 = \mathbf{0}.$$

But α_1 and α_2 are linearly independent; therefore $z_1 + z_3 + 2z_4 = 0$ and $z_2 - z_3 + z_4 = 0$. Hence $\zeta + z_3\beta_1 + z_4\beta_2 = (0, 0, 0, 0)$, i.e., $\zeta = -z_3\beta_1 - z_4\beta_2$. This proves that ζ is a linear combination of β_1 and β_2. We have established that $\{(1, -1, -1, 0), (2, 1, 0, -1)\}$ is a basis for the subspace of vector solutions of the system (2). We point out that our subspace has dimension 2.

Let us consider the significance of Corollary 3.3.1. Now, the rank of a matrix is the maximum number of linearly independent column vectors of the matrix. Therefore the coefficient matrix of a homogeneous system consisting of m equations has rank which does not exceed m (since the column vectors are members of R_m, and R_m has dimension m). We conclude that a homogeneous system of m equations in n unknowns possesses a nontrivial solution if $m < n$.

We have seen that the vector solutions of a homogeneous system can be characterized as the set of all linear combinations of a certain set of linearly independent vector solutions of the system. It is a simple matter of characterize the vector solutions of *any* linear system in terms of one solution of the system and the solutions of the related homogeneous system. Consider the following linear system:

(3)
$$\begin{cases} a_{11}x_1 + a_{12}x_2 + \cdots + a_{1n}x_n + b_1 = 0 \\ a_{21}x_1 + a_{22}x_2 + \cdots + a_{2n}x_n + b_2 = 0 \\ \vdots \\ a_{m1}x_1 + a_{m2}x_2 + \cdots + a_{mn}x_n + b_m = 0. \end{cases}$$

Let $\eta = (y_1, y_2, \cdots, y_n)$ be a particular vector solution of (3). If $\gamma = (c_1, c_2, \cdots, c_n)$ is a vector solution of the related homogeneous system (1), then it is easily seen that

$$\eta + \gamma = (y_1 + c_1, y_2 + c_2, \cdots, y_n + c_n)$$

is a vector solution of (3). Thus $\{\eta + \gamma \,|\, \gamma$ is a vector solution of (1)$\}$ is a set of vector solutions of (3); notice that corresponding to each vector solution of (1) we have a vector solution of (3). Furthermore, there are no other vector solutions of (3). To see this, suppose that ζ is a vector solution of (3); then $\zeta - \eta$ is a vector solution of (1); but $\eta + (\zeta - \eta) = \zeta$ Thus ζ is one of the vector solutions of (3) obtained by adding η to a vector solution of (1). We have proved that the set of all vector solutions of (3) is obtained by adding a particular vector solution of (3) to each vector solution of (1).

We now consider the question: under what circumstances does the system (3) have a unique solution?

THEOREM 3.3.3.   The linear system (3) has a unique solution iff n is the rank of both the coefficient matrix and the augmented matrix.

Proof: By Theorem 3.2.1 it is necessary that the coefficient matrix and the augmented matrix have the same rank in order that the system (3) possess a solution at all. Furthermore, we require that the corresponding homogeneous system have a unique solution (namely, the trivial solution **0**) in order that the system (3) have no more than one solution. By Corollary 3.3.1, this means that the coefficient matrix must have rank n. This establishes Theorem 3.3.3.

E X E R C I S E S

1. Prove Theorem 3.3.1.

2. a. Show that the linear homogeneous system

$$x_1 + 2x_2 - x_3 = 0$$
$$2x_1 - x_2 + x_3 = 0$$

has a nontrivial solution.

b. Find a nontrivial solution of this system.

c. Construct a basis for the subspace of vector solutions of the given system.

3. By applying Theorem 3.3.3, show that the following linear system has a unique solution:

$$x_1 + 2x_2 - x_3 + 3x_4 - 15 = 0$$

$$3x_1 - x_2 + 2x_3 + x_4 + 5 = 0$$

$$4x_1 + 2x_2 - 3x_3 + 5x_4 - 27 = 0$$

$$2x_1 + 7x_2 + 5x_3 - x_4 - 24 = 0.$$

3.4   Computing the Rank of a Matrix

We wish to determine the rank of a matrix, say

$$\begin{pmatrix} a_{11} & a_{12} & \cdots & a_{1n} \\ a_{21} & a_{22} & \cdots & a_{2n} \\ & \vdots & & \\ a_{m1} & a_{m2} & \cdots & a_{mn} \end{pmatrix}$$

This matrix is the coefficient matrix of the homogeneous linear system

(1)
$$\begin{cases} a_{11}x_1 + a_{12}x_2 + \cdots + a_{1n}x_n = 0 \\ a_{21}x_1 + a_{22}x_2 + \cdots + a_{2n}x_n = 0 \\ \qquad\qquad \vdots \\ a_{m1}x_1 + a_{m2}x_2 + \cdots + a_{mn}x_n = 0. \end{cases}$$

Let the rank of the given matrix be r; then, by Theorem 3.3.2, the subspace of vector solutions of the system (1) has dimension $n - r$. Hence any homogeneous linear system equivalent to (1) (i.e., having the same solution set) has a matrix with rank r. It follows from this observation that our process for reducing a matrix does not affect the rank of the matrix. Recall that the matrix operations involved in reducing a matrix are the following: (i) interchange two rows, (ii) multiply a row by a nonzero real number, (iii) add one row to another row. We emphasize that these operations do not affect rank because the corresponding homogeneous linear systems are equivalent. Of course, once we have reduced our matrix, we can read off the rank of the matrix.

EXAMPLE 1.   Compute the rank of

$$\begin{pmatrix} 2 & 1 & 0 & -1 & 3 \\ 1 & 2 & 1 & 2 & 0 \\ 0 & 3 & 1 & 1 & 1 \\ -1 & -5 & -3 & -7 & 3 \end{pmatrix}.$$

Solution:

$$\begin{pmatrix} 2 & 1 & 0 & -1 & 3 \\ 1 & 2 & 1 & 2 & 0 \\ 0 & 3 & 1 & 1 & 1 \\ -1 & -5 & -3 & -7 & 3 \end{pmatrix} \sim \begin{pmatrix} 1 & 2 & 1 & 2 & 0 \\ 0 & -3 & -2 & -5 & 3 \\ 0 & 3 & 1 & 1 & 1 \\ 0 & -3 & -2 & -5 & 3 \end{pmatrix} \sim \begin{pmatrix} 1 & 2 & 1 & 2 & 0 \\ 0 & 3 & 1 & 1 & 1 \\ 0 & 0 & -1 & -4 & 4 \\ 0 & 0 & -1 & -4 & 4 \end{pmatrix}$$

$$\sim \begin{pmatrix} 3 & 0 & 1 & 4 & -2 \\ 0 & 3 & 0 & -3 & 5 \\ 0 & 0 & -1 & -4 & 4 \\ 0 & 0 & 0 & 0 & 0 \end{pmatrix} \sim \begin{pmatrix} 3 & 0 & 0 & 0 & 2 \\ 0 & 3 & 0 & -3 & 5 \\ 0 & 0 & -1 & -4 & 4 \\ 0 & 0 & 0 & 0 & 0 \end{pmatrix}.$$

Clearly, the vectors $(3, 0, 0, 0)$, $(0, 3, 0, 0)$, and $(0, 0, -1, 0)$ are linearly independent. Furthermore, 0 is the fourth term of each of the five column vectors of our final matrix; therefore the column vectors are essentially 3-vectors. Recalling that any set of 3-vectors with more than three members is linearly dependent, we see that our matrix has rank 3.

Note: Since the matrix of this example is the augmented matrix of the linear system

$$2x_1 + x_2 \quad\quad - x_4 + 3 = 0$$

$$x_1 + 2x_2 + x_3 + 2x_4 \quad\quad = 0$$

$$3x_2 + x_3 + x_4 + 1 = 0$$

$$-x_1 - 5x_2 - 3x_3 - 7x_4 + 3 = 0,$$

we see that the coefficient matrix and the augmented matrix of this system both have rank 3; therefore, by Theorem 3.2.1, this system possesses at least one solution. In view of Theorem 3.3.3, we see that this linear system possesses more than one solution.

EXERCISES

Determine the rank of each of the following matrices.

1. $\begin{pmatrix} 1 & 2 & 3 & 1 \\ 3 & 1 & 2 & 0 \\ 0 & -1 & -2 & 1 \end{pmatrix}$.

2. $\begin{pmatrix} -1 & 0 & 1 & 2 \\ 3 & 1 & 2 & -1 \\ 5 & 1 & 0 & -5 \end{pmatrix}$.

3. $\begin{pmatrix} 1 & 1 & 2 & 1 \\ -2 & 2 & 5 & 4 \\ 4 & 0 & -1 & -2 \end{pmatrix}$.

4. $\begin{pmatrix} -1 & 1 & 0 & 2 & 3 \\ 1 & 1 & -1 & -1 & 2 \\ 3 & 0 & -1 & 1 & -2 \\ 2 & -1 & 0 & 2 & -1 \end{pmatrix}$.

5. $\begin{pmatrix} 2 & 0 & -1 & 3 & 2 & 1 \\ -1 & 1 & 0 & 1 & 3 & -2 \\ 3 & 1 & -2 & 5 & 7 & 0 \\ -5 & 1 & 2 & -3 & -1 & -4 \\ 1 & 3 & -2 & 7 & 13 & -4 \end{pmatrix}$.

6. Does the linear system whose augmented matrix is the matrix of Exercise 1 possess a solution?

7. Does the linear system whose augmented matrix is the matrix of Exercise 5 possess a solution?

8. Let $n \in N$ and let $\alpha = (a_1, a_2, \cdots, a_n)$ and $\beta = (b_1, b_2, \cdots, b_n)$ be any n-vectors; then α is said to be *orthogonal* to β iff $a_1 b_1 + a_2 b_2 + \cdots + a_n b_n = 0$.

   a. Show that there is a nonzero vector $\xi = (x_1, x_2, x_3, x_4)$ such that ξ is orthogonal to each of the vectors $(1, 0, -1, 2)$, $(2, 1, 3, -1)$, and $(3, 0, 1, 4)$.

   b. Compute ξ.

3.5 Rank and the Mapping Determinant

The notion of the *rank* of a matrix can be characterized in terms of the matrices which can be constructed from the given matrix by deleting various rows and columns of the matrix. The resulting matrices are said to be the *submatrices* of the given matrix. Actually, we shall be concerned primarily with the *square* submatrices of a given matrix. We shall say that a square matrix, say (a_{ij}), is *singular* iff $|a_{ij}| = 0$, and we shall say that (a_{ij}) is *nonsingular* iff $|a_{ij}| \neq 0$.

We now present the main theorem of this section.

THEOREM 3.5.1.   A matrix, say A, has rank r iff

(i) A possesses a nonsingular $r \times r$ submatrix

(ii) If $t > r$ then each $t \times t$ submatrix of A is singular.

In order to prove this theorem we need to establish several preliminary results.

THEOREM 3.5.2.   Let $n \in N$ and let A be any $n \times n$ matrix; then A has rank n iff A is nonsingular.

Proof: There are two parts to our proof.

1. Assume that the column vectors of the matrix A are linearly dependent. Then one of the column vectors is a linear combination of the other column vectors. So, one of the columns of the given matrix A is a linear combination of the other columns. Considering the properties of the mapping *determinant*, we see that $|A| = 0$.

2. Assume that the column vectors of A are linearly independent. Then the process of reducing A produces a matrix with 1's on the main diagonal and 0's off the diagonal. But the reduced matrix is obtained from A by row operations only; thus, each step in the reduction produces a matrix whose determinant is a nonzero multiple of $|A|$. Since the determinant of the reduced matrix is not zero, it follows that $|A| \neq 0$. This establishes Theorem 3.5.2.

THEOREM 3.5.3.   Let A be any matrix with rank r; then

(i) A possesses a nonsingular $r \times r$ submatrix

(ii) If $t > r$ then each $t \times t$ submatrix of A is singular.

Proof: By assumption there are r column vectors of A that are linearly independent, say $\alpha_1, \cdots, \alpha_r$. Consider the matrix B whose column vectors are $\alpha_1, \cdots, \alpha_r$. Since our process for reducing a matrix does not affect rank (see Section 3.4), it is clear that B can be reduced to a matrix whose first r rows consist of 0's off the main diagonal and 1's on the main diagonal. Moreover, this reduced matrix can be obtained from B by using only r rows of B; therefore, the submatrix of B which consists of these r rows, has rank r. Notice that this submatrix of B is an $r \times r$ matrix. So, by Theorem 3.5.2, this submatrix is nonsingular. Finally, let $t > r$; we must prove that each $t \times t$ submatrix of A is singular. By assumption, any t column vectors of A are linearly dependent. Let $\beta_1, \cdots, \beta_t$ be any t column vectors of A. Since these vectors are linearly dependent, it follows that the t-vectors constructed from them by deleting any $n - t$ rows of the matrix A, are also linearly dependent (here, n is the number of rows of the matrix A). Hence, the corresponding $t \times t$ submatrix of A does not have rank t; so, by Theorem 3.5.2, this $t \times t$ submatrix of A is singular. We have established Theorem 3.5.3.

This theorem possesses two useful corollaries.

COROLLARY 3.5.1.   If A possesses a nonsingular $r \times r$ submatrix, then rank A $\geq r$.

Proof: If the rank of A is less than r, then each $r \times r$ submatrix of A is singular.

COROLLARY 3.5.2.   Let $r \in N$ and suppose that each $t \times t$ submatrix of A is singular whenever $t > r$; then rank $A \leq r$.

Proof: Let rank $A = r_1$ and suppose that $r_1 > r$. Then, by Theorem 3.5.3, A possesses a nonsingular $r_1 \times r_1$ submatrix.

We are now in a position to establish the following theorem; this theorem is the converse of Theorem 3.5.3.

THEOREM 3.5.4.   A matrix, say A, has rank r if
  (i) A possesses a nonsingular $r \times r$ submatrix.
  (ii) If $t > r$ then each $t \times t$ submatrix of A is singular.

Proof: Let r_1 be the rank of A. By assumption, A possesses a nonsingular $r \times r$ submatrix; therefore, by Corollary 3.5.1, $r_1 \geq r$. By assumption, if $t > r$ then each $t \times t$ submatrix of A is singular. Therefore, by Corollary 3.5.2, $r_1 \leq r$. We conclude that $r_1 = r$.

Of course, Theorems 3.5.3 and 3.5.4 together constitute a proof of Theorem 3.5.1; so we have established our main theorem.

Notice that Theorem 3.5.2 is a special case of Theorem 3.5.1; in particular, using Theorem 3.5.2 we obtain a condition under which a linear system which consists of n equations in n unknowns has a unique solution.

THEOREM 3.5.5.   A linear system which consists of n equations in n unknowns has a unique solution iff its coefficient matrix is nonsingular.

Proof: Apply Theorems 3.3.3 and 3.5.2.

We shall now bring out an interesting consequence of Theorem 3.5.1. By the *row* vectors of an $m \times n$ matrix, say

$$
\begin{pmatrix}
a_{11} & a_{12} & \cdots & a_{1n} \\
a_{21} & a_{22} & \cdots & a_{2n} \\
& & \vdots & \\
a_{m1} & a_{m2} & \cdots & a_{mn}
\end{pmatrix} = (a_{ij}),
$$

we mean the vectors $(a_{11}, a_{12}, \cdots, a_{1n}), (a_{21}, a_{22}, \cdots, a_{2n}), \cdots, (a_{m1}, a_{m2}, \cdots, a_{mn})$. Notice that this $m \times n$ matrix has m row vectors and n column vectors. Now, let r be the rank of (a_{ij}). Then, by Theorem 3.5.1, there is a nonsingular $r \times r$ submatrix of (a_{ij}), whereas each $t \times t$ submatrix of (a_{ij}) is singular if $t > r$. Consider the transpose of (a_{ij}); this is an $n \times m$ matrix (see Definition 2.3.2). Since each square matrix and its transpose have the same determinant, it follows that there is a nonsingular $r \times r$ submatrix of $(a_{ij})^t$, whereas each $t \times t$ submatrix of $(a_{ij})^t$ is singular if $t > r$. Therefore, by Theorem 3.5.1, the matrix $(a_{ij})^t$ has rank r. We have established the following result.

THEOREM 3.5.6.   Let A be any matrix; then A and A^t have the same rank.

In other words, we have established the following theorem.

THEOREM 3.5.7.   Let A be any matrix and let $r \in N$; then r column vectors of A are linearly independent iff r row vectors of A are linearly independent.

E X E R C I S E S

1. List the submatrices of the matrix

$$
\begin{pmatrix}
1 & 0 & 3 \\
2 & -1 & 4
\end{pmatrix}.
$$

2. By computing the determinant of the following matrix, show that this matrix has rank 4:

$$
\begin{pmatrix}
1 & 0 & -1 & 2 \\
2 & 1 & 2 & -1 \\
-2 & 2 & -1 & 3 \\
3 & 4 & -1 & -2
\end{pmatrix}.
$$

3. Show that the following linear system has a unique solution for any choice of $b_1, b_2, b_3,$ and b_4:

$$
\begin{aligned}
x_1 \quad\quad - \; x_3 + 2x_4 &= b_1 \\
2x_1 + \; x_2 + 2x_3 - \; x_4 &= b_2 \\
-2x_1 + 2x_2 - \; x_3 + 3x_4 &= b_3 \\
3x_1 + 4x_2 - \; x_3 - 2x_4 &= b_4 \;.
\end{aligned}
$$

4. Given that the vectors (a_1, a_2, a_3), (b_1, b_2, b_3), and (c_1, c_2, c_3) are linearly independent, prove that the vectors (a_1, b_1, c_1), (a_2, b_2, c_2), and (a_3, b_3, c_3) are linearly independent.

5. Given that the vectors (a_1, a_2, a_3), (b_1, b_2, b_3), and (c_1, c_2, c_3) are linearly dependent, prove that the vectors (a_1, b_1, c_1), (a_2, b_2, c_2), and (a_3, b_3, c_3) are linearly dependent.

6. Given that α, β, and γ are linearly independent 3-vectors, prove that there is exactly one vector orthogonal to each of α, β, and γ. Find this vector. (For a definition of *orthogonal*, see Exercise 8, Section 3.4.)

7. Given t linearly independent n-vectors, $t < n$, show that there is a vector, other than $\mathbf{0}$, which is orthogonal to each of the given vectors.

3.6 The Inner Product; Length

The purpose of this section is to investigate the properties of vectors that enable us to use vectors in geometry. First, we present the notion of the *inner product*.

DEFINITION 3.6.1.   Let $n \in N$ and let $\alpha = (a_1, a_2, \cdots, a_n)$ and $\beta = (b_1, b_2, \cdots, b_n)$ be any n-vectors. Then by the *inner product* of α and β we mean the real number $a_1 b_1 + a_2 b_2 + \cdots + a_n b_n$. This real number is denoted by "$\alpha \cdot \beta$".

We point out that the inner product is a mapping of $R_n \times R_n$ into R. The following theorem brings out the basic properties of this mapping.

THEOREM 3.6.1.   Let $n \in N$ and let α, β, and γ be any n-vectors; then

$\qquad$ (i) $\alpha \cdot \beta = \beta \cdot \alpha$,

$\qquad$ (ii) $\alpha \cdot (\beta + \gamma) = \alpha \cdot \beta + \alpha \cdot \gamma$,

$\qquad$ (iii) $(k\alpha) \cdot \beta = k(\alpha \cdot \beta)$ whenever $k \in R$,

$\qquad$ (iv) $\alpha \cdot \alpha > 0$ iff $\alpha \neq \mathbf{0}$; $\mathbf{0} \cdot \mathbf{0} = 0$.

Proof: The details are straightforward and are left as an exercise.

This theorem is important because many properties of the inner product can be established algebraically on the basis of the properties exhibited in the theorem. In this way we avoid a detailed calculation based on Definition 3.6.1.

THEOREM 3.6.2.   Let $n \in N$ and let $\alpha, \beta_1, \cdots, \beta_t$ be any n-vectors; then $\alpha \cdot (\beta_1 + \cdots + \beta_t) = \alpha \cdot \beta_1 + \cdots + \alpha \cdot \beta_t$.

Proof: Use mathematical induction on t and apply Theorem 3.6.1(ii).

THEOREM 3.6.3. Let $n \in N$, let $\alpha, \beta_1, \cdots, \beta_t$ be any n-vectors, and let $k_1, k_2, \cdots, k_t$ be any real numbers; then $\alpha \cdot (k_1\beta_1 + \cdots + k_t\beta_t) = k_1(\alpha \cdot \beta_1) + \cdots + k_t(\alpha \cdot \beta_t)$.

Proof:

$$\alpha \cdot (k_1\beta_1 + \cdots + k_t\beta_t) = \alpha \cdot (k_1\beta_1) + \cdots + \alpha \cdot (k_t\beta_t) \qquad \text{by Th. 3.6.2}$$
$$= (k_1\beta_1) \cdot \alpha + \cdots + (k_t\beta_t) \cdot \alpha \qquad \text{by Th. 3.6.1(i)}$$
$$= k_1(\alpha \cdot \beta_1) + \cdots + k_t(\alpha \cdot \beta_t) \qquad \text{by Th. 3.6.1(iii), (i).}$$

THEOREM 3.6.4. If $\alpha \neq \mathbf{0}$, $\beta \neq \mathbf{0}$, and $\alpha \cdot \beta = 0$, then α and β are linearly independent.

Proof: Suppose that there are real numbers k_1 and k_2 such that $k_1\alpha + k_2\beta = \mathbf{0}$; then $(k_1\alpha) \cdot \alpha + (k_2\beta) \cdot \alpha = \mathbf{0} \cdot \alpha = 0$. Thus $k_1(\alpha \cdot \alpha) = 0$; so $k_1 = 0$. Similarly, we see that $k_2 = 0$. Therefore α and β are linearly independent.

COROLLARY 3.6.1. Let $n \in N$ and let $\beta_1, \beta_2, \cdots, \beta_m$ be nonzero n-vectors such that $\beta_i \cdot \beta_j = 0$ whenever $i \neq j$. Then $\beta_1, \beta_2, \cdots, \beta_m$ are linearly independent.

Proof: Apply the argument of Theorem 3.6.4.

It will soon be clear that the ideas of this section are slanted toward geometry. In Chapter 4 we shall develop a geometry which relies heavily on vectors. Consider the following concept.

DEFINITION 3.6.2. Let $n \in N$ and let α and β be any n-vectors; then we shall write "$\alpha \perp \beta$" (read "α is orthogonal to β") iff $\alpha \cdot \beta = 0$.

We point out that $\perp$ is a binary relation. For example, $(5, -1, 2) \perp (2, 8, -1)$.

THEOREM 3.6.5. Let $n \in N$ and let α and β be any n-vectors; then $\alpha \perp \beta$ iff $\beta \perp \alpha$.

Proof: Theorem 3.6.1(i).

THEOREM 3.6.6. Let $n \in N$, let V be the subspace of $\mathscr{V}_n(\mathscr{R})$ spanned by the n-vectors $\beta_1, \beta_2, \cdots, \beta_t$, and let $\alpha \perp \beta_i$ whenever $1 \leq i \leq t$. Then $\alpha \perp \beta$ whenever $\beta \in V$.

Proof: Let $\beta \in V$; then there are real numbers $k_1, k_2, \cdots, k_t$ such that $\beta = k_1\beta_1 + k_2\beta_2 + \cdots + k_t\beta_t$. Thus

$$\alpha \cdot \beta = \alpha \cdot (k_1\beta_1 + k_2\beta_2 + \cdots + k_t\beta_t)$$
$$= k_1(\alpha \cdot \beta_1) + k_2(\alpha \cdot \beta_2) + \cdots + k_t(\alpha \cdot \beta_t) \qquad \text{by Th. 3.6.3}$$
$$= 0 \qquad \text{by assumption.}$$

This completes our proof.

THEOREM 3.6.7.   Let $n \in N$ and let $\alpha_1, \alpha_2, \cdots, \alpha_m$ be any n-vectors, where $m < n$. Then there is a nonzero n-vector which is orthogonal to each of the α's.

Proof: Consider the m vector equations $\alpha_i \cdot \zeta = 0$, $i = 1, 2, \cdots, m$. These equations represent a homogeneous system which consists of m equations in n unknowns; the unknowns are the terms of ζ. Since $m < n$, the rank of the coefficient matrix of this system is less than n. Therefore, by Corollary 3.3.1, the system has a nontrivial solution. This establishes our result.

EXAMPLE 1.   Find a 4-vector orthogonal to each of $(1, 0, 2, -3), (0, 1, -1, 3)$, and $(2, 0, 0, 2)$.

Solution: Now, (x_1, x_2, x_3, x_4) is a suitable vector iff

$$\begin{cases} x_1 + 2x_3 - 3x_4 = 0 \\ x_2 - x_3 + 3x_4 = 0 \\ 2x_1 + 2x_4 = 0 \end{cases}$$

We shall reduce the matrix of this homogeneous linear system:

$$\begin{pmatrix} 1 & 0 & 2 & -3 \\ 0 & 1 & -1 & 3 \\ 2 & 0 & 0 & 2 \end{pmatrix} \sim \begin{pmatrix} 1 & 0 & 2 & -3 \\ 0 & 1 & -1 & 3 \\ 0 & 0 & -4 & 8 \end{pmatrix} \sim \begin{pmatrix} 1 & 0 & 2 & -3 \\ 0 & 1 & -1 & 3 \\ 0 & 0 & -1 & 2 \end{pmatrix} \sim \begin{pmatrix} 1 & 0 & 0 & 1 \\ 0 & 1 & 0 & 1 \\ 0 & 0 & -1 & 2 \end{pmatrix}$$

Notice that the solution set of this linear system is $\{k(-1, -1, 2, 1) \mid k \in R\}$. In particular, $(1, 1, -2, -1)$ is a member of this set; so $(1, 1, -2, -1)$ is orthogonal to each of the given vectors

We can sharpen Theorem 3.6.7 as follows.

THEOREM 3.6.8.   Let $n \in N$, let V be any subspace of $\mathscr{V}_n(\mathscr{R})$ with dimension t, $t > 0$, and let $\{\alpha_1, \cdots, \alpha_m\}$ be a proper subset of a basis for V. Then there is a nonzero member of V which is orthogonal to each of the α's.

Proof: We are given that $\alpha_1, \cdots, \alpha_m$ are linearly independent members of V and that $m < t$. Let $\{\gamma_1, \cdots, \gamma_t\}$ be any basis for V; our goal is to find scalars $k_1, \cdots, k_t$ such that $\beta = k_1\gamma_1 + \cdots + k_t\gamma_t$ is orthogonal to α_i, $1 \le i \le m$, and such that $\beta \ne 0$. Consider the m equations $\beta \cdot \alpha_1 = 0, \cdots, \beta \cdot \alpha_m = 0$. Let us write out these equations in more detail. Using Theorem 3.6.1 we obtain:

$$\begin{cases} k_1(\gamma_1 \cdot \alpha_1) + \cdots + k_t(\gamma_t \cdot \alpha_1) = 0 \\ \qquad \vdots \\ k_1(\gamma_1 \cdot \alpha_m) + \cdots + k_t(\gamma_t \cdot \alpha_m) = 0 \end{cases}$$

We face a homogeneous linear system which consists of m equations in the t unknowns $k_1, \cdots, k_t$. The rank of the matrix of this system cannot exceed the number of equations, namely m. By assumption, $m < t$; therefore, by Corollary 3.3.1, the given system possesses a nontrivial solution. Since the k's are not all zero and since the γ's are linearly independent, we see that $\beta \neq \mathbf{0}$. This establishes our result.

It is easy, now, to prove the following important theorem.

THEOREM 3.6.9 (Gram-Schmidt).   Let $n \in N$ and let V be any subspace of $\mathscr{V}_n(\mathscr{R})$ other than $\{\mathbf{0}\}$. Then there is a basis for V, say $\{\beta_1, \cdots, \beta_t\}$, such that $\beta_i \cdot \beta_j = 0$ whenever $i \neq j$.

Proof: We shall build up a suitable basis for V by applying Theorem 3.6.8 $t - 1$ times. Since $V \neq \{\mathbf{0}\}$, V possesses a nonzero member, say β_1. By Theorem 3.6.8 there is a nonzero member of V, say β_2, which is orthogonal to β_1. By Corollary 3.6.1, β_1 and β_2 are linearly independent. Therefore, by the Steinitz Replacement Theorem, $\{\beta_1, \beta_2\}$ is a proper subset of a basis for V if $t > 2$. So, if $t > 2$, by Theorem 3.6.8 there is a nonzero member of V, say β_3, which is orthogonal to β_1 and β_2. Again, if $t > 3$ then $\{\beta_1, \beta_2, \beta_3\}$ is a proper subset of a basis for V. So, by Theorem 3.6.8, there is a nonzero member of V, say β_4, which is orthogonal to β_1, β_2, and β_3. Continuing this process, we apply Theorem 3.6.8 a total of $t - 1$ times to obtain $\{\beta_1, \cdots, \beta_t\}$ where $\beta_i \cdot \beta_j = 0$ whenever $i \neq j$ and each β is a nonzero member of V. Therefore, by Corollary 3.6.1, the β's are linearly independent; so $\{\beta_1, \cdots, \beta_t\}$ is a basis for V with the required properties. This completes our proof.

Note: A set of vectors is said to be *orthogonal* if any two of its members are orthogonal. Thus our result asserts that each subspace of $\mathscr{V}_n(\mathscr{R})$ other than $\{\mathbf{0}\}$, possesses an orthogonal basis.

We now present an example which illustrates the Gram-Schmidt process.

EXAMPLE 2.   Find an orthogonal basis for $V = S(\alpha_1, \alpha_2, \alpha_3)$ where $\alpha_1 = (1, 1, 0, 0, 0)$, $\alpha_2 = (0, 1, 1, 0, 0)$, and $\alpha_3 = (0, 0, 1, 1, 1)$.
Solution: By reducing the matrix

$$\begin{pmatrix} 1 & 0 & 0 \\ 1 & 1 & 0 \\ 0 & 1 & 1 \\ 0 & 0 & 1 \\ 0 & 0 & 1 \end{pmatrix}$$

we readily verify that this matrix has rank 3; so α_1, α_2, and α_3 are linearly independent. We shall apply the method of the proof of Theorem 3.6.8 to build up the required basis. Let $\beta_1 = \alpha_1$; we want a nonzero member of V, say β_2, orthogonal to β_1. Let $\beta_2 = k_1 \alpha_1 + k_2 \alpha_2 + k_3 \alpha_3$; then we require that

$$k_1(\alpha_1 \cdot \beta_1) + k_2(\alpha_2 \cdot \beta_1) + k_3(\alpha_3 \cdot \beta_1) = 0$$

i.e.,

$$2k_1 + k_2 = 0$$

Take $k_3 = 0$, $k_2 = -2$, and $k_1 = 1$. Thus

$$\beta_2 = \alpha_1 - 2\alpha_2 = (1, -1, -2, 0, 0)$$

Next, we want a nonzero member of V, say β_3, orthogonal to β_1 and β_2. Let $\beta_3 = x_1\alpha_1 + x_2\alpha_2 + x_3\alpha_3$; then

$$\begin{cases} x_1(\alpha_1 \cdot \beta_1) + x_2(\alpha_2 \cdot \beta_1) + x_3(\alpha_3 \cdot \beta_1) = 0 \\ x_1(\alpha_1 \cdot \beta_2) + x_2(\alpha_2 \cdot \beta_2) + x_3(\alpha_3 \cdot \beta_2) = 0 \end{cases}$$

i.e., $2x_1 + x_2 = 0$ and $-3x_2 - 2x_3 = 0$

We now solve this homogeneous linear system:

$$\begin{pmatrix} 2 & 1 & 0 \\ 0 & -3 & -2 \end{pmatrix} \sim \begin{pmatrix} 6 & 0 & -2 \\ 0 & 3 & 2 \end{pmatrix} \sim \begin{pmatrix} 3 & 0 & -1 \\ 0 & 3 & 2 \end{pmatrix}$$

Here, the subspace of vector solutions has dimension 1; in particular, $(1, -2, 3)$ is a member of the subspace. Thus, $\beta_3 = \alpha_1 - 2\alpha_2 + 3\alpha_3 = (1, -1, 1, 3, 3)$. We conclude that $\{(1, 1, 0, 0, 0), (1, -1, -2, 0, 0), (1, -1, 1, 3, 3)\}$ is an orthogonal basis for V.

Next, we introduce another term with geometric flavor: the notion of the *length* of a vector.

DEFINITION 3.6.3.   Let $n \in N$ and let α be any n-vector. Then by the *length* of α we mean the real number $\sqrt{\alpha \cdot \alpha}$; this number is denoted by " $\|\alpha\|$ ".

In view of Theorem 3.6.1(iv), it is clear that each n-vector possesses a length. We shall now establish some properties of *length*.

THEOREM 3.6.10.   Let $n \in N$ and let α be any n-vector. Then $\|\alpha\| > 0$ if $\alpha \neq \mathbf{0}$; moreover, $\|\mathbf{0}\| = 0$.
Proof: Theorem 3.6.1(iv).

THEOREM 3.6.11.   Let $n \in N$, let α be any n-vector, and let $k \in R$. Then $\|k\alpha\| = |k| \|\alpha\|$.
Proof: Apply Definition 3.6.3.

COROLLARY 3.6.2.   Let $n \in N$ and let α be any n-vector other than $\mathbf{0}$. Then $\alpha/\|\alpha\|$ is an n-vector of length 1.
Proof: Apply Theorem 3.6.11.

THEOREM 3.6.12.   Let $n \in N$ and let α and β be any n-vectors. Then $\|\alpha + \beta\| = \sqrt{\alpha \cdot \alpha + \beta \cdot \beta + 2\alpha \cdot \beta}$.

Proof:
$$\|\alpha + \beta\| = \sqrt{(\alpha + \beta) \cdot (\alpha + \beta)} \qquad \text{by Def. 3.6.3}$$

$$= \sqrt{(\alpha + \beta) \cdot \alpha + (\alpha + \beta) \cdot \beta} \qquad \text{by Th. 3.6.1(ii)}$$

$$= \sqrt{\alpha \cdot (\alpha + \beta) + \beta \cdot (\alpha + \beta)} \qquad \text{by Th. 3.6.1(i)}$$

$$= \sqrt{\alpha \cdot \alpha + \alpha \cdot \beta + \beta \cdot \alpha + \beta \cdot \beta} \qquad \text{by Th. 3.6.1(ii)}$$

$$= \sqrt{\alpha \cdot \alpha + \beta \cdot \beta + \alpha \cdot \beta + \alpha \cdot \beta} \qquad \text{by Th. 3.6.1(i)}$$

$$= \sqrt{\alpha \cdot \alpha + \beta \cdot \beta + 2\alpha \cdot \beta}.$$

COROLLARY 3.6.3.   Let $n \in N$ and let α and β be any n-vectors. Then $\|\alpha - \beta\| = \sqrt{\alpha \cdot \alpha + \beta \cdot \beta - 2\alpha \cdot \beta}$.

Proof:

$$\|\alpha - \beta\| = \|\alpha + -\beta\|$$

$$= \sqrt{\alpha \cdot \alpha + (-\beta) \cdot (-\beta) + 2\alpha \cdot (-\beta)} \qquad \text{by Th. 3.6.12}$$

$$= \sqrt{\alpha \cdot \alpha + \beta \cdot \beta - 2\alpha \cdot \beta} \qquad \text{by Th. 3.6.1(iii)}$$

THEOREM 3.6.13.   Let $n \in N$ and let α and β be any n-vectors of length 1. Then $|\alpha \cdot \beta| \leq 1$.

Proof: As we have seen in the proof of Theorem 3.6.12,

$$(\alpha + \beta) \cdot (\alpha + \beta) = \alpha \cdot \alpha + \beta \cdot \beta + 2\alpha \cdot \beta = 2 + 2\alpha \cdot \beta \qquad \text{by assumption.}$$

Therefore, from Theorem 3.6.1(iv), $2 + 2\alpha \cdot \beta \geq 0$; thus $\alpha \cdot \beta \geq -1$. Similarly, $(\alpha - \beta) \cdot (\alpha - \beta) = \alpha \cdot \alpha + \beta \cdot \beta - 2\alpha \cdot \beta = 2 - 2\alpha \cdot \beta$, by assumption. Thus, by Theorem 3.6.1(iv), $2 - 2\alpha \cdot \beta \geq 0$, i.e., $\alpha \cdot \beta \leq 1$. We conclude that $|\alpha \cdot \beta| \leq 1$.

We are now in a position to establish the following fundamental result.

THEOREM 3.6.14 (Schwartz Inequality).   Let $n \in N$ and let α and β be any n-vectors. Then $|\alpha \cdot \beta| \leq \|\alpha\| \|\beta\|$.

Proof: If $\alpha = 0$ or $\beta = 0$, then $\alpha \cdot \beta = 0$ and $\|\alpha\| \|\beta\| = 0$. Assume, then, that $\alpha \neq 0$ and that $\beta \neq 0$. By Corollary 3.6.2, both $\alpha/\|\alpha\|$ and $\beta/\|\beta\|$ are n-vectors of length 1. Therefore, by Theorem 3.6.13, $\left| \dfrac{\alpha}{\|\alpha\|} \cdot \dfrac{\beta}{\|\beta\|} \right| \leq 1$; thus, by Theorem 3.6.1(iii), $\left| \dfrac{1}{\|\alpha\| \|\beta\|} \alpha \cdot \beta \right|$ ≤ 1; i.e., $\dfrac{1}{\|\alpha\| \|\beta\|} \left| \alpha \cdot \beta \right| \leq 1$; so $|\alpha \cdot \beta| \leq \|\alpha\| \|\beta\|$.

We can now establish the important *triangle inequality*.

THE TRIANGLE INEQUALITY.   Let $n \in N$ and let α and β be any n-vectors. Then $\|\alpha + \beta\| \leq \|\alpha\| + \|\beta\|$.

Proof: By Theorem 3.6.12,

$$\|\alpha + \beta\|^2 = |\alpha \cdot \alpha + \beta \cdot \beta + 2\alpha \cdot \beta|$$

$$\leq |\alpha \cdot \alpha| + |\beta \cdot \beta| + 2|\alpha \cdot \beta| \qquad \text{by the triangle inequality for the real number system}$$

$$\leq \|\alpha\|^2 + \|\beta\|^2 + 2\|\alpha\| \ \|\beta\| \qquad \text{by Th. 3.16.14}$$

$$= (\|\alpha\| + \|\beta\|)^2.$$

But $\|\gamma\| \geq 0$ if $\gamma \in R_n$; therefore $\|\alpha + \beta\| \leq \|\alpha\| + \|\beta\|$. This completes our proof.

There is one more geometric concept that we wish to consider in our algebraic setting—the notion of an *angle*.

DEFINITION 3.6.4.   Let $n \in N$ and let $\alpha \in N$ and let α and β be any nonzero n-vectors. Then the real number $\arccos \dfrac{\alpha \cdot \beta}{\|\alpha\| \ \|\beta\|}$ is said to be the angle between α and β. This real number is denoted by "(α, β)".

For example, let $\alpha = (1, 0, 0)$ and $\beta = (0, 1, 0)$; then $(\alpha, \beta) = \arccos 0 = \pi/2$. Again, let $\alpha = (\sqrt{8}, 0, 2, -2)$ and $\beta = (0, 0, -1, 0)$; then $(\alpha, \beta) = \arccos -2/4 = \arccos -.5 \simeq 2.0944$.
Since the domain of arccos is $\{t | -1 \leq t \leq 1\}$, we need to know that $-1 \leq \dfrac{\alpha \cdot \beta}{\|\alpha\| \ \|\beta\|} \leq 1$
whenever α and β are nonzero n-vectors. Of course, this follows from Theorem 3.6.14.
The following theorem displays some properties of this notion of angle; the proofs are straightforward and are left as exercises.

THEOREM 3.6.15.   Let $n \in N$ and let α and β be any nonzero n-vectors. Then

(i) $\alpha \perp \beta$ iff $(\alpha, \beta) = \pi/2$;

(ii) $(\alpha, \beta) = (\beta, \alpha)$;

(iii) $(\alpha, \alpha) = 0$;

(iv) $(\alpha, k\alpha) = 0$ whenever $k > 0$;

(v) $(\alpha, -\alpha) = \pi$;

(vi) $(\alpha, k\alpha) = \pi$ whenever $k < 0$.

As we have said, the purpose of this section is to develop ideas about vectors that we can use in our work in geometry. As a bonus we now present an important application to analysis. Consider the vector space of Example 5, Section 1.8; there, by a vector we mean any function, say f, such that f is continuous and $\mathscr{D}_f = [0, 1]$. Now, any such function is integrable on $[0, 1]$; indeed, the product of two functions with these properties is integrable on $[0, 1]$. Accordingly, we consider the mapping of $V \times V$ into R which associates $\int_0^1 f \cdot g$ with the vectors f and g. This mapping is usually regarded as an *inner product* in this vector space because it possesses the properties listed in Theorem 3.6.1. It is evident that this mapping has properties (i), (ii) and (iii); for a proof that our mapping has property (iv), see Theorem 13.4.1 Now, we have very carefully established many of the theorems of this section by appealing to Theorem 3.6.1 rather than to the definition of the inner product. Thus each of these theorems holds for the inner product of the vector space of continuous functions. We shall define *length* in this vector space in accordance with Definition 3.6.3; i.e., $\|f\| = \left[\int_0^1 f^2\right]^{1/2}$ whenever $f \in V$. Since we deduced the properties of *length* directly from the definition or from Theorem 3.6.1, we see that *length* in this vector space has these same properties (this should be carefully checked by the reader). We therefore obtain the following two theorems.

THEOREM 3.6.16 (Schwartz Inequality).   Let f and g be any continuous functions with domain $[0, 1]$; then

$$\left|\int_0^1 f \cdot g\right| \leq \left[\int_0^1 f^2 \int_0^1 g^2\right]^{1/2}.$$

THEOREM 3.6.17 (Minkowski Inequality).   Let f and g be any continuous functions with domain $[0, 1]$; then

$$\left[\int_0^1 (f + g)^2\right]^{1/2} \leq \left[\int_0^1 f^2\right]^{1/2} + \left[\int_0^1 g^2\right]^{1/2}.$$

E X E R C I S E S

1. Prove Theorem 3.6.1.

2. Let $n \in N$ and let α be any n-vector. Prove that $\mathbf{0} \cdot \alpha = 0$. Present a direct proof based on Definition 3.6.1, and present an algebraic proof based on Theorem 3.6.1.

3. Prove Theorem 3.6.2.

4. Prove Corollary 3.6.1.

5. Show that there is exactly one vector, say $\zeta = (x_1, x_2, x_3)$, which is orthogonal to each of $(1, 0, 0)$, $(0, 1, 0)$, and $(0, 0, 1)$. Determine ζ.

6. Find a nonzero member of R_4 which is orthogonal to each of $(2, 1, -1, 0)$, $(1, 0, 2, -1)$, and $(3, 1, -1, 1)$.

7. Let $n \in N$ and let γ be any n-vector. Prove that $\{\alpha \mid \alpha \perp \gamma\}$ is a subspace of $\mathscr{V}_n(\mathscr{R})$.

8. Let $n \in N$ and let $\gamma_1, \gamma_2, \cdots, \gamma_t$ be any n-vectors. Prove that $\{\alpha \mid \alpha \perp \gamma_i, i = 1, 2, \cdots, t\}$ is a subspace of $\mathscr{V}_n(\mathscr{R})$.

9. Let $n \in N$ and let $\alpha_1, \alpha_2, \cdots, \alpha_m$ be any linearly independent n-vectors, where $m \leq n$. Prove that $\{\zeta \mid \zeta \perp \alpha_i, i = 1, 2, \cdots, m\}$ is a subspace of $\mathscr{V}_n(\mathscr{R})$ with dimension $n - m$.

10. Find an orthogonal basis for the subspace of $\mathscr{V}_3(\mathscr{R})$ which is spanned by $(2, -1, 0)$, $(3, 1, 1)$, and $(0, 5, 2)$.

11. Find an orthogonal basis for the subspace of $\mathscr{V}_4(\mathscr{R})$ spanned by $(1, 2, -1, 0)$, $(2, 0, 0, -1)$, and $(3, 1, 0, 1)$.

12. Let $\alpha = (1, 2, 2)$ and let $\beta = (7, 0, 0)$.
  a. Compute $\|\alpha + \beta\|$ in two ways.
  b. Compute $\|\alpha - \beta\|$ in two ways.
  c. Compute $\alpha \cdot \beta$.
  d. Compute $\|\alpha\|\,\|\beta\|$.
  e. Compute $\|\alpha\| + \|\beta\|$.
  f. Compute (α, β).

13. Prove Theorem 3.6.15.

14. Let f and g be any continuous functions with domain $[0, 1]$ such that $\int_0^1 f^2 = \int_0^1 g^2 = 1$. Prove that $\left| \int_0^1 f \cdot g \right| \leq 1$.

3.7 Matrix Algebra; Inverse of a Matrix

In order to develop a useful algebra of matrices, we now introduce suitable operations on matrices, namely addition, multiplication by a real number, and multiplication. To add two matrices, we add corresponding entries; to multiply a matrix by a real number, we multiply each entry of the matrix by the real number; the product of matrices (a_{ij}) and (b_{ij}) is the matrix (c_{ij}), where c_{ij} is the inner product of the ith row vector of (a_{ij}) and the jth column vector of (b_{ij}).

DEFINITION 3.7.1.   Let (a_{ij}) and (b_{ij}) be any $m \times n$ matrices; then $(a_{ij}) + (b_{ij}) = (a_{ij} + b_{ij})$.

DEFINITION 3.7.2.   Let (a_{ij}) be any matrix and let k be any real number; then $k(a_{ij}) = (ka_{ij})$.

DEFINITION 3.7.3.   Let (a_{ij}) and (b_{ij}) be matrices such that (a_{ij}) has n column vectors and (b_{ij}) has n row vectors, for some natural number n; then $(a_{ij}) \cdot (b_{ij}) = (c_{ij})$, where $c_{ij} = a_{i1}b_{1j} + a_{i2}b_{2j} + \cdots + a_{in}b_{nj}$.

For example,
$$\begin{pmatrix} 1 & 4 \\ 2 & 5 \\ 3 & 6 \end{pmatrix} + \begin{pmatrix} 2 & 0 \\ 1 & 3 \\ -2 & 4 \end{pmatrix} = \begin{pmatrix} 3 & 4 \\ 3 & 8 \\ 1 & 10 \end{pmatrix},$$

$$3 \begin{pmatrix} 1 & 0 & 2 \\ 3 & -2 & -3 \end{pmatrix} = \begin{pmatrix} 3 & 0 & 6 \\ 9 & -6 & -9 \end{pmatrix},$$

and

$$\begin{pmatrix} 1 & 2 & -1 & 3 \\ -2 & 3 & -3 & 5 \end{pmatrix} \cdot \begin{pmatrix} 4 & -1 & 5 \\ 2 & 1 & 0 \\ 1 & 3 & 1 \\ 0 & 2 & -2 \end{pmatrix} = \begin{pmatrix} 7 & 4 & -2 \\ -5 & 6 & -23 \end{pmatrix}.$$

We point out that the dot for matrix multiplication is sometimes omitted.

Since addition of real numbers is commutative and associative, it follows that addition of matrices is commutative and associative. However, multiplication of matrices is not commutative; i.e., there are matrices (a_{ij}) and (b_{ij}) such that $(a_{ij}) \cdot (b_{ij}) \neq (b_{ij}) \cdot (a_{ij})$. For example,

$$\begin{pmatrix} 2 & 3 \\ 1 & 4 \end{pmatrix} \cdot \begin{pmatrix} -1 & 4 \\ 5 & 3 \end{pmatrix} = \begin{pmatrix} 13 & 17 \\ 19 & 16 \end{pmatrix},$$

whereas

$$\begin{pmatrix} -1 & 4 \\ 5 & 3 \end{pmatrix} \cdot \begin{pmatrix} 2 & 3 \\ 1 & 4 \end{pmatrix} = \begin{pmatrix} 2 & 13 \\ 13 & 27 \end{pmatrix}.$$

Although multiplication of square matrices is not commutative, it turns out that this binary operation satisfies the associative law.

THEOREM 3.7.1. Let $n \in N$ and let (a_{ij}), (b_{ij}), and (c_{ij}) be any $n \times n$ matrices; then $[(a_{ij}) \cdot (b_{ij})] \cdot (c_{ij}) = (a_{ij}) \cdot [(b_{ij}) \cdot (c_{ij})]$.

Proof: We have only to apply Definition 3.7.3. Now,

$$(a_{ij}) \cdot (b_{ij}) = \left(\sum_{t=1}^{n} a_{it} b_{tj} \right);$$

therefore

$$[(a_{ij}) \cdot (b_{ij})] \cdot (c_{ij}) = (d_{ij}),$$

where

$$d_{ij} = c_{1j} \sum_{t=1}^{n} a_{it} b_{t1} + c_{2j} \sum_{t=1}^{n} a_{it} b_{t2} + \cdots + c_{nj} \sum_{t=1}^{n} a_{it} b_{tn}.$$

Moreover,

$$(b_{ij}) \cdot (c_{ij}) = \left(\sum_{t=1}^{n} b_{it} c_{tj} \right);$$

therefore

$$(a_{ij}) \cdot [(b_{ij}) \cdot (c_{ij})] = (e_{ij}),$$

where

$$e_{ij} = a_{i1} \sum_{t=1}^{n} b_{1t} c_{tj} + a_{i2} \sum_{t=1}^{n} b_{2t} c_{tj} + \cdots + a_{in} \sum_{t=1}^{n} b_{nt} c_{tj}$$

$$= c_{1j}(a_{i1} b_{11} + a_{i2} b_{21} + \cdots + a_{in} b_{n1}) + c_{2j}(a_{i1} b_{12} + a_{i2} b_{22} + \cdots + a_{in} b_{n2})$$

$$+ \cdots + c_{nj}(a_{i1} b_{1n} + a_{i2} b_{2n} + \cdots + a_{in} b_{nn})$$

$$= d_{ij}.$$

Hence $(d_{ij}) = (e_{ij})$. This establishes Theorem 3.7.1.

The following property of matrix multiplication is useful.

THEOREM 3.7.2.   Let $(c_{ij}) = (a_{ij}) \cdot (b_{ij})$; then $|c_{ij}| = |a_{ij}| \cdot |b_{ij}|$.

Proof: Our theorem asserts that the determinant of the product of two matrices is the product of the determinants of the matrices. To prove this theorem, apply Theorem 2.4.13.

Next, we consider the $n \times n$ matrix with 1's on the main diagonal and 0's off the main diagonal, namely

$$\begin{pmatrix} 1 & 0 & 0 & \cdots & 0 & 0 \\ 0 & 1 & 0 & \cdots & 0 & 0 \\ & & \vdots & & & \\ 0 & 0 & 0 & \cdots & 0 & 1 \end{pmatrix},$$

which we shall denote by "I_n". The following theorem, which states that I_n is a multiplicative identity, is easy to prove.

THEOREM 3.7.3.   Let $n \in N$ and let (a_{ij}) be any $n \times n$ matrix; then $(a_{ij}) \cdot I_n = I_n \cdot (a_{ij}) = (a_{ij})$.

Proof: The details are left as an exercise.

By an *inverse* of an $n \times n$ matrix (a_{ij}) we mean an $n \times n$ matrix (b_{ij}) such that $(a_{ij}) \cdot (b_{ij}) = I_n$. Note that if $a \neq 0$ then $(1/a)$ is an inverse of the 1×1 matrix (a). It is easy to see that some $n \times n$ matrices do not have inverses.

THEOREM 3.7.4. (a_{ij}) does not have an inverse if $|a_{ij}| = 0$.

Proof: Suppose that (b_{ij}) is an inverse of (a_{ij}); then $(a_{ij}) \cdot (b_{ij}) = I_n$. Therefore $|a_{ij}| \cdot |b_{ij}| = |I_n| = 1$, by Theorem 2.3.1. But $|a_{ij}| = 0$; thus $|a_{ij}| \cdot |b_{ij}| = 0$. This contradiction establishes our result.

The problem of computing an inverse of an $n \times n$ matrix requires one more notion.

DEFINITION 3.7.4.   Let $n > 1$ and let (a_{ij}) be an $n \times n$ matrix; then by the *adjoint* matrix of (a_{ij}) we mean the transpose of (A_{ij}), where A_{ij} is the cofactor of a_{ij} in the matrix (a_{ij}).

For example, the adjoint matrix of $\begin{pmatrix} 1 & 3 \\ 2 & 4 \end{pmatrix}$ is the transpose of $\begin{pmatrix} 4 & -2 \\ -3 & 1 \end{pmatrix}$, namely $\begin{pmatrix} 4 & -3 \\ -2 & 1 \end{pmatrix}$. The adjoint matrix of

$$\begin{pmatrix} 2 & 1 & 0 \\ 3 & -2 & 1 \\ 4 & 0 & -1 \end{pmatrix}$$

is the transpose of

$$\begin{pmatrix} 2 & 7 & 8 \\ 1 & -2 & 4 \\ 1 & -2 & -7 \end{pmatrix}, \quad \text{namely} \quad \begin{pmatrix} 2 & 1 & 1 \\ 7 & -2 & -2 \\ 8 & 4 & -7 \end{pmatrix}.$$

THEOREM 3.7.5. Let (b_{ij}) be the adjoint matrix of the $n \times n$ matrix (a_{ij}) where $n > 1$; then $|b_{ij}| = |a_{ij}|^{n-1}$, provided $|a_{ij}| \neq 0$.

Proof:

$$(a_{ij}) \cdot (b_{ij}) = (a_{ij}) \cdot (A_{ij})^t = \begin{pmatrix} a_{11} & a_{12} & \cdots & a_{1n} \\ a_{21} & a_{22} & \cdots & a_{2n} \\ & & \vdots & \\ a_{n1} & a_{n2} & \cdots & a_{nn} \end{pmatrix} \begin{pmatrix} A_{11} & A_{21} & \cdots & A_{n1} \\ A_{12} & A_{22} & \cdots & A_{n2} \\ & & \vdots & \\ A_{1n} & A_{2n} & \cdots & A_{nn} \end{pmatrix}$$

$$= \begin{pmatrix} |a_{ij}| & 0 & 0 & \cdots & 0 & 0 \\ 0 & |a_{ij}| & 0 & \cdots & 0 & 0 \\ & & \vdots & & & \\ 0 & 0 & 0 & \cdots & 0 & |a_{ij}| \end{pmatrix} \quad \text{by Cor. 2.4.3 and Ex. 16d, Section 2.4}$$

Therefore $|a_{ij}| \cdot |b_{ij}| = |a_{ij}|^n$ by Theorem 3.7.2. Hence $|b_{ij}| = |a_{ij}|^{n-1}$, provided $|a_{ij}| \neq 0$. This establishes Theorem 3.7.5.

THEOREM 3.7.6. Let (b_{ij}) be the adjoint matrix of the $n \times n$ matrix (a_{ij}) where $n > 1$; then $(a_{ij}) \cdot (b_{ij}) = |a_{ij}| I_n$.

Proof: Consider the proof of Theorem 3.7.5.

THEOREM 3.7.7. Let (b_{ij}) be the adjoint matrix of the $n \times n$ matrix (a_{ij}) where $n > 1$; then $(b_{ij}/|a_{ij}|)$ is an inverse of (a_{ij}), provided $|a_{ij}| \neq 0$.

Proof: $(a_{ij}) \cdot (b_{ij}/|a_{ij}|) = I_n$, by Theorem 3.7.6.

This result is important because it shows us how to compute an inverse of an $n \times n$ matrix; furthermore, Theorem 3.7.7 provides us with a necessary and sufficient condition for the *existence* of an inverse.

THEOREM 3.7.8. A square matrix has an inverse iff it is nonsingular.

Proof: Theorems 3.7.3 and 3.7.7.

EXAMPLE 1. Compute an inverse of $\begin{pmatrix} 1 & 3 \\ -1 & 2 \end{pmatrix}$.

Solution: Note that $\begin{vmatrix} 1 & 3 \\ -1 & 2 \end{vmatrix} = 5$; therefore, by Theorem 3.7.7, an inverse of $\begin{pmatrix} 1 & 3 \\ -1 & 2 \end{pmatrix}$ is $\begin{pmatrix} \frac{2}{5} & -\frac{3}{5} \\ \frac{1}{5} & \frac{1}{5} \end{pmatrix}$. Checking, we see that

$$\begin{pmatrix} 1 & 3 \\ -1 & 2 \end{pmatrix} \cdot \begin{pmatrix} \frac{2}{5} & -\frac{3}{5} \\ \frac{1}{5} & \frac{1}{5} \end{pmatrix} = \begin{pmatrix} 1 & 0 \\ 0 & 1 \end{pmatrix}.$$

Many useful properties of inverses are freely available once we establish the kind of algebraic system that we face. Let $n \in N$; the algebraic system $(G, \cdot, I_n)$, where G is the set of all nonsingular $n \times n$ matrices and " $\cdot$ " denotes matrix multiplication, is a group. It is easy to check that the group postulates are satisfied (see Definition 1.4.1). We can now utilize the information that we possess about groups.

THEOREM 3.7.9.   Each nonsingular $n \times n$ matrix possesses a unique inverse.

Proof: This is true for any group; see Theorem 1.4.6.

In view of this result, we are entitled to speak of *the* inverse of a nonsingular square matrix. Let A be any nonsingular square matrix; then the inverse of A is denoted by "A^{-1}".

THEOREM 3.7.10.   Let A and B be any nonsingular $n \times n$ matrices such that $AB = I_n$; then $BA = I_n$.

Proof: This is true for any group; see Theorem 1.4.2.

THEOREM 3.7.11.   Let A and B be any nonsingular $n \times n$ matrices; then $(AB)^{-1} = B^{-1}A^{-1}$.

Proof: This is true for any group; see Theorem 1.4.10.

We can use Theorem 3.7.9 to solve the matrix equation $AX = B$ for the unknown matrix X, where A and B are given $n \times n$ matrices. If A is nonsingular, then by Theorem 3.7.9 A has a unique inverse, namely A^{-1}. We claim that the matrix $A^{-1}B$ satisfies the given equation; clearly,

$$A(A^{-1}B) = (AA^{-1})B \qquad \text{by the associative law}$$
$$= I_n B$$
$$= B$$

Moreover, $A^{-1}B$ is the only solution of our equation; for if D is any solution, then

$$AD = B$$

hence
$$A^{-1}(AD) = A^{-1}B$$

so
$$(A^{-1}A)D = A^{-1}B$$

but $A^{-1}A = I_n$ by Theorem 3.7.10, so $D = A^{-1}B$. We have established the following result.

THEOREM 3.7.12.   Let $n \in N$, let A be a given nonsingular $n \times n$ matrix, and let B be a given $n \times n$ matrix; then the matrix equation $AX = B$ has the unique matrix solution $A^{-1}B$.

So far we have concentrated on the algebraic properties of matrix multiplication. At the beginning of this section we introduced matrix addition and the operation of multiplying a matrix by a real number, which we shall call *scalar* multiplication. Turning to these operations, we point out that the mathematical system $(\mathcal{R}, \mathcal{M}, \circ)$ is a vector space, given that $\mathcal{M} = (M, +, (0))$ where M is the set of all $m \times n$ matrices, "+" denotes matrix addition, (0) is the $m \times n$ matrix each of whose entries is 0, and "$\circ$" denotes scalar multiplication.

THEOREM 3.7.13. $(\mathcal{R}, \mathcal{M}, \circ)$ is a vector space.

Proof: Consider Definition 1.8.1; the details are left as an exercise.

E X E R C I S E S

1. Prove Theorem 3.7.3.

2. Compute the adjoint matrix of each of the following:

$$\begin{pmatrix} 2 & 1 & 0 \\ 0 & 2 & 1 \\ 1 & -1 & 4 \end{pmatrix} \quad \text{and} \quad \begin{pmatrix} 1 & 2 & 3 & -2 \\ 0 & 1 & 2 & 3 \\ -1 & -2 & 0 & -1 \\ 2 & 1 & -1 & 1 \end{pmatrix}.$$

3. Given that $(a_{ij}) \cdot (b_{ij}) = I_n$, prove directly that $(b_{ij}) \cdot (a_{ij}) = I_n$.

4. Prove that $(a_{ij}) \cdot (b_{ij}) = I_n$ iff $(b_{ij}) \cdot (a_{ij}) = I_n$.

Compute the adjoint of each of the following matrices.

5. $\begin{pmatrix} 2 & 1 \\ -1 & 3 \end{pmatrix}$.

6. $\begin{pmatrix} 3 & 1 & 2 \\ 2 & 0 & 1 \\ 0 & 0 & 0 \end{pmatrix}$.

7. $\begin{pmatrix} 1 & -1 & 2 & 1 \\ 2 & 0 & 1 & -2 \\ 1 & 3 & 4 & 2 \\ 0 & 1 & 5 & -1 \end{pmatrix}$.

8. I_4.

Compute the inverse of each of the following matrices.

9. $\begin{pmatrix} 2 & 1 \\ -1 & 3 \end{pmatrix}$.

10. $\begin{pmatrix} 1 & -1 & 2 & 1 \\ 2 & 0 & 1 & -2 \\ 1 & 3 & 4 & 2 \\ 0 & 1 & 5 & -1 \end{pmatrix}$.

11. Find a matrix X such that $\begin{pmatrix} 2 & 1 \\ -1 & 3 \end{pmatrix} \cdot X = \begin{pmatrix} 4 & 1 \\ 1 & 2 \end{pmatrix}$.

12. Find a matrix X such that

$$\begin{pmatrix} 1 & -1 & 2 & 1 \\ 2 & 0 & 1 & -2 \\ 1 & 3 & 4 & 2 \\ 0 & 1 & 5 & -1 \end{pmatrix} \cdot X = \begin{pmatrix} 2 & 0 & 1 & 2 \\ 0 & 1 & 0 & 3 \\ -1 & 1 & -1 & 1 \\ 1 & 2 & 1 & 2 \end{pmatrix}.$$

13. Find a matrix X such that

$$\begin{pmatrix} 1 & -1 & 2 & 1 \\ 2 & 0 & 1 & -2 \\ 1 & 3 & 4 & 2 \\ 0 & 1 & 5 & -1 \end{pmatrix} \cdot X = \begin{pmatrix} 2 \\ 0 \\ -1 \\ 1 \end{pmatrix}.$$

14. Let (a_{ij}) and (b_{ij}) be any $t \times m$ matrices and let (c_{ij}) be any $m \times n$ matrix. Prove the distributive law:

$$[(a_{ij}) + (b_{ij})] \cdot (c_{ij}) = (a_{ij}) \cdot (c_{ij}) + (b_{ij}) \cdot (c_{ij}).$$

3.8 Cramer's Rule

We have seen that the linear system

$$(1) \qquad \begin{cases} a_{11}x_1 + a_{12}x_2 + \cdots + a_{1n}x_n = b_1 \\ a_{21}x_1 + a_{22}x_2 + \cdots + a_{2n}x_n = b_2 \\ \vdots \\ a_{n1}x_1 + a_{n2}x_2 + \cdots + a_{nn}x_n = b_n \end{cases}$$

has a unique solution iff $|a_{ij}| \neq 0$. Suppose, then, that $|a_{ij}| \neq 0$; we want to compute the unique solution of the system (1). To this purpose we represent (1) by the matrix equation

$$(2) \qquad (a_{ij}) \cdot X = (b_i),$$

where (a_{ij}) is the coefficient matrix of (1), (b_i) is

$$\begin{pmatrix} b_1 \\ b_2 \\ \vdots \\ b_n \end{pmatrix},$$

an $n \times 1$ matrix, and X is the unique vector solution of (1),

$$\begin{pmatrix} x_1 \\ x_2 \\ \vdots \\ x_n \end{pmatrix}.$$

By the method of the proof of Theorem 3.7.12, the unique vector solution of (2) is $(a_{ij})^{-1} \cdot (b_i)$; hence

$$X = \frac{1}{|a_{ij}|} \begin{pmatrix} A_{11} & A_{21} & \cdots & A_{n1} \\ A_{12} & A_{22} & \cdots & A_{n2} \\ & & \vdots & \\ A_{1n} & A_{2n} & \cdots & A_{nn} \end{pmatrix} \cdot \begin{pmatrix} b_1 \\ b_2 \\ \vdots \\ b_n \end{pmatrix}$$

But

$$b_1 A_{11} + b_2 A_{21} + \cdots + b_n A_{n1} = \begin{vmatrix} b_1 & a_{12} & \cdots & a_{1n} \\ b_2 & a_{22} & \cdots & a_{2n} \\ & & \vdots & \\ b_n & a_{n2} & \cdots & a_{nn} \end{vmatrix}.$$

$$b_1 A_{12} + b_2 A_{22} + \cdots + b_n A_{n2} = \begin{vmatrix} a_{11} & b_1 & a_{13} & \cdots & a_{1n} \\ a_{21} & b_2 & a_{23} & \cdots & a_{2n} \\ & & & \vdots & \\ a_{n1} & b_n & a_{n3} & \cdots & a_{nn} \end{vmatrix},$$

$$\vdots$$

$$b_1 A_{1n} + b_2 A_{2n} + \cdots + b_n A_{nn} = \begin{vmatrix} a_{11} & \cdots & a_{1,n-1} & b_1 \\ a_{21} & \cdots & a_{2,n-1} & b_2 \\ & & \vdots & \\ a_{n1} & \cdots & a_{n,n-1} & b_n \end{vmatrix}.$$

This establishes the following result, which is known as *Cramer's Rule*: the unique solution of system (1) is

$$x_1 = \frac{1}{|a_{ij}|} \begin{vmatrix} b_1 & a_{12} & \cdots & a_{1n} \\ b_2 & a_{22} & \cdots & a_{2n} \\ & & \vdots & \\ b_n & a_{n2} & \cdots & a_{nn} \end{vmatrix}, \qquad x_2 = \frac{1}{|a_{ij}|} \begin{vmatrix} a_{11} & b_1 & a_{13} & \cdots & a_{1n} \\ a_{21} & b_2 & a_{23} & \cdots & a_{2n} \\ & & & \vdots & \\ a_{n1} & b_n & a_{n3} & \cdots & a_{nn} \end{vmatrix},$$

$$\cdots, \qquad x_n = \frac{1}{|a_{ij}|} \begin{vmatrix} a_{11} & \cdots & a_{1,n-1} & b_1 \\ a_{21} & \cdots & a_{2,n-1} & b_2 \\ & & \vdots & \\ a_{n1} & \cdots & a_{n,n-1} & b_n \end{vmatrix}.$$

EXAMPLE 1. Solve the linear system

$$3x_1 - x_2 + 2x_3 = 1, \quad x_1 + x_2 - x_3 = 0, \quad 2x_1 - x_2 + x_3 = 2.$$

Solution: First, we compute the determinant of the coefficient matrix:

$$\begin{vmatrix} 3 & -1 & 2 \\ 1 & 1 & -1 \\ 2 & -1 & 1 \end{vmatrix} = 3(0) + 1(3) + 2(-3) = -3.$$

Therefore

$$x_1 = \frac{1}{-3} \begin{vmatrix} 1 & -1 & 2 \\ 0 & 1 & -1 \\ 2 & -1 & 1 \end{vmatrix} = \frac{1}{-3}[2(-1)] = \frac{2}{3},$$

$$x_2 = \frac{1}{-3} \begin{vmatrix} 3 & 1 & 2 \\ 1 & 0 & -1 \\ 2 & 2 & 1 \end{vmatrix} = \frac{1}{-3}[6 - 1(-3) + 2(-1)] = \frac{-7}{3},$$

$$x_3 = \frac{1}{-3} \begin{vmatrix} 3 & -1 & 1 \\ 1 & 1 & 0 \\ 2 & -1 & 2 \end{vmatrix} = \frac{1}{-3}[6 + 2 + 1(-3)] = \frac{-5}{3}.$$

EXERCISES

1. Develop Cramer's Rule without the use of matrices. (*Hint:* To obtain x_1, multiply the ith equation of the system (1) by A_{i1}, $i = 1, 2, \cdots, n$, and then add.)

2. Solve the linear system

$$x_1 + x_2 - x_3 = 1, \quad 2x_1 - 3x_2 + x_3 = 0, \quad x_1 - 2x_2 + x_3 = 2.$$

3. Find x_2, given that $2x_1 - x_2 + x_3 + 2x_4 = 2$, $x_1 + x_2 - 2x_3 - x_4 = 0$, $x_1 - 2x_2 + x_4 = 1$, and $2x_1 + x_2 - x_3 - x_4 = 0$.

3.9 Linear Transformations; Linear Operators

We come now to an interesting and important application of matrices. By a *vector function* we mean any mapping of a set of vectors into a set of vectors; essentially, then, a vector function is a rule which associates a vector with a vector. In the customary functional notation "$\mathbf{f}(\alpha)$" denotes the vector which the vector function $\mathbf{f}$ associates with α. A vector function possesses both a domain and a range; the domain of $\mathbf{f}$ is the set of all first terms of members of $\mathbf{f}$, and the range of $\mathbf{f}$ is the set of all second terms of members of $\mathbf{f}$.

In this section we shall confine our attention to certain vector functions known as *linear transformations*.

DEFINITION 3.9.1.   Let $(\mathscr{F}, \mathscr{V}, \circ)$ and $(\mathscr{F}, \mathscr{V}', \circ')$ be any vector spaces, where $\mathscr{V} = (V, +, 0)$ and $\mathscr{V}' = (V', +', 0')$. Then T is said to be a *linear transformation of V into V'* iff

(i) T is a mapping of V into V',

(ii) $T(\alpha + \beta) = T(\alpha) +' T(\beta)$ whenever $\alpha \in V$ and $\beta \in V$,

(iii) $T(k\alpha) = kT(\alpha)$ whenever $\alpha \in V$ and $k \in F$.

EXAMPLE 1.   Consider the vector spaces $\mathscr{V}_3(\mathscr{R})$ and $\mathscr{V}_4(\mathscr{R})$, and let $T(a, b, c) = (a, b, c, a+b+c)$ whenever $(a, b, c) \in R_3$. Then T is a mapping of R_3 into R_4. If $\alpha = (a_1, a_2, a_3)$, $\beta = (b_1, b_2, b_3)$, and $k \in R$, then

$$T(\alpha + \beta) = (a_1 + b_1, a_2 + b_2, a_3 + b_3, a_1 + a_2 + a_3 + b_1 + b_2 + b_3)$$
$$= (a_1, a_2, a_3, a_1 + a_2 + a_3) + (b_1, b_2, b_3, b_1 + b_2 + b_3)$$
$$= T(\alpha) + T(\beta),$$

and
$$T(k\alpha) = T(ka_1, ka_2, ka_3)$$
$$= (ka_1, ka_2, ka_3, ka_1 + ka_2 + ka_3)$$
$$= k(a_1, a_2, a_3, a_1 + a_2 + a_3)$$
$$= kT(\alpha).$$

Thus T is a linear transformation of R_3 into R_4.

EXAMPLE 2.   Consider the vector space which involves all continuous functions with domain [0, 1] (see Example 5, Section 1.8), and consider the vector space $\mathscr{V}_2(\mathscr{R})$. Let $T(f) = (f(0), f(1))$ whenever f is a continuous function with domain [0, 1]. Clearly,

$$T(f + g) = (f(0) + g(0), f(1) + g(1)) = (f(0), f(1)) + (g(0), g(1)) = T(f) + T(g)$$

and $T(kf) = (kf(0), kf(1)) = k(f(0), f(1)) = kT(f)$.

Thus T is a linear transformation of the set of all continuous functions with domain [0, 1] into R_2.

In view of Definition 3.9.1, it is easy to see that the image of a subspace under a linear transformation is a subspace.

THEOREM 3.9.1.   Let T be any linear transformation of V into V', and let V_1 be any subspace of $(\mathscr{F}, \mathscr{V}, \circ)$; then $\{T(\alpha) \mid \alpha \in V_1\}$ is a subspace of $(\mathscr{F}, \mathscr{V}', \circ')$.
   Proof: Let $\alpha \in V_1, \beta \in V_1$, and $k \in F$; then $T(\alpha) +' T(\beta) = T(\alpha + \beta)$ and $kT(\alpha) = T(k\alpha)$. Therefore $\{T(\alpha) \mid \alpha \in V_1\}$ is a subspace of $(\mathscr{F}, \mathscr{V}', \circ')$.

COROLLARY 3.9.1.   Let T be any linear transformation of V into V'; then the range of T is a subspace of $(\mathscr{F}, \mathscr{V}', \circ')$.

Next, we introduce the notion of the *null space* of a linear transformation.

DEFINITION 3.9.2.   Let T be any linear transformation of V into V'; then $\{\alpha \mid \alpha \in V \text{ and } T(\alpha) = \mathbf{0}'\}$ is said to be the *null space* of T. This set is denoted by "N_T" or by "$n(T)$".

We point out that the null space of the linear transformation of Example 1 is $\{\mathbf{0}\}$, and that the null space of the linear transformation of Example 2 is $\{f \mid f$ is continuous, $\mathscr{D}_f = [0, 1]$, and $f(0) = f(1) = 0\}$. Notice that each of these null spaces is a subspace of the vector space involved. This is always so.

THEOREM 3.9.2.   Let T be any linear transformation of V into V'; then the null space of T is a subspace of $(\mathscr{F}, \mathscr{V}, \circ)$.

Proof: Let $\alpha \in N_T$, let $\beta \in N_T$, and let $k \in F$. Then $T(\alpha + \beta) = T(\alpha) +' T(\beta) = \mathbf{0}' + \mathbf{0}' = \mathbf{0}'$; thus $\alpha + \beta \in N_T$. Also, $T(k\alpha) = kT(\alpha) = k\mathbf{0}' = \mathbf{0}'$; thus $k\alpha \in N_T$. Therefore N_T is a subspace of $(\mathscr{F}, \mathscr{V}, \circ)$.

THEOREM 3.9.3.   Let T be any linear transformation of V into V'; then T is a one–one mapping of V into V' iff $N_T = \{\mathbf{0}\}$.

Proof: We point out that $\mathbf{0} \in N_T$ whenever T is a linear transformation of V into V' [note that $\mathbf{0} = \mathbf{0} + \mathbf{0}$; thus $T(\mathbf{0}) = T(\mathbf{0} + \mathbf{0}) = T(\mathbf{0}) +' T(\mathbf{0})$; therefore $T(\mathbf{0}) = \mathbf{0}'$]. Now, suppose that T is a one–one mapping of V into V'. Then $\alpha = \beta$ whenever $T(\alpha) = T(\beta)$. Let $\gamma \in N_T$, i.e., $T(\gamma) = \mathbf{0}'$. By assumption, then, $\gamma = \mathbf{0}$ since $T(\mathbf{0}) = \mathbf{0}'$. Thus $N_T = \{\mathbf{0}\}$. Next, suppose that $N_T = \{\mathbf{0}\}$; we want to show that T is a one–one mapping of V into V'. If $\alpha \neq \beta$ and $T(\alpha) = T(\beta)$, then $T(\alpha - \beta) = \mathbf{0}'$, and so $\alpha - \beta \in N_T$. But $N_T = \{\mathbf{0}\}$; therefore $\alpha - \beta = \mathbf{0}$, i.e., $\alpha = \beta$. This contradiction establishes that T is a one–one mapping of V into V'.

We now bring out an important feature of linear transformations. If T is a linear transformation of V into V' and if $\{\alpha_1, \alpha_2, \cdots, \alpha_s\}$ is a basis for V, then T is completely determined by the vectors $T(\alpha_1), T(\alpha_2), \cdots, T(\alpha_s)$.

THEOREM 3.9.4.   Let T be any linear transformation of V into V', where V is finite-dimensional, let $\{\alpha_1, \alpha_2, \cdots, \alpha_s\}$ be any basis for V, and let $\beta = \sum\limits_{i=1}^{s} k_i \alpha_i$ be any member of V. Then $T(\beta) = \sum\limits_{i=1}^{s} k_i T(\alpha_i)$.

Proof: Apply Definition 3.9.1(ii).

We have already seen that the range of T is a subspace; moreover, from Theorem 3.9.4 it is clear that each member of the range of T is a linear combination of $T(\alpha_1)$, $T(\alpha_2)$, $\cdots$, $T(\alpha_s)$ if each member of V is a linear combination of $\alpha_1, \alpha_2, \cdots, \alpha_s$. So we have the following theorem.

THEOREM 3.9.5.   Let T be any linear transformation of V into V', where V is finite-dimensional, and let V be spanned by $\alpha_1, \alpha_2, \cdots, \alpha_s$. Then the range of T is spanned by $T(\alpha_1), T(\alpha_2), \cdots, T(\alpha_s)$.

We might think that if $\{\alpha_1, \alpha_2, \cdots, \alpha_s\}$ is a basis for V, then $\{T(\alpha_1), T(\alpha_2), \cdots, T(\alpha_s)\}$ is a basis for the range of T. However, this is not generally true, as the following example shows.

EXAMPLE 3.   Consider the vector spaces $\mathscr{V}_3(\mathscr{R})$ and $\mathscr{V}_1(\mathscr{R})$, and let $T(a, b, c) = (a)$ whenever $(a, b, c) \in R_3$. Clearly, T is a linear transformation of R_3 into R_1. Now, $\{(1, 0, 0), (0, 1, 0), (0, 0, 1)\}$ is a basis for R_3; the image of this basis under T is $\{(1), (0)\}$, which is *not* a basis for the range of T.

So far our discussion has been quite general; although generality is a good thing, it can be overdone. Let us fix our attention on a particular kind of linear transformation. Now, a linear transformation of V into V' involves the vector spaces $(\mathscr{F}, \mathscr{V}, \circ)$ and $(\mathscr{F}, \mathscr{V}', \circ')$, which may or may not be the same. Let us simplify the situation by insisting that they are the same; i.e., we require that $(\mathscr{F}, \mathscr{V}, \circ) = (\mathscr{F}, \mathscr{V}', \circ')$, and therefore $V = V'$. We shall assign a special name to a linear transformation under this circumstance: it is called a *linear operator on V*.

DEFINITION 3.9.3.   Let $(\mathscr{F}, \mathscr{V}, \circ)$ be any vector space and let T be any linear transformation of V into V; then T is said to be a *linear operator on V*.

EXAMPLE 4.   Consider the vector space $\mathscr{V}_n(\mathscr{R})$, where $n \in N$, and let $\{\gamma_1, \gamma_2, \cdots, \gamma_n\}$ be any basis for R_n. Let $T(\alpha) = (k_1, k_2, \cdots, k_n)$ if $\alpha = \sum_{i=1}^{n} k_i \gamma_i$. Then T is a linear operator on R_n. To see this, let $\alpha = \sum_{i=1}^{n} k_i \gamma_i$ and let $\beta = \sum_{i=1}^{n} k_i' \gamma_i$; then

$$T(\alpha + \beta) = T\left(\sum_{i=1}^{n} (k_i + k_i')\gamma_i\right) = (k_1, k_2, \cdots, k_n) + (k_1', k_2', \cdots, k_n') = T(\alpha) + T(\beta).$$

Moreover, if $k \in R$, then $T(k\alpha) = T\left(\sum_{i=1}^{n} k k_i \gamma_i\right) = k(k_1, k_2, \cdots, k_n) = kT(\alpha)$. Thus T is a linear operator on R_n.

EXAMPLE 5.   Consider the vector space which involves all continuous functions with domain $[0, 1]$ such that the nth derivative of the function also has domain $[0, 1]$ whenever $n \in N$. Let $T(f) = f'$ whenever f is a member of this set of vectors. Then T is a linear operator on this set of vectors.

Perhaps the most significant property of linear transformations is that each linear transformation of a finite-dimensional vector space can be characterized by a matrix.

To make our point as painlessly as possible, we shall consider only linear operators; however, we point out that the idea generalizes to any linear transformation of a finite-dimensional vector space. Let us see how a matrix enters the scene. Let $(\mathscr{F}, \mathscr{V}, \circ)$ be any finite-dimensional vector space, let $\{\alpha_1, \alpha_2, \cdots, \alpha_s\}$ be a basis for V, and let T be any linear operator on V. Moreover, let $T(\alpha_i) = a_{i1}\alpha_1 + a_{i2}\alpha_2 + \cdots + a_{is}\alpha_s$, $i = 1, 2, \cdots, s$. Then the $s \times s$ matrix (a_{ij}) is said to be the *matrix of* T with respect to the ordered basis $(\alpha_1, \alpha_2, \cdots, \alpha_s)$.

EXAMPLE 6. Consider the vector space $\mathscr{V}_3(\mathscr{R})$. Let $\alpha_1 = (2, 1, 0)$, $\alpha_2 = (0, 1, 1)$, and $\alpha_3 = (1, -1, 0)$. Then $(\alpha_1, \alpha_2, \alpha_3)$ is an ordered basis for R_3. Let T be the linear operator on R_3 such that $T(\alpha_1) = (3, 3, 0)$, $T(\alpha_2) = (4, 0, 1)$, and $T(\alpha_3) = (-3, 2, 2)$. It is easy to see that $T(\alpha_1) = 2\alpha_1 - \alpha_3$, $T(\alpha_2) = \alpha_1 + \alpha_2 + 2\alpha_3$, and $T(\alpha_3) = -\alpha_1 + 2\alpha_2 - \alpha_3$. Thus the matrix of T with respect to the ordered basis $(\alpha_1, \alpha_2, \alpha_3)$ is the 3×3 matrix

$$\begin{pmatrix} 2 & 0 & -1 \\ 1 & 1 & 2 \\ -1 & 2 & -1 \end{pmatrix}.$$

In connection with this example, let us work out $T(\beta)$, where $\beta = 3\alpha_1 - 2\alpha_2 + 4\alpha_3$. Here, we need Theorem 3.9.4; thus

$$T(\beta) = 3T(\alpha_1) - 2T(\alpha_2) + 4T(\alpha_3)$$

$$= 3[2\alpha_1 - \alpha_3] - 2[\alpha_1 + \alpha_2 + 2\alpha_3] + 4[-\alpha_1 + 2\alpha_2 - \alpha_3]$$

$$= 6\alpha_2 - 11\alpha_3.$$

Notice that β is represented by $(3, -2, 4)$ with respect to the given ordered basis. Let us compute the inner product of $(3, -2, 4)$ with the columns of the matrix of T with respect to the same ordered basis. Now, $(3, -2, 4) \cdot (2, 1, -1) = 0$, $(3, -2, 4) \cdot (0, 1, 2) = 6$, $(3, -2, 4) \cdot (-1, 2, -1) = -11$. Our point is that $T(\beta)$ is represented by $(0, 6, -11)$ with respect to the given ordered basis. From an examination of our computation for $T(\beta)$ given above, it is clear that this is no accident. Let us formulate this observation as a theorem.

THEOREM 3.9.6.   Let (a_{ij}) be the matrix of the linear operator T with respect to the ordered basis $(\alpha_1, \alpha_2, \cdots, \alpha_s)$, and let $\beta = \sum_{i=1}^{s} k_i \alpha_i$. Then $T(\beta) = \sum_{i=1}^{s} k_i' \alpha_i$, where $k_i' = (k_1, k_2, \cdots, k_s) \cdot (a_{1i}, a_{2i}, \cdots, a_{si})$, $1 \leq i \leq s$.

Proof: Now, $\beta = \sum_{i=1}^{s} k_i \alpha_i$; therefore

$$T(\beta) = T\left(\sum_{i=1}^{s} k_i \alpha_i\right) = \sum_{i=1}^{s} k_i T(\alpha_i) \qquad \text{by Th. 3.9.4}$$

$$= k_1 \sum_{j=1}^{s} a_{1j}\alpha_j + k_2 \sum_{j=1}^{s} a_{2j}\alpha_j + \cdots + k_s \sum_{j=1}^{s} a_{sj}\alpha_j$$

$$= [k_1 a_{11} + \cdots + k_s a_{s1}]\alpha_1 + \cdots + [k_1 a_{1s} + \cdots + k_s a_{ss}]\alpha_s$$

$$= k_1' \alpha_1 + \cdots + k_s' \alpha_s.$$

This establishes our result.

A special case of Theorem 3.9.6 is of particular importance. Consider the vector space $\mathcal{V}_n(\mathcal{R})$ and choose $(e_1, e_2, \cdots, e_n)$ as our ordered basis for R_n, where e_i is the n-vector whose ith term is 1 and other terms are 0, $1 \leq i \leq n$. Let T be any linear operator on R_n and let $T(e_i) = (a_{i1}, a_{i2}, \cdots, a_{in})$, $1 \leq i \leq n$. Then (a_{ij}) is the matrix of T with respect to the given ordered basis. Moreover, if $\beta = (b_1, b_2, \cdots, b_n)$, then $\beta = \sum_{i=1}^{n} b_i e_i$; thus, by Theorem 3.9.6, $T(\beta) = \sum_{i=1}^{n} b_i' e_i = (b_1', b_2', \cdots, b_n')$, where $b_i' = \beta \cdot (a_{i1}, a_{i2}, \cdots, a_{in})$, $1 \leq i \leq n$. This means that $T(\beta)$ is the matrix $\beta(a_{ij})$. This establishes the following result.

THEOREM 3.9.7.   Let $n \in N$, let T be any linear operator on R_n, and let (a_{ij}) be the matrix of T with respect to the ordered basis $(e_1, e_2, \cdots, e_n)$. Then $T(\beta) = \beta(a_{ij})$ whenever $\beta \in R_n$.

EXAMPLE 7.   Compute $T(2, 5, -7, 1)$, given that T is a linear operator on R_4 such that $T(e_1) = (0, -1, 3, 2)$, $T(e_2) = (-2, 1, 4, -1)$, $T(e_3) = (4, 2, 0, -3)$, and $T(e_4) = (3, 0, -1, -2)$.
Solution: The matrix of T is

$$\begin{pmatrix} 0 & -1 & 3 & 2 \\ -2 & 1 & 4 & -1 \\ 4 & 2 & 0 & -3 \\ 3 & 0 & -1 & -2 \end{pmatrix}.$$

Therefore, by Theorem 3.9.7,

$$T(2, 5, -7, 1) = (2, 5, -7, 1) \begin{pmatrix} 0 & -1 & 3 & 2 \\ -2 & 1 & 4 & -1 \\ 4 & 2 & 0 & -3 \\ 3 & 0 & -1 & -2 \end{pmatrix} = (-35, -11, 25, 18).$$

E X E R C I S E S

1. Let f be the vector function such that $f(a_1, a_2, a_3) = (a_2, 0)$ whenever $(a_1, a_2, a_3) \in R_3$.
  a. Show that f is a linear transformation of R_3 into R_2.
  b. Compute the dimension of the subspace $f(R_3)$.
2. Let f be the vector function such that $f(a_1, a_2, a_3) = (a_1, a_2)$ whenever $(a_1, a_2, a_3) \in R_3$.
  a. Show that f is a linear transformation of R_3 into R_2.
  b. Compute the dimension of $f(R_3)$.
3. Let f be the vector function such that $f(a_1, a_2, a_3) = (0, a_1)$ whenever $(a_1, a_2, a_3) \in R_3$.
  a. Show that f is a linear transformation of R_3 into R_2.
  b. Compute the dimension of $f(R_3)$.
4. Let f be the vector function such that $f(a_1, a_2, a_3) = (a_1 + a_2, 0, 0)$ whenever $(a_1, a_2, a_3) \in R_3$.
  a. Show that f is a linear transformation of R_3 into R_3.
  b. Compute the dimension of $f(R_3)$.

5. Let **f** be the vector function such that $\mathbf{f}(a_1, a_2, a_3) = (a_1 + a_2, a_2, a_3)$ whenever $(a_1, a_2, a_3) \in R_3$.
  a. Show that **f** is a linear transformation of R_3 into R_3.
  b. Find a basis for the subspace $\mathbf{f}(R_3)$.

6. Show that T is a linear transformation of V into V, given that $T(\alpha) = \alpha$ whenever $\alpha \in V$.

7. Show that **f** is *not* a linear operator on R_3, given that $\mathbf{f}(a_1, a_2, a_3) = (1 + a_1, a_2, a_3)$ whenever $(a_1, a_2, a_3) \in R_3$.

8. Show that **f** is *not* a linear transformation of R_3 into R_2, given that $\mathbf{f}(a_1, a_2, a_3) = (a_1, 1)$ whenever $(a_1, a_2, a_3) \in R_3$.

9. Given that **f** is a vector function whose domain is a subspace V and given that **f** is *not* a linear transformation of V, does it follow that $\mathbf{f}(V)$ is *not* a subspace?

10. Compute $T(1, 2, -3)$, given that T is a linear operator on R_3, $T(1, 0, 0) = (2, 2, 1)$, $T(0, 1, 0) = (-1, 1, 1)$, and $T(0, 0, -3) = (4, -2, 5)$.

11. Compute $T(3, 0, -1)$, given that T is a linear operator on R_3, $T(1, 0, 0) = (-1, -2, 1)$, $T(0, 1, 0) = (1, -1, 1)$, and $T(0, 0, 1) = (2, 2, 2)$.

12. Prove that $T(\alpha_1), T(\alpha_2), \cdots, T(\alpha_s)$ are linearly dependent if $\alpha_1, \alpha_2, \cdots, \alpha_s$ are linearly dependent and T is a linear operator on the subspace spanned by $\alpha_1, \alpha_2, \cdots, \alpha_s$.

13. Let T be a linear transformation of V into V', where V is finite-dimensional. Prove that $\dim V = \dim T(V) + \dim N_T$, where "dim" stands for "dimension of" and $T(V)$ is the range of T.

14. Let T_1 and T_2 be any linear transformations of V into V'. By the *sum* of T_1 and T_2 we mean the vector function $\{(\alpha, \beta) \mid \alpha \in V \text{ and } \beta = T_1(\alpha) +' T_2(\alpha)\}$. This vector function is denoted by "$T_1 + T_2$". Prove that $T_1 + T_2$ is a linear transformation of V into V'.

15. Let T be any linear transformation of V into V' and let $k \in F$. The vector function $\{(\alpha, \beta) \mid \alpha \in V \text{ and } \beta = kT(\alpha)\}$ is denoted by "kT" and is said to be a *scalar product*. Prove that kT is a linear transformation of V into V'.

16. Let $L(V, V')$ be the set of all linear transformations of V into V'. Show that the algebraic system $(L(V, V'), +, \varphi)$ is an abelian group, where $+$ is the binary operation defined in Exercise 14 and φ is the linear transformation which associates $0'$ with each member of V.

17. Show that $(\mathscr{F}, \mathscr{V}, \circ)$ is a vector space, where $\mathscr{V}$ is the abelian group of Exercise 16, $\mathscr{F}$ is the field involved in the vector spaces of the linear transformations, and "$\circ$" denotes the scalar multiplication defined in Exercise 15.

18. Let T_1 and T_2 be any linear operators on V. By the *product* of T_1 and T_2 we mean the vector function $\{(\alpha, \beta) \mid \alpha \in V \text{ and } \beta = T_1(T_2(\alpha))\}$; this vectors function is denoted by "$T_1 T_2$". Prove that $T_1 T_2$ is a linear operator on V.

19. Find a vector space $(\mathscr{F}, \mathscr{V}, \circ)$ and two linear operators on V, say T_1 and T_2, such that $T_1 T_2 \neq T_2 T_1$.

20. Let $(\mathscr{F}, \mathscr{V}, \circ)$ be any vector space, and let "I" denote the identity function $\{(\alpha, \alpha) \mid \alpha \in V\}$. Show that I is a linear operator on V.

21. Let $(\mathscr{F}, \mathscr{V}, \circ)$ be any vector space, let B be the set of all linear operators on V, and let "$\times$" denote the binary operation on linear operators of Exercise 18. Is the algebraic system $(B, \times, I)$ a group?

22. Let $(\mathscr{F}, \mathscr{V}, \circ)$ be any vector space and let T_1, T_2, T_3 be any linear operators on V. Prove that

$$T_1(T_2 + T_3) = T_1 T_2 + T_1 T_3$$

and

$$(T_2 + T_3)T_1 = T_2 T_1 + T_3 T_1.$$

23. Let $(\mathscr{F}, \mathscr{V}, \circ)$ be any vector space, let T_1 and T_2 be any linear operators on V, and let $k \in F$. Prove that $(kT_1)T_2 = T_1(kT_2) = k(T_1T_2)$.

24. Let T be any linear transformation of V into V' such that T is one–one and onto. The vector function $\{(\alpha, \beta) \mid (\beta, \alpha) \in T\}$ is denoted by "T^{-1}" and is said to be the *inverse* of T. Prove that T^{-1} is a linear transformation of V' into V.

25. Let T be a linear transformation of V into V'; then T is said to be *nonsingular* iff $N_T = \{0\}$. Prove that T is one–one and onto iff T is nonsingular and $T(V) = V'$.

26. Let T_1 and T_2 be linear operators on V which are one–one and onto.
  a. Prove that T_1T_2 is one–one and onto.
  b. Prove that $(T_1T_2)^{-1} = T_2^{-1}T_1^{-1}$.

27. Let B be the set of all linear operators on V which are one–one and onto. Prove that the algebraic system $(B, \times, I)$ is a group, where $\times$ is the binary operation of Exercise 18 and I is the linear operator of Exercise 20.

28. Let T be the linear operator on R_3 such that $T(1, 0, 0) = (\cos\theta, \sin\theta, 0)$, $T(0, 1, 0) = (-\sin\theta, \cos\theta, 0)$, and $T(0, 0, 1) = (0, 0, 1)$, where θ is a given real number.
  a. Write down the matrix of T.
  b. Show that T is nonsingular.
  c. Compute $T(2, -3, 4)$.
  d. Prove that $[T(\alpha) - T(\beta)] \cdot [T(\alpha) - T(\beta)] = [\alpha - \beta] \cdot [\alpha - \beta]$ whenever $\alpha \in R_3$ and $\beta \in R_3$.

29. Let $n \in N$ and let T be any linear operator on R_n. Prove that T is nonsingular iff the matrix of T is nonsingular.

30. Let $n \in N$ and let T be any linear operator on R_n; then T is said to be an orthogonal transformation on R_n iff $T(\alpha) \cdot T(\alpha) = \alpha \cdot \alpha$ whenever $\alpha \in R_n$. Prove each of the following statements.
  a. If T is orthogonal, then T is nonsingular.
  b. If T_1 and T_2 are orthogonal, then T_1T_2 is orthogonal.
  c. If T is orthogonal, then T^{-1} exists and T^{-1} is orthogonal.

31. Show that T is an orthogonal transformation on R_3, given that

$$T(1, 0, 0) = \tfrac{1}{3}(2, 1, 2), \quad T(0, 1, 0) = \tfrac{1}{3}(1, 2, -2), \quad \text{and} \quad T(0, 0, 1) = \tfrac{1}{3}(-2, 2, 1).$$

32. Let $n \in N$, let B be the set of all orthogonal transformations on R_n, and let $\times$ be the binary operation of Exercise 18. Prove that the algebraic system $(B, \times, I)$ is a group.

33. Let $n \in N$ and let T be any orthogonal transformation on R_n. Prove that T preserves angles; i.e., the angle between $T(\alpha)$ and $T(\beta)$ is the same as the angle between α and β, whenever $\alpha \in R_n$ and $\beta \in R_n$.
  (*Hint:* Observe that $[\alpha - \beta] \cdot [\alpha - \beta] = [T(\alpha) - T(\beta)] \cdot [T(\alpha) - T(\beta)]$.)

34. Let $n \in N$. Show that the algebraic system $(B, +, \times, 0, 1)$ is a ring with identity, where B is the set of all linear operators on R_n, $+$ and $\times$ are the binary operations of Exercises 14 and 18, $0 = \{(\alpha, 0) \mid \alpha \in R_n\}$, and $1 = \{(\alpha, \alpha) \mid \alpha \in R_n\}$.

35. Let $n \in N$. Let T_1 and T_2 be any linear operators on R_n, let (a_{ij}) be the matrix of T_1 with respect to the ordered basis $(e_1, \cdots, e_n)$ and let (b_{ij}) be the matrix of T_2 with respect to the ordered basis $(e_1, \cdots, e_n)$. Prove that $(b_{ij})(a_{ij})$ is the matrix of the linear operator T_1T_2 with respect to the ordered basis $(e_1, \cdots, e_n)$.

36. Let $n \in N$; consider the algebraic system $(B, +, \cdot, 0, 1)$ which is obtained from the ring of Exercise 34 by replacing its third term by $\cdot$, where $\cdot$ is the binary operation on B defined as follows: $\alpha \cdot \beta = \beta \times \alpha$ whenever $\alpha \in R_n$ and $\beta \in R_n$. Show that $(B, +, \cdot, 0, 1)$ is a ring with identity.

37. Let $n \in N$. Prove that the ring of Exercise 36, namely $(B, +, \cdot, 0, 1)$, is isomorphic to the ring which involves all $n \times n$ matrices.

3.10   Characteristic Vectors; Characteristic Roots

Let $n \in N$ and let T be any linear operator on R_n. We are interested in whether there is a vector, say α, which is related to its image under T as follows: $T(\alpha) = k\alpha$, where $k \in R$. Any nonzero vector which has this property is said to be a *characteristic vector of T* and the real number involved is said to be a *characteristic root of T*.

> DEFINITION 3.10.1.   Let $n \in N$, let T be any linear operator on R_n, and let α be any nonzero n-vector. Then α is said to be a *characteristic vector of T* iff there is a real number k such that $T(\alpha) = k\alpha$.

> DEFINITION 3.10.2.   Let $n \in N$, let T be any linear operator on R_n, and let $k \in R$. Then k is said to be a *characteristic root of T* iff there is a nonzero vector α such that $T(\alpha) = k\alpha$.

For example, let T be the linear operator on R_3 such that $T(a, b, c) = (a, 0, 0)$ whenever $(a,b,c) \in R_3$. Then $T(a, 0, 0) = (a, 0, 0)$ whenever $a \in R$. Thus $(a, 0, 0)$ is a characteristic vector of T whenever $a \neq 0$, and 1 is a characteristic root of T. Clearly, T has no other characteristic vectors or characteristic roots.

Here is another example. Let T be the linear operator on R_3 whose matrix with respect to (e_1, e_2, e_3) is

$$\begin{pmatrix} 1 & 2 & 2 \\ 2 & 1 & -2 \\ 2 & -2 & -8 \end{pmatrix}.$$

Let $(a, b, c) \in R_3$; then

$$T(a, b, c) = (a, b, c) \cdot \begin{pmatrix} 1 & 2 & 2 \\ 2 & 1 & -2 \\ 2 & -2 & -8 \end{pmatrix}$$

$$= (a + 2b + 2c, \; 2a + b - 2c, \; 2a - 2b - 8c).$$

Therefore (a, b, c) is a characteristic vector of T iff $(a, b, c) \neq 0$ and there is a real number k such that $(a + 2b + 2c, \; 2a + b - 2c, \; 2a - 2b - 8c) = k(a, b, c)$. Thus to find the characteristic vectors of T, we must solve the linear system

$$(1 - k)a + 2b + 2c = 0$$

$$2a + (1 - k)b - 2c = 0$$

$$2a - 2b - (8 + k)c = 0.$$

Let us regard k as a parameter, so that the unknowns are a, b, and c. Now, there is a non-trivial solution of this linear system iff the coefficient matrix is singular, i.e.,

$$\begin{vmatrix} 1-k & 2 & 2 \\ 2 & 1-k & -2 \\ 2 & -2 & -8-k \end{vmatrix} = 0.$$

This equation enables us to determine the values of the parameter k. We obtain $-k^3 - 6k^2 + 27k = 0$, and so $-k(k+9)(k-3) = 0$. Thus $k = 0, 3, -9$. This means that 0, 3, and -9 are the characteristic roots of T. Using these values of the parameter k, we readily determine the corresponding characteristic vectors. They are $(2t, -2t, t)$ whenever $t \neq 0$; $(t, t, 0)$ whenever $t \neq 0$; and $(t, -t, -4t)$ whenever $t \neq 0$. Notice that each characteristic vector associated with the characteristic root 0 is a multiple of $(2, -2, 1)$, that each characteristic vector associated with the characteristic root 3 is a multiple of $(1, 1, 0)$, and that each characteristic vector associated with the characteristic root -9 is a multiple of $(1, -1, -4)$. The following theorem brings out the general situation.

THEOREM 3.10.1.   Let $n \in N$, let T be any linear operator on R_n, and let k be any characteristic root of T. Then $\{\alpha \mid T(\alpha) = k\alpha\}$ is a subspace $\mathscr{V}_n(\mathscr{R})$.

Proof: Suppose that $T(\alpha) = k\alpha$ and that $T(\beta) = k\beta$. Then $T(\alpha + \beta) = T(\alpha) + T(\beta) = k\alpha + k\beta = k(\alpha + \beta)$. Also, $T(c\alpha) = cT(\alpha) = c(k\alpha) = k(c\alpha)$ whenever $c \in R$. Therefore $\{\alpha \mid T(\alpha) = k\alpha\}$ is a subspace of $\mathscr{V}_n(\mathscr{R})$.

THEOREM 3.10.2   Let $n \in N$, let T be any linear operator on R_n, and let k_1 and k_2 be two characteristic roots of T. Then $\{\alpha \mid T(\alpha) = k_1\alpha\} \cap \{\alpha \mid T(\alpha) = k_2\alpha\} = \{\mathbf{0}\}$.

Proof: Clearly, $\mathbf{0}$ is a member of both sets. Suppose that $T(\alpha) = k_1\alpha$ and that $T_2(\alpha) = k_2\alpha$. Then $k_1\alpha = k_2\alpha$; thus $(k_1 - k_2)\alpha = \mathbf{0}$. Since $k_1 \neq k_2$ by assumption, we conclude that $\alpha = \mathbf{0}$. This establishes our result.

Let us examine our method for determining the characteristic vectors of a linear operator on R_n, say T. First, we consider the matrix of T with respect to $(\mathbf{e}_1, \cdots, \mathbf{e}_n)$, say (a_{ij}). Next, we form the matrix equation

(1) $$\alpha \cdot (a_{ij}) = k\alpha,$$

where α is any nonzero n-vector, and so is a $1 \times n$ matrix. This leads us to a homogeneous linear system which consists of n equations in n unknowns. Observe that $(a_{ij}) - kI_n$ is the coefficient matrix of this linear system. We point out that $(a_{ij}) - kI_n = (b_{ij})$, where

$$b_{ij} = \begin{cases} a_{ij} & \text{if } i \neq j \\ a_{ij} - k & \text{if } i = j. \end{cases}$$

Now, our linear system has a nontrivial solution iff its coefficient matrix is singular. Therefore we must consider the equation $|b_{ij}| = 0$; this equation is called the *characteristic equation* of the matrix (a_{ij}). Its zeros are the characteristic roots of T. Finally, we substitute a characteristic root of T for the parameter k in (1); this gives us a homogeneous linear system which we can solve for the characteristic vectors of T corresponding to the characteristic root involved.

The point of all this is that we can slap down the key matrix $(a_{ij}) - kI_n$ to begin our solution. Next, we read off the characteristic equation of (a_{ij}) and find its zeros. Finally, we substitute a characteristic root for k in our coefficient matrix and reduce the resulting matrix. We can then read off the corresponding characteristic vectors. The idea is to work directly from the matrix $(a_{ij}) - kI_n$.

For example, let us find the characteristic vectors of the linear operator on R_3 whose matrix with respect to $(\mathbf{e}_1, \mathbf{e}_2, \mathbf{e}_3)$ is

$$\begin{pmatrix} 3 & 1 & 1 \\ 1 & 0 & 2 \\ 1 & 2 & 0 \end{pmatrix} = (a_{ij}).$$

Here,

$$(a_{ij}) - kI_3 = \begin{pmatrix} 3-k & 1 & 1 \\ 1 & -k & 2 \\ 1 & 2 & -k \end{pmatrix};$$

and so the characteristic equation is

$$(3-k)(k^2 - 4) - (-k - 2) + (2 + k) = 0,$$

i.e.,

$$-k^3 + 3k^2 + 6k - 8 = 0.$$

Thus $k = 1, 4, -2$. We have found the characteristic roots of the linear operator. Now we substitute for the parameter in our key matrix.

$$k = 1: \quad \begin{pmatrix} 2 & 1 & 1 \\ 1 & -1 & 2 \\ 1 & 2 & -1 \end{pmatrix} \sim \begin{pmatrix} 0 & 0 & 0 \\ 1 & -1 & 2 \\ 0 & 3 & -3 \end{pmatrix} \sim \begin{pmatrix} 1 & -1 & 2 \\ 0 & 1 & -1 \end{pmatrix} \sim \begin{pmatrix} 1 & 0 & 1 \\ 0 & 1 & -1 \end{pmatrix};$$

therefore $(t, -t, -t)$ is a characteristic vector whenever $t \neq 0$.

$$k = 4: \quad \begin{pmatrix} -1 & 1 & 1 \\ 1 & -4 & 2 \\ 1 & 2 & -4 \end{pmatrix} \sim \begin{pmatrix} -1 & 1 & 1 \\ 0 & -3 & 3 \\ 0 & 3 & -3 \end{pmatrix} \sim \begin{pmatrix} -1 & 1 & 1 \\ 0 & -1 & 1 \end{pmatrix} \sim \begin{pmatrix} -1 & 0 & 2 \\ 0 & -1 & 1 \end{pmatrix};$$

therefore $(2t, t, t)$ is a characteristic vector whenever $t \neq 0$.

$$k = -2: \quad \begin{pmatrix} 5 & 1 & 1 \\ 1 & 2 & 2 \\ 1 & 2 & 2 \end{pmatrix} \sim \begin{pmatrix} 0 & -9 & -9 \\ 1 & 2 & 2 \end{pmatrix} \sim \begin{pmatrix} 0 & 1 & 1 \\ 1 & 0 & 0 \end{pmatrix} :$$

therefore $(0, t, -t)$ is a characteristic vector whenever $t \neq 0$.

To emphasize the fact that we can work directly from the matrix of a linear operator, it is customary to extend our terminology as follows. Let (a_{ij}) be the matrix of T with respect to $(e_1, \cdots, e_n)$. By the *characteristic vectors* of (a_{ij}) we mean the characteristic vectors of T; by the *characteristic roots* of (a_{ij}) we mean the characteristic roots of T.

EXERCISES

1. Find the characteristic vectors and the characteristic roots of T, given that $T(a, b, c) = (0, b, 0)$ whenever $(a, b, c) \in R_3$.

2. Find the characteristic vectors and the characteristic roots of T, given that $T(a, b, c) = (3a, 0, 0)$ whenever $(a, b, c) \in R_3$.

3. Find the characteristic vectors and the characteristic roots of T, given that $T(a, b, c, d) = (-a, -b, -c, -d)$ whenever $(a, b, c, d) \in R_4$.

4. Find the characteristic vectors and the characteristic roots of T, given that $T(a, b, c, d) = (a + b + c + d, 0, 0, 0)$ whenever $(a, b, c, d) \in R_4$.

Find the characteristic vectors and the characteristic roots of the following matrices.

5. $\begin{pmatrix} 1 & 2 & -1 \\ 2 & 4 & -2 \\ -1 & -2 & 1 \end{pmatrix}$.

6. $\begin{pmatrix} 1 & -3 & 0 \\ -3 & 9 & 0 \\ 0 & 0 & 0 \end{pmatrix}$.

7. $\begin{pmatrix} 1 & 0 & 0 \\ 0 & 1 & 2 \\ 0 & 2 & 4 \end{pmatrix}$.

8. $\begin{pmatrix} 9 & -6 & 0 \\ -6 & 5 & 0 \\ 0 & 0 & -1 \end{pmatrix}$.

9. $\begin{pmatrix} 1 & -1 & 2 \\ -1 & 2 & -2 \\ 2 & -2 & 5 \end{pmatrix}$.

10. $\begin{pmatrix} 9 & -3 & 0 \\ -3 & 13 & 6 \\ 0 & 6 & 3 \end{pmatrix}$.

PART

II

Three-Dimensional Analytic Geometry

Chapter 4   The Line

4.1   Three-Dimensional Euclidean Space

Those of us who have been exposed to Euclid's *Elements* are aware that one can study geometry without knowing what a *point* or a *line* is. It is enough to know that points and lines have certain properties; Euclid called these fundamental properties the postulates (axioms) of geometry.

We shall not follow Euclid's approach here. Instead we shall carefully define, or construct, each geometric entity as we meet it. To this purpose we shall draw on the mathematical objects and concepts associated with the vector space $\mathscr{V}_3(\mathscr{R})$.

Let us give a name to the mathematical system that we shall now construct. We shall call it *three-dimensional Euclidean space* and we shall denote it by "E_3". This mathematical system involves four concepts: points, lines, planes, and distance between points. Thus E_3 is an ordered 4-tuple. By a *point* we mean any ordered triple of real numbers; therefore R_3 is the set of all points. By a *line* we mean any set, such as $\{\alpha + t\beta \mid t \in R\}$, where α and β are points and $\beta \neq \mathbf{0}$. Next we define *distance*: let α and β be any points; then $\|\alpha - \beta\|$ is the distance between α and β. Using the concept of *distance*, we can define a *plane*: the set $\{\gamma \mid \|\gamma - \alpha\| = \|\gamma - \beta\|\}$ is said to be a plane provided α and β are distinct points. Thus a plane is the set of all points equidistant from two given points.

The usual Cartesian coordinate system can now be constructed in terms of E_3. We select three lines X, Y, and Z as follows:

$$X = \{t(1, 0, 0) \mid t \in R\},$$

$$Y = \{t(0, 1, 0) \mid t \in R\},$$

$$Z = \{t(0, 0, 1) \mid t \in R\}.$$

These lines are called the *coordinate axes*. Notice that $X \cap Y \cap Z = \{\mathbf{0}\}$; $\mathbf{0}$ is said to be the *origin*. Clearly, there is a one–one correspondence between X and R, between Y and R, and between Z and R; e.g., with each member of X, say $(a, 0, 0)$, we shall associate the real number a. Notice that $|a|$ is the distance between $(a, 0, 0)$ and the origin. Similarly, $|b|$ is the distance between $(0, b, 0)$ and the origin, and $|c|$ is the distance between $(0, 0, c)$ and the origin. Later we shall see that there is a unique plane which contains two given lines meeting at a point. The plane which contains X and Y is called the XY-plane; the plane which contains Y and Z is called the YZ-plane; and the plane which contains Z and X is called the ZX-plane. These planes are said to be the *coordinate planes*.

The terms of a point are said to be its coordinates; indeed, a is called the *first* co-ordinate of (a, b, c), b is called the *second* coordinate of this point, and c is called the *third* coordinate of the point. Later we shall prove that $|a|$ is the distance between (a, b, c) and the YZ-plane; $|b|$ is the distance between (a, b, c) and the ZX-plane; and $|c|$ is the distance between (a, b, c) and the XY-plane. Does this mean anything to you? It should not, for we have not yet defined what we mean by the distance between a point and a plane. This will come later.

We now illustrate the concepts that we have introduced above.

EXAMPLE 1.   Find the distance between the points $(1, 2, -4)$ and $(3, -1, 2)$.

Solution: Let $\alpha = (1, 2, -4)$ and let $\beta = (3, -1, 2)$; by definition, the distance between α and β is

$$\|\alpha - \beta\| = \|(-2, 3, -6)\| = (4 + 9 + 36)^{1/2} = 7.$$

Thus 7 is the distance between the given points.

EXAMPLE 2.   Find the points on the line $\{(1, 0, 0) + t(1, 2, 3) \mid t \in R\}$ at a distance of $4\sqrt{14}$ from $(3, 4, 6)$.

Solution: Let γ be a point on the given line at a distance of $4\sqrt{14}$ from $(3, 4, 6)$; then there is a real number t such that $\gamma = (1, 0, 0) + t(1, 2, 3) = (1 + t, 2t, 3t)$ and $\|\gamma - (3, 4, 6)\| = 4\sqrt{14}$. Thus $(t - 2)^2 + (2t - 4)^2 + (3t - 6)^2 = 224$; i.e., $t^2 - 4t - 12 = 0$, and so $t = 6$ or $t = -2$. Therefore the required points are $(7, 12, 18)$ and $(-1, -4, -6)$. Checking, we readily verify that these points are at a distance of $4\sqrt{14}$ from $(3, 4, 6)$.

EXAMPLE 3.   Find a line L such that $(1, 0, 2) \in L$ and $(2, -1, 0) \in L$.

Solution: Let $\alpha = (1, 0, 2)$ and let $\beta = (2, -1, 0)$. Now, $\{\alpha + t(\beta - \alpha) \mid t \in R\}$ is a line since $\beta - \alpha \neq 0$. Clearly, α and β are members of this line (take $t = 0, 1$). Thus the line $\{(1, 0, 2) + t(1, -1, -2) \mid t \in R\}$ has the required properties.

EXAMPLE 4.   Characterize the set of all points equidistant from $(1, 0, 0)$ and $(-1, 0, 0)$.

Solution: Denote the required set of points by "$\mathscr{P}$"; then $(a, b, c) \in \mathscr{P}$ iff

$$\|(a - 1, b, c)\| = \|(a + 1, b, c)\|;$$

i.e., $(a - 1)^2 + b^2 + c^2 = (a + 1)^2 + b^2 + c^2$, and so $a = 0$. Thus $\mathscr{P} = \{(0, b, c) \mid b \in R \text{ and } c \in R\}$. We point out that $\mathscr{P}$ is the YZ-plane since $Y \subset \mathscr{P}$ and $Z \subset \mathscr{P}$.

EXAMPLE 5.   Characterize the set of all points equidistant from $(2, -3, 1)$ and $(-1, 1, 3)$.

Solution: Let $\mathscr{P}$ be the required set of points; then $(a, b, c) \in \mathscr{P}$ iff

$$\|(a - 2, b + 3, c - 1)\| = \|(a + 1, b - 1, c - 3)\|;$$

thus $(a - 2)^2 + (b + 3)^2 + (c - 1)^2 = (a + 1)^2 + (b - 1)^2 + (c - 3)^2$; i.e., $-6a + 8b + 4c + 3 = 0$; therefore $\mathscr{P} = \{(a, b, c) \mid -6a + 8b + 4c + 3 = 0\}$.

We call this geometry *three-dimensional* because the vector space $\mathscr{V}_3(\mathscr{R})$ involved is three-dimensional. It is just as easy to discuss *n*-dimensional Euclidean space, E_n, where $n \in N$. This mathematical system is constructed from the vector space $\mathscr{V}_n(\mathscr{R})$. Since points of this geometry are *n*-vectors, R_n is the set of all points. Here, a line is defined just as in the three-dimensional case: so, by a *line* we mean any set of points $\{\alpha + t\beta \mid t \in R\}$, where α and β are points and $\beta \neq \mathbf{0}$. Distance between points is the same concept as in the three-dimensional case: $\|\alpha - \beta\|$ is the distance between α and β. However, the notion of a plane generalizes to a *hyperplane*; i.e., the set of all points equidistant from two given points is called a *hyperplane*. Notice that if $n = 2$, then a hyperplane is a line.

EXERCISES

1. Find the distance between the points $(2, -1, 3)$ and $(-4, 1, 5)$.
2. Show that $(1, 5, -2)$ is equidistant from $(3, 7, 0)$ and $(-1, 3, -4)$.
3. Find a point which is equidistant from $(2, -4, 6)$ and $(8, 0, 4)$.
4. Show that $\{(a, 0, 0) \mid a \in R\}$ is a line.
5. Show that $\{(0, a, 0) \mid a \in R\}$ is a line.
6. Show that $\{(0, 0, a) \mid a \in R\}$ is a line.
7. Show that $\{(3 - a, 2, 1) \mid a \in R\}$ is a line.
8. Show that $\{(-t, 1 + t, 2t) \mid t \in R\}$ is a line.
9. Find a line L such that $(2, -1, 3) \in L$ and $(4, 0, 1) \in L$.
10. Characterize the set of all points equidistant from $(0, 1, 0)$ and $(0, -1, 0)$. Show that this plane is the ZX-plane.
11. Characterize the set of all points equidistant from $(0, 0, 1)$ and $(0, 0, -1)$. Show that this plane is the XY-plane.
12. Characterize the set of all points equidistant from $(3, 0, -1)$ and $(5, 4, 1)$. Is $(-1, 2, 4)$ a member of this set?

4.2 The Line Through Two Points

One of Euclid's postulates for geometry is this: "there is exactly one line through two points". When we say that a line is through (or passes through) a point, we mean that the point is a member of the line. (Similarly, when we say that a plane passes through a point, we mean that the point is a member of the plane.) Now, our definition of a line involves two 3-vectors (or possibly just one 3-vector), say α and β, where the line is $\{\alpha + t\beta \mid t \in R\}$. Our first theoretical observation about this concept is that we obtain the same line if we replace β by any nonzero member of the subspace spanned by β (i.e., any nonzero multiple of β).

THEOREM   4.2.1.   Let $k \neq 0$ and let $\beta \neq \mathbf{0}$; then $\{\alpha + t\beta \mid t \in R\} = \{\alpha + t(k\beta) \mid t \in R\}$.

Proof: Show that each of these sets is a subset of the other.

Next, let us see how we can vary α without changing the line $\{\alpha + t\beta \mid t \in R\}$. We shall prove that we can replace α by any member of the given line and still have the original line.

THEOREM 4.2.2. Let $L_1 = \{\alpha + t\beta \mid t \in R\}$ be a line, and let $L_2 = \{\gamma + t\beta \mid t \in R\}$, where $\gamma \in L_1$; then $L_1 = L_2$.

Proof: We shall show that $L_1 \subset L_2$ and $L_2 \subset L_1$. By assumption, there is a real number, say t_1, such that $\gamma = \alpha + t_1\beta$. Let $\alpha + t_2\beta$ be any member of L_1; now,

$$\alpha + t_2\beta = (\alpha + t_1\beta) + (t_2 - t_1)\beta = \gamma + (t_2 - t_1)\beta.$$

Therefore $\alpha + t_2\beta \in L_2$. Thus $L_1 \subset L_2$. Similarly, let $\gamma + t_3\beta$ be any member of L_2. But

$$\gamma + t_3\beta = (\alpha + t_1\beta) + t_3\beta = \alpha + (t_1 + t_3)\beta,$$

and so $\gamma + t_3\beta \in L_1$. Thus $L_2 \subset L_1$. This proves that $L_1 = L_2$.

Putting our two results together, we have the following corollary.

COROLLARY 4.2.1. Let $L = \{\alpha + t\beta \mid t \in R\}$ be any line, let $\gamma \in L$, and let β_1 be any nonzero multiple of β. Then $\{\gamma + t\beta_1 \mid t \in R\} = L$.

Proof: Theorems 4.2.1 and 4.2.2.

The following theorem shows that in this connection there is a limit to our freedom of choice.

THEOREM 4.2.3. Let L_1 and L_2 be any lines, say $\{\alpha_1 + t\beta_1 \mid t \in R\}$ and $\{\alpha_2 + t\beta_2 \mid t \in R\}$, respectively; then $L_1 = L_2$ iff β_1 and β_2 are linearly dependent, $\alpha_1 \in L_2$, and $\alpha_2 \in L_1$.

Proof: In view of our preceding results, we have only to show that if $L_1 = L_2$, then β_1 and β_2 are linearly dependent, $\alpha_1 \in L_2$, and $\alpha_2 \in L_1$. Assume, then, that $\{\alpha_1 + t\beta_1 \mid t \in R\} = \{\alpha_2 + t\beta_2 \mid t \in R\}$. Now, $\alpha_1 \in L_1$; therefore $\alpha_1 \in L_2$, by assumption. Similarly, $\alpha_2 \in L_1$. Moreover, $\alpha_1 + \beta_1 \in L_1$, and so $\alpha_1 + \beta_1 \in L_2$. Therefore there is a real number, say t_1, such that $\alpha_1 + \beta_1 = \alpha_2 + t_1\beta_2$. But $\alpha_1 = \alpha_2 + t_2\beta_2$ for some real number t_2; thus $\alpha_2 + t_2\beta_2 + \beta_1 = \alpha_2 + t_1\beta_2$. Hence $(t_2 - t_1)\beta_2 + \beta_1 = 0$. Therefore β_1 and β_2 are linearly dependent. This completes our proof.

Now let us see about Euclid's postulate. First, we present a method of obtaining a line through two points.

THEOREM 4.2.4. Suppose that $\alpha \neq \beta$; then $\{\alpha + t(\beta - \alpha) \mid t \in R\}$ is a line through α and β.

Proof: Since $\beta - \alpha \neq 0$, we have a line. Moreover, we have seen that $\{\alpha, \beta\} \subset \{\alpha + t(\beta - \alpha) \mid t \in R\}$. Thus we have our result.

Next, we shall demonstrate that $\{\alpha + t(\beta - \alpha)\,|\,t \in R\}$ is the *only* line through α and β, given that $\alpha \neq \beta$.

THEOREM 4.2.5.   Suppose that $\alpha \neq \beta$, and let L be any line through α and β. Then $L = \{\alpha + t(\beta - \alpha)\,|\,t \in R\}$.

Proof: Let L be any line such that $\alpha \in L$ and $\beta \in L$, and let α_1 and β_1 be 3-vectors such that $L = \{\alpha_1 + t\beta_1\,|\,t \in R\}$. Since $\alpha \in L$, $L = \{\alpha + t\beta_1\,|\,t \in R\}$, by Theorem 4.2.2. Since $\beta \in L$, there is a real number t_1 such that $\beta = \alpha + t_1\beta_1$. But $\alpha \neq \beta$; thus $t_1 \neq 0$, and so $\beta_1 = (1/t_1)(\beta - \alpha)$. Hence, by Theorem 4.2.1, $L = \{\alpha + t(\beta - \alpha)\,|\,t \in R\}$. This establishes Theorem 4.2.5.

We now present some examples.

EXAMPLE 1.   Find the line through $(3, 0, -2)$ and $(4, -1, -1)$.
Solution: By Theorem 4.2.5, the required line is $\{(3, 0, -2) + t(1, -1, 1)\,|\,t \in R\}$.

EXAMPLE 2.   Is the point $(2, 0, 1)$ on the line through $(7, -3, 4)$ and $(1, 2, 5)$?
Solution: The line through $(7, -3, 4)$ and $(1, 2, 5)$ is $\{(7, -3, 4) + t(-6, 5, 1)\,|\,t \in R\}$. Now, $(2, 0, 1)$ is on this line iff there is a real number t such that $(2, 0, 1) = (7, -3, 4) + t(-6, 5, 1)$; i.e., $2 = 7 - 6t$, $0 = -3 + 5t$, $1 = 4 + t$. Since this linear system has no solution, we conclude that $(2, 0, 1)$ is not on the given line.

THEOREM 4.2.6.   If the points (x_1, y_1, z_1), (x_2, y_2, z_2), (x_3, y_3, z_3) are on one line, then

$$\begin{vmatrix} x_1 & y_1 & z_1 \\ x_2 & y_2 & z_2 \\ x_3 & y_3 & z_3 \end{vmatrix} = 0.$$

Proof: In view of Theorem 2.4.7 we may assume that the given points are distinct. Suppose that the given points are on one line. By Theorem 4.2.5, the point (x_3, y_3, z_3) is on the line through (x_1, y_1, z_1) and (x_2, y_2, z_2). Hence there is a number t such that $x_3 = x_1 + t(x_2 - x_1)$, $y_3 = y_1 + t(y_2 - y_1)$, and $z_3 = z_1 + t(z_2 - z_1)$. Therefore

$$\begin{vmatrix} x_1 & y_1 & z_1 \\ x_2 & y_2 & z_2 \\ x_3 & y_3 & z_3 \end{vmatrix} = \begin{vmatrix} x_1 & y_1 & z_1 \\ x_2 & y_2 & z_2 \\ x_3 - x_1 & y_3 - y_1 & z_3 - z_1 \end{vmatrix} = \begin{vmatrix} x_1 & y_1 & z_1 \\ x_2 & y_2 & z_2 \\ t(x_2 - x_1) & t(y_2 - y_1) & t(z_2 - z_1) \end{vmatrix}$$

$$= t\begin{vmatrix} x_1 & y_1 & z_1 \\ x_2 & y_2 & z_2 \\ x_2 - x_1 & y_2 - y_1 & z_2 - z_1 \end{vmatrix} = 0,$$

since the third row of the last matrix is a linear combination of the other rows. This establishes Theorem 4.2.6.

It is customary to say that three or more points are *collinear* iff all of the points are members of the same line. We now rewrite the preceding theorem.

THEOREM 4.2.7. If $\begin{vmatrix} x_1 & y_1 & z_1 \\ x_2 & y_2 & z_2 \\ x_3 & y_3 & z_3 \end{vmatrix} \neq 0$, then (x_1, y_1, z_1), (x_2, y_2, z_2), and (x_3, y_3, z_3) are *not* collinear.

It is tempting to formulate the following conjecture.

CONJECTURE. The points (x_1, y_1, z_1), (x_2, y_2, z_2), and (x_3, y_3, z_3) are collinear iff

$$\begin{vmatrix} x_1 & y_1 & z_1 \\ x_2 & y_2 & z_2 \\ x_3 & y_3 & z_3 \end{vmatrix} = 0.$$

However, it is not difficult to disprove this conjecture by presenting a counterexample. We now consider the significance of the vectors that appear in our definition of a line. Let $\alpha \in R_3$ and let β be any nonzero 3-vector, so that $\{\alpha + t\beta \mid t \in R\}$ is a line, say L. As we have already indicated, $\alpha \in L$; indeed, we can take for α any member of L. Now consider β; we shall say that β is a *direction* of L. In particular, if $\alpha_1 \in L$ and $\alpha_2 \in L$, $\alpha_1 \neq \alpha_2$, then $\alpha_1 - \alpha_2$ is a direction of L (this follows from Theorem 4.2.4). If β_1 and β_2 are directions of the same line, we shall say that β_1 is equivalent to β_2. Notice that this gives us an equivalence relation on $R_3 - \{0\}$. In the following section we shall refine the notion of a direction of a line so that each line will possess precisely two directions.

EXERCISES

1. Find the line through $(2, -3, 1)$ and $(1, 0, 5)$.

2. Find the line through $(0, 2, -3)$ and $(0, 1, 1)$.

3. Is the point $(-1, 2, 8)$ on the line through $(1, 0, 2)$ and $(2, -1, -1)$?   (*Answer:* yes)

4. Is the point $(7, -1, 3)$ on the line through $(1, 2, 0)$ and $(3, 1, 1)$?   (*Answer:* yes)

5. Is the point $(6, 2, 2)$ on the line through $(0, 1, -5)$ and $(2, 0, -2)$?   (*Answer:* no)

6. Do the lines $\{(1, 0, 0) + t(-1, 2, 1) \mid t \in R\}$ and $\{(2, -1, 3) + t(1, 0, 2) \mid t \in R\}$ intersect?   (*Answer:* no)

7. Do the lines $\{(3, -2, 1) + t(1, -1, 1) \mid t \in R\}$ and $\{(0, -1, -3) + t(2, 0, 3) \mid t \in R\}$ intersect?   (*Answer:* yes, at $(2, -1, 0)$)

8. Show that the line through $(1, 0, 2)$ and $(2, -1, 4)$ intersects the line through $(2, 1, 3)$ and $(6, -7, 13)$.

9. Do the lines $\{(2t, 0, 3 - t) \mid t \in R\}$ and $\{(4 + 2t, 3 - t, t - 5) \mid t \in R\}$ intersect?

10. Do the lines $\{(t, 2 - t, 4 + 3t) \mid t \in R\}$ and $\{(1 + t, 3 - 2t, 1 + 6t) \mid t \in R\}$ intersect?   (*Answer:* yes, at $(3, -1, 13)$)

11. Show that the lines $\{(1 - t, t + 1, t + 2) \mid t \in R\}$ and $\{(3t, 1 - t, 2 + 3t) \mid t \in R\}$ do not intersect.

12. A line through the origin has direction $(2, -1, 3)$. Find the line.

13. Prove that L is a line through α iff there is a one-dimensional subspace of $\mathscr{V}_3(\mathscr{R})$, say V, such that $L = \{\alpha + \beta \mid \beta \in V\}$.

14. Let $\{\alpha + t\beta \mid t \in R\}$ be any line. What is the geometric significance of the parameter t? (*Hint:* Assume that β has length 1; consider the distance between α and $\alpha + t\beta$.)

15. Show that the conjecture of the text is false.

16. Use Theorem 4.2.7 to show that the points $(2, 5, -1)$, $(0, 3, 1)$, and $(1, 2, -1)$ are *not* collinear.

4.3 Directed Lines; Direction Cosines

Intuitively, we know that a line in space points out exactly two directions. Thus we should be able to reduce the set of all directions of a given line to just two directions. This is achieved as follows. Let $\{\alpha + t\beta \mid t \in R\}$ be any line L; then $\{k\beta \mid k \neq 0\}$ is the set of all directions of L. We partition $\{k\beta \mid k \neq 0\}$ into two disjoint subsets: $\{k\beta \mid k > 0\}$ and $\{k\beta \mid k < 0\}$. We shall regard β_1 and β_2 as equivalent iff they are members of the same subset. Notice that this is an equivalence relation on $R_3 - \{\mathbf{0}\}$. For example, consider the line $\{t(1, 2, -1) \mid t \in R\}$. This line has essentially two directions: $(1, 2, -1)$ is one of its directions, whereas $(-1, -2, 1)$ is its other direction. Of course, $(2, 4, -2)$ is also a direction of this line, but we have agreed to regard the directions $(2, 4, -2)$ and $(1, 2, -1)$ as equivalent. In general, we shall regard nonzero 3-vectors β_1 and β_2 as equivalent iff there is a positive real number k such that $\beta_2 = k\beta_1$; in this case we shall write "$\beta_1 \equiv \beta_2$".

> DEFINITION 4.3.1.   Let β_1 and β_2 be any nonzero 3-vectors; then $\beta_1 \equiv \beta_2$ iff there is a positive real number k such that $\beta_2 = k\beta_1$.

As usual, the equivalence class $\{\alpha \mid \alpha \equiv \beta\}$ is denoted by "$[\beta]$"; thus $[\beta] = [\alpha]$ iff $\alpha \in [\beta]$.

Let us examine our position. We have agreed to associate exactly two equivalence classes with each line; i.e., given any line L, we have available essentially just two directions, either one of which we can associate with L. Notice that once we carry out the act of associating a specific equivalence class (i.e., direction) with a line, we obtain a new object, namely a *directed* line. The point is this: each line carries with it exactly two equivalence classes. If we select one of the equivalence classes, we have in fact *directed* the line; i.e., we have given a direction to the line. The possibility of being directed belongs to any line; the fact of possessing a specific direction belongs only to a *directed* line. It is easy to represent a directed line by a precise mathematical object: a directed line is an ordered pair whose first term is a line and whose second term is one of the equivalence classes associated with the line. For example, if β is a direction of a line L, then $(L, [\beta])$ is a directed line. To simplify our notation, we shall characterize an equivalence class by any one of its members. Thus we shall write "(L, β)" in place of "$(L, [\beta])$"; this is a bracket-omitting convention. Of course, (L, β_1) and (L, β_2) are the same directed line iff β_1 and β_2 are equivalent directions; i.e., $(L, \beta_1) = (L, \beta_2)$ iff $\beta_1 \equiv \beta_2$.

Next, we introduce the notion of the angle between two directed lines. To this purpose we use the concept of the angle between nonzero vectors.

DEFINITION 4.3.2. Let (L_1, β_1) and (L_2, β_2) be any directed lines; then $\arccos \dfrac{\beta_1 \cdot \beta_2}{\|\beta_1\| \, \|\beta_2\|}$ is said to be the *angle* between these directed lines.

This means that the angle between (L_1, β_1) and (L_2, β_2) is the angle between the vectors β_1 and β_2.

Notice that the angle between (L_1, β_1) and (L_2, β_2) does not depend upon which members of the equivalence classes are used. That is, if $k_1 > 0$ and $k_2 > 0$, then the angle between $(L_1, k_1\beta_1)$ and $(L_2, k_2\beta_2)$ is the same as the angle between (L_1, β_1) and (L_2, β_2).

In setting up a coordinate system, it is customary to use *directed* lines as the coordinate axes. Thus for our coordinate axes we take $(X, (1, 0, 0))$, $(Y, (0, 1, 0))$, $(Z, (0, 0, 1))$. Now that our coordinate axes are directed lines, let us consider the angles that a given directed line, say (L, β), makes with each of the coordinate axes. Let $\beta = (l, m, n)$; then these angles are

$$\arccos \frac{l}{\|\beta\|}, \quad \arccos \frac{m}{\|\beta\|}, \quad \arccos \frac{n}{\|\beta\|}.$$

We are free to choose β so that $\|\beta\| = 1$ [in this case β is denoted by "(λ, μ, ν)"]. Then the angles between (L, β) and the directed coordinate axes are $\arccos \lambda$, $\arccos \mu$, $\arccos \nu$. These angles are said to be the *direction angles* of the directed line (L, β). The cosines of the direction angles are said to be the *direction cosines* of the directed line. Clearly, the direction cosines of the directed line (L, β) are the terms of β, if $\|\beta\| = 1$. Of course, this reflects the geometric significance of the *direction* of a directed line. The point is that if $\|\beta\| = 1$, then the cosines of the angles that the directed line (L, β) makes with the directed coordinate axes are given by the terms of β.

For example, the direction cosines of $(X, (1, 0, 0))$ are given by $(1, 0, 0)$; thus the angles that this directed line makes with the directed coordinate axes are $\arccos 1$, $\arccos 0$, and $\arccos 0$, respectively, i.e., 0, $\pi/2$, $\pi/2$.

EXAMPLE 1. Determine the angles that the directed line $(X, (-1, 0, 0))$ makes with the directed coordinate axes.

Solution: The cosines of the required angles are the terms of $(-1, 0, 0)$; therefore the angles are $\arccos -1$, $\arccos 0$, and $\arccos 0$, i.e., π, $\pi/2$, $\pi/2$.

EXAMPLE 2. Determine the direction cosines of the directed line (L, β), where $L = \{t(0, \sqrt{3}, 1) \mid t \in R\}$ and $\beta = (0, \sqrt{3}, 1)$.

Solution: Since $\|\beta\| = 2$, we consider $(L, \beta/2)$. Clearly, the required direction cosines are the terms of $\beta/2$, namely 0, $.5\sqrt{3}$, $.5$.

Here is a simple way of characterizing a directed line. Let us agree that by "the line directed from α_1 to α_2" we mean the directed line (L, β), where L is the line through α_1 and α_2, and $\beta = \alpha_2 - \alpha_1$.

EXAMPLE 3. Determine the direction cosines of the line directed from $(1, 3, 2)$ to $(4, -1, 0)$.

Solution: Our directed line is (L, β), where $\beta = (3, -4, -2)$. Now, $\|\beta\| = \sqrt{29}$; therefore the direction cosines of our directed line are the terms of $(3/\sqrt{29}, -4\sqrt{29}, -2/\sqrt{29})$.

EXAMPLE 4.   Find the angle between the line directed from $(-1, 0, 2)$ to $(2, 1, 1)$ and the line directed from $(3, -1, 2)$ to $(0, 0, 0)$.

Solution: Our directed lines are $(L_1, (3, 1, -1))$ and $(L_2, (-3, 1, -2))$. Therefore the angle between these directed lines is

$$\arccos \frac{(3, 1, -1) \cdot (-3, 1, -2)}{\|(3, 1, -1)\| \, \|(-3, 1, -2)\|} = \arccos \frac{-6}{\sqrt{11}\sqrt{14}} \approx \arccos - .4835 \approx 2.075.$$

One of the most significant of Euclid's postulates is the famous postulate of *parallel lines*: "Given any line and any point not on the line, there is exactly one line through the given point which is parallel to the given line". To establish this proposition, we must first define the term *parallel*. We shall talk about *directed* lines rather than lines.

DEFINITION 4.3.3.   Two directed lines are said to be *parallel* iff they have the same direction. No directed line is parallel to itself.

You may think it odd that a directed line is not parallel to itself; however, most geometers prefer to use this term in this sense.

Let us now establish Euclid's postulate.

THEOREM 4.3.1.   Let (L, β) be any directed line and suppose that $\alpha \,\bar{\in}\, L$; then there is exactly one directed line parallel to (L, β), say (L_1, β), such that $\alpha \in L_1$.

Proof: Let $\alpha_1 \in L$; then $L = \{\alpha_1 + t\beta \,|\, t \in R\}$. Let $L_1 = \{\alpha + t\beta \,|\, t \in R\}$; then (L_1, β) is parallel to (L, β) since $L_1 \neq L$. Let us show that there is no other directed line through α which is parallel to (L, β). Suppose that (L_2, β) is parallel to (L, β) and that $\alpha \in L_2$. Then, by Theorem 4.2.2, $L_2 = \{\alpha + t\beta \,|\, t \in R\} = L_1$. This completes our proof.

We shall find it convenient to use the term *parallel* in connection with lines as well as directed lines. Thus we shall say that two lines are *parallel* iff they possess a common direction. For example, $\{(1, 0, 0) + t(2, -1, 1) \,|\, t \in R\}$ and $\{(3, 2, 5) + t(2, -1, 1) \,|\, t \in R\}$ are parallel. No line is parallel to itself.

E X E R C I S E S

1. Determine the angle between the line directed from $(1, 0, -1)$ to $(2, 1, 3)$ and the line directed from $(2, 2, 1)$ to $(0, 1, -1)$.
2. Determine the angle between the line directed from $(-1, 1, 1)$ to $(1, 0, 0)$ and the line directed from $(0, 0, 0)$ to $(1, -1, -1)$.
3. Compute the angle between the directed lines (L_1, β) and $(L_2, -\beta)$.
4. Find the direction cosines of the line directed from $(2, -1, -2)$ to $(1, 0, 0)$.
5. Find the angle between $(Y, (0, 1, 0))$ and $(Z, (0, 0, 1))$.
6. Find the angle between $(X, (-1, 0, 0))$ and $(Z, (0, 0, -1))$.
7. Show that two directed lines are parallel iff the angle between them is zero.

8. Two lines, say $\{\alpha_1 + t\beta_1 \mid t \in R\}$ and $\{\alpha_2 + t\beta_2 \mid t \in R\}$, are said to be *perpendicular* (or *orthogonal*) iff $\beta_1 \perp \beta_2$. Show that any two coordinate axes are perpendicular.

9. Are the lines $\{t(1, 2, -1) \mid t \in R\}$ and $\{(1, 0, 1) + t(2, -1, 0) \mid t \in R\}$ perpendicular?

(*Answer:* yes)

10. Find a line which is perpendicular to $\{(2, -1, 1) + t(1, 0, 1) \mid t \in R\}$.

11. Find a line through $(1, 0, 2)$ which is perpendicular to $\{(0, 0, 1) + t(2, -1, 0) \mid t \in R\}$.

4.4   Directed Distance

Let (L, β) be any directed line and let $\alpha \in L$; then $L = \{\alpha + t\beta \mid t \in R\}$. We can refine the geometric significance of the parameter t by introducing the notion of the *directed distance* from a point of L to a point of L. Let $\alpha_1 \in L$ and let $\alpha_2 \in L$; then we shall say that $\|\alpha_2 - \alpha_1\|$ is the directed distance from α_1 to α_2 in case $\alpha_2 - \alpha_1 \equiv \beta$; otherwise we say that $-\|\alpha_2 - \alpha_1\|$ is the directed distance from α_1 to α_2. Thus the directed distance from one point of a directed line to another point of that directed line depends upon the direction of the directed line.

EXAMPLE 1.   Determine the directed distance from $(2, -1, 1)$ to $(3, 0, 1)$ along the directed line (L, β), where $L = \{(1, -2, 1) + t(1, 1, 0) \mid t \in R\}$ and $\beta = (-1, -1, 0)$.

Solution: Here, $(3, 0, 1) - (2, -1, 1) = (1, 1, 0)$, which is not equivalent to $(-1, -1, 0)$. Therefore the directed distance from $(2, -1, 1)$ to $(3, 0, 1)$ is $-\|(1, 1, 0)\|$, namely $-\sqrt{2}$.

Let us consider the geometric significance of the parameter t for the line $\{\alpha + t\beta \mid t \in R\} = L$. Assume that $\|\beta\| = 1$, and consider the directed line (L, β). We claim that if t_1 is the value of the parameter corresponding to α_1, where $\alpha_1 \in L$, then t_1 is the directed distance from α to α_1 along the directed line (L, β). By assumption, $\alpha_1 = \alpha + t_1\beta$; therefore $\alpha_1 - \alpha = t_1\beta$, and so $\|\alpha_1 - \alpha\| = |t_1| \|\beta\| = |t_1|$. There are two cases: (1) if $t_1 > 0$, then $\alpha_1 - \alpha \equiv \beta$, and so t_1 is the directed distance from α to α_1; (2) if $t_1 < 0$, then $\alpha_1 - \alpha$ is not equivalent to β, and so $-|t_1| = t_1$ is the directed distance from α to α_1. In either case, t_1, the value of the parameter, is the directed distance from α to α_1 along the directed line. Let us state this result as a theorem.

THEOREM 4.4.1.   Let $L = \{\alpha + t\beta \mid t \in R\}$, where $\|\beta\| = 1$, let $\alpha_1 \in L$, and let $\alpha_1 = \alpha + t_1\beta$. Then t_1 is the directed distance from α to α_1 along the directed line (L, β).

EXAMPLE 2.   Find the midpoint of the line segment with endpoints $(2, 3, -1)$ and $(5, -1, -1)$.

Solution: Consider the line directed from $(2, 3, -1)$ to $(5, -1, -1)$, namely (L, β), where $L = \{(2, 3, -1) + t\beta \mid t \in R\}$ and $\beta = .2(3, -4, 0)$. Clearly, the directed distance from $(2, 3, -1)$ to $(5, -1, -1)$ is 5; therefore the midpoint of the given line segment is at a directed distance from $(2, 3, -1)$ of 2.5. Thus the required point is

$$(2, 3, -1) + 2.5\beta = (2, 3, -1) + .5(3, -4, 0) = (3.5, 1, -1).$$

EXERCISES

1. Consider the line directed from the origin to $(1, 2, -2)$.
   a. Find the directed distance from $(2, 4, -4)$ to $(3, 6, -6)$.
   b. Find the directed distance from $(-1, -2, 2)$ to $(-2, -4, 4)$.
   c. Find the directed distance from the origin to $(-1, -2, 2)$.
   d. Find the midpoint of the line segment with endpoints $(2, 4, -4)$ and $(4, 8, -8)$.

2. Find the midpoint of the line segment with endpoints $(0, 1, 2)$ and $(-3, 4, 1)$.

3. Find the point on the line directed from $(0, 1, 2)$ to $(4, -3, -1)$ whose directed distance from $(1, 0, -1)$ is -3.

4.5   Perpendicular Lines; the Vector Product

We begin with a definition.

DEFINITION 4.5.1.   Let $\{\alpha_1 + t\beta_1 \mid t \in R\}$ and $\{\alpha_2 + t\beta_2 \mid t \in R\}$ be any lines; then these lines are said to be *perpendicular* (or orthogonal) iff $\beta_1 \perp \beta_2$.

Thus lines with directions β_1 and β_2 are perpendicular iff $\beta_1 \cdot \beta_2 = 0$.

EXAMPLE 1.   Find the line through $(1, -1, 0)$ which is perpendicular to lines with directions $(1, 5, -2)$ and $(2, -7, 3)$.

Solution: Let (l, m, n) be a direction of the required line. Then

$$l + 5m - 2n = 0$$
$$2l - 7m + 3n = 0.$$

This linear system is represented by

$$\begin{pmatrix} 1 & 5 & -2 \\ 2 & -7 & 3 \end{pmatrix} \sim \begin{pmatrix} 1 & 5 & -2 \\ 0 & -17 & 7 \end{pmatrix} \sim \begin{pmatrix} 17 & 0 & 1 \\ 0 & -17 & 7 \end{pmatrix}.$$

Therefore one solution of our linear system is $n = 17$, $m = 7$, $l = -1$. This means that $(-1, 7, 17)$ is a direction of the required line. Hence our line is $\{(1, -1, 0) + t(-1, 7, 17) \mid t \in R\}$.

Because the problem of Example 1 occurs frequently, it is worthwhile to develop a formula which gives a direction orthogonal to two nonzero directions. Such a formula is contained in the following theorem.

THEOREM 4.5.1.   Let

$$l = \begin{vmatrix} m_1 & n_1 \\ m_2 & n_2 \end{vmatrix}, \quad m = \begin{vmatrix} n_1 & l_1 \\ n_2 & l_2 \end{vmatrix}, \quad \text{and} \quad n = \begin{vmatrix} l_1 & m_1 \\ l_2 & m_2 \end{vmatrix};$$

then the vector (l, m, n) is orthogonal to both (l_1, m_1, n_1) and (l_2, m_2, n_2).

Proof:

$$(l, m, n) \cdot (l_1, m_1, n_1) = l_1 \begin{vmatrix} m_1 & n_1 \\ m_2 & n_2 \end{vmatrix} - m_1 \begin{vmatrix} l_1 & n_1 \\ l_2 & n_2 \end{vmatrix} + n_1 \begin{vmatrix} l_1 & m_1 \\ l_2 & m_2 \end{vmatrix} \qquad \text{by assumption}$$

$$= \begin{vmatrix} l_1 & m_1 & n_1 \\ l_1 & m_1 & n_1 \\ l_2 & m_2 & n_2 \end{vmatrix} = 0 \qquad \text{by Cor. 2.4.2 and Th. 2.4.7;}$$

$$(l, m, n) \cdot (l_2, m_2, n_2) = l_2 \begin{vmatrix} m_1 & n_1 \\ m_2 & n_2 \end{vmatrix} - m_2 \begin{vmatrix} l_1 & n_1 \\ l_2 & n_2 \end{vmatrix} + n_2 \begin{vmatrix} l_1 & m_1 \\ l_2 & n_2 \end{vmatrix}$$

$$= \begin{vmatrix} l_2 & m_2 & n_2 \\ l_1 & m_1 & n_1 \\ l_2 & m_2 & n_2 \end{vmatrix} = 0 \qquad \text{by Cor. 2.4.2 and Th. 2.4.7.}$$

This establishes our result.

EXAMPLE 2. Find a direction of a line perpendicular to the lines $\{(2 - t, 3t, 2) \mid t \in R\}$ and $\{(5t, 1 + 2t, t) \mid t \in R\}$.

Solution: The given lines have directions $(-1, 3, 0)$ and $(5, 2, 1)$. To apply Theorem 4.5.1, we construct the matrix

$$\begin{pmatrix} -1 & 3 & 0 \\ 5 & 2 & 1 \end{pmatrix}.$$

Now, $\qquad \begin{vmatrix} 3 & 0 \\ 2 & 1 \end{vmatrix} = 3, \quad \begin{vmatrix} 0 & -1 \\ 1 & 5 \end{vmatrix} = 1, \quad \text{and} \quad \begin{vmatrix} -1 & 3 \\ 5 & 2 \end{vmatrix} = -17;$

therefore a suitable direction is $(3, 1, -17)$.

THEOREM 4.5.2. Let (l_1, m_1, n_1) and (l_2, m_2, n_2) be unit vectors; then

$$\begin{vmatrix} l_1 & m_1 \\ l_2 & m_2 \end{vmatrix}^2 + \begin{vmatrix} m_1 & n_1 \\ m_2 & n_2 \end{vmatrix}^2 + \begin{vmatrix} n_1 & l_1 \\ n_2 & l_2 \end{vmatrix}^2 = \sin^2 \theta,$$

where θ is the angle between the given vectors.

Proof: We can establish that

$$\begin{vmatrix} l_1 & m_1 \\ l_2 & m_2 \end{vmatrix}^2 + \begin{vmatrix} m_1 & n_1 \\ m_2 & n_2 \end{vmatrix}^2 + \begin{vmatrix} n_1 & l_1 \\ n_2 & l_2 \end{vmatrix}^2 = (l_1^2 + m_1^2 + n_1^2)(l_2^2 + m_2^2 + n_2^2)$$
$$- (l_1 l_2 + m_1 m_2 + n_1 n_2)^2$$

by expanding both sides of this equation. Therefore

$$\begin{vmatrix} l_1 & m_1 \\ l_2 & m_2 \end{vmatrix}^2 + \begin{vmatrix} m_1 & n_1 \\ m_2 & n_2 \end{vmatrix}^2 + \begin{vmatrix} n_1 & l_1 \\ n_2 & l_2 \end{vmatrix}^2 = 1 - \cos^2 \theta = \sin^2 \theta,$$

where θ is the angle between the given vectors. This establishes our result.

COROLLARY 4.5.1.   Let (l_1, m_1, n_1) and (l_2, m_2, n_2) be unit orthogonal vectors; then

$$\begin{vmatrix} l_1 & m_1 \\ l_2 & m_2 \end{vmatrix}^2 + \begin{vmatrix} m_1 & n_1 \\ m_2 & n_2 \end{vmatrix}^2 + \begin{vmatrix} n_1 & l_1 \\ n_2 & l_2 \end{vmatrix}^2 = 1.$$

THEOREM 4.5.3.   Let γ_1 and γ_2 be any linearly independent 3-vectors; then $\{\alpha \,|\, \alpha \perp \gamma_1 \text{ and } \alpha \perp \gamma_2\}$ is a subspace of $\mathscr{V}_3(\mathscr{R})$ with dimension 1.

Proof: Let $\gamma_1 = (l_1, m_1, n_1)$ and let $\gamma_2 = (l_2, m_2, n_2)$; then $\alpha = (l, m, n)$ is orthogonal to both γ_1 and γ_2 iff

(1) $l_1 l + m_1 m + n_1 n = 0, \qquad l_2 l + m_2 m + n_2 n = 0.$

The coefficient matrix of this homogeneous linear system is

$$\begin{pmatrix} l_1 & m_1 & n_1 \\ l_2 & m_2 & n_2 \end{pmatrix}.$$

By Theorem 3.3.1, the set of all vector solutions of (1) is a subspace of $\mathscr{V}_3(\mathscr{R})$. Furthermore, γ_1 and γ_2 are linearly independent; therefore the above matrix has rank 2. Thus, by Theorem 3.3.2, our subspace has dimension 1. This establishes Theorem 4.5.3.

Considering this result, we see that if we are given two nonparallel lines, there is a direction, say (l, m, n), such that each direction perpendicular to both given lines is a member of $\{k(l, m, n) \,|\, k \in R\}$, a subspace of $\mathscr{V}_3(\mathscr{R})$.

EXAMPLE 3.   Characterize the lines which are perpendicular to

$$\{(2 - 3t, 7, 2t) \,|\, t \in R\} \qquad \text{and} \qquad \{(-t, 3 + 5t, 1 + 3t) \,|\, t \in R\}.$$

Solution: First, we find a direction perpendicular to both given lines. Considering the matrix $\begin{pmatrix} -3 & 0 & 2 \\ -1 & 5 & 3 \end{pmatrix}$, we see from Theorem 4.5.1 that the direction $(-10, 7, -15)$ is perpendicular to both lines. In view of Theorem 4.5.3, we conclude that each line perpendicular to the given lines has direction $(-10, 7, -15)$.

EXAMPLE 4.   Find the line through the point $(2, -3, 4)$ which is perpendicular to the lines

$$\{(2 - 3t, 7, 2t) \,|\, t \in R\} \qquad \text{and} \qquad \{(-t, 3 + 5t, 1 + 3t) \,|\, t \in R\}.$$

Solution: Considering the result of Example 3, we find that the required line is

$$\{(2 - 10t, -3 + 7t, 4 - 15t) \,|\, t \in R\}.$$

We shall find the following theorems useful later.

THEOREM 4.5.4. If (l_1, m_1, n_1), (l_2, m_2, n_2), and (l_3, m_3, n_3) are mutually orthogonal, unit vectors, then

$$\begin{vmatrix} l_1 & m_1 & n_1 \\ l_2 & m_2 & n_2 \\ l_3 & m_3 & n_3 \end{vmatrix}^2 = 1.$$

Proof: By assumption

$$\begin{pmatrix} l_1 & m_1 & n_1 \\ l_2 & m_2 & n_2 \\ l_3 & m_3 & n_3 \end{pmatrix} \begin{pmatrix} l_1 & l_2 & l_3 \\ m_1 & m_2 & m_3 \\ n_1 & n_2 & n_3 \end{pmatrix} = \begin{pmatrix} 1 & 0 & 0 \\ 0 & 1 & 0 \\ 0 & 0 & 1 \end{pmatrix} = I_3$$

Let $A = \begin{pmatrix} l_1 & m_1 & n_1 \\ l_2 & m_2 & n_2 \\ l_3 & m_3 & n_3 \end{pmatrix}$; then $AA^t = I_3$. Therefore $|AA^t| = 1$.

Now,
$$|AA^t| = |A||A^t| \qquad \text{by Th. 3.7.2}$$
$$= |A||A| \qquad \text{by Th. 2.3.3}$$
$$= |A|^2$$

So
$$|A|^2 = 1.$$

THEOREM 4.5.5. If (l_1, m_1, n_1), (l_2, m_2, n_2), and (l_3, m_3, n_3) are mutually orthogonal, unit vectors such that

$$\begin{vmatrix} l_1 & m_1 & n_1 \\ l_2 & m_2 & n_2 \\ l_3 & m_3 & n_3 \end{vmatrix} = 1,$$

then
$$l_1 = \begin{vmatrix} m_2 & n_2 \\ m_3 & n_3 \end{vmatrix}, \quad m_1 = -\begin{vmatrix} l_2 & n_2 \\ l_3 & n_3 \end{vmatrix}, \quad \text{and} \quad n_1 = \begin{vmatrix} l_2 & m_2 \\ l_3 & m_3 \end{vmatrix}.$$

Proof: Let

$$l = \begin{vmatrix} m_2 & n_2 \\ m_3 & n_3 \end{vmatrix}, \quad m = -\begin{vmatrix} l_2 & n_2 \\ l_3 & n_3 \end{vmatrix}, \quad \text{and} \quad n = \begin{vmatrix} l_2 & m_2 \\ l_3 & m_3 \end{vmatrix};$$

then (l, m, n) is orthogonal to both (l_2, m_2, n_2) and (l_3, m_3, n_3). Therefore there is a real number t such that $l = tl_1$, $m = tl_2$, and $n = tl_3$. Now,

$$1 = \begin{vmatrix} l_1 & m_1 & n_1 \\ l_2 & m_2 & n_2 \\ l_3 & m_3 & n_3 \end{vmatrix} = l_1 \begin{vmatrix} m_2 & n_2 \\ m_3 & n_3 \end{vmatrix} - m_1 \begin{vmatrix} l_2 & n_2 \\ l_3 & n_3 \end{vmatrix} + n_1 \begin{vmatrix} l_2 & m_2 \\ l_3 & m_3 \end{vmatrix}$$

$$= l_1 l + m_1 m + n_1 n$$

$$= t(l_1^2 + m_1^2 + n_1^2)$$

$$= t.$$

Therefore $l = l_1$, $m = m_1$, and $n = n_1$. This establishes Theorem 4.5.5.

THEOREM 4.5.6.   If (l_1, m_1, n_1), (l_2, m_2, n_2), and (l_3, m_3, n_3) are mutually orthogonal, unit vectors, then so are (l_1, l_2, l_3), (m_1, m_2, m_3), and (n_1, n_2, n_3).

Proof: Let

$$A = \begin{pmatrix} l_1 & m_1 & n_1 \\ l_2 & m_2 & n_2 \\ l_3 & m_3 & n_3 \end{pmatrix}.$$

By assumption A^t is the inverse of A, i.e., $AA^t = I_3$. Therefore, by Theorem 3.7.10, $A^t A = I_3$, i.e.,

$$\begin{pmatrix} l_1 & l_2 & l_3 \\ m_1 & m_2 & m_3 \\ n_1 & n_2 & n_3 \end{pmatrix} \begin{pmatrix} l_1 & m_1 & n_1 \\ l_2 & m_2 & n_2 \\ l_3 & m_3 & n_3 \end{pmatrix} = \begin{pmatrix} 1 & 0 & 0 \\ 0 & 1 & 0 \\ 0 & 0 & 1 \end{pmatrix}.$$

Thus, (l_1, l_2, l_3), (m_1, m_2, m_3), and (n_1, n_2, n_3) are mutually orthogonal, unit vectors.

The operation involved in determining a vector which is orthogonal to two given vectors can be formalized as a binary operation on R_3; this operation is called the *vector product* or *cross product* and is denoted by "$\times$" (read "cross").

DEFINITION 4.5.2.   Let $\alpha = (a_1, a_2, a_3)$ and $\beta = (b_1, b_2, b_3)$ be any 3-vectors; then $\alpha \times \beta = (a_2 b_3 - a_3 b_2, a_3 b_1 - a_1 b_3, a_1 b_2 - a_2 b_1)$.

For example, $(2, 0, 1) \times (-1, 2, -2) = (-2, 3, 4)$. The following algebraic properties of the vector product are easy to establish.

THEOREM 4.5.7.   Let α and β be any 3-vectors; then $\alpha \times \beta = -\beta \times \alpha$.

THEOREM 4.5.8.   Let α and β be any 3-vectors and let $k \in R$; then $(k\alpha) \times \beta = k(\alpha \times \beta)$.

THEOREM 4.5.9.   Let α, β, and γ be any 3-vectors; then $\alpha \times (\beta + \gamma) = \alpha \times \beta + \alpha \times \gamma$.

We must emphasize one point: the vector product is a binary operation on R_3 only. Unlike vector addition and scalar multiplication, this operation does not generalize to vector spaces of higher dimension.

E X E R C I S E S

1. Are the lines $\{(1 + t, t, 2t) \mid t \in R\}$ and $\{(2 - t, 3, 4 + t/2) \mid t \in R\}$ perpendicular?
2. Find a direction of a line which is perpendicular to both lines of Exercise 1.

3. Find a direction of a line perpendicular to the lines $\{(t, -t, 3t) \mid t \in R\}$ and $\{(2 + 3t, 1 - t, 5) \mid t \in R\}$.

4. Characterize the lines which are perpendicular to the lines $\{(5, 2, 4) + t(-3, 1, 7) \mid t \in R\}$ and $\{(0, 1, -2) + t(2, 3, 0) \mid t \in R\}$.

5. Find the line through the point $(2, 5, -1)$ which is perpendicular to the lines $\{(5, 2, 4) + t(-3, 1, 7) \mid t \in R\}$ and $\{(0, 1, -2) + t(2, 3, 0) \mid t \in R\}$.

6. Find the line through $(1, -3, 2)$ which is perpendicular to $\{t(1, 2, 3) \mid t \in R\}$ and $\{(-3, 4, 1) + t(2, -1, 1) \mid t \in R\}$.

7. Let $n \in N$ and let (a_{ij}) be any $n \times n$ matrix. Prove that $(A_{11}, A_{12}, \cdots, A_{1n}) \perp (a_{i1}, a_{i2}, \cdots, a_{in})$, $i = 2, 3, \cdots, n$, where, for each j, A_{1j} is the cofactor of a_{1j} in the matrix (a_{ij}).

8. Find a vector orthogonal to each of $(2, 1, 6, 0)$, $(1, -2, 0, 2)$, $(-3, 0, 1, 4)$.

9. Find a vector orthogonal to each of $(3, 0, 0, 1, -2)$, $(2, 1, 4, 0, -1)$, $(1, 0, -1, 0, 1)$, $(2, 1, 0, 0, 0)$.

10. Let $n \in N$ and let $\gamma_1, \gamma_2, \cdots, \gamma_{n-1}$ be any $n - 1$ linearly independent n-vectors. Prove that $\{\alpha \mid \alpha \perp \gamma_i, i = 1, 2, \cdots, n - 1\}$ is a one-dimensional subspace of $\mathscr{V}_n(\mathscr{R})$.

11. Let $\gamma_1, \gamma_2, \cdots, \gamma_n$ be mutually orthogonal, unit vectors, where $\gamma_i = (a_{i1}, a_{i2}, \cdots, a_{in})$, $i = 1, 2, \cdots, n$. Prove that $|a_{ij}|^2 = 1$.

12. Let L be any line in three-dimensional space. Show that $\{\alpha - \beta \mid \alpha \in L \text{ and } \beta \in L\}$ is a subspace of $\mathscr{V}_3(\mathscr{R})$. Compute the dimension of this subspace.

13. Prove Theorem 4.5.7.

14. Prove Theorem 4.5.8.

15. Prove Theorem 4.5.9.

16. Let $\mathbf{i} = (1, 0, 0)$, $\mathbf{j} = (0, 1, 0)$, $\mathbf{k} = (0, 0, 1)$.
   a. Prove that $\mathbf{i} \times \mathbf{i} = \mathbf{j} \times \mathbf{j} = \mathbf{k} \times \mathbf{k} = \mathbf{0}$.
   b. Prove that $\mathbf{i} \times \mathbf{j} = \mathbf{k}$.
   c. Prove that $\mathbf{j} \times \mathbf{k} = \mathbf{i}$.
   d. Prove that $\mathbf{k} \times \mathbf{i} = \mathbf{j}$.

17. Let α and β be any 3-vectors. Prove the following.
   a. $\|\alpha \times \beta\|^2 = \|\alpha\|^2 \|\beta\|^2 - [\alpha \cdot \beta]^2$.
   b. $\|\alpha \times \beta\| = \|\alpha\| \|\beta\| \sin \theta$, where θ is the angle between α and β.

18. Let α and β be any 3-vectors. Prove that α and β are linearly dependent iff $\alpha \times \beta = \mathbf{0}$.

19. Find 3-vectors α, β, and γ such that $\alpha \times [\beta \times \gamma] \neq [\alpha \times \beta] \times \gamma$.

20. Let α, β, and γ be any 3-vectors. Prove that $\alpha \times [\beta \times \gamma] = [\alpha \cdot \gamma]\beta - [\alpha \cdot \beta]\gamma$.

4.6 The Distance Between a Point and a Line

The distance between a point α and a line L, where $\alpha \in L$, is said to be zero. The distance between a point α and a line L, where $\alpha \bar\in L$, is said to be $\|\alpha - \gamma\|$ provided that $\gamma \in L$ and the line through α and γ is perpendicular to L. To make sense of this definition, we shall prove that the point γ is unique.

THEOREM 4.6.1. If $\alpha \bar\in L$, then there is a unique member of L, say γ, such that $(\alpha - \gamma) \perp \beta$, where β is a direction of L.

Proof: Let $L = \{\alpha_1 + t\beta \,|\, t \in R\}$. We want to find γ such that $\beta \cdot (\alpha - \gamma) = 0$ and $\gamma = \alpha_1 + t_1\beta$, where $t_1 \in R$. This means that we must find a real number t_1 such that

$$\beta \cdot [\alpha - \alpha_1 - t_1\beta] = 0;$$

thus
$$\beta \cdot \alpha - \beta \cdot \alpha_1 - t_1\beta \cdot \beta = 0;$$

hence
$$t_1 = \frac{\beta \cdot \alpha - \beta \cdot \alpha_1}{\beta \cdot \beta}.$$

Since our argument is reversible, we conclude that γ is unique. This establishes our result.

EXAMPLE 1.   Compute the distance between $(1, -1, 2)$ and $\{(2, 0, 1) + t(1, 2, -2) \,|\, t \in R\}$.

Solution: Let $\gamma = (2, 0, 1) + t_1(1, 2, -2)$ be the point on the given line such that the line through γ and the given point $(1, -1, 2)$ is perpendicular to the given line. Then $(1, 2, -2) \cdot [(1, -1, 2) - \gamma] = 0$; i.e., $(1, 2, -2) \cdot [(-1, -1, 1) - t_1(1, 2, -2)] = 0$; therefore $9t_1 = -1 - 2 - 2 = -5$; thus $t_1 = -5/9$. Hence $\gamma = \frac{1}{9}(13, -10, 19)$. Therefore the required distance is $\|\alpha - \gamma\| = \frac{1}{9}(-4, 1, -1) = \frac{1}{9}\sqrt{18} = \sqrt{2}/3$.

E X E R C I S E S

1. Compute the distance between the point $(4, -2, 3)$ and the line $\{(2, 0, 0) + t(1, 0, -1) \,|\, t \in R\}$.
2. Compute the distance between the point $(1, 0, 0)$ and the line $\{(0, 0, 1) + t(1, 2, 3) \,|\, t \in R\}$.
3. Show that the distance between the origin and the line $\{\alpha + t\beta \,|\, t \in R\}$, where $\|\beta\| = 1$, is $\sqrt{\|\alpha\|^2 - [\alpha \cdot \beta]^2}$.
4. Show that the distance between the point α and the line $\{t\beta \,|\, t \in R\}$, where $\|\beta\| = 1$, is $\sqrt{\|\alpha\|^2 - [\alpha \cdot \beta]^2}$.

4.7   The Distance Between Two Lines

The distance between intersecting lines is said to be zero. The distance between two nonintersecting lines is said to be $\|\gamma_1 - \gamma_2\|$ provided γ_1 is a member of one line, γ_2 is a member of the other line, and the line through γ_1 and γ_2 is perpendicular to the given lines. To make sense of this definition, we must show that, given two nonintersecting lines, $\|\gamma_1 - \gamma_2\|$ is independent of the choice of γ_1 and γ_2; moreover, we must show that there is at least one pair γ_1, γ_2 with the required properties. Intuitively, we see that there will be more than one suitable pair only if the given lines are parallel. Let us dispose of this case.

THEOREM 4.7.1.   Let $L_1 = \{\alpha_1 + t\beta \,|\, t \in R\}$ and $L_2 = \{\alpha_2 + t\beta \,|\, t \in R\}$ be any parallel lines. Let γ_1 and γ_2 be members of L_1 and L_2 such that $(\gamma_1 - \gamma_2) \perp \beta$. Then $\|\gamma_1 - \gamma_2\|$ is independent of the choice of γ_1 and γ_2.

Proof: Let $\gamma_1 \in L_1$ and consider the problem of finding the distance between γ_1 and L_2. By Theorem 4.6.1, there is a unique member of L_2, say γ_2, such that $(\gamma_1 - \gamma_2) \perp \beta$.

Therefore the line through γ_1 and γ_2 is perpendicular to L_1 and L_2. It is a simple exercise to verify that

$$\gamma_1 - \gamma_2 = \alpha_1 - \alpha_2 - \frac{\beta \cdot (\alpha_1 - \alpha_2)}{\beta \cdot \beta} \beta;$$

thus $\|\gamma_1 - \gamma_2\|$ is independent of the choice of γ_1. This establishes our result.

THEOREM 4.7.2.   Let $L_1 = \{\alpha_1 + t\beta_1 \mid t \in R\}$ and $L_2 = \{\alpha_2 + t\beta_2 \mid t \in R\}$ be any nonintersecting, nonparallel lines. Then there are unique members of L_1 and L_2, say γ_1 and γ_2, such that the line through γ_1 and γ_2 is perpendicular to both L_1 and L_2.

Proof: Let $\gamma_1 = \alpha_1 + t_1\beta_1$ and $\gamma_2 = \alpha_2 + t_2\beta_2$ be members of L_1 and L_2 such that the line through γ_1 and γ_2 is perpendicular to both L_1 and L_2. Then

$$(\gamma_1 - \gamma_2) \cdot \beta_1 = 0 \qquad \text{and} \qquad (\gamma_1 - \gamma_2) \cdot \beta_2 = 0.$$

Thus

$$t_1\beta_1 \cdot \beta_1 - t_2\beta_1 \cdot \beta_2 = (\alpha_2 - \alpha_1) \cdot \beta_1$$

$$t_1\beta_1 \cdot \beta_2 - t_2\beta_2 \cdot \beta_2 = (\alpha_2 - \alpha_1) \cdot \beta_2.$$

Now, this linear system has a unique solution iff the coefficient matrix is nonsingular, i.e.,

$$\begin{vmatrix} \beta_1 \cdot \beta_1 & -\beta_1 \cdot \beta_2 \\ \beta_1 \cdot \beta_2 & -\beta_2 \cdot \beta_2 \end{vmatrix} \neq 0.$$

But the coefficient matrix is singular iff its row vectors are linearly dependent. This means that there is a real number k such that $\beta_1 \cdot \beta_2 = k\beta_1 \cdot \beta_1$ and $\beta_2 \cdot \beta_2 = k\beta_1 \cdot \beta_2$; hence $k\beta_1 = \beta_2 + \gamma$ where $\gamma \cdot \beta_1 = \gamma \cdot \beta_2 = 0$. It follows that $\gamma \cdot \gamma = 0$; thus $\beta_2 = k\beta_1$. This contradicts our assumption that L_1 and L_2 are not parallel; we conclude that the coefficient matrix is nonsingular. Thus γ_1 and γ_2 are unique. This establishes our result.

The proofs of the preceding theorems have indicated how to compute the distance between two lines. We now illustrate the idea.

EXAMPLE 1.   Find the points, one on each of $\{(2, 0, 3) + t(1, -2, 1) \mid t \in R\}$ and $\{(5, 2, -3) + t(1, -1, -1) \mid t \in R\}$, such that the line through these points is perpendicular to the given lines. Find the distance between these lines.

Solution: Let $\gamma_1 = (2, 0, 3) + t_1(1, -2, 1)$ and $\gamma_2 = (5, 2, -3) + t_2(1, -1, -1)$ be the required points. Then

$$[\gamma_1 - \gamma_2] \cdot (1, -2, 1) = 0 \qquad \text{and} \qquad [\gamma_1 - \gamma_2] \cdot (1, -1, -1) = 0;$$

i.e., $6t_1 - 2t_2 = -7$ and $2t_1 - 3t_2 = 7$. Solving, we find that $t_1 = -5/2$ and $t_2 = -4$. Therefore $\gamma_1 = (-.5, 5, .5)$ and $\gamma_2 = (1, 6, 1)$. Thus the distance between the given lines is $.5\sqrt{14}$.

There is a simple and elegant method for finding the distance between two lines which involves the parallel planes that contain the given lines. We shall see about this in the next chapter.

E X E R C I S E S

1. Compute the distance between the lines $\{(1, t, -t) \mid t \in R\}$ and $\{(t, 2t, 3t) \mid t \in R\}$.

2. Compute the distance between the lines $\{(2 - t, 2t, 0) \mid t \in R\}$ and $\{(3t, 1 + 2t, -t) \mid t \in R\}$.

Chapter 5

The Plane

5.1 The Plane Defined by Two Points

So far we have discussed the concepts of *point* and *line* in three-dimensional space and related ideas such as the distance between two points and the distance between two lines. There is good reason for this apparent preoccupation with the concept of distance; the fact is that many geometers regard *distance* as a fundamental concept of geometry (on the other hand, there are distance-free geometries). Our discussion of geometry is based upon two basic concepts: the notion of a point and the notion of the distance between two points. As we have seen, we can define a *plane* in terms of these concepts. We now repeat our definition.

DEFINITION 5.1.1. A set which consists of all points equidistant from two points is called a *plane*.

Note: Two means two, not one.
We now present an example.

EXAMPLE 1. Determine the set of all points equidistant from $(2, 0, 3)$ and $(6, -2, 5)$.

Solution: Let $\gamma = (x, y, z)$ be any point equidistant from $(2, 0, 3)$ and $(6, -2, 5)$. Then

$$\|\gamma - (2, 0, 3)\| = \|\gamma - (6, -2, 5)\|;$$

i.e.,

$$\sqrt{(x-2)^2 + y^2 + (z-3)^2} = \sqrt{(x-6)^2 + (y+2)^2 + (z-5)^2};$$

therefore

$$(x-2)^2 + y^2 + (z-3)^2 = (x-6)^2 + (y+2)^2 + (z-5)^2;$$

thus

$$8x - 4y + 4z = 52.$$

Hence the required set of points is $\{(x, y, z) \mid 2x - y + z = 13\}$, i.e., $\{\gamma \mid \gamma \cdot (2, -1, 1) = 13\}$.

We now define the phrase "the plane *defined* by two points".

DEFINITION 5.1.2. Let $\alpha \neq \beta$; then the set of all points equidistant from α and β is said to be the plane *defined* by α and β.

THEOREM 5.1.1.   Let $\alpha \neq \beta$; then the plane defined by α and β is $\{\gamma \mid \gamma \cdot (\beta - \alpha)$
$= d\}$, where $d = .5[\|\beta\|^2 - \|\alpha\|^2]$.

Proof: Let $\mathcal{P}$ be the plane defined by α and β. Then $\gamma \in \mathcal{P}$ iff $\|\gamma - \alpha\| = \|\gamma - \beta\|$;

thus
$$\|\gamma - \alpha\|^2 = \|\gamma - \beta\|^2;$$

i.e.,
$$\|\gamma\|^2 + \|\alpha\|^2 - 2\gamma \cdot \alpha = \|\gamma\|^2 + \|\beta\|^2 - 2\gamma \cdot \beta;$$

therefore
$$\gamma \cdot (\beta - \alpha) = .5[\|\beta\|^2 - \|\alpha\|^2].$$

Thus $\{\gamma \mid \gamma \cdot (\beta - \alpha) = d\}$, where $d = .5[\|\beta\|^2 - \|\alpha\|^2]$, is the plane defined by α and β.
We now bring out an important property of the plane defined by two points.

THEOREM 5.1.2.   Let γ_1 and γ_2 be any two members of the plane defined by
α and β; then the line through γ_1 and γ_2 is perpendicular to the line through α
and β.

Proof: The plane defined by α and β is $\{\gamma \mid \alpha \cdot (\beta - \alpha) = d\}$, where $d = .5[\|\beta\|^2 -$
$\|\alpha\|^2]$. Therefore

$$\gamma_1 \cdot (\beta - \alpha) = d \qquad \text{and} \qquad \gamma_2 \cdot (\beta - \alpha) = d;$$

Thus $\gamma_1 \cdot (\beta - \alpha) = \gamma_2 \cdot (\beta - \alpha)$; hence $(\gamma_1 - \gamma_2) \cdot (\beta - \alpha) = 0$. But $\gamma_1 - \gamma_2$ is a direction
of the line through γ_1 and γ_2, and $\beta - \alpha$ is a direction of the line through β and α. There-
fore these lines are perpendicular.

THEOREM 5.1.3.   Let γ_1 and γ_2 be any two members of $\mathcal{P}$, the plane defined by
α and β; then each point on the line through γ_1 and γ_2 is a member of $\mathcal{P}$.

Proof: By Theorem 5.1.1., $\mathcal{P} = \{\gamma \mid \gamma \cdot (\beta - \alpha) = d\}$, where $d = .5[\|\beta\|^2 - \|\alpha\|^2]$.
Now, the line through γ_1 and γ_2 is $\{\gamma_1 + t(\gamma_2 - \gamma_1) \mid t \in R\}$. Let $t \in R$; then

$$\begin{aligned}
[\gamma_1 + t(\gamma_2 - \gamma_1)] \cdot [\beta - \alpha] &= \gamma_1 \cdot (\beta - \alpha) + t[(\gamma_2 - \gamma_1)] \cdot [\beta - \alpha] \\
&= d + t[(\gamma_2 - \gamma_1) \cdot (\beta - \alpha)] \qquad \text{since } \gamma_1 \in \mathcal{P} \\
&= d + t[0] \qquad\qquad\qquad\quad \text{by Th. 5.1.2} \\
&= d.
\end{aligned}$$

Therefore $\gamma_1 + t(\gamma_2 - \gamma_1) \in \mathcal{P}$ whenever $t \in R$. This establishes Theorem 5.1.3.
Consider the following concept.

DEFINITION 5.1.4.   Any line which is perpendicular to each line contained in a
given plane is said to be a *normal* to the plane.
For example, let $\alpha \neq \beta$; then the line through α and β is a normal to the plane defined
by α and β.

EXAMPLE 2. Find the plane through the point $(5, 1, -2)$ such that the line $\{(0, 1, 2) + t(1, 2, -1) \mid t \in R\}$ is a normal to the plane.

Solution: Let γ be any member of the required plane other than $(5, 1, -2)$; then the line through γ and $(5, 1, -2)$ is perpendicular to the given line. Therefore

$$[\gamma - (5, 1, -2)] \quad (1, 2, -1);$$

so

$$\gamma \cdot (1, 2, -1) = (5, 1, -2) \cdot (1, 2, -1) = 9.$$

Thus $\{\gamma \mid \gamma \cdot (1, 2, -1) = 9\}$ is the required plane, provided this set is a plane.

The following theorem functions as an *existence* theorem for problems like Example 2.

THEOREM 5.1.4.   Let α be any point and let $\beta \neq \mathbf{0}$; then $\{\gamma \mid \beta \cdot (\gamma - \alpha) = 0\}$ is a plane.

Proof: We must show that $\{\gamma \mid \beta \cdot (\gamma - \alpha) = 0\}$ is a plane. Consider the plane defined by the points $\alpha + \beta$ and $\alpha - \beta$, namely $\{\gamma \mid \gamma \cdot (2\beta) = .5[\|\alpha + \beta\|^2 - \|\alpha - \beta\|^2]\}$. Now, $\|\alpha + \beta\|^2 - \|\alpha - \beta\|^2 = 4\alpha \cdot \beta$; therefore the plane defined by $\alpha + \beta$ and $\alpha - \beta$ is $\{\gamma \mid \gamma \cdot (2\beta) = 2\alpha \cdot \beta\}$, i.e., $\{\gamma \mid \beta \cdot (\gamma - \alpha) = 0\}$. This establishes Theorem 5.1.4.

THEOREM 5.1.5.   Let $\beta \neq \mathbf{0}$ and let $d \in R$; then $\{\gamma \mid \beta \cdot \gamma = d\}$ is a plane.

Proof: Let α be a 3-vector such that $\beta \cdot \alpha = d$[e.g., if $\beta = (b_1, b_2, b_3)$ and $b_1 \neq 0$, take $\alpha = (d/b_1, 0, 0)$]. Then the given set of points is $\{\gamma \mid \beta \cdot (\gamma - \alpha) = 0\}$. By Theorem 5.1.4, this set is a plane.

EXAMPLE 3.   Find a plane through the points $(1, 2, 3)$, $(2, 0, 5)$, and $(8, 4, 21)$.

Solution 1:   Suppose that there is a plane through the three given points; let it be $\{(x, y, z) \mid Ax + By + Cz + D = 0\}$; then

$$A + 2B + 3C + D = 0, \quad 2A + 5C + D = 0. \quad 8A + 4B + 21C + D = 0.$$

We have three equations in four unknowns A, B, C, and D. However, if we are to have a plane, then at least one of A, B, C is not zero; dividing through by the one which is not zero, we essentially eliminate one unknown. In other words, we are really faced with a system of three equations in three unknowns. To solve this system, we use matrices. Now,

$$\begin{pmatrix} 1 & 2 & 3 & 1 \\ 2 & 0 & 5 & 1 \\ 8 & 4 & 21 & 1 \end{pmatrix} \sim \begin{pmatrix} 1 & 2 & 3 & 1 \\ 0 & -4 & -1 & -1 \\ 0 & 4 & 1 & -3 \end{pmatrix} \sim \begin{pmatrix} 2 & 0 & 5 & 1 \\ 0 & -4 & -1 & -1 \\ 0 & 0 & 0 & -4 \end{pmatrix}.$$

Thus $D = 0$, $2A + 5C = 0$, and $-4B - C = 0$; hence $A = -5C/2$ and $B = -C/4$. Take $C = -4$; then $A = 10$ and $B = 1$. Therefore, if there is a plane through the given points, it is $\{(x, y, z) \mid 10x + y - 4z = 0\}$. Checking, we see that the given points are on this plane.

We now present another solution of Example 3 which makes more use of geometry.

Solution 2: Suppose that there is a plane through the given points, say $\{\gamma \mid \beta \cdot [\gamma - (1, 2, 3)] = 0\}$. Then β is a direction of a normal to the required plane. Let us determine β. The line through $(1, 2, 3)$ and $(2, 0, 5)$ has direction $(-1, 2, -2)$, and the line through $(1, 2, 3)$ and $(8, 4, 21)$ has direction $(7, 2, 18)$. Therefore $\beta \perp (-1, 2, -2)$ and $\beta \perp (7, 2, 18)$. In view of the properties of the vector product, we take $\beta = (-1, 2, -2) \times (7, 2, 18) = (40, 4, -16)$. Thus $(10, 1, -4)$ is a direction of a normal to our plane. Hence, if there is a plane through the given points, it is $\{\gamma \mid (10, 1, -4) \cdot [\gamma - (1, 2, 3)] = 0\}$, i.e., $\{\gamma \mid (10, 1, -4) \cdot \gamma = 0\}$. Checking, we see that the given points are on this plane.

We now establish a *unique-existence* theorem for the problem of Example 3 (i.e., a theorem which asserts the existence of a unique object which possesses a specified property).

THEOREM 5.1.6. There is a unique plane through the points $\alpha_1, \alpha_2, \alpha_3$ iff these points are not collinear.

Proof: There are two parts to the proof.

1. Suppose that there is no line through the points $\alpha_1, \alpha_2, \alpha_3$. Then no two of $\alpha_1, \alpha_2, \alpha_3$ are the same; therefore there is a unique line through α_1 and α_2. By assumption, α_3 is not on this line; so $\alpha_3 - \alpha_1$ is not a multiple of $\alpha_2 - \alpha_1$. In other words, $\alpha_3 - \alpha_1$ and $\alpha_2 - \alpha_1$ are linearly independent. Therefore $\{\beta \mid \beta \perp (\alpha_3 - \alpha_1) \text{ and } \beta \perp (\alpha_2 - \alpha_1)\}$ is a one-dimensional subspace of $\mathscr{V}_3(\mathscr{R})$. Thus, up to scalar multiplication, there is a unique vector β such that

$$\beta \cdot (\alpha_3 - \alpha_1) = 0 \quad \text{and} \quad \beta \cdot (\alpha_2 - \alpha_1) = 0.$$

Since $\alpha_3 - \alpha_1$ and $\alpha_2 - \alpha_1$ are directions of lines in the required plane, we see that each normal to our plane has direction β. Thus the required plane is $\{\gamma \mid \beta \cdot (\gamma - \alpha_1) = 0\}$. More precisely, if there is a plane which contains the given points, it can only be this plane. It is easy to verify that $\{\gamma \mid \beta \cdot (\gamma - \alpha_1) = 0\}$ contains the given points. Clearly, $\beta \cdot (\alpha_1 - \alpha_1) = 0$, $\beta \cdot (\alpha_2 - \alpha_1) = 0$, and $\beta \cdot (\alpha_3 - \alpha_1) = 0$. This proves that there is a unique plane through three points that are not collinear.

2. Suppose that there is a line through $\alpha_1, \alpha_2, \alpha_3$. Let α_4 be a point such that $\alpha_1, \alpha_2, \alpha_4$ are not collinear. Then there is a plane through $\alpha_1, \alpha_2, \alpha_4$, say $\mathscr{P}$. Since α_3 is on the line through α_1 and α_2, it follows that $\alpha_3 \in \mathscr{P}$. By choosing a point α_5 which is not a member of $\mathscr{P}$, we readily find another plane through $\alpha_1, \alpha_2, \alpha_3$. This establishes Theorem 5.1.6.

THEOREM 5.1.7. Suppose that $\alpha \bar{\in} L$, where L is a line and α is a point; then there is a unique plane which contains the line L and the point α.

Proof: Let α_1 and α_2 be two points on the given line. Then $\alpha, \alpha_1,$ and α_2 are three points which are not on one line. Therefore, by Theorem 5.1.6, there is a unique plane through these points. Since this plane contains α_1 and α_2, it contains the line through α_1 and α_2, namely L. This establishes our result.

EXAMPLE 4. Find the plane which contains the line $\{(1, 0, 3) + t(-1, 2, 1) | t \in R\}$ and the point $(2, 2, 2)$.

Solution: Suppose that β is a direction of a normal to the required plane. Then $\beta \cdot (-1, 2, 1) = 0$. Now, the required plane contains the line through $(1, 0, 3)$ and $(2, 2, 2)$; thus $\beta \cdot (1, 2, -1) = 0$. But $(-1, 2, 1) \times (1, 2, -1) = (-4, 0, -4)$. So $(1, 0, 1)$ is a direction of a normal to our plane. Thus our plane is $\{\gamma | (1, 0, 1) \cdot [\gamma - (2, 2, 2)] = 0\}$, i.e., $\{\gamma | (1, 0, 1) \cdot \gamma = 4\}$. Checking, we verify that this plane contains the given line and the given point.

E X E R C I S E S

1. Determine the set of all points equidistant from the points $(5, 1, -2)$ and $(1, -3, 2)$.
2. Determine the plane defined by the points $(-1, 0, 1)$ and $(2, 1, 0)$.
3. Find a direction of a normal to the plane $\{\gamma | \gamma \cdot (2, -1, 1) = 3\}$.
4. Find a direction of a normal to the plane defined by the points $(2, 0, 1)$ and $(3, 2, 4)$.
5. Find the plane through the point $(2, -1, 3)$ such that $\{(1, 0, 0) + t(-1, 1, 0) | t \in R\}$ is a normal to the plane.
6. **a.** Find a direction of a normal to the plane through the points $(2, -1, 0)$, $(3, 4, 1)$, and $(4, 5, 0)$.
   b. Find the plane through the points $(2, -1, 0)$, $(3, 4, 1)$, and $(4, 5, 0)$.
7. Find the plane through $(1, 0, 0)$, $(0, 1, 0)$, and $(0, 0, 1)$.
8. Find the plane through $(0, 1, 1)$, $(1, 0, 1)$, and $(1, 1, 0)$.
9. Find the plane through $(2, -1, 4)$, $(5, 2, -3)$, and $(3, 4, 2)$.
10. Find a point of intersection of the line $\{t(1, 2, 3) | t \in R\}$ and the plane $\{\gamma | \gamma \cdot (2, -1, 3) = 18\}$.
11. Find a point of intersection of the line through $(0, -1, 2)$ and $(2, 3, 1)$ and the plane $\{\gamma | \gamma \cdot (1, 1, -2) = 10\}$.
12. Find a point of intersection of the line through $(1, -2, 1)$ and $(2, 0, 1)$ and the plane $\{(x, y, z) | 2x - y + z = 5\}$.
13. Present a line and a plane which do not intersect.
14. Find the plane which contains the line $\{(2, 0, 0) + t(-1, 3, 0) | t \in R\}$ and the point $(1, 2, -2)$.
15. Show that $\{(1, 0, -8) + t(1, 5, 7) | t \in R\} \subset \{\gamma | \gamma \cdot (2, 1, -1) = 10\}$.
16. Let $\mathscr{P}$ be any plane which contains the origin.
    a. Show that $\mathscr{P}$ is a subspace of $\mathscr{V}_3(\mathscr{R})$.
    b. Find a basis for $\mathscr{P}$.
    c. Compute the dimension of $\mathscr{P}$.
17. Find a basis for $\{\gamma | \gamma \cdot (2, -3, 5) = 0\}$.
18. Let $\mathscr{P}$ be any plane through α.
    a. Show that $V = \{\gamma - \alpha | \gamma \in \mathscr{P}\}$ is a subspace of $\mathscr{V}_3(\mathscr{R})$.
    b. Find a basis for V.
    c. Determine the dimension of V.
19. Let $\mathscr{P} = \{\gamma | \gamma \cdot (5, 2, -1) = 3\}$. Find a basis for the subspace $\{\gamma - (0, 0, -3) | \gamma \in \mathscr{P}\}$.

5.2   The Intersection of Two Planes

Let $\mathscr{P}_1$ and $\mathscr{P}_2$ be any planes; we shall say that $\mathscr{P}_1$ and $\mathscr{P}_2$ are *parallel* iff there is a line which is normal to both $\mathscr{P}_1$ and $\mathscr{P}_2$. Applying this definition, we easily establish the following theorem.

THEOREM 5.2.1.   Let $\mathscr{P}_1 = \{\gamma \,|\, \beta_1 \cdot \gamma = d_1\}$ and $\mathscr{P}_2 = \{\gamma \,|\, \beta_2 \cdot \gamma = d_2\}$ be any planes; then $\mathscr{P}_1$ and $\mathscr{P}_2$ are parallel iff β_1 and β_2 are linearly dependent.

We shall need the following fact.

THEOREM 5.2.2.   Let $l_2 m_1 = l_1 m_2$, $l_2 n_1 = l_1 n_2$, and let $l_1 \neq 0$; then (l_1, m_1, n_1) and (l_2, m_2, n_2) are linearly dependent.

Proof: Let us show that there is a real number k such that $kl_1 = l_2$, $km_1 = m_2$, and $kn_1 = n_2$. Since $l_1 \neq 0$, let $k = l_2/l_1$. Then

$$km_1 = (l_2/l_1) \cdot m_1 = l_2 m_1/l_1 = l_1 m_2/l_1 = m_2$$

and

$$kn_1 = (l_2/l_1) \cdot n_1 = l_2 n_1/l_1 = l_1 n_2/l_1 = n_2.$$

This establishes our result.

In view of Theorem 5.2.2, we can now prove the following theorem.

THEOREM 5.2.3.   Suppose that $\{\gamma \,|\, (l_1, m_1, n_1) \cdot \gamma = d_1\}$ and $\{\gamma \,|\, (l_2, m_2, n_2) \cdot \gamma = d_2\}$ are nonparallel planes and that $l_1 \neq 0$; then $l_2 m_1 \neq l_1 m_2$ or $l_2 n_1 \neq l_1 n_2$.

Proof: Assume that $l_2 m_1 = l_1 m_2$ and that $l_2 n_1 = l_1 n_2$; now apply Theorem 5.2.2.

We now make a start on determining the intersection of two nonparallel planes.

THEOREM 5.2.4.   Let $\mathscr{P}_1$ and $\mathscr{P}_2$ be any nonparallel planes; then $\mathscr{P}_1 \cap \mathscr{P}_2 \neq \varnothing$.

Proof: Let $\mathscr{P}_1 = \{\gamma \,|\, (l_1, m_1, n_1) \cdot \gamma = d_1\}$ and $\mathscr{P}_2 = \{\gamma \,|\, (l_2, m_2, n_2) \cdot \gamma = d_2\}$ be any nonparallel planes. There is no loss of generality in assuming that $l_1 \neq 0$. Then, by Theorem 5.2.3, $l_2 m_1 \neq l_1 m_2$ or $l_2 n_1 \neq l_1 n_2$. We want to show that the linear system

(1) $(l_1, m_1, n_1) \cdot \gamma = d_1, \qquad (l_2, m_2, n_2) \cdot \gamma = d_2$

possesses a solution. But the coefficient matrix of this system, namely $\begin{pmatrix} l_1 & m_1 & n_1 \\ l_2 & m_2 & n_2 \end{pmatrix}$, has rank 2 since

$$\begin{vmatrix} l_1 & m_1 \\ l_2 & m_2 \end{vmatrix} \neq 0 \qquad \text{or} \qquad \begin{vmatrix} l_1 & n_1 \\ l_2 & n_2 \end{vmatrix} \neq 0.$$

Moreover, the augmented matrix of (1) also has rank 2. Hence, by Theorem 3.2.1, the system (1) has a solution. This establishes Theorem 5.2.4.

We are now in a position to characterize the intersection of two nonparallel planes.

THEOREM 5.2.5.   Let $\mathscr{P}_1$ and $\mathscr{P}_2$ be any nonparallel planes; then $\mathscr{P}_1 \cap \mathscr{P}_2$ is a line.

Proof: By Theorem 5.2.4, $\mathscr{P}_1 \cap \mathscr{P}_2$ is nonempty; let α be a point on both planes. Furthermore, let $\beta_1 = (l_1, m_1, n_1)$ be a direction of a normal to $\mathscr{P}_1$, and let $\beta_2 = (l_2, m_2, n_2)$ be a direction of a normal to $\mathscr{P}_2$. Then

$$\mathscr{P}_1 = \{\gamma \,|\, \beta_1 \cdot (\gamma - \alpha) = 0\} \qquad \text{and} \qquad \mathscr{P}_2 = \{\gamma \,|\, \beta_2 \cdot (\gamma - \alpha) = 0\}.$$

There is no loss of generality in assuming that $l_1 \neq 0$; therefore, by Theorem 5.2.3, $l_2 m_1 \neq l_1 m_2$ or $l_2 n_1 \neq l_1 n_2$. Consider the homogeneous linear system

(2)
$$\beta_1 \cdot \beta = 0, \qquad \beta_2 \cdot \beta = 0.$$

The coefficient matrix of this system is $\begin{pmatrix} l_1 & m_1 & n_1 \\ l_2 & m_2 & n_2 \end{pmatrix}$, which has rank 2. Therefore, by Corollary 3.3.1 the system (2) has a nontrivial solution, say the 3-vector β_3. Now, consider the line $\{\alpha + t\beta_3 \,|\, t \in R\}$. Clearly, this line is contained in both $\mathscr{P}_1$ and $\mathscr{P}_2$; therefore $\{\alpha + t\beta_3 \,|\, t \in R\} \subset \mathscr{P}_1 \cap \mathscr{P}_2$. It remains to show that $\mathscr{P}_1 \cap \mathscr{P}_2$ has no other members. If there are other members, it follows from Theorem 5.1.7 that $\mathscr{P}_1 = \mathscr{P}_2$; hence $\mathscr{P}_1$ and $\mathscr{P}_2$ are parallel. This contradiction establishes Theorem 5.2.5.

The proofs of Theorems 5.2.4 and 5.2.5 actually provide us with a method of determining the line of intersection of nonparallel planes. We need a point on the line and a direction of the line, or we need two points on the line. Of course, the vector product will give us the direction of our line, but it is simpler to obtain this while solving (1) for a member of the line. We now illustrate the technique.

EXAMPLE 1.   Find the intersection of the planes $\{\gamma \,|\, (1, -2, 3) \cdot \gamma = 3\}$ and $\{\gamma \,|\, (2, 3, -1) \cdot \gamma = -1\}$.

Solution: The matrix that gives us a point on both planes also gives us a direction of the line of intersection of the planes:

$$\begin{pmatrix} 1 & -2 & 3 & -3 \\ 2 & 3 & -1 & 1 \end{pmatrix} \sim \begin{pmatrix} 1 & -2 & 3 & -3 \\ 0 & 7 & -7 & 7 \end{pmatrix} \sim \begin{pmatrix} 1 & 0 & 1 & -1 \\ 0 & 1 & -1 & 1 \end{pmatrix}.$$

From the last matrix we can read off the coordinates of a point on both planes; also, we can read off a direction of the line of intersection of the planes. Let a point of intersection be $(a, b, 0)$; then $a = 1$ and $b = -1$. Thus the point $(1, -1, 0)$ is on both planes. Let (l_0, m_0, n_0) be a direction of the line of intersection of the given planes; considering only the first three columns of our matrix, we see that

$$l_0 + n_0 = 0 \qquad \text{and} \qquad m_0 - n_0 = 0.$$

Take $n_0 = -1$; then $l_0 = 1$ and $m_0 = -1$. Therefore $(1, -1, -1)$ is a direction of our line. Hence the line of intersection of the given planes is $\{(1, -1, 0) + t(1, -1, -1) \,|\, t \in R\}$. Checking, we see that this line is a subset of both planes.

The result of this section is interesting for an unexpected reason: it provides us with an alternative method of characterizing a line, namely, as the intersection of two non-parallel planes. Given a line, it is a simple matter to find one plane which contains the line: merely choose a point which is not on the given line. A second plane containing the given line is easily found by choosing a point which is not on the first plane.

EXAMPLE 2.   Characterize the line $\{(4, -5, 2) + t(2, -3, 1) \mid t \in R\}$ as the intersection of two planes.

Solution: The point $(0, 0, 0)$ is not on the given line. The plane through the given line and the point $(0, 0, 0)$ contains lines with directions $(2, -3, 1)$ and $(4, -5, 2)$. Therefore $(2, -3, 1) \times (4, -5, 2) = (-1, 0, 2)$ is a direction of a normal to our plane. Thus one plane which contains the given line is $\{\gamma \mid (-1, 0, 2) \cdot \gamma = 0\}$. Noting that the point $(1, 0, 0)$ is not on this plane, we next determine the plane containing the point $(1, 0, 0)$ and the given line. This plane contains lines with directions $(2, -3, 1)$ and $(3, -5, 2)$. Therefore $(2, -3, 1) \times (3, -5, 2) = (-1, -1, -1)$ is a direction of a normal to our plane. Thus $(1, 1, 1)$ is a direction of a normal to the required plane. Hence our plane is $\{\gamma \mid (1, 1, 1) \cdot \gamma = 1\}$. We conclude that the given line is the intersection of the planes $\{\gamma \mid (1, 0, -2) \cdot \gamma = 0\}$ and $\{\gamma \mid (1, 1, 1) \cdot \gamma = 1\}$; thus

$$\{(4, -5, 2) + t(2, -3, 1) \mid t \in R\} = \{\gamma \mid (1, 0, -2) \cdot \gamma = 0 \text{ and } (1, 1, 1) \cdot \gamma = 1\}.$$

E X E R C I S E S

1. Show that the planes $\{\gamma \mid (2, -1, 3) \cdot \gamma = 2\}$ and $\{\gamma \mid (-6, 3, -9) \cdot \gamma = 3\}$ are parallel.

2. Given that $m_2 n_1 = m_1 n_2$, $m_2 l_1 = m_1 l_2$, and $m_1 \neq 0$, prove that (l_1, m_1, n_1) and (l_2, m_2, n_2) are linearly dependent.

3. Given that $n_2 l_1 = n_1 l_2$, $n_2 m_1 = n_1 m_2$, and $n_1 \neq 0$, prove that (l_1, m_1, n_1) and (l_2, m_2, n_2) are linearly dependent.

4. Given that the planes $\{\gamma \mid (l_1 m_1, n_1) \cdot \gamma = d_1\}$ and $\{\gamma \mid (l_2, m_2, n_2) \cdot \gamma = d_2\}$ are not parallel, and that $m_1 \neq 0$, prove that $m_2 n_1 \neq m_1 n_2$ or $m_2 l_1 \neq m_1 l_2$.

5. Given that the planes $\{\gamma \mid (l_1, m_1 n_1) \cdot \gamma = d_1\}$ and $\{\gamma \mid (l_2, m_2, n_2) \cdot \gamma = d_2\}$ are not parallel, and given that $n_1 \neq 0$, prove that $n_2 l_1 \neq n_1 l_2$ or $n_2 m_1 \neq n_1 m_2$.

6. a. Prove Theorem 5.2.4, assuming that $m_1 \neq 0$.
   b. Prove Theorem 5.2.4, assuming that $n_1 \neq 0$.

7. Find the intersection of the planes $\{\gamma \mid (1, -2, 0) \cdot \gamma = 2\}$ and $\{\gamma \mid (2, 1, -1) \cdot \gamma = 4\}$.

8. Find the intersection of the planes $\{(x, y, z) \mid x = z\}$ and $\{(x, y, z) \mid y = z\}$.

9. Characterize the line $\{(0, 1, 2) + t(1, 1, 1) \mid t \in R\}$ as the intersection of two planes.

10. Characterize the line $\{(1, 2, 1) + t(-2, 0, 1) \mid t \in R\}$ as the intersection of two planes.

5.3   The Distance Between a Point and a Plane

We have seen that $\{\gamma \mid \gamma \cdot \beta = d\}$ is a plane provided that $\beta \neq 0$. The vector β possesses geometric significance since any line with direction β is a normal to this plane. The number d also possesses geometric significance. Let $\|\beta\| = 1$; then d is the directed distance from the origin to the point α_1 along the line directed from the origin to β, where

α_1 is the intersection of this directed line and the given plane. Intuitively, then, we see that $|d|$ is the distance between the origin and the given plane.

In this connection, the following fact is relevant.

THEOREM 5.3.1.   Let $\|\beta\| = 1$; then d is the directed distance along the directed line $\{t\beta \mid t \in R\}$ with direction β, from the origin to the point $d\beta$.

Proof: Consider Definition 4.5.1.

We now define the concept of the distance between a point and a plane.

DEFINITION 5.3.1.   The distance between a plane and any member of the plane is zero; the distance between a plane and a point not on the plane, say α, is $\|\gamma - \alpha\|$, where γ is the point of intersection of the given plane and the normal to the plane through α.

The following theorem illustrates this concept.

THEOREM 5.3.2.   Let $\|\beta\| = 1$; then $|d|$ is the distance between the origin and the plane $\{\gamma \mid \gamma \cdot \beta = d\}$.

Proof: If the origin is a member of the given plane, then $d = 0$ and the distance between the origin and the plane is also 0. Assume, then, that $(0, 0, 0)$ is not a member of the given plane. In this case there is a unique normal to the plane through the origin, namely $\{t\beta \mid t \in R\}$. This line intersects the plane at the point $d\beta$. Therefore the distance between the origin and the plane is $\|d\beta - (0, 0, 0)\| = \|d\beta\| = |d|$.

EXAMPLE 1.   Compute the distance between the origin and the plane $\{\gamma \mid (5, -2, 3) \cdot \gamma = -4\}$.

Solution: The given plane is $\{\gamma \mid (\gamma/\sqrt{38}) \cdot (5, -2, 3) = -4/\sqrt{38}\}$. Therefore, by Theorem 5.3.2, $4/\sqrt{38}$ is the required distance.

We now extend Theorem 5.3.2.

THEOREM 5.3.3.   Let $\|\beta\| = 1$; then $|\alpha \cdot \beta - d|$ is the distance between the point α and the plane $\{\gamma \mid \gamma \cdot \beta = d\}$.

Proof: If α is a member of the given plane, then $\alpha \cdot \beta = d$, and so $|\alpha \cdot \beta - d| = 0$; in this case the distance between α and the plane is also 0. Assume, then, that α is not a member of the given plane. Then there is a unique normal to the plane through α, namely $\{\alpha + t\beta \mid t \in R\}$. Let the intersection of this line and the given plane be the point $\alpha + t_0\beta$; then $(\alpha + t_0\beta) \cdot \beta = d$; therefore $\alpha \cdot \beta + t_0 = d$; so $t_0 = d - \alpha \cdot \beta$. Since $|t_0|$ is the distance between the points α and $\alpha + t_0\beta$, we see that $|\alpha \cdot \beta - d|$ is the distance between the point α and the given plane. This establishes Theorem 5.3.3.

COROLLARY 5.3.1. $\dfrac{|\alpha \cdot \beta - d|}{\|\beta\|}$ is the distance between the point α and the plane $\{\gamma \mid \gamma \cdot \beta = d\}$.

Proof: The given plane is $\left\{\gamma \mid \dfrac{\gamma \cdot \beta}{\|\beta\|} = \dfrac{d}{\|\beta\|}\right\}$; therefore, by Theorem 5.3.3, the distance between α and the given plane is

$$\left| \frac{\alpha \cdot \beta}{\|\beta\|} - \frac{d}{\|\beta\|} \right| = \frac{|\alpha \cdot \beta - d|}{\|\beta\|}$$

This establishes our result.

EXAMPLE 2. Compute the distance between the point $(2, -1, 3)$ and the plane $\{\gamma \mid (4, 2, -3) \cdot \gamma = 5\}$.

Solution: By Corollary 5.3.1, the required distance is

$$\frac{|(2, -1, 3) \cdot (4, 2, -3) - 5|}{\|(4, 2, -3)\|} = 8/\sqrt{29}.$$

Notice that Theorem 5.3.1 involves a *directed* line. This result helps us to determine the distance between parallel planes. Consider the parallel planes $\{\gamma \mid \beta \cdot \gamma = d_1\}$ and $\{\gamma \mid \beta \cdot \gamma = d_2\}$, where $\|\beta\| = 1$ and $d_1 \neq d_2$. Now, the distance between these planes is said to be the distance between two points, one on each plane, such that the line through the two points is normal to both planes. Consider the directed line $\{t\beta \mid t \in R\}$ with direction β; this directed line is normal to both planes and passes through the origin. Suppose that $\{t\beta \mid t \in R\}$ intersects the first plane at the point α_1 and the second plane at the point α_2. Then $-d_1$ is the directed distance from α_1 to the origin, along our directed line, and d_2 is the directed distance from the origin to α_2, along our directed line. Therefore $d_2 - d_1$ is the directed distance, along the directed line, from α_1 to α_2. Thus $|d_2 - d_1|$ is the distance between the given planes. We have established the following result.

THEOREM 5.3.4. Let $\|\beta\| = 1$; then the distance between the parallel planes $\{\gamma \mid \gamma \cdot \beta = d_1\}$ and $\{\gamma \mid \gamma \cdot \beta = d_2\}$ is $|d_2 - d_1|$.

Note: The distance between a plane and itself is said to be zero.

EXAMPLE 3. Compute the distance between the planes $\{\gamma \mid (2, 1, -4) \cdot \gamma = 5\}$ and $\{\gamma \mid (-6, -3, 12) \cdot \gamma = 6\}$.

Solution: The given planes are $\{\gamma \mid \gamma \cdot \beta = 5/\sqrt{21}\}$ and $\{\gamma \mid \gamma \cdot \beta = -2/\sqrt{21}\}$, where $\beta = (1/\sqrt{21})(2, 1, -4)$. Therefore, by Theorem 5.3.4, the distance between the given planes is $|5/\sqrt{21} + 2/\sqrt{21}| = 7/\sqrt{21} = \sqrt{21}/3$.

E X E R C I S E S

1. Compute the distance between the origin and the plane
$$\{\gamma \mid (1/\sqrt{2})(1, 0, -1) \cdot \gamma = 2\}.$$

2. Compute the distance between the origin and $\{\gamma \mid (2, 1, -3) \cdot \gamma = 5\}$.

3. Compute the distance between $(1, -2, 0)$ and $\{\gamma \mid (1, 1, 1) \cdot \gamma = 2\}$.

4. Compute the distance between $(2, 3, -2)$ and $\{\gamma \mid (1, -2, 1) \cdot \gamma = -5\}$.

5. Compute the distance between $\{\gamma \mid (1, 1, -2) \cdot \gamma = 3\}$ and $\{\gamma \mid (5, 5, -10) \cdot \gamma = 3\}$.

6. Compute the distance between $\{\gamma \mid (2, 3, -1) \cdot \gamma = 2\}$ and $\{\gamma \mid (6, 9, -3) \cdot \gamma = -1\}$.

7. Compute the distance between $\{\gamma \mid (-1, 0, 2) \cdot \gamma = -3\}$ and $\{\gamma \mid (1, 0, -2) \cdot \gamma = 0\}$.

8. Compute the distance between $\{\gamma \mid (2, -2, 1) \cdot \gamma = -4\}$ and $\{\gamma \mid (6, -6, 3) \cdot \gamma = 2\}$.

9. Let γ be the point of intersection of the plane $\{\gamma \mid \gamma \cdot \beta = d\}$ and the normal to the plane through α, where α is not on the plane. Then the *directed* distance from $\{\gamma \mid \gamma \cdot \beta = d\}$ to α in the direction β, is said to be the directed distance from γ to α. Given that $\|\beta\| = 1$, prove that $\alpha \cdot \beta - d$ is the directed distance from $\{\gamma \mid \gamma \cdot \beta = d\}$ to α along the line directed from α to $\alpha + \beta$.

10. Prove that $(\alpha \cdot \beta - d)/\|\beta\|$ is the directed distance from $\{\gamma \mid \gamma \cdot \beta = d\}$ to α, where α is not on the plane, along the line directed from α to $\alpha + \beta$.

5.4   The Family of Planes Containing a Given Line

We need to be able to characterize the planes which contain a given line. Consider the following theorem.

THEOREM 5.4.1.   Let $\mathscr{P}_1 = \{\gamma \mid \beta_1 \cdot \gamma = d_1\}$ and $\mathscr{P}_2 = \{\gamma \mid \beta_2 \cdot \gamma = d_2\}$ be any nonparallel planes, and let L be the line of intersection of $\mathscr{P}_1$ and $\mathscr{P}_2$. Then $\mathscr{P}$ is a plane which contains L iff there are real numbers k_1 and k_2, not both zero, such that

$$\mathscr{P} = \{\gamma \mid [k_1\beta_1 + k_2\beta_2] \cdot \gamma = k_1 d_1 + k_2 d_2\}.$$

Proof: There are two parts to the proof.

1. Suppose that k_1 and k_2 are real numbers not both zero. Now, β_1 and β_2 are linearly independent since $\mathscr{P}_1$ and $\mathscr{P}_2$ are not parallel. Therefore $k_1\beta_1 + k_2\beta_2 \neq \mathbf{0}$; thus $\{\gamma \mid [k_1\beta_1 + k_2\beta_2] \cdot \gamma = k_1 d_1 + k_2 d_2\}$ is a plane. Clearly, this plane contains the given line L.

2. Let $\mathscr{P}$ be any plane which contains the given line L. We must find real numbers k_1 and k_2, not both zero, such that $\mathscr{P} = \{\gamma \mid [k_1\beta_1 + k_2\beta_2] \cdot \gamma = k_1 d_1 + k_2 d_2\}$. The key to our construction is the selection of a member of $\mathscr{P}$ which is not on L. Thus let $\gamma_0 \in \mathscr{P} - L$. Now, let $t_1 = \beta_1 \cdot \gamma_0 - d_1$ and let $t_2 = \beta_2 \cdot \gamma_0 - d_2$. Since $\gamma_0 \bar{\in} \mathscr{P}_1$ or $\gamma_0 \bar{\in} \mathscr{P}_2$, $t_1 \neq 0$ or $t_2 \neq 0$. We claim that $k_1 = t_2$ and $k_2 = -t_1$ are the required real numbers. To see this, consider the plane $\{\gamma \mid [t_2\beta_1 - t_1\beta_2] \cdot \gamma = t_2 d_1 - t_1 d_2\}$. By part 1 of the proof, this plane contains the given line L; furthermore, γ_0 is a member of this plane since

$$[t_2\beta_1 - t_1\beta_2] \cdot \gamma_0 = [(\beta_2 \cdot \gamma_0 - d_2)\beta_1 - (\beta_1 \cdot \gamma_0 - d_1)\beta_2] \cdot \gamma_0$$
$$= d_1\beta_2 \cdot \gamma_0 - d_2\beta_1 \cdot \gamma_0$$
$$= d_1(t_2 + d_2) - d_2(t_1 + d_1)$$
$$= t_2 d_1 - t_1 d_2.$$

But there is exactly one plane which contains a given line and a given point not on the line. Therefore $\mathscr{P} = \{\gamma \mid [t_2\beta_1 - t_1\beta_2] \cdot \gamma = t_2 d_1 - t_1 d_2\}$. This establishes Theorem 5.4.1.

EXAMPLE 1. Determine the plane which contains the line $\{(3, 0, 1) + t(-2, 1, 5) \mid t \in R\}$ and the point $(1, 2, -1)$.

Solution: It is easy to see that the given line is the intersection of the planes $\{\gamma \mid (1, 2, 0) \cdot \gamma = 3\}$ and $\{\gamma \mid (0, 5, -1) \cdot \gamma = -1\}$. Therefore, by Theorem 5.4.1, there are real numbers k_1 and k_2, not both zero, such that the required plane is $\{\gamma \mid [k_1(1, 2, 0) + k_2(0, 5, -1)] \cdot \gamma = 3k_1 - k_2\}$. Since $(1, 2, -1) \bar{\in} \{\gamma \mid (1, 2, 0) \cdot \gamma = 3\}$, we see that $k_2 \neq 0$; therefore we may assume that $k_2 = 1$. Since the point $(1, 2, -1)$ is a member of the required plane, we see that $[k_1(1, 2, 0) + (0, 5, -1)] \cdot (1, 2, -1) = 3k_1 - 1$, i.e., $2k_1 + 12 = 0$; thus $k_1 = -6$. Hence our plane is $\{\gamma \mid [-6(1, 2, 0) + (0, 5, -1)] \cdot \gamma = -19\}$, i.e., $\{\gamma \mid (6, 7, 1) \cdot \gamma = 19\}$.

The idea of this section provides us with a sophisticated method of computing the distance between two lines. Now, the distance between two lines is the distance between the parallel planes containing the given lines; therefore we consider the family of planes which contain the first line and we consider the family of planes which contain the second line. Finally, we choose a plane from each family such that the two planes are parallel. An example will illustrate the technique.

EXAMPLE 2. Compute the distance between $\{(2, 0, 3) + t(1, -2, 1) \mid t \in R\}$ and $\{(5, 2, -3) + t(1, -1, -1) \mid t \in R\}$.

Solution: The first line is the intersection of the planes $\{\gamma \mid (2, 1, 0) \cdot \gamma = 4\}$ and $\{\gamma \mid (1, 0, -1) \cdot \gamma = -1\}$; the second line is the intersection of the planes $\{\gamma \mid (1, 1, 0) \cdot \gamma = 7\}$ and $\{\gamma \mid (0, 1, -1) \cdot \gamma = 5\}$. Therefore, by choosing k_1 and k_2 appropriately, we find that each plane containing the first line is given by

$$\{\gamma \mid [k_1(2, 1, 0) + k_2(1, 0, -1)] \cdot \gamma = 4k_1 - k_2\}.$$

Similarly, by choosing K_1 and K_2 appropriately, we find that each plane containing the second line is given by

$$\{\gamma \mid [K_1(1, 1, 0) + K_2(0, 1, -1)] \cdot \gamma = 7K_1 + 5K_2\}.$$

Suppose, now, that k_1, k_2, K_1, and K_2 have been chosen so that our planes are parallel. Since the planes $\{\gamma \mid (2, 1, 0) \cdot \gamma = 4\}$ and $\{\gamma \mid (1, 1, 0) \cdot \gamma = 7\}$ are not parallel, we see that $k_2 \neq 0$ and $K_2 \neq 0$; therefore we can assume that $k_2 = 1$ and $K_2 = 1$ (notice how this simplifies the algebra). Thus we want real numbers k_1 and K_1 such that the planes $\{\gamma \mid [k_1(2, 1, 0) + (1, 0, -1)] \cdot \gamma = 4k_1 - 1\}$ and $\{\gamma \mid [K_1(1, 1, 0) + (0, 1, -1)] \cdot \gamma = 7K_1 + 5\}$ are parallel. Hence $(2k_1 + 1)/K_1 = k_1/(K_1 + 1) = -1/-1 = 1$; therefore $2k_1 - K_1 = -1$ and $k_1 - K_1 = 1$. Solving, we find that $k_1 = -2$ and $K_1 = -3$. Therefore the parallel planes which contain the given lines are $\{\gamma \mid (3, 2, 1) \cdot \gamma = 9\}$ and $\{\gamma \mid (3, 2, 1) \cdot \gamma = 16\}$. The distance between these planes is $7/\sqrt{14}$; therefore the distance between the given lines is $7/\sqrt{14}$.

E X E R C I S E S

1. Determine the plane which contains the line $\{(0, -5, 2) + t(1, 0, 3) \mid t \in R\}$ and the point $(1, 5, 6)$.

2. Find the plane through $\{(1, 0, 1) + t(2, 0, 0) \mid t \in R\}$ and $(0, 0, 0)$.

3. Find parallel planes $\mathscr{P}_1$ and $\mathscr{P}_2$ such that $\mathscr{P}_1$ contains the line $\{(0, 1, 2) + t(2, -1, 0) \mid t \in R\}$ and $\mathscr{P}_2$ contains the line $\{(0, 1, 0) + t(5, 0, 4) \mid t \in R\}$.

4. Find parallel planes $\mathscr{P}_1$ and $\mathscr{P}_2$ such that $\mathscr{P}_1$ contains the line $\{t(1, 0, 0) \mid t \in R\}$ and $\mathscr{P}_2$ contains the line $\{(1, 0, 0) + t(2, -1, -2) \mid t \in R\}$.

5. Let L_1 and L_2 be any lines. Prove that there exist parallel planes $\mathscr{P}_1$ and $\mathscr{P}_2$ such that $\mathscr{P}_1$ contains L_1 and $\mathscr{P}_2$ contains L_2. (*Hint:* Use Corollary 3.3.1.)

6. Find the distance between the lines $\{(t, 0, 0) \mid t \in R\}$ and $\{(1 + 2t, -t, -2t) \mid t \in R\}$.

7. Find the distance between the lines $\{(2t, 1 - t, 2) \mid t \in R\}$ and $\{(5t, 1, 4t) \mid t \in R\}$.

5.5 The Angle Between Two Planes

By the angle between two nonparallel planes we mean the acute angle between two normals to the planes. Two nonparallel planes mark out a solid angle in space, and the measure of this angle is given by the acute angle between the normals to the planes. As an aid to visualizing the solid angle formed by two planes, place a book on your desk and raise the cover slightly. Regard the cover as a portion of a plane, and regard the first page of the book as a portion of another plane; the line of intersection of these planes is before your eyes. Indeed, you can examine the angles formed by these planes and the acute angle formed by normals to each plane. Hence we formulate the following definition.

DEFINITION 5.5.1. Let β_1 and β_2 be any nonzero vectors; then the angle between the planes $\{\gamma \mid \beta_1 \cdot \gamma = d_1\}$ and $\{\gamma \mid \beta_2 \cdot \gamma = d_2\}$ is said to be $\arccos \dfrac{|\beta_1 \cdot \beta_2|}{\|\beta_1\| \, \|\beta_2\|}$.

EXAMPLE 1. Compute the angle between the planes $\{\gamma \mid (2, -1, 2) \cdot \gamma = 3\}$ and $\{\gamma \mid (4, 3, 5) \cdot \gamma = -2\}$.

Solution: The angle between the given planes is

$$\arccos \frac{|(2, -1, 2) \cdot (4, 3, 5)|}{\|(2, -1, 2)\| \, \|(4, 3, 5)\|} = \arccos \frac{15}{\sqrt{9}\sqrt{50}} = \arccos \frac{1}{\sqrt{2}} = \frac{\pi}{4}$$

EXAMPLE 2. Determine the plane through the point $(1, -2, 0)$ which is perpendicular to the planes $\{\gamma \mid (1, 2, -1) \cdot \gamma = 5\}$ and $\{\gamma \mid (3, 1, -4) \cdot \gamma = -2\}$.

Solution: Clearly, $(1, 2, -1) \times (3, 1, -4) = (-7, 1, -5)$ is a direction of a normal to the required plane. Thus the required plane is $\{\gamma \mid (7, -1, 5) \cdot \gamma = 9\}$.

EXAMPLE 3. Determine the plane which contains the line $\{(2, -1, 1) + t(1, 3, -1) \mid t \in R\}$ and is perpendicular to the plane $\{\gamma \mid (1, -1, 2) \cdot \gamma = 3\}$.

Solution: The family of all planes through the given line is given by $\{\gamma \mid [k_1(3, -1, 0) + k_2(1, 0, 1)] \cdot \gamma = 7k_1 + 3k_2\}$. Suppose that k_1 and k_2 have been chosen to give us the required plane. Now, the plane $\{\gamma \mid (3, -1, 0) \cdot \gamma = 7\}$ is not perpendicular to the plane $\{\gamma \mid (1, -1, 2) \cdot \gamma = 3\}$; therefore $k_2 \neq 0$. To simplify the algebra, we take $k_2 = 1$. Hence $(1, -1, 2) \cdot (3k_1 + 1, -k_1, 1) = 0$; therefore $k_1 = -\frac{3}{4}$. Thus the required plane is $\{\gamma \mid (5, -3, -4) \cdot \gamma = 9\}$.

The concept of the angle between two planes is especially important because of the following application. Suppose that θ is the angle between two nonperpendicular planes $\mathscr{P}_1$ and $\mathscr{P}_2$. Consider a region R_1 of the plane $\mathscr{P}_1$ which possesses an area; let A_1 be the area of R_1. We shall associate a region of the plane $\mathscr{P}_2$ with the given region of $\mathscr{P}_1$ as follows. Consider the set of all lines normal to $\mathscr{P}_1$ which intersect R_1; each line in this set intersects the plane $\mathscr{P}_2$ in a unique point. Let R_2 be the set of all such points; then R_2 is the region that we shall associate with the given region R_1. We shall say that R_2 is the *projection* of R_1 into the plane $\mathscr{P}_2$. It is a simple exercise in elementary calculus to prove the following theorem.

THEOREM 5.5.1.   Area of $R_1 = (\text{area of } R_2) \cos \theta$.

Proof: The proof is obvious once we consider the line of intersection of the two given planes and break up the region R_1 into rectangles with base parallel to this line. Consider one of these rectangles; the corresponding rectangle in R_2 has a base of the same length; however, the height of the rectangle in R_2 is sec θ times the height of the rectangle in R_1. This establishes Theorem 5.5.1.

Here is a special case of Theorem 5.5.1.

THEOREM 5.5.2.   Let $\mathscr{P}_1 = \{\gamma \,|\, (0, 0, 1) \cdot \gamma = 0\}$ and let $\mathscr{P}_2 = \{\gamma \,|\, \beta \cdot \gamma = d\}$; then

$$\text{Area of } R_1 = \frac{|n|(\text{area of } R_2)}{\|\beta\|},$$

where n is the third term of β.

Proof: The details are left as an exercise.

EXERCISES

1. Compute the angle between the planes $\{\gamma \,|\, (0, 0, 1) \cdot \gamma = 0\}$ and $\{\gamma \,|\, (1, 1, 1) \cdot \gamma = 1\}$.
2. Compute the angle between $\{\gamma \,|\, (0, 1, 0) \cdot \gamma = 0\}$ and $\{\gamma \,|\, (1, 1, 1) \cdot \gamma = 1\}$.
3. Compute the angle between $\{\gamma \,|\, (2, 0, -1) \cdot \gamma = 3\}$ and $\{\gamma \,|\, (0, 1, 1) \cdot \gamma = 4\}$.
4. Determine the plane through $\mathbf{0}$ which is perpendicular to the planes $\{\gamma \,|\, (1, 0, 1) \cdot \gamma = 1\}$ and $\{\gamma \,|\, (2, 1, 0) \cdot \gamma = 2\}$.
5. Determine the plane which contains the line $\{(1, 2, 0) + t(-1, 2, 3) \,|\, t \in R\}$ and is perpendicular to the plane $\{\gamma \,|\, (1, 2, 3) \cdot \gamma = 5\}$.
6. Determine the plane through $(-1, 2, 5)$ which is perpendicular to the planes $\{\gamma \,|\, (2, 0, 3) \cdot \gamma = -1\}$ and $\{\gamma \,|\, (3, 1, -2) \cdot \gamma = 2\}$.
7. Determine the plane through $(2, 0, 1)$ and $(-1, 1, 2)$ which is perpendicular to the plane $\{\gamma \,|\, (3, 0, 0) \cdot \gamma = 4\}$.
8. Determine the plane through $(1, 3, -2)$ and $(0, 1, 0)$ which is parallel to the plane $\{\gamma \,|\, (1, -1, 0) \cdot \gamma = -2\}$.
9. Prove Theorem 5.5.2.

5.6 Polynomials; Quadric Surfaces

We have acquired a great deal of experience in handling vector spaces in which the vectors are ordered n-tuples of real numbers, where n is a specific natural number. We now present an important vector space in which the vectors are all possible ordered n-tuples of real numbers with nonzero final term, and the 1-tuple (0). These objects are called polynomials; thus (0) is a polynomial, and if n is any natural number, then each n-vector with nonzero final term is a polynomial. For example, $(1, 0, 3)$, $(0, 1, -1, 0, 0, 0, 5)$, $(0, 0, 0, 0, 1)$, $(0, 5)$, (-3), $(1, 1, 1, 1)$ are polynomials, whereas none of $(1, 0, 3, -2, 0)$, $(0, 0, 0)$, $(1, 0)$ is a polynomial.

To construct a vector space over the real number field, we must introduce scalar multiplication and vector addition. Unfortunately, there is a basic distinction between polynomials which complicates matters; some polynomials are ordered triples, some are ordered 7-tuples, and so on. To avoid this difficulty, we shall adopt a notation for polynomials which presents all polynomials in a uniform manner: we shall represent each polynomial, say $(a_1, a_2, \cdots, a_t)$, by the sequence of real numbers whose first t terms are the corresponding terms of the given polynomial, and whose remaining terms are 0. That is, given $(a_1, a_2, \cdots, a_t)$, we consider the sequence (b_n) such that

$$b_i = \begin{cases} a_i \text{ if } i \leq t \\ 0 \text{ otherwise.} \end{cases}$$

Clearly, there is a one–one correspondence between polynomials and sequences which have only a finite number of nonzero terms. Let us agree to identify a polynomial with the corresponding sequence. For example, the polynomial $(3, -2, 4)$ and the sequence $(3, -2, 4, 0, 0, \cdots, 0, \cdots)$ are identified, and the polynomial (0) and the sequence $(0, 0, \cdots, 0, \cdots)$ are identified. Recall that a sequence is a mapping of N into R, and that the sequence which associates the real number a_n with n whenever $n \in N$ is denoted by "(a_n)" (actually, a_n is a prescription for obtaining a real number from the natural number n). Now we are in a position to define scalar multiplication and vector addition. Let (a_n) and (b_n) be any polynomials, and let $k \in R$; then

$$k(a_n) = (ka_n)$$

$$(a_n) + (b_n) = (a_n + b_n).$$

It is easy to verify that these operations possess the required properties. For the null vector we take the polynomial (0). Thus we have our vector space.

We can do much more with this mathematical system. Let us show that we can construct a ring from our vector space. The basic set of the ring will be the set of all polynomials; for $+$ we take vector addition. We need a second binary operation on polynomials, called *multiplication*. Here, we do not need the language of sequences. Let $(a_0, a_1, \cdots, a_s)$ and $(b_0, b_1, \cdots, b_t)$ be any polynomials other than (0); then we say that

$$(a_0, a_1, \cdots, a_s) \cdot (b_0, b_1, \cdots, b_t) = (c_0, c_1, \cdots, c_{s+t}),$$

where $c_k = \sum\limits_{i=0}^{k} a_i b_{k-i}$ whenever $0 \le k \le s + t$; also, we say that if p is any polynomial, then $p \cdot (0) = (0) \cdot p = (0)$.

It can be shown directly that multiplication is commutative and associative and that the distributive law holds; this is left as an exercise. So we have a ring. Moreover, $p \cdot (1) = p$ whenever p is a polynomial; thus the polynomial (1) is the multiplicative identity.

The polynomial $(0, 1)$ is especially important. Let us denote $(0, 1)$ by "X", and let us define powers of X in the usual way, i.e., $X^1 = X$ and $X^{n+1} = X^n \cdot X$ whenever $n \in N$; moreover, we take $X^0 = (1)$. Then $X^2 = X^1 \cdot X = (0, 1) \cdot (0, 1) = (0, 0, 1)$. Using mathematical induction, we can prove that if $n \in N$, then $X^n = (0, 0, \cdots, 0, 1)$, the $n + 1$-tuple whose first n terms are each 0.

It follows from this result that if $p = (a_0, a_1, \cdots, a_t)$ is any polynomial, then p is a linear combination of $X^0, X^1, \cdots, X^t$; indeed, $p = a_0 X^0 + a_1 X^1 + \cdots + a_t X^t$. Thus each polynomial can be represented in terms of its coefficients and certain powers of $(0, 1)$. Of course, this is the familiar method of representing a polynomial. It is customary, however, to omit writing "X^0".

Each polynomial, say $p = a_0 + a_1 X^1 + a_2 X^2 + \cdots + a_t X^t$, provides us with a mapping of R into R, as follows: let $b \in R$; then "$p(b)$" denotes the real number $\sum\limits_{i=0}^{t} a_i b^i$. This mapping is said to be a *polynomial function*.

Although we used a field, the real number field, to begin our construction, the results of this section rely only on the ring properties of this field (more precisely, we need a ring with identity). This means that given any ring with identity we can construct a ring of polynomials with coefficients in the given ring. Let B be the basic set of a ring with identity; then "$B[X]$" denotes the set of all polynomials with coefficients in B, where "X" is a name of the polynomial $(0, 1)$. These polynomials are also called *polynomials with one argument*.

Of course, we can use our ring of polynomials with basic set $R[X]$ to construct another ring of polynomials. The resulting set of polynomials is denoted by "$R[X, Y]$"; here, Y is the polynomial $(0, 1)$, where 0 and 1 are the additive and multiplicative identities of the ring with basic set $R[X]$, namely (0) and (1); thus $Y = ((0), (1))$. Just as in the case of the polynomials $R[X]$, each member of $R[X, Y]$ is a linear combination of certain powers of Y. Since the coefficients are members of $R[X]$, we see that each member of $R[X, Y]$ is a sum of terms of the form "$kX^r Y^s$". Thus each member of $R[X, Y]$, say p, provides us with a mapping of R_2 into R as follows: let $(a, b) \in R_2$, then "$p(a, b)$" denotes the real number obtained by replacing each term of p, say $kX^r Y^s$, by $ka^r b^s$ and summing. This mapping is said to be a *polynomial function*. The members of $R[X, Y]$ are also called *polynomials with two arguments*.

We need to carry our procedure one step further. From the ring of polynomials with basic set $R[X, Y]$ we construct another ring of polynomials whose basic set is denoted by "$R[X, Y, Z]$"; here Z is the polynomial $(0, 1)$, where 0 and 1 are the additive and multiplicative identities of the ring with basic set $R[X, Y]$. Again, it is evident that each member of $R[X, Y, Z]$ is a sum of terms of the form "$kX^r Y^s Z^t$". Thus each member of $R[X, Y, Z]$, say p, provides us with a mapping of R_3 into R as follows: let $(a, b, c) \in R_3$; then "$p(a, b, c)$" denotes the real number obtained by replacing each term of p, say

$kX^rY^sZ^t$, by $ka^rb^sc^t$ and summing. Again, this mapping is said to be a *polynomial function*. The members of $R[X, Y, Z]$ are also called *polynomials with three arguments*. For example, let $p = 5XY^2 + Z^3 - 2X^4Y^5 + 7$; then $p(2, -1, 1) = 50$.

The degree of a polynomial with three arguments, say X, Y, and Z, is the largest sum of powers of X, Y, and Z associated with any one term of the polynomial with nonzero coefficient. For example, the polynomial $5XY^2 + Z^3 - 2X^4Y^5 + 7$ has degree 9.

We now introduce the notion of an *algebraic surface*.

DEFINITION 5.6.1.   Let p be any polynomial with three arguments; then $\{\gamma \mid \gamma \in R_3$ and $p(\gamma) = 0\}$ is said to be an *algebraic surface*.

For example, the plane $\{\gamma \mid (1, -2, 3) \cdot \gamma = 2\}$ is an algebraic surface; here, $p = X - 2Y + 3Z - 2$. Notice that $\{(x, y, z) \mid x^4 + y^2z^4 + 1 = 0\}$ is also an algebraic surface; here, $p = X^4 + Y^2Z^4 + 1$. This algebraic surface is the empty set.

By contrast, we define the notion of a *curve*. Let f, g, and h be any functions with one argument which are continuous on an interval $\mathscr{I}$; then the set of all 3-vectors $(f(t), g(t), h(t))$, where $t \in \mathscr{I}$, is called a *curve*.

DEFINITION 5.6.2. $\{(f(t), g(t), h(t)) \mid t \in \mathscr{I}\}$ is said to be a *curve* provided that $\mathscr{I}$ is an interval and f, g, and h are continuous on $\mathscr{I}$.

For example, the line $\{(2, -1, 5) + t(3, 1, 0) \mid t \in R\}$ is a curve.

Next, we introduce the notion of a *quadric surface*.

DEFINITION 5.6.3.   A set $\mathscr{Q}$ is said to be a *quadric surface* iff there exists a polynomial with three arguments, of degree two, say p, such that $\mathscr{Q} = \{\gamma \mid \gamma \in R_3$ and $p(\gamma) = 0\}$.

For example, the sphere $\{(x, y, z) \mid x^2 + y^2 + z^2 - 1 = 0\}$ is a quadric surface; here, $p = X^2 + Y^2 + Z^2 - 1$. The plane $\{(x, y, z) \mid z = 0\}$ is a quadric surface since $\{(x, y, z) \mid z = 0\} = \{(x, y, z) \mid z^2 = 0\}$.

We shall say that a quadric surface $\mathscr{Q}$ is *imaginary* iff $\mathscr{Q}$ is the empty set. For example, $\{(x, y, z) \mid x^2 + y^2 + 1 = 0\}$ is an imaginary quadric surface. We shall say that a quadric surface is *real* iff it is not imaginary. For example, $\{(x, y, z) \mid x^2 + y^2 - 1 = 0\}$ is real.

It is well known that the real quadric surfaces can be sorted into the following fourteen types, where a, b, and c are any nonzero real numbers.

1. $\{(x, y, z) \mid x^2/a^2 + y^2/b^2 + z^2/c^2 - 1 = 0\}$.   This quadric surface is called an *ellipsoid*. To sketch the graph of this surface, we consider the intersection of the surface with a plane parallel to a coordinate plane. The intersection of a quadric surface and a plane is called the *trace* of the surface in the plane. Consider the trace of our quadric surface in the plane $\{(x, y, z) \mid z = k\}$, namely $\{(x, y, k) \mid x^2/a^2 + y^2/b^2 = 1 - k^2/c^2\}$, which is an ellipse if $|k| < |c|$. Again, the trace of our quadric surface in the plane $\{(x, y, z) \mid y = k\}$ is the ellipse $\{(x, k, z) \mid x^2/a^2 + z^2/c^2 = 1 - k^2/b^2\}$ if $|k| < |b|$; and the trace of our quadric surface in the plane $\{(x, y, z) \mid x = k\}$ is the ellipse $\{(k, y, z) \mid y^2/b^2 + z^2/c^2 = 1 - k^2/a^2\}$ if $|k| < |a|$. Thus we obtain the sketch of the ellipsoid shown in Figure 5.6.1.

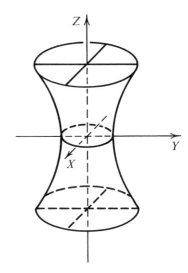

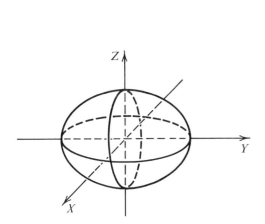

Figure 5.6.1

Figure 5.6.2

2. $\{(x, y, z) \mid x^2/a^2 + y^2/b^2 - z^2/c^2 - 1 = 0\}$. This quadric surface is called a *hyperboloid of one sheet*. The trace of this surface in any plane parallel to the XY-plane is an ellipse; the trace in a plane parallel to either of the remaining coordinate planes is a hyperbola or a pair of lines. Thus we obtain the hyperboloid of one sheet shown in Figure 5.6.2.

3. $\{(x, y, z) \mid x^2/a^2 + y^2/b^2 - z^2/c^2 + 1 = 0\}$. This quadric surface is called a *hyperboloid of two sheets*. The trace of this surface in the plane $\{(x, y, z) \mid z = k\}$ is an ellipse provided $|k| > |c|$. The trace of this surface in any plane parallel to the YZ-plane or the ZX-plane is a hyperbola. Notice that this surface has two parts (see Figure 5.6.3).

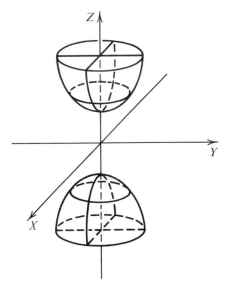

Figure 5.6.3

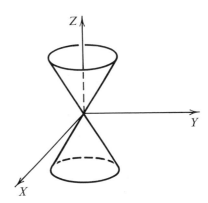

Figure 5.6.4

4. $\{(x, y, z) \mid x^2/a^2 + y^2/b^2 - z^2/c^2 = 0\}$. This quadric surface is called an *elliptic cone*. The trace of this surface in the plane $\{(x, y, z) \mid z = k\}$, $k \neq 0$, is an ellipse. The trace of this surface in the plane $\{(x, y, z) \mid y = k\}$, $k \neq 0$, is a hyperbola. The trace of this surface in the plane $\{(x, y, z) \mid x = k\}$, $k \neq 0$, is a hyperbola. Thus we obtain the elliptic cone (shown in Figure 5.6.4).

5. $\{(x, y, z) \mid x^2/a^2 + y^2/b^2 + z^2/c^2 = 0\}$. This quadric surface consists of the point $(0, 0, 0)$.

6. $\{(x, y, z) \mid x^2/a^2 + y^2/b^2 - 2z = 0\}$. This quadric surface is called an *elliptic para-boloid*. The trace of this surface in the plane $\{(x, y, z) \mid z = k\}$, $k > 0$, is an ellipse. Each trace in a plane parallel to the YZ-plane or the ZX-plane is a parabola. Thus we obtain the elliptic paraboloid (shown in Figure 5.6.5).

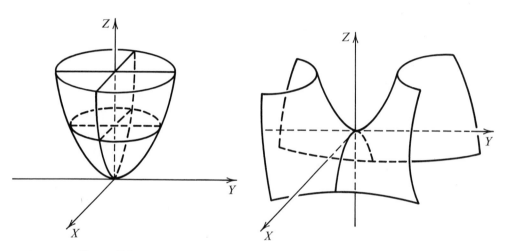

Figure 5.6.5

Figure 5.6.6

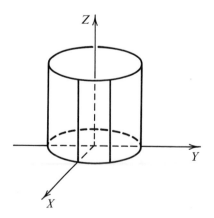

Figure 5.6.7

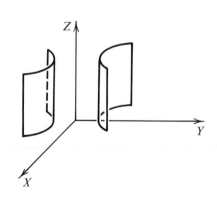

Figure 5.6.8

7. $\{(x, y, z) \,|\, x^2/a^2 - y^2/b^2 + 2z = 0\}$. This quadric surface is called a *hyperbolic paraboloid*. The trace in the plane $\{(x, y, z) \,|\, z = k\}$, $k \neq 0$, is a hyperbola. The trace in any plane parallel to the YZ-plane or the ZX-plane is a parabola. Notice that this surface is saddle-shaped (see Figure 5.6.6).

8. $\{(x, y, z) \,|\, x^2/a^2 + y^2/b^2 - 1 = 0\}$. This quadric surface is called an *elliptic cylinder*. This surface consists of lines, namely the normals to the XY-plane which pass through a point of the ellipse $\{(x, y, 0) \,|\, x^2/a^2 + y^2/b^2 = 1\}$. (See Figure 5.6.7).

9. $\{(x, y, z) \,|\, x^2/a^2 - y^2/b^2 - 1 = 0\}$. This quadric surface is called a *hyperbolic cylinder*. This surface consists of lines, namely the normals to the XY-plane which pass through a point of the hyperbola $\{(x, y, 0) \,|\, x^2/a^2 - y^2/b^2 = 1\}$. (See Figure 5.6.8).

10. $\{(x, y, z) \,|\, x^2/a^2 - y^2/b^2 = 0\}$. This quadric surface consists of two nonparallel planes.

11. $\{(x, y, z) \,|\, x^2/a^2 + y^2/b^2 = 0\}$. This is the line $\{(0, 0, t) \,|\, t \in R\}$.

12. $\{(x, y, z) \,|\, x^2/a^2 - 2z = 0\}$. This quadric surface is called a *parabolic cylinder*. This surface consists of lines, namely the normals to the ZX-plane which pass through a point of the parabola $\{(x, 0, z) \,|\, x^2 = 2a^2z\}$. (See Figure 5.6.9).

13. $\{(x, y, z) \,|\, x^2/a^2 - 1 = 0\}$. This quadric surface consists of two parallel planes, namely the planes $\{(x, y, z) \,|\, x = a\}$ and $\{(x, y, z) \,|\, x = -a\}$.

14. $\{(x, y, z) \,|\, x^2/a^2 = 0\}$. This quadric surface is the YZ-plane.

We shall say that an equation is in *standard form* if it is one of the fourteen equations considered above. Furthermore, we shall say that the equations $x^2/a^2 + y^2/b^2 + z^2/c^2 + 1 = 0$, $x^2/a^2 + y^2/b^2 + 1 = 0$, $x^2/a^2 + 1 = 0$ are in standard form; the latter equations give rise to imaginary quadric surfaces.

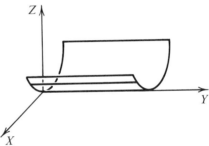

Figure 5.6.9

EXERCISES

Identify and sketch the following quadric surfaces.

1. $\{(x, y, z) \,|\, x^2 + 4y^2 + 9z^2 = 36\}$.
2. $\{(x, y, z) \,|\, 4x^2 + 4y^2 + 4z^2 = 16\}$.
3. $\{(x, y, z) \,|\, 2x^2 + y^2 - z^2 = 1\}$.
4. $\{(x, y, z) \,|\, 2x^2 + y^2 - z^2 = -1\}$.
5. $\{(x, y, z) \,|\, 2x^2 + y^2 - z^2 = 0\}$.
6. $\{(x, y, z) \,|\, 2x^2 - y^2 + z^2 = 0\}$.
7. $\{(x, y, z) \,|\, 4x^2 - y^2 + 2z^2 = 1\}$.
8. $\{(x, y, z) \,|\, 9x^2 - 4y^2 + z^2 = 10\}$.
9. $\{(x, y, z) \,|\, x^2 + 2y^2 = 4z\}$.
10. $\{(x, y, z) \,|\, 6x = y^2 + 4z^2\}$.

11. $\{(x, y, z) \,|\, 2x^2 - y^2 + 2z = 0\}$.
12. $\{(x, y, z) \,|\, z = y^2 - 4x^2\}$.
13. $\{(x, y, z) \,|\, x = y^2 - 6z^2\}$.
14. $\{(x, y, z) \,|\, x^2 + y^2 = 1\}$.
15. $\{(x, y, z) \,|\, 2x^2 + y^2 = 16\}$.
16. $\{(x, y, z) \,|\, x^2 + 4z^2 = 1\}$.
17. $\{(x, y, z) \,|\, 4y^2 + 9z^2 = 36\}$.
18. $\{(x, y, z) \,|\, 4x^2 - 9y^2 = 36\}$.
19. $\{(x, y, z) \,|\, 4x^2 - 9z^2 = 36\}$.
20. $\{(x, y, z) \,|\, x^2 = y^2\}$.

21. $\{(x, y, z) \mid x^2 = z^2\}$.

22. $\{(x, y, z) \mid y^2 = 4x^2\}$.

23. $\{(x, y, z) \mid y^2 + 2x = 0\}$.

24. $\{(x, y, z) \mid x = 4z^2\}$.

25. $\{(x, y, z) \mid y = 18z^2\}$.

26. $\{(x, y, z) \mid x^2 = 4\}$.

27. $\{(x, y, z) \mid z^2 = 9\}$.

28. $\{(x, y, z) \mid x = 0\}$.

29. $\{(x, y, z) \mid z = 0\}$.

30. Let C be a *plane* curve (i.e., C is a subset of some plane) and let (l, m, n) be any direction; then the surface which consists of the lines with direction (l, m, n) passing through a point of C is said to be a *cylinder*. A cylinder is called a *right* cylinder if the lines of the cylinder are normals to the plane of the given curve.

    a. Show that $\{(x, y, 0) \mid x^2 + y^2 = 9\}$ is a right cylinder.

    b. Show that any elliptic cylinder, hyperbolic cylinder, or parabolic cylinder is a right cylinder.

31. a. Show that $C = \{(x, y, z) \mid x^2 + (10 - x - z)^2 = 9\}$ is a plane curve. [*Hint:* Consider $\{(x, y, z) \mid x + y + z = 10$ and $x^2 + y^2 = 9\}$.]

    b. Show that the surface consisting of all lines through a point of C with direction $(0, 0, 1)$ is a cylinder.

32. By a *surface of revolution* we mean the surface obtained by rotating a plane curve about a line in its plane.

    a. Show that $\{(x, y, z) \mid x^2 + y^2 + z^2 = 1\}$ is the surface obtained by rotating the curve $\{(\cos t, \sin t, 0) \mid t \in [0, \pi]\}$ about the X-axis.

    b. Show that $\{(x, y, z) \mid x^2/a^2 + y^2/b^2 + z^2/b^2 = 1\}$ is the surface obtained by rotating the curve $\{(a \cos t, b \sin t, 0) \mid t \in [0, \pi]\}$ about the X-axis.

    c. Show that $\{(x, y, z) \mid x^2 + y^2 = z^4\}$ is the surface obtained by rotating the curve $\{(t^2, 0, t) \mid t \in R\}$ about the Z-axis.

    d. Show that $\{(x, y, z) \mid x^2 + z^2 = 4y^2 - 4y + 1\}$ is the surface obtained by rotating the curve $\{(0, t, 2t - 1) \mid t \in R\}$ about the Y-axis.

PART

III

Calculus

Chapter 6

Functions with Several Arguments

6.1 Functions with Two Arguments

Just as any mapping of a subset of R into R is called a *function with one argument*, so any mapping of a subset of R_2 into R is called a *function with two arguments*. Recall that the notion of a mapping of a set A into a set B enables us to associate with each member of A some member of B. Loosely speaking, then, a function with two arguments correlates certain real numbers with certain ordered pairs of real numbers. Since a mapping is a set of ordered pairs, the objects that are associated together under the mapping are linked together physically as well as conceptually. The point is that a function with two arguments is a set of ordered pairs whose first terms are ordered pairs of real numbers and whose second terms are real numbers. For example, each of the following sets is a function with two arguments: $\{((a, b), c) \mid (a, b) \in R_2$ and $c = a^2 + 5b\}$, $\{((a, b), 10) \mid (a, b) \in R_2\}$, $\{((a, b), b + 2) \mid (a, b) \in R_2\}$, $\{((1, 0), 5), ((1, 1), 5)\}$, $\{((1, 1), 1)\}$, $\{((a, b), \sin a) \mid (a, b) \in R_2\}$. On the other hand, neither of the following sets is a function with two arguments: $\{((1, 0), 5), ((1, 0), 3)\}$, $\{((a, b), c) \mid (a, b) \in R_2$ and $a^2 + b^2 + c^2 = 4\}$. Just as in the case of functions with one argument, it is necessary that we extend our notion of *function* by calling $\varnothing$, the empty set, a function with two arguments.

Let F be any function with two arguments. By the *domain* of F we mean $\{(a, b) \mid$ there is a real number, say c, such that $((a, b), c) \in F\}$; we shall denote this set by "$\mathscr{D}_F$". Note that $\mathscr{D}_F$ is a set of ordered pairs of real numbers, i.e., $\mathscr{D}_F \subset R_2$. By the *range* of F we mean $\{c \mid$ there is an ordered pair, say (a, b), such that $((a, b), c) \in F\}$; we shall denote this set by "$\mathscr{R}_F$". Note that $\mathscr{R}_F \subset R$. For example, the domain of $\{((1, 0), 5), ((1, 1), 3), ((4, 2), 5)\}$ is $\{(1, 0), (1, 1), (4, 2)\}$, and the range of this function is $\{3, 5\}$. Here is a well-known and useful convention. Let F be any function with two arguments, let $(a, b) \in \mathscr{D}_F$, and let c be the unique real number associated with the ordered pair (a, b) by the function F. Then we shall denote the number c by prefixing "F" to "(a, b)"; this means that c is denoted by writing "$F(a, b)$". In other words, $F(a, b) = c$ iff $((a, b), c) \in F$. For example,

$$\{((a, b), c) \mid (a, b) \in R_2 \text{ and } c = a^2 + 5b\}(2, -1) = -1.$$

Since a function with two arguments is a set of ordered pairs, it is clear that two functions are the same iff they have the same members. Thus $F = G$ iff

(i) $\mathscr{D}_F = \mathscr{D}_G$,

(ii) $F(a, b) = G(a, b)$ whenever $(a, b) \in \mathscr{D}_F$.

Just as the study of functions with one argument is facilitated by a systematic method of *naming* functions, so the study of functions with several arguments is facilitated by a systematic method of naming such functions. Let us agree to denote the constant function $\{((a, b), k) \mid (a, b) \in R_2\}$, where k is a real number, by writing "**k**". Notice the use of boldface type; this is logically necessary in order to distinguish between the "k" appearing in the name of the function, and the "k" appearing in the expression for the set. However, since we generally use italic type for names of functions, let us agree to denote **k** by writing "k". This convention is unambiguous if a particular constant function is mentioned; e.g., $5 = \{((a, b), 5) \mid (a, b) \in R_2\}$. Here, the two 5's are distinct. However, should we use italic type to mention a constant function **k**, where k is a variable (i.e., place-holder), we must rely on the context to indicate that a function is being mentioned.

There is another possible source of ambiguity present. Notice that "5" is also a name of a function with one argument, namely $\{(a, 5) \mid a \in R\}$. Fortunately, the number of arguments of the function mentioned is usually clear from the context. Nonetheless, it will be helpful if our notation distinguishes between functions with one argument and functions with two arguments. For this reason, whenever possible we shall denote functions with one argument by small letters, and we shall denote functions with two arguments by capital letters. In particular, we shall denote the function $\{((a, b), a) \mid (a, b) \in R_2\}$ by "X", and we shall denote the function $\{((a, b), b) \mid (a, b) \in R_2\}$ by "Y". So far we have obtained the following definitions.

DEFINITION 6.1.1. $k = \{((a, b), k) \mid (a, b) \in R_2\}$ whenever k is a real number.

DEFINITION 6.1.2. $X = \{((a, b), a) \mid (a, b) \in R_2\}$.

DEFINITION 6.1.3. $Y = \{((a, b), b) \mid (a, b) \in R_2\}$.

Note that $\mathscr{D}_k = \mathscr{D}_X = \mathscr{D}_Y = R_2$, the range of k is $\{k\}$, whereas the range of X is R, and the range of Y is R.

We shall use these functions with two arguments to construct additional functions with two arguments, following the same pattern as in the case of functions with one argument. Let F and G be any functions with two arguments; then we shall construct the following functions with two arguments—$F + G$, $F - G$, $F \cdot G$, F/G.

DEFINITION 6.1.4. $F + G = \{((a, b), c) \mid (a, b) \in R_2 \text{ and } c = F(a, b) + G(a, b)\}$.

DEFINITION 6.1.5. $F - G = \{((a, b), c) \mid (a, b) \in R_2 \text{ and } c = F(a, b) - G(a, b)\}$.

DEFINITION 6.1.6. $F \cdot G = \{((a, b), c) \mid (a, b) \in R_2 \text{ and } c = F(a, b) \cdot G(a, b)\}$.

DEFINITION 6.1.7. $F/G = \{((a, b), c) \mid (a, b) \in R_2 \text{ and } c = F(a, b)/G(a, b)\}$.

Furthermore, from a function with one argument, say h, and a function with two arguments, say F, we construct a function with two arguments, which we denote by "$h(F)$".

DEFINITION 6.1.8. $h(F) = \{((a, b), c) \mid (a, b) \in R_2$ and $c = h(F(a, b))\}$.

Finally, we present one more important method of naming functions with two arguments. Let F, G, and H be any functions with two arguments; then by "$H(F, G)$" we mean the function $\{((a, b), c) \mid (a, b) \in R_2$ and $c = H(F(a, b), G(a, b))\}$.

DEFINITION 6.1.9. $H(F, G) = \{((a, b), c) \mid (a, b) \in R_2$ and $c = H(F(a, b), G(a, b))\}$.

Let us consider the preceding definitions. First, it is important to recall that the expression "$\{z \mid z$ has property $P\}$" denotes the set of *all* objects which possess property P. Furthermore, in case one of the required properties of z is that z is a member of a set S, it may be convenient to transfer that property of z from the right of "$\mid$" to the left of "$\mid$"; thus we write "$\{z \in S \mid z$ has property $P\}$" in place of "$\{z \mid z \in S$ and z has property $P\}$". Moreover, if S is the set of all objects possessing a certain form, we may express z directly in the required form; we have used this convention freely in the preceding nine definitions. Consider Definition 6.1.4; this definition asserts that $F + G$ consists of *all* objects of the form $((a, b), c)$ such that $c = F(a, b) + G(a, b)$. Suppose that $(a, b) \in \mathcal{D}_F$ and $(a, b) \in \mathcal{D}_G$; then $((a, b), F(a, b) + G(a, b)) \in F + G$. Hence, $\mathcal{D}_{F+G} = \mathcal{D}_F \cap \mathcal{D}_G$. In the same way, we see that $\mathcal{D}_{F-G} = \mathcal{D}_F \cap \mathcal{D}_G$ and $\mathcal{D}_{F \cdot G} = \mathcal{D}_F \cap \mathcal{D}_G$. Now consider Definition 6.1.7; recalling that in the real number system division by zero is excluded, we see that F/G consists of all objects having the form $((a, b), c)$ such that $G(a, b) \neq 0$ and $c = F(a, b)/G(a, b)$. Thus the domain of F/G is the common domain of F and G, with zeros of G excluded; i.e.,

$$\mathcal{D}_{F/G} = \{(a, b) \mid (a, b) \in \mathcal{D}_F, (a, b) \in \mathcal{D}_G, \text{ and } G(a, b) \neq 0\}.$$

Now consider Definition 6.1.8; an ordered pair, say (a, b), is a member of the domain of $h(F)$ provided that (a, b) is a member of the domain of F and $F(a, b)$ is a member of the domain of h; i.e.,

$$\mathcal{D}_{h(F)} = \{(a, b) \mid (a, b) \in \mathcal{D}_F \text{ and } F(a, b) \in \mathcal{D}_h\}.$$

In the same way, considering Definition 6.1.9, we see that

$$\mathcal{D}_{H(F,G)} = \{(a, b) \mid (a, b) \in \mathcal{D}_F, (a, b) \in \mathcal{D}_G, \text{ and } (F(a, b), G(a, b)) \in \mathcal{D}_H\}.$$

Now let us illustrate with some examples. From Definition 6.1.4, "$3 + X$" is a name of $\{((a, b), c) \mid (a, b) \in R_2$ and $c = 3 + a.\}$ From Definition 6.1.5, "$X - Y$" is a name of $\{((a, b), c) \mid (a, b) \in R_2$ and $c = a - b\}$. From Definition 6.1.6, "$7 \cdot Y$" is a name of $\{((a, b), c) \mid (a, b) \in R_2$ and $c = 7b\}$. From Definition 6.1.7, "Y/X" is a name of $\{((a, b),$

c)$|(a, b) \in R_2$ and $c = b/a\}$. From Definition 6.1.8, "$\sin(X + 2 \cdot Y)$" is a name of $\{((a, b), c)|(a, b) \in R_2$ and $c = \sin(a + 2b)\}$. From Definition 6.1.9, "$Y(Y + X, \tan Y/X)$" is a name of $\{((a, b), c)|c = \tan b/a\}$. In particular, note that $Y(Y + X, \tan Y/X) = \tan(Y/X)$. Indeed, $Y(F, G) = G$ provided $\mathcal{D}_G \subset \mathcal{D}_F$, and $X(F, G) = F$ provided $\mathcal{D}_F \subset \mathcal{D}_G$.

Let F be any function with two arguments. It is convenient to denote the function $F \cdot F$ by writing "F^2", $F^2 \cdot F$ by writing "F^3", and so on. The function F^n, where n is any natural number, is defined as follows: $F^1 = F$, $F^{k+1} = F^k \cdot F$ whenever k is a natural number. Using mathematical induction, it is easy to prove the following theorem.

THEOREM 6.1.1. $F^n = \{((a, b), c)|c = [F(a, b)]^n\}$ whenever n is a natural number.

Proof: $F^1 = F = \{((a, b), c)|c = [F(a, b)]^1\}$, and so the natural number 1 has the required property. Assume that the natural number k also satisfies the theorem, i.e., assume $F^k = \{((a, b), c)|c = [F(a, b)]^k\}$. Then

$$F^{k+1} = F^k \cdot F = \{((a, b), c)|c = [F(a, b)]^k\} \cdot \{((a, b), c)|c = F(a, b)\}$$
$$= \{((a, b), c)|c = [F(a, b)]^k \cdot F(a, b)\}$$
$$= \{((a, b), c)|c = [F(a, b)]^{k+1}\}.$$

Thus the natural number $k + 1$ has the required property. By mathematical induction, the theorem is established.

It follows from Theorem 6.1.1 that $X^n = \{((a, b), c)|(a, b) \in R_2$ and $c = a^n\}$ and $Y^n = \{((a, b), c)|(a, b) \in R_2$ and $c = b^n\}$ whenever n is a natural number.

EXAMPLE 1. Express $1 + X^2 \cdot Y$ as a set.

Solution: $X^2 \cdot Y = \{((a, b), c)|(a, b) \in R_2$ and $c = a^2b\}$, by Definition 6.1.6. Therefore, by Definition 6.1.4, $1 + X^2 \cdot Y = \{((a, b), c)|(a, b) \in R_2$ and $c = 1 + a^2b\}$.

EXAMPLE 2. Express $(X + \cos(Y))^3$ as a set.

Solution: By Definition 6.1.4, $X + \cos(Y) = \{((a, b), c)|(a, b) \in R_2$ and $c = a + \cos b\}$. Hence, by Theorem 6.1.1, $(X + \cos(Y))^3 = \{((a, b), c)|(a, b) \in R_2$ and $c = (a + \cos b)^3\}$.

EXAMPLE 3. Express $[Y \cdot X^2](\sin(X \cdot Y), \cos X)$ as a set.

Solution: By Definition 6.1.9 $[Y \cdot X^2](\sin(X \cdot Y), \cos X) = \cos X \cdot [\sin(X \cdot Y)]^2 = \{((a, b), c)|(a, b) \in R_2$ and $c = \cos a \cdot \sin^2 ab\}$.

Finally, we note that the operations of subtraction and division can be expressed in terms of the other operations on functions. The following three theorems are easy to establish.

THEOREM 6.1.2. $F - G = F + (-1) \cdot G$ whenever F and G are functions with two arguments.

THEOREM 6.1.3. $1/G = \dfrac{1}{x}(G)$ whenever G is a function with two arguments.

THEOREM 6.1.4. $F/G = F \cdot \dfrac{1}{x}(G)$ whenever F and G are functions with two arguments.

Note: It is customary and convenient to suppress the multiplication dot; thus $F \cdot G$ is denoted by "FG".

E X E R C I S E S

1. Show that $X \neq \{(a, b) \,|\, (a, b) \in R_2 \text{ and } b = a\}$.
2. Is $X \neq \{(a, b, c) \,|\, a \in R, \, b \in R, \text{ and } c = a\}$?
3. Distinguish between the functions x and X.
4. Simplify $\{((a, b), c) \,|\, (a, b) \in R_2 \text{ and } c = a + 2b\} + \{((a, b), c) \,|\, (a, b) \in R_2 \text{ and } c = -b\}$.
5. Simplify $\{((a, b), c) \,|\, (a, b) \in R_2 \text{ and } c = a/b\} \cdot \{((a, b), c) \,|\, (a, b) \in R_2 \text{ and } c = 2b\}$.
6. Simplify $\{((a, b), c) \,|\, (a, b) \in R_2 \text{ and } c = \sin b\} \cdot \{((a, b), c) \,|\, (a, b) \in R_2 \text{ and } c = a\}$.
7. Simplify $\{((a, b), c) \,|\, (a, b) \in R_2 \text{ and } c = a + \log b\}$.
8. What is the domain of $X + 5 \cdot Y$?
9. What is the domain of $X/(Y - 2)$?
10. Which set is denoted by $X/(Y - 2)$?
11. a. What is the domain of $\tan$?
    b. What is the domain of $\tan(X + Y)$?
    c. What is the domain of $\sin(X + Y)$?
12. Show that $x(F) = F$ whenever F is a function with two arguments.
13. Prove that $F^n = x^n(F)$ whenever n is a natural number.
14. a. Show that $f(X) = \{((a, b), c) \,|\, c = f(a)\}$ whenever f is a function with one argument.
    b. Show that $f(X) \neq f$ whenever f is a function with one argument.
15. a. Show that $f(Y) = \{((a, b), c) \,|\, (a, b) \in R_2 \text{ and } c = f(b)\}$ whenever f is a function with one argument.
    b. Show that $f(Y) \neq f$ whenever f is a function with one argument.
16. Show that $F(X, Y) = F$.
17. Show that $X(F, G) = \{((a, b), c) \,|\, c = F(a, b) \text{ and } (a, b) \in \mathscr{D}_G\}$.
18. Show that $Y(F, G) = \{((a, b), c) \,|\, c = G(a, b) \text{ and } (a, b) \in \mathscr{D}_F\}$.
19. Show that $H(F, Y) = \{((a, b), c) \,|\, c = H(F(a, b), b)\}$.
20. Show that $H(X, G) = \{((a, b), c) \,|\, c = H(a, G(a, b))\}$.
21. Show that $H(F, X) = \{((a, b), c) \,|\, c = H(F(a, b), a)\}$.
22. Show that $H(X, X) = \{((a, b), c) \,|\, c = H(a, a)\}$.
23. Prove $(f + g)(H) = f(H) + g(H)$.
24. Prove that $(f \cdot g)(H) = f(H) \cdot g(H)$.
25. Prove that $(H_1 + H_2)(F, G) = H_1(F, G) + H_2(F, G)$.

26. Prove that $(H_1 \cdot H_2)(F, G) = H_1(F, G) \cdot H_2(F, G)$.

27. Prove that $[f(G)](H_1, H_2) = f(G(H_1, H_2))$.

28. Prove Theorem 6.1.2.

29. Prove Theorem 6.1.3.

30. Prove Theorem 6.1.4.

6.2 The Limit Concept; Continuity

The theory of functions with two arguments parallels the theory of functions with one argument. The fundamental idea is the notion of a sequence. Here, by a sequence we mean any mapping of the natural numbers into R_2, the set of all ordered pairs of real numbers. For example, $\{(n, (a, b)) \mid n \in N, a = n^2 \text{ and } b = 1\}$ is a sequence, as is $\{(n, (a, b)) \mid n \in N, a = 2 \text{ and } b = 10^{-n}\}$. Following the usual convention, we shall denote the sequence

$$\{(n, (a, b)) \mid n \in N \text{ and } a = a_n \text{ and } b = b_n\}$$

by writing "$((a_1, b_1), (a_2, b_2), (a_3, b_3), \cdots, (a_n, b_n), \cdots)$", which we abbreviate to "$((a_n, b_n))$". For each natural number n, (a_n, b_n) is called the *nth term* of the sequence. For example, the fifth term of the sequence $((-2n, n + 3))$ is $(-10, 8)$, an ordered pair of real numbers.

The first important concept that we need is that of the *limit* of a sequence. Given the sequence $((a_n, b_n))$ of ordered pairs, we consider two sequences: the sequence of first terms (a_n) and the sequence of second terms (b_n). It may happen that each of these sequences of real numbers possesses a limit. Suppose that $\lim(a_n) = a$ and $\lim(b_n) = b$; then we shall say that the ordered pair (a, b) is the limit of the given sequence $((a_n, b_n))$. The limit of $((a_n, b_n))$ is denoted by writing "$\lim(a_n, b_n)$"; thus our definition is as follows.

DEFINITION 6.2.1. $\lim(a_n, b_n) = (a, b)$ iff $\lim(a_n) = a$ and $\lim(b_n) = b$.

In other words, $\lim(a_n, b_n) = (\lim(a_n), \lim(b_n))$. For example, $\lim(2, 10^{-n}) = (2, 0)$ and $\lim(5 - 1/n, 3 + 1/n^2) = (5, 3)$. A sequence which possesses a limit is said to be *convergent*, and a sequence which does not possess a limit is said to be *divergent*. Note that the sequence of ordered pairs $((a_n, b_n))$ is divergent if either (a_n) is divergent or (b_n) is divergent. For example, the sequence $((1/n, n^2))$ is divergent.

We shall now establish the usual four theorems which assist in computing the limit of a sequence.

THEOREM 6.2.1. $\lim(a_n + a'_n, b_n + b'_n) = (a + a', b + b')$ provided that $\lim(a_n) = a$, $\lim(a'_n) = a'$, $\lim(b_n) = b$, $\lim(b'_n) = b'$.

Proof: By definition, $\lim(a_n + a'_n, b_n + b'_n) = (\lim(a_n + a'_n), \lim(b_n + b'_n))$; but $\lim(a_n + a'_n) = \lim(a_n) + \lim(a'_n) = a + a'$ by assumption, and $\lim(b_n + b'_n) = \lim(b_n) + \lim(b'_n) = b + b'$ by assumption. Hence $\lim(a_n + a'_n, b_n + b'_n) = (a + a', b + b')$.

THEOREM 6.2.2. $\lim(a_n \cdot a_n', b_n \cdot b_n') = (a \cdot a', b \cdot b')$ provided that $\lim(a_n) = a$, $\lim(a_n') = a'$, $\lim(b_n) = b$, $\lim(b_n') = b'$.

Proof: $\lim(a_n \cdot a_n') = \lim(a_n) \cdot \lim(a_n') = a \cdot a'$,

and $\lim(b_n \cdot b_n') = \lim(b_n) \cdot \lim(b_n') = b \cdot b'$.

THEOREM 6.2.3. $\lim(a_n - a_n', b_n - b_n') = (a - a', b - b')$ provided that $\lim(a_n) = a$, $\lim(a_n') = a'$, $\lim(b_n) = b$, $\lim(b_n') = b'$.

Proof: $\lim(a_n - a_n') = \lim(a_n) - \lim(a_n') = a - a'$,

and $\lim(b_n - b_n') = \lim(b_n) - \lim(b_n') = b - b'$.

THEOREM 6.2.4. $\lim\left(\dfrac{a_n}{a_n'}, \dfrac{b_n}{b_n'}\right) = \left(\dfrac{a}{a'}, \dfrac{b}{b'}\right)$ provided that $\lim(a_n) = a$, $\lim(a_n') = a'$, $\lim(b_n) = b$, $\lim(b_n') = b'$, $a' \neq 0$, $b' \neq 0$, and, for each n, $a_n' \neq 0$ and $b_n' \neq 0$.

Proof: $\lim\left(\dfrac{a_n}{a_n'}\right) = \dfrac{\lim(a_n)}{\lim(a_n')} = \dfrac{a}{a'}$ and $\lim\left(\dfrac{b_n}{b_n'}\right) = \dfrac{\lim(b_n)}{\lim(b_n')} = \dfrac{b}{b'}$.

EXAMPLE 1.   Compute $\lim\left(3 + 2/10^n, \dfrac{2 - 1/n}{3 + 1/n}\right)$.

Solution: $\lim\left(3 + \dfrac{2}{10^n}, \dfrac{2 - 1/n}{3 + 1/n}\right) = \left(\lim\left(3 + \dfrac{2}{10^n}\right), \lim\left(\dfrac{2 - 1/n}{3 + 1/n}\right)\right)$ by definition

$\qquad\qquad = \left(3 + \lim\left(\dfrac{2}{10^n}\right), \dfrac{\lim(2 - 1/n)}{\lim(3 + 1/n)}\right)$ by Th. 6.2.1 and Th. 6.2.4

$\qquad\qquad = \left(3, \dfrac{2 - \lim(1/n)}{3 + \lim(1/n)}\right)$ by Th. 6.2.3 and Th. 6.2.1

$\qquad\qquad = (3, 2/3)$.

We now introduce the idea of the limit of a function at an ordered pair. First, we need the notion of an $[F, (a, b)]$-sequence.

DEFINITION 6.2.2.   Let F be any function with two arguments, and let (a, b) be any ordered pair of real numbers; we shall say that $((a_n, b_n))$ is an $[F, (a, b)]$-sequence iff

(i) $\lim(a_n, b_n) = (a, b)$,

(ii) $(a_n, b_n) \in \mathcal{D}_F$ whenever $n \in N$,

(iii) $(a_n, b_n) \neq (a, b)$ whenever $n \in N$.

For example, $((3, 1/n))$ is an $[X, (3, 0)]$-sequence.

Now consider the sequence of real numbers $(F(a_n, b_n))$, where $((a_n, b_n))$ is an $[F, (a, b)]$-sequence. It may happen that this sequence possesses a limit; furthermore, it may happen that $\lim(F(a'_n, b'_n)) = \lim(F(a_n, b_n))$ whenever $((a'_n, b'_n))$ is a sequence of ordered pairs with the three properties listed above. If so, then we shall say that the real number $\lim(F(a_n, b_n))$ is the limit of F at (a, b). We shall denote this number by writing "$\lim_{(a,b)} F$".

DEFINITION 6.2.3. $\lim_{(a,b)} F = L$ iff

(i) $\lim(F(a_n, b_n)) = L$ whenever $((a_n, b_n))$ is an $[F, (a, b)]$-sequence,

(ii) there is at least one $[F, (a, b)]$-sequence.

Thus the statement "$\lim_{(a,b)} F = L$" asserts the existence of an $[F, (a, b)]$-sequence; moreover, we require that $\lim(F(a_n, b_n)) = L$ whenever $((a_n, b_n))$ is an $[F, (a, b)]$-sequence.

To illustrate Definition 6.2.3, we compute $\lim_{(3,4)} X$. Clearly, an $[X, (3, 4)]$-sequence exists, e.g., $((3, 4 + 1/n))$. But $X(3, 4 + 1/n) = 3$ for each n; therefore $\lim(X(3, 4 + 1/n)) = \lim(3) = 3$. Furthermore, if $((a_n, b_n))$ is any $[X, (3, 4)]$-sequence, then $\lim(X(a_n, b_n)) = \lim(a_n) = 3$. This demonstrates that $\lim_{(3,4)} X = 3$.

As another illustration, we demonstrate that $\lim_{(2,5)} X \cdot Y^2 = 50$. Clearly, an $[X \cdot Y^2, (2, 5)]$-sequence exists. Let $((a_n, b_n))$ be any such sequence; then $\lim_{(2,5)} X \cdot Y^2 = \lim(X \cdot Y^2(a_n, b_n)) = \lim(a_n \cdot b_n^2) = \lim(a_n) \cdot [\lim(b_n)]^2 = 50$, since $\lim(a_n) = 2$ and $\lim(b_n) = 5$, by assumption.

We now turn to the concept of continuity. We shall say that F is continuous at (a, b) iff $(a, b) \in \mathcal{D}_F$ and $\lim_{(a,b)} F = F(a, b)$. We shall say that F is continuous on E, where $E \subset R_2$ iff F is continuous at each member of E. We shall say that F is continuous iff F is continuous on $\mathcal{D}_F$. Now the notion of discontinuity: we shall say that F is discontinuous at (a, b) iff $(a, b) \in \mathcal{D}_F$ and $\lim_{(a,b)} F \neq F(a, b)$. This means that either F has no limit at (a, b) or else the number $F(a, b)$ is not the limit of F at (a, b).

Notice that F is continuous at (a, b) iff $\lim(F(a_n, b_n)) = F(\lim(a_n), \lim(b_n))$ whenever $((a_n, b_n))$ is an $[F, (a, b)]$-sequence; and F is continuous iff $\lim(F(a_n, b_n)) = F(\lim(a_n), \lim(b_n))$ whenever $\lim((a_n, b_n))$ exists and is a member of the domain of F, and each term of $((a_n, b_n))$ is a member of the domain of F. Recall that the same kind of statement is true in the case of functions with one argument; f is continuous at a iff $\lim(f(a_n)) = f(\lim(a_n))$ whenever (a_n) is a sequence such that $\lim(a_n) = a$ and $a_n \in D_f$ for each natural number n. Also, f is continuous iff $\lim(f(a_n)) = f(\lim(a_n))$ whenever $\lim(a_n)$ exists and is a member of the domain of f, and each term of (a_n) is a member of the domain of f.

The concept of the limit of a function at an ordered pair enables us to construct a function with two arguments from a given function with two arguments. From F we shall construct a function which we shall call the limit of F and denote by "$\lim F$". First, we say that (a, b) is a member of the domain of $\lim F$ iff $\lim_{(a,b)} F$ exists. Secondly, we say that $\lim F$ associates with (a, b) the real number $\lim_{(a,b)} F$. In other words, we have the following definition.

DEFINITION 6.2.4. $\lim F = \{((a, b), c) \mid (a, b) \in R_2 \text{ and } c = \lim_{(a,b)} F\}.$

Note that $(\lim F)(a, b) = \lim_{(a,b)} F$. To illustrate the definition, observe that $\lim X = X$, $\lim Y = Y$. Also, $\lim\{((a, b), c) \mid a \text{ is rational, } b \text{ is rational, and } c = 2\} = 2$.

EXERCISES

1. Show that $\lim(5 + 2/n, 1/n - 1/n^2) = (5, 0)$.
2. Show that $\lim(1 - 4/10^n, 2 + 3/10^{2n}) = (1, 2)$.
3. Show that $((3 + 1/n, n^2/[1 + n]))$ is divergent.
4. Show that $((10^n/n!, 3^{2n}/n!))$ is convergent.
5. Prove that $\lim(a_n, b_n) = (A, B)$ iff given any natural number p, there is a natural number q such that $|a_n - A| < 10^{-p}$ and $|b_n - B| < 10^{-p}$ whenever $n > q$.
6. Compute $\lim_{(3,-1)} 10$.
7. Compute $\lim_{(a,b)} 10$.
8. Compute $\lim_{(a,b)} \sin(X \cdot Y)$.
9. Compute $\lim_{(a,b)} [(Y^2 + 1) \cdot (X + Y)]$.
10. Prove that $\lim_{(a,b)} (F + G) = \lim_{(a,b)} F + \lim_{(a,b)} G$.
11. Prove that $\lim_{(a,b)} (F \cdot G) = \lim_{(a,b)} F \cdot \lim_{(a,b)} G$.
12. Prove that $\lim_{(a,b)} (F - G) = \lim_{(a,b)} F - \lim_{(a,b)} G$.
13. Prove that $\lim_{(a,b)} \dfrac{F}{G} = \dfrac{\lim_{(a,b)} F}{\lim_{(a,b)} G}$ provided $\lim_{(a,b)} G \neq 0$.
14. Prove that $\lim_{(a,b)} F = L$ iff given any natural number p, there is a natural number q such that $|F(s, t) - L| < 10^{-p}$ if $0 < |s - a| < 10^{-q}$, $0 < |t - b| < 10^{-q}$, and $(s, t) \in \mathcal{D}_F$.
15. Show that X is continuous.
16. Show that Y is continuous.
17. Prove that $F + G$ is continuous at (a, b) if F is continuous at (a, b) and G is continuous at (a, b).
18. Prove that $F \cdot G$ is continuous at (a, b) if F is continuous at (a, b) and G is continuous at (a, b).
19. Prove that $F - G$ is continuous at (a, b) if F is continuous at (a, b) and G is continuous at (a, b).
20. Prove that F/G is continuous at (a, b) if F is continuous at (a, b), G is continuous at (a, b), and $G(a, b) \neq 0$.
21. Prove that $F + G$ is continuous if F is continuous and G is continuous.
22. Prove that F is continuous iff $F \subset \lim F$.
23. Is the function $\{((1, 2), 3)\}$ continuous?

24. Show that the conjecture "If F is continuous, then $F = \lim F$" is false.

25. Given that F is continuous at (a, b), prove that $\lim(F(a_n, b_n)) = F(\lim(a_n), \lim(b_n))$ whenever (a_n, b_n) is an $[F, (a, b)]$-sequence.

6.3 The Elementary Functions

The concept of a function with two arguments presented in this chapter is extremely broad in scope; e.g., the set with one member $\{((1, 1), 1)\}$ is a function with two arguments. In point of fact, a small subset of the collection of all functions with two arguments suffices for most purposes. In this section we shall define and study a certain family of functions of great importance; these functions are called *elementary functions with two arguments,* or *elementary functions* for short. The method of defining the elementary functions is extremely sophisticated and deserves close attention; we shall see that many properties of the elementary functions are evident once we consider the definition of these functions. But more about this later; first, we define the elementary functions.

The *method* used in defining the elementary functions with two arguments is rather unusual but highly effective. We begin by defining the atomic functions.

> DEFINITION 6.3.1. The *atomic* functions are
>
> (i) X,
>
> (ii) Y,
>
> (iii) the constant functions with two arguments.

The atomic functions, together with the elementary functions with one argument, constitute the raw material from which the elementary functions with two arguments are constructed. We shall permit three construction processes. In Section 6.1 we introduced six methods of constructing functions with two arguments. Two of these, namely $F - G$ and F/G, can readily be defined in terms of the others; another, namely $H(F, G)$, turns out to be unnecessary also. The remaining three methods of constructing functions with two arguments constitute the three construction processes that we apply in constructing the elementary functions with two arguments. Notice our point of view: we regard the functions $F + G$ and $F \cdot G$ as being constructed from the functions F and G; the function $h(F)$ is constructed from the function with one argument h and the function with two arguments F. Using these construction steps, we now define the elementary functions with two arguments.

> DEFINITION 6.3.2. The elementary functions with two arguments are defined as follows, where only a finite number of construction steps are permitted.
>
> (i) Each atomic function is an elementary function with two arguments;
>
> (ii) $F + G$ is an elementary function with two arguments if F and G are elementary functions with two arguments;

(iii) $F \cdot G$ is an elementary function with two arguments if F and G are elementary functions with two arguments;
(iv) $h(F)$ is an elementary function with two arguments if F is an elementary function with two arguments and h is an elementary function with one argument.

These are the only elementary functions with two arguments.

Thus a function with two arguments is an elementary function if it can be constructed from a *finite* number of atomic functions and a *finite* number of elementary functions with one argument, by applying the three permitted construction steps a *finite* number of times. Notice the emphasis on *finiteness* throughout this definition; of course, by a *finite* number we mean a natural number or zero. To illustrate the definition, we shall show that the function $\{((a, b), c) \mid c = 3a^2 + \log(5ab)\}$ is an elementary function with two arguments. This function can be constructed from the raw material X, Y, 3, 5, and log; six construction steps are involved, as follows. The function $3 \cdot X^2$ is constructed in two steps, the function $5 \cdot X \cdot Y$ is constructed in two steps, and the next step is to construct the function $\log(5 \cdot X \cdot Y)$, which requires one more construction step; finally, another construction step and we obtain the function $3 \cdot X^2 + \log(5 \cdot X \cdot Y)$. Thus a total of six construction steps are required.

The number of construction steps involved in constructing a given elementary function is of extreme importance, as we shall soon see. In particular, this number provides us with a measure of the complexity of the function. For, if F and G are elementary functions such that F can be constructed in three steps, whereas G requires ten construction steps, then the function F is less complicated than the function G. Notice, however, that any elementary function can be constructed in many ways; e.g., $\{((a, b), c) \mid c = 4a\}$ can be represented as $4 \cdot X$ and as $((X + X) + X) + X$, and notice that $F = F + X - X$ whenever F is a function with two arguments. Hence the number of construction steps merely reflects the complexity of a particular method of constructing the given function. Thus it is the *representation* of the function, not the function itself, that is involved. For this reason we shall refer to the number of construction steps involved in a particular method of constructing an elementary function as the *length* of the given representation of the function. We see that we must express the function so that the method of construction of the function is apparent. In this connection the following theorem is helpful.

THEOREM 6.3.1.   If F is an elementary function with two arguments, then at least one of the following statements is true:

(1) F is atomic,
(2) there exist elementary functions with two arguments G and H such that $F = G + H$ or $F = G \cdot H$,
(3) there exists an elementary function with one argument h and an elementary function with two arguments G such that $F = h(G)$.

Proof: Read the definition of an elementary function with two arguments.

Note that this theorem states that each representation of an elementary function which is not atomic possesses a final construction step.

The preceding discussion of the number of construction steps appearing in a given representation of an elementary function is largely intuitive and hence possesses an element of ambiguity. For example, if the elementary function F involves five construction steps, how many are involved in $F + F$—six or eleven? To answer this question, we formulate a precise definition of this notion. Let F be a particular representation of an elementary function; then we shall denote the length of this particular representation of the function involved by writing "$\lambda(F)$".

DEFINITION 6.3.3. If F is a particular representation of an elementary function with two arguments, then

(1) $\lambda(F) = 0$ if F is atomic,
(2) $\lambda(F) = 1 + \lambda(G) + \lambda(H)$ if F is $G + H$ or F is $G \cdot H$,
(3) $\lambda(F) = 1 + \lambda(G)$ if F is $h(G)$, where h is an elementary function with one argument.

For example,

$$\lambda(\sin(X^2) + (\log + \cos)(X + 3 \cdot Y)) = 1 + \lambda(\sin(X^2)) + \lambda((\log + \cos)(X + 3 \cdot Y)) \qquad \text{by (2)}$$

$$= 1 + [1 + \lambda(X^2)] + [1 + \lambda(X + 3 \cdot Y)] \qquad \text{by (3)}$$

$$= 3 + \lambda(X \cdot X) + [1 + \lambda(X) + \lambda(3 \cdot Y)] \qquad \text{by (2)}$$

$$= 4 + [1 + \lambda(X) + \lambda(X)] + \lambda(3 \cdot Y) \qquad \text{by (1)}$$

$$= 5 + [1 + \lambda(3) + \lambda(Y)] \qquad \text{by (2)}$$

$$= 6 \qquad \text{by (1).}$$

Now that we have a firm grasp on the notion of the length of a particular representation of an elementary function, we are in a position to study a simple yet powerful technique for demonstrating that each elementary function possesses a stated property. Consider a property, say P, which each elementary function with two arguments either possesses or does not possess. It may happen that we can prove that each atomic function has property P; furthermore, we may be able to prove that each elementary function constructed from elementary functions which possess property P also possesses property P. If so, then each elementary function has property P. We shall call this statement a *metatheorem* in order to emphasize the point that this is a theorem about theorems.

METATHEOREM 6.3.1. Each elementary function with two arguments has property P if

(1) each atomic elementary function has property P,
(2) $G + H$ and $G \cdot H$ each has property P whenever G and H are elementary functions with property P,
(3) $h(G)$ has property P whenever G is an elementary function with two arguments which possesses property P, and h is an elementary function with one argument.

Proof: Suppose there exists an elementary function which does not have property *P*. Let "*S*" denote the set of all elementary functions with two arguments which do not have property *P*. By assumption, *S* is nonempty. Now consider $\{\lambda(F)\,|\,F \in S\}$; this is the set of all numbers $\lambda(F)$ where *F* is an elementary function which does not have property *P*. Clearly, $\{\lambda(F)\,|\,F \in S\}$ contains a smallest number. Suppose that this smallest number is $\lambda(F)$. Since *F* is an elementary function with two arguments, we can apply Theorem 6.3.1. Either

(a) *F* is atomic, or
(b) there exist elementary functions with two arguments *G* and *H* such that $F = G + H$ or $F = G \cdot H$, or
(c) there exists an elementary function with one argument *h* and an elementary function with two arguments *G* such that $F = h(G)$.

Clearly (a) is impossible, since assumption (1) of Metatheorem 6.3.1 is that each atomic function has property *P*.

Now consider (b). If $F = G + H$, then $\lambda(F) = 1 + \lambda(G) + \lambda(H)$; therefore $\lambda(G) < \lambda(F)$ and $\lambda(H) < \lambda(F)$. It follows that neither *G* nor *H* is a member of *S*. That is, *G* and *H* each possess property *P*. Hence, by assumption (2) of Metatheorem 6.3.1, $G + H$ has property *P*. Therefore $F \neq G + H$. In exactly the same way, we can show that $F \neq G \cdot H$. This dispenses with (b).

Now consider (c). Suppose that $F = h(G)$. Then $\lambda(F) = 1 + \lambda(G)$; therefore $\lambda(G) < \lambda(F)$. Thus *G* has property *P*. Therefore, by assumption (3) of Metatheorem 6.3.1, $h(G)$ has property *P*. We can only conclude that $F \neq h(G)$.

We have now exhausted all the possibilities listed under Theorem 6.3.1; so we have reached a contradiction. It follows that the initial assumption of this argument is false. In other words, the set *S* is empty. This demonstrates Metatheorem 6.3.1.

We now apply our metatheorem to establish the following important theorem.

THEOREM 6.3.2.   Each elementary function is continuous.

Proof: We must show that if *F* is any elementary function with two arguments, then $\lim_{(a, b)} F = F(a, b)$ whenever $(a, b) \in \mathcal{D}_F$. Throughout this proof we shall assume that $((a_n, b_n))$ is any $[F, (a, b)]$-sequence; i.e., we shall assume that $\lim(a_n, b_n) = (a, b)$, that each term of $((a_n, b_n))$ belongs to the domain of the function involved, and that (a, b) is not a term of $((a_n, b_n))$.

1. We show that each atomic elementary function is continuous.

$$\lim_{(a,b)} X = \lim(X(a_n, b_n)) = \lim(a_n) = a = X(a, b).$$

$$\lim_{(a,b)} Y = \lim(Y(a_n, b_n)) = \lim(b_n) = b = Y(a, b).$$

$$\lim_{(a,b)} k = \lim(k(a_n, b_n)) = \lim(k) = k = k(a, b).$$

2. Now suppose that G and H are elementary functions with two arguments which are continuous. Then

$$\lim_{(a,b)}[G+H] = \lim([G+H](a_n, b_n)) = \lim(G(a_n, b_n) + H(a_n, b_n))$$

$$= \lim(G(a_n, b_n)) + \lim(H(a_n, b_n))$$

$$= G(a, b) + H(a, b) = [G+H](a, b).$$

$$\lim_{(a,b)}[G \cdot H] = \lim([G \cdot H](a_n, b_n)) = \lim(G(a_n, b_n) \cdot H(a_n, b_n))$$

$$= \lim(G(a_n, b_n)) \cdot \lim(H(a_n, b_n))$$

$$= G(a, b) \cdot H(a, b) = [G \cdot H](a, b).$$

3. Now suppose that G is an elementary function with two arguments which is continuous, and suppose that h is any elementary function with one argument. Recalling that each elementary function with one argument is continuous, we see that

$$\lim_{(a,b)} h(G) = \lim([h(G)](a_n, b_n)) = \lim(h(G(a_n, b_n))) = h(\lim(G(a_n, b_n)))$$

$$= h(G(a, b)) = [h(G)](a, b).$$

This establishes Theorem 6.3.2 by appealing to Metatheorem 6.3.1.

We turn now to the problem of demonstrating that $F(G, H)$ is an elementary function whenever F, G, and H are elementary functions. We shall achieve this in two steps. First, we shall fix G and H, and we shall prove that $F(G, H)$ is an elementary function whenever F is an elementary function with two arguments; this maneuver frees us to concentrate on F, so we can apply Metatheorem 6.3.1. Finally, a simple argument leads us to our general result.

THEOREM 6.3.3.   Let G and H be given elementary functions with two arguments; then $F(G, H)$ is an elementary function with two arguments whenever F is an elementary function with two arguments.

Proof: We shall show that each elementary function F has the property that $F(G, H)$ is an elementary function.

1.   We show that $F(G, H)$ is an elementary function whenever F is atomic:

$$X(G, H) = \{((a, b), c) \mid c = X(G(a, b), H(a, b))\} = \{((a, b), c) \mid c = G(a, b) \text{ and } (a, b) \in \mathcal{D}_H\}$$

$$= G \mathrel{R} \mathcal{D}_H \quad (\text{here, } G \mathrel{R} \mathcal{D}_H = \{((a, b), c) \mid (a, b) \in \mathcal{D}_H \text{ and } ((a, b), c) \in G\})$$

$$= G + (H - H) \quad (\text{but } G + (H - H) \text{ is an elementary function}).$$

$$Y(G, H) = \{((a, b), c) \mid c = H(a, b) \text{ and } (a, b) \in \mathcal{D}_G\} = H + (G - G).$$

$$k(G, H) = \{((a, b), c) \mid c = k \text{ and } (a, b) \in \mathcal{D}_{G \cap H}\} = k + (G - G) + (H - H).$$

2. Now suppose that M and N are elementary functions with two arguments such that $M(G, H)$ and $N(G, H)$ are both elementary functions. Then

$$[M + N](G, H) = \{((a, b), c) \,|\, c = M(G(a, b), H(a, b)) + N(G(a, b), H(a, b))\}$$
$$= M(G, H) + N(G, H), \quad \text{which is an elementary function;}$$
$$[M \cdot N](G, H) = \{((a, b), c) \,|\, c = M(G(a, b), H(a, b)) \cdot N(G(a, b), H(a, b))\}$$
$$= M(G, H) \cdot N(G, H), \quad \text{which is an elementary function.}$$

3. Now suppose that T is an elementary function with two arguments such that $T(G, H)$ is an elementary function with two arguments, and let h be any elementary function with one argument. Then

$$[h(T)](G, H) = \{((a, b), c) \,|\, c = h(T(G(a, b), H(a, b)))\} = h(T(G, H)).$$

But $T(G, H)$ is an elementary function, by assumption; hence $h(T(G, H))$ is an elementary function with two arguments.

Applying the metatheorem, Theorem 6.3.3 is established.

COROLLARY 6.3.1. $F(G, H)$ is an elementary function with two arguments whenever F, G, and H are elementary functions with two arguments.

Proof: Suppose that there are elementary functions with two arguments, say F, G, and H, such that $F(G, H)$ is not an elementary function. This contradicts Theorem 6.3.3.

EXERCISES

1. Prove that $F - G$ is an elementary function with two arguments, provided both F and G are elementary functions with two arguments.
2. **a.** Show that $\{((a, b), c) \,|\, c = 3 + 5b + \sin a^3\}$ is an elementary function.
   b. How many construction steps are required to obtain this function from the raw material involved?
3. Compute $\lambda((3 + Y)/X \cdot (\log + \exp)(X^2 \cdot Y))$.
4. Compute $\lambda\left(\tan\left(\dfrac{Y^2 + X}{1 + \cos X^2}\right)\right)$.
5. Compute $\lambda(\sin^2(X) + \cos^2(X))$.
6. Using Theorem 6.3.2 and the Corollary 6.3.1, prove that $F(G, H)$ is continuous, provided F, G, and H are elementary functions with two arguments.
7. Without using Theorem 6.3.2, prove that $F(G, H)$ is continuous, provided F, G, and H are elementary functions with two arguments which are continuous.
8. Is $X + 5$ atomic?

9. Is $X + (5 - 5)$ atomic?

10. Is $X + 0$ atomic?

11. Represent $[(3 + Y)/X](Y, 1 + X^2)$ as an elementary function.

12. Define the function "dual F" as follows: dual $F = \{((a, b), c) \mid c = F(b, a)\}$.

    a. Show that dual $X = Y$; dual $Y = X$; dual $k = k$ whenever k is a real number.

    b. Show that dual $(F + G) =$ dual $F +$ dual G; dual $F \cdot G =$ dual $F \cdot$ dual G; dual $F/G =$ dual F/dual G.

    c. Show that dual $h(F) = h(\text{dual } F)$.

    d. Apply Metatheorem 6.3.1 to prove that dual F is an elementary function with two arguments whenever F is an elementary function with two arguments.

    e. Prove that dual F is continuous, provided that F is an elementary function with two arguments.

13. Prove that $G/H = G \cdot 1/H$ whenever G and H are functions with two arguments. Prove that $1/H = [1/x](H)$ whenever H is a function with two arguments, where $1/x = \{(a, b) \mid b = 1/a\}$.

14. Prove Theorem 6.3.1.

6.4   The Tangent Plane

    In Section 6.5 we shall introduce the notion of the *partial derivatives* of a function with several arguments. The purpose of this section is to expose the intuitive ideas underlying the notion of a partial derivative by investigating an important geometric concept, namely the notion of the tangent plane to a surface at a point on the surface.

    Let us explain these terms. Suppose that a Cartesian coordinate system has been chosen in the usual way so that an ordered triple of real numbers is associated with each point of space. Let F be any function with two arguments; by the *graph* of F we mean the set of points of space associated with members of F, namely $\{(a, b, c) \mid ((a, b), c) \in F\}$. The graph of F is said to be a surface in case F is continuous. Thus a surface is a set of points of space; each of these points is said to be on the surface. We now introduce the notion of the tangent plane to a surface at a point, say (a, b, c), on the surface.

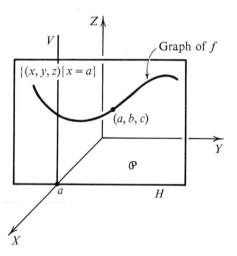

Figure 6.4.1

    Let $\mathscr{P}$ be any plane through (a, b, c) which is perpendicular to the XY-plane. The curve of intersection of the surface and $\mathscr{P}$ may possess a tangent line at (a, b, c), say $T(\mathscr{P})$. Furthermore, there may exist a plane which contains $T(\mathscr{P})$ for each possible choice of $\mathscr{P}$; then this plane is said to be the *tangent plane to the surface* at (a, b, c).

    Let us consider the problem of actually computing the tangent plane to the graph of F at (a, b, c), where $c = F(a, b)$. (See Figure 6.4.1.) As a first choice for $\mathscr{P}$, we use the plane $\{(x, y, z) \mid x = a\}$. This plane intersects the graph of F in a curve. We wish to determine the tangent line to this curve at (a, b, c).

Clearly, we are involved in a two-dimensional situation. Therefore it is to our advantage to represent the curve as the graph of a function with one argument, say f. This is achieved by setting up coordinates in the plane $\{(x, y, z) \,|\, x = a\}$, as follows. Choose for H the line of intersection of $\{(x, y, z) \,|\, x = a\}$ and $\{(x, y, z) \,|\, z = 0\}$, and choose for V the line of intersection of $\{(x, y, z) \,|\, x = a\}$ and $\{(x, y, z) \,|\, y = 0\}$. It follows that our curve is the graph of f, where $f = \{(y, z) \,|\, z = F(a, y)\}$; thus $f'(b)$ is the slope of the required tangent line.

In three-dimensional space our curve is $\{(a, y, z) \,|\, z = F(a, y)\}$. Notice that each point of this curve has first coordinate a. Thus, in representing the curve as the graph of a function with one argument, we have in effect merely deleted all first coordinates.

We now compute a direction of the tangent line. We know that (a, b, c) is on this line; we need to determine the coordinates of another point on the tangent line. First we work out the coordinates of a point on the tangent line in terms of the two-dimensional co-ordinate system we have imposed on the plane $\{(x, y, z) \,|\, x = a\}$. Since $f'(b)$ is the slope of the tangent line, it is easy to see (Figure 6.4.2) that $(b + 1, c + f'(b))$ is on the tangent line. Therefore, in terms of the original three-dimensional coordinate system, the point $(a, b + 1, c + f'(b))$ is on the tangent line. Hence $(0, 1, f'(b))$ is a direction of the tangent line.

We now make a second choice of $\mathscr{P}$. Consider the plane $\{(x, y, z) \,|\, y = b\}$, shown in Figure 6.4.3. This plane intersects the graph of F in a curve, which we may represent as the graph of a function with one argument, say g. This is achieved by setting up coordinates in the plane $\{(x, y, z) \,|\, y = b\}$ as follows. Choose for H the line of intersection of $\{(x, y, z) \,|\, y = b\}$ and $\{(x, y, z) \,|\, z = 0\}$, and choose for V the line of intersection of $\{(x, y, z) \,|\, y = b\}$ and $\{(x, y, z) \,|\, x = 0\}$. It follows that our curve is the graph of g, where $g = \{(x, z) \,|\, z = F(x, b)\}$; thus $g'(a)$ is the slope of the required tangent line.

In three-dimensional space our curve is $\{(x, b, z) \,|\, z = F(x, b)\}$. Note that each point of this curve has second coordinate b. Thus, in representing the curve as the graph of a function with one argument, we have in effect merely deleted all second coordinates.

As before, we now compute a direction of the tangent line. Taking advantage of the two-dimensional coordinate system which we have imposed on the plane $\{(x, y, z) \,|\, y = b\}$,

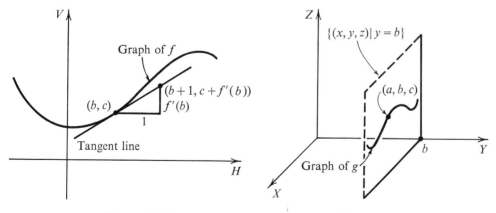

Figure 6.4.2   Figure 6.4.3

we see that $(a + 1, c + g'(a))$ is on the tangent line. In the original three-dimensional coordinate system, this point has coordinates $(a + 1, b, c + g'(a))$. Knowing two points on the tangent line, we easily see that $(1, 0, g'(a))$ is a direction of this line.

We are now in a position to compute a direction of a normal to the tangent plane. This direction must be perpendicular to the directions $(0, 1, f'(b))$ and $(1, 0, g'(a))$; but $(0, 1, f'(b)) \times (1, 0, g'(a)) = (g'(a), f'(b), -1)$. We conclude that the tangent plane to the graph of F at (a, b, c) can only be $\{(x, y, z) \mid g'(a)(x - a) + f'(b)(y - b) - (z - c) = 0\}$. In Section 6.7 we shall prove that this plane contains the tangent line $T(\mathscr{P})$ whenever $\mathscr{P}$ is a plane through (a, b, c) which is perpendicular to the XY-plane.

To illustrate this result, let us determine the tangent plane to the graph of $X^2 + X \cdot Y - 2Y^3$ at $(3, 0, 9)$, assuming that it exists. The curve of intersection of this surface and the plane $\{(x, y, z) \mid x = 3\}$ is $\{(x, y, z) \mid x = 3 \text{ and } z = 9 + 3y - 2y^3\}$. Thus we are involved with the function $9 + 3x - 2x^3$, a function with one argument. The derivative of this function is $3 - 6x^2$; hence the tangent line to the curve of intersection at $(0, 9)$ has slope 3. Thus $(0, 1, 3)$ is a direction of the tangent line. Now consider the curve of intersection of the given surface and the plane $\{(x, y, z) \mid y = 0\}$, namely $\{(x, y, z) \mid y = 0 \text{ and } z = x^2\}$. Clearly, we are involved with the function x^2; the derivative of this function is $2x$. Hence the tangent line to the curve of intersection at $(3, 9)$ has slope 6. Thus $(1, 0, 6)$ is a direction of this tangent line. It is now easy to see that $(6, 3, -1)$ is a direction which is perpendicular to the two tangent lines. We conclude that if our surface possesses a tangent plane at $(3, 0, 9)$, it can only be $\{(x, y, z) \mid 6(x - 3) + 3y - (z - 9) = 0\}$.

E X E R C I S E S

Determine the tangent plane to each of the following surfaces at the indicated point on the surface.

1. $\{(x, y, z) \mid z = x^2 + y^2\}$ at $(3, -1, 10)$.

2. $\{(x, y, z) \mid z = xy^3 - 4x^2y^2 + 5\}$ at $(2, 3, -85)$.

3. $\{(x, y, z) \mid z = \log(xy) + \sin x\}$ at $(1, 1, \sin 1)$.

4. $\{(x, y, z) \mid x^2 + y^2 + z^2 = 1 \text{ and } 0 \le z\}$ at $(0, 0, 1)$.

5. $\{(x, y, z) \mid x^2 + y^2 + z^2 = 1 \text{ and } z \le 0\}$ at $(0, 1/\sqrt{2}, -1/\sqrt{2})$.

6. The graph of $X^3 + X^2Y^2 - XY$ at $(-2, 1, -2)$.

7. The graph of Y/X at $(1, 2, 2)$.

8. The graph of $\cos Y + \cos X$ at $(0, 0, 2)$.

9. The graph of $\sin(X^2 + XY)$ at $(1, 0, \sin 1)$.

10. The graph of $\exp(3X - XY^2)$ at $(0, 2, 1)$.

11. $\{(x, y, z) \mid z = x + y^2\}$ at $(a, b, a + b^2)$.

12. $\{(x, y, z) \mid z = xy - 5x^3\}$ at $(s, t, st - 5s^3)$.

13. $\{(x, y, z) \mid z = y^2 + y^3\}$ at $(u, v, v^2 + v^3)$.

14. $\{(x, y, z) \mid z = x^2 + x^3\}$ at $(c, d, c^2 + c^3)$.

15. $\{(x, y, z) \mid z = \sin(x + y)\}$ at $(p, q, \sin(p + q))$.

6.5 Partial Derivatives

We shall now formalize the operations on functions with two arguments introduced in the preceding section. Let F be any function with two arguments; consider the function with one argument obtained from F by first restricting the domain of F to ordered pairs with second term b, and then dropping out the b. Denoting this function by "$_bF_1$," we obtain the following definition.

DEFINITION 6.5.1. $_bF_1 = \{(a, c) \mid c = F(a, b)\}$.

For example, if $F = X^2 \cdot Y + \sin(X + Y)$, then $_5F_1 = \{(a, c) \mid c = 5a^2 + \sin(a + 5)\} = 5x^2 + \sin(x + 5)$. We point out that $_bF_1 = \{(a, c) \mid c = ba^2 + \sin(a + b)\}$ whenever $b \in R$.

In case the graph of F is a surface, it follows that the graph of $_bF_1$ is the curve of intersection of the surface and the plane $\{(x, y, z) \mid y = b\}$ with respect to the coordinate system imposed on this plane, as in Section 6.4. We are interested in the slope of this curve at a point on the curve, say $(a, F(a, b))$. In this way we are led to the number $(_bF_1)'(a)$, obtained by evaluating the derivative of $_bF_1$ at a. Notice that we have constructed a function with two arguments from the given function F: for, starting with an ordered pair (a, b) in the domain of F, we have been led to the number $(_bF_1)'(a)$. This function is called the *partial derivative of F with respect to the first argument of F* and is denoted by "$\partial F/\partial x$", "F_x", or "F_1". Hence we have the following important definition.

DEFINITION 6.5.2. $F_1 = \{((a, b), c) \mid c = (_bF_1)'(a)\}$.

For example, if $F = X^2 \cdot Y + \sin(X + Y)$, then $F_1(a, b) = (_bF_1)'(a)$; but $(_bF_1)' = 2bx + \cos(x + b)$. Therefore $(_bF_1)'(a) = 2ab + \cos(a + b)$ whenever $(a, b) \in \mathcal{D}_F$; hence $F_1 = \{((a, b), c) \mid c = 2ab + \cos(a + b)\} = 2 \cdot X \cdot Y + \cos(X + Y)$.

In the same way we construct a function with one argument from a given function with two arguments, say F, by first restricting the domain of F to ordered pairs with first term a, and then dropping out the a. We shall denote this function by "$_aF_2$".

DEFINITION 6.5.3. $_aF_2 = \{(b, c) \mid c = F(a, b)\}$.

For example, if $F = X^2 \cdot Y + \sin(X + Y)$, then $_5F_2 = \{(b, c) \mid c = 25b + \sin(5 + b)\} = 25x + \sin(5 + x)$. We point out that $_aF_2 = \{(b, c) \mid c = a^2b + \sin(a + b)\}$ whenever $a \in R$.

In case the graph of F is a surface, it follows that the graph of $_aF_2$ is the curve of intersection of the surface and the plane $\{(x, y, z) \mid x = a\}$ with respect to the coordinate system imposed on this plane, as in Section 6.4. Again, we are interested in computing the slope of this curve at a point on the curve, say $(b, F(a, b))$. Thus, starting with the ordered pair (a, b) in the domain of F, we are led to the number $(_aF_2)'(b)$. Notice that we have constructed a function with two arguments from the given function F. This function is called the *partial derivative of F with respect to the second argument of F* and is denoted by "$\partial F/\partial y$", "F_y", or "F_2". So we have the following important definition.

DEFINITION 6.5.4. $F_2 = \{((a, b), c) \,|\, c = (_aF_2)'(b)\}$.

For example, if $F = X^2 \cdot Y + \sin(X + Y)$, then $(_aF_2)'(b) = a^2 + \cos(a + b)$; thus $F_2(a, b) = a^2 + \cos(a + b)$ whenever $(a, b) \in \mathscr{D}_F$. Therefore $F_2 = X^2 + \cos(X + Y)$.

The result of Section 6.4 can now be rephrased as follows: the tangent plane to the graph of F at (a, b, c), where $c = F(a, b)$, is $\{(x, y, z) \,|\, F_1(a, b)(x - a) + F_2(a, b)(y - b) - (z - c) = 0\}$, provided the surface possesses a tangent plane at (a, b, c).

The definitions of F_1 and F_2 presented above are short and snappy. For this very reason the content of the definitions may not be clear. The following two theorems are intended to rectify this situation.

THEOREM 6.5.1. $(a, b) \in \mathscr{D}_{F_1}$ and $F_1(a, b) = L$ iff

(i) $\lim \left(\dfrac{F(a_n, b) - F(a, b)}{a_n - a} \right) = L$ whenever $((a_n, b))$ is an $[F, (a, b)]$-sequence;

(ii) there is at least one $[F, (a, b)]$-sequence.

Proof: By Definition 6.5.2, $(a, b) \in \mathscr{D}_{F_1}$ iff $a \in \mathscr{D}_{(_bF_1)'}$; but $a \in \mathscr{D}_{(_bF_1)'}$ and $(_bF_1)'(a) = L$ iff

(i) $\lim \left(\dfrac{_bF_1(a_n) - {_bF_1(a)}}{a_n - a} \right) = L$ whenever (a_n) is a $(_bF_1, a)$-sequence;

(ii) there is at least one $(_bF_1, a)$-sequence.

Clearly, (a_n) is a $(_bF_1, a)$-sequence iff $((a_n, b))$ is an $[F, (a, b)]$-sequence. Moreover, $_bF_1(a_n) - {_bF_1(a)} = F(a_n, b) - F(a, b)$. This establishes our result.

THEOREM 6.5.2. $(a, b) \in \mathscr{D}_{F_2}$ and $F_2(a, b) = L$ iff

(i) $\lim \left(\dfrac{F(a, b_n) - F(a, b)}{b_n - b} \right) = L$ whenever $((a, b_n))$ is an $[F, (a, b)]$-sequence;

(ii) there is at least one $[F, (a, b)]$-sequence.

Proof: The proof parallels the proof of Theorem 6.5.1.

It is convenient to use Theorems 6.5.1 and 6.5.2 to compute partial derivatives. For example, we compute X_1 and X_2. Recall that $X = \{((a, b), a) \,|\, (a, b) \in R_2\}$; let (a_n) be any (x, a)-sequence. Now,

$$\lim \left(\frac{X(a_n, b) - X(a, b)}{a_n - a} \right) = \lim \left(\frac{a_n - a}{a_n - a} \right) = \lim(1) = 1.$$

Thus, $X_1(a, b) = 1$ whenever $(a, b) \in R_2$. Hence $X_1 = \{((a, b), c) \mid (a, b) \in R_2 \text{ and } c = 1\}$ $= 1$. Also,

$$\lim\left(\frac{X(a, b_n) - X(a, b)}{b_n - b}\right) = \lim\left(\frac{a - a}{b_n - b}\right) = \lim(0) = 0.$$

Thus $X_2(a, b) = 0$ whenever $(a, b) \in R_2$. Therefore $X_2 = \{((a, b), c) \mid (a, b) \in R_2 \text{ and } c = 0\}$ $= 0$.

Similarly, it is easy to show that $Y_1 = 0$ and $Y_2 = 1$; recall that $Y = \{((a, b), b) \mid (a, b) \in R_2\}$.

We shall require the following theorem.

THEOREM 6.5.3.   Let F be any function with two arguments such that $(a, b) \in \mathcal{D}_{F_1}$; suppose that (a_n) is any sequence such that $\lim(a_n) = a$, $a_n \neq a$, and $(a_n, b) \in \mathcal{D}_F$ for each n. Then $\lim(F(a_n, b)) = F(a, b)$.

Proof: By Theorem 6.5.1,

$$F_1(a, b) = \lim\left(\frac{F(a_n, b) - F(a, b)}{a_n - a}\right);$$

hence $\lim(F(a_n, b) - F(a, b)) = 0$. Therefore $\lim(F(a_n, b)) = F(a, b)$.

We want to develop a technique for computing partial derivatives; furthermore, we want to prove that F_1 and F_2 are elementary functions whenever F is an elementary function. All this is based on the following six theorems.

THEOREM 6.5.4. $X_1 = 1$, $X_2 = 0$, $Y_1 = 0$, $Y_2 = 1$, $k_1 = k_2 = 0$ whenever k is a real number.

THEOREM 6.5.5. $(G + H)_1 = G_1 + H_1$ and $(G + H)_2 = G_2 + H_2$,   provided $\mathcal{D}_{G_1} = \mathcal{D}_{G_2} = \mathcal{D}_G$ and $\mathcal{D}_{H_1} = \mathcal{D}_{H_2} = \mathcal{D}_H$.

THEOREM 6.5.6. $(G \cdot H)_1 = G \cdot H_1 + G_1 \cdot H$ and $(G \cdot H)_2 = G \cdot H_2 + G_2 \cdot H$, provided $\mathcal{D}_{G_1} = \mathcal{D}_{G_2} = \mathcal{D}_G$ and $\mathcal{D}_{H_1} = \mathcal{D}_{H_2} = \mathcal{D}_H$.

THEOREM 6.5.7. $(G/H)_1 = \dfrac{H \cdot G_1 - H_1 \cdot G}{H^2}$ and $(G/H)_2 = \dfrac{H \cdot G_2 - H_2 \cdot G}{H^2}$, provided $\mathcal{D}_{G_1} = \mathcal{D}_{G_2} = \mathcal{D}_G$ and $\mathcal{D}_{H_1} = \mathcal{D}_{H_2} = \mathcal{D}_H$.

THEOREM 6.5.8. $[h(G)]_1 = h'(G) \cdot G_1$ and $[h(G)]_2 = h'(G) \cdot G_2$, provided $\mathcal{D}_{G_1} = \mathcal{D}_{G_2} = \mathcal{D}_G$ and $\mathcal{D}_{h'} = \mathcal{D}_h$.

THEOREM 6.5.9. $[F(G, H)]_1 = F_1(G, H) \cdot G_1 + F_2(G, H) \cdot H_1$ and $[F(G, H)]_2 = F_1(G, H) \cdot G_2 + F_2(G, H) \cdot H_2$, provided $\mathscr{D}_{F_1} = \mathscr{D}_{F_2} = \mathscr{D}_F$, $\mathscr{D}_{G_1} = \mathscr{D}_{G_2} = \mathscr{D}_G$, $\mathscr{D}_{H_1} = \mathscr{D}_{H_2} = \mathscr{D}_H$, and provided F_1 and F_2 are continuous.

Theorem 6.5.4 has already been established; we now present elementary proofs of the remaining theorems. In Section 6.6 we shall establish a fundamental theorem about partial derivatives which can be used to establish these theorems and other theorems concerning partial derivatives. Nevertheless, the following proofs should be studied carefully since a basic approach to these theorems is valuable.

Proof of Theorem 6.5.5:   Let (a, b) be any member of the domain of $G + H$, and let (a_n) be any sequence such that $\lim(a_n) = a$, $a_n \neq a$, and $(a_n, b) \in \mathscr{D}_{G+H}$ for each n. Now,

$$\lim\left(\frac{[G + H](a_n, b) - [G + H](a, b)}{a_n - a}\right)$$

$$= \lim\left(\frac{G(a_n, b) - G(a, b)}{a_n - a}\right) + \lim\left(\frac{H(a_n, b) - H(a, b)}{a_n - a}\right)$$

$$= G_1(a, b) + H_1(a, b).$$

Hence $(G + H)_1(a, b) = G_1(a, b) + H_1(a, b)$ whenever $(a, b) \in \mathscr{D}_{G+H}$. Thus $(G + H)_1 = \{((a, b), c) \mid c = G_1(a, b) + H_1(a, b)\} = G_1 + H_1$. This establishes the first part of Theorem 6.5.5; the second part of the theorem can be established in the same way.

Proof of Theorem 6.5.6:   Let (a, b) be any member of the domain of $G \cdot H$. Let (a_n) be any sequence such that $\lim(a_n) = a$, $a_n \neq a$, and $(a_n, b) \in \mathscr{D}_{G \cdot H}$ for each n. Now,

$$\lim\left(\frac{G(a_n, b) \cdot H(a_n, b) - G(a, b) \cdot H(a, b)}{a_n - a}\right)$$

$$= \lim\left(\frac{G(a_n, b) \cdot H(a_n, b) - G(a, b) \cdot H(a_n, b)}{a_n - a}\right)$$

$$+ \lim\left(\frac{G(a, b) \cdot H(a_n, b) - G(a, b) \cdot H(a, b)}{a_n - a}\right)$$

$$= \lim\left(\frac{G(a_n, b) - G(a, b)}{a_n - a}\right) \cdot \lim(H(a_n, b))$$

$$+ \lim(G(a, b)) \cdot \lim\left(\frac{H(a_n, b) - H(a, b)}{a_n - a}\right)$$

$$= G_1(a, b) \cdot H(a, b) + G(a, b) \cdot H_1(a, b) \quad \text{by Th. 6.5.3. and assumptions.}$$

Hence $(G \cdot H)_1(a, b) = G_1(a, b) \cdot H(a, b) + G(a, b) \cdot H_1(a, b)$ whenever $(a, b) \in \mathcal{D}_{G \cdot H}$. Thus

$$(G \cdot H)_1 = \{((a, b), c) \mid c = G(a, b) \cdot H_1(a, b) + G_1(a, b) \cdot H(a, b)\}$$
$$= G \cdot H_1 + G_1 \cdot H.$$

This establishes the first part of Theorem 6.5.6; the second part of the theorem can be established in the same way.

Theorem 6.5.7 is actually a consequence of Theorems 6.5.6 and 6.5.8.

Proof of Theorem 6.5.8:   Let (a, b) be any member of the domain of $h(G)$. We wish to prove that $[h(G)]_1(a, b) = h'(G(a, b)) \cdot G_1(a, b)$; this we shall accomplish by appealing directly to the definition of the partial derivative, making use of the function $_b[h(G)]_1$. Note that $_b[h(G)]_1 = \{(a, c) \mid c = h(G(a, b))\} = h(_bG_1)$; therefore

$$[h(G)]_1(a, b) = (_b[h(G)]_1)'(a) = [h(_bG_1)]'(a) = h'(_bG_1(a)) \cdot (_bG_1)'(a) = h'(G(a, b)) \cdot G_1(a, b).$$

Hence $[h(G)]_1 = \{((a, b), c) \mid c = h'(G(a, b)) \cdot G_1(a, b)\} = h'(G) \cdot G_1$. This establishes the first part of Theorem 6.5.8; the second part of the theorem can be established in the same way.

We can now establish Theorem 6.5.7.

Proof of Theorem 6.5.7:   We shall prove that $(G/H)_1 = (H \cdot G_1 - H_1 \cdot G)/H^2$ under the assumptions of the theorem. Now, $1/H = [1/x](H)$; therefore, by Theorem 6.5.8, $(1/H)_1 = [(1/x)(H)]_1 = [-1/x^2](H) \cdot H_1 = -H_1/H^2$. Hence

$$(G/H)_1 = (G \cdot [/1H])_1 = G \cdot (1/H)_1 + G_1 \cdot 1/H \qquad \text{by Th. 6.5.6}$$
$$= G \cdot (-H_1/H^2) + G_1/H = \frac{H \cdot G_1 - H_1 \cdot G}{H^2}.$$

This establishes the first part of Theorem 6.5.7; the second part of the theorem can be established in the same way.

Proof of Theorem 6.5.9:   Let (a, b) be any member of the domain of $F(G, H)$. Let (a_n) be any sequence such that $\lim(a_n) = a$, $a_n \neq a$, and $(a_n, b) \in \mathcal{D}_{F(G,H)}$ for each n. Now,

$$\lim \left(\frac{F(G(a_n, b), H(a_n, b)) - F(G(a, b), H(a, b))}{a_n - a} \right)$$
$$= \lim \left(\frac{F(G(a_n, b), c_n) - F(G(a, b), c_n)}{a_n - a} \right)$$
$$+ \lim \left(\frac{F(G(a, b), c_n) - F(G(a, b), H(a, b))}{a_n - a} \right)$$

where $c_n = H(a_n, b)$ whenever $n \in N$. But

$$\lim\left(\frac{F(G(a_n, b), c_n) - F(G(a, b), c_n)}{a_n - a}\right) = \lim\left(\frac{c_n F_1(G(a_n, b)) - c_n F_1(G(a, b))}{a_n - a}\right)$$

$$= \lim\left(\frac{[c_n F_1]'(t_n) \cdot [G(a_n, b) - G(a, b)]}{a_n - a}\right)$$

by the Mean Value Theorem, where t_n is between $G(a_n, b)$ and $G(a, b)$ whenever $n \in N$.

$$= \lim(F_1(t_n, c_n)) \cdot \lim\left(\frac{G(a_n, b) - G(a, b)}{a_n - a}\right)$$

$$= F_1(\lim(t_n), \lim(H(a_n, b))) \cdot G_1(a, b) \qquad \text{since } F_1 \text{ is continuous}$$

$$= F_1(G(a, b), \lim(H(a_n, b))) \cdot G_1(a, b) \qquad \begin{aligned}&\text{since } \lim(G(a_n, b)) = G(\lim(a_n, b)) \\ &\qquad\qquad = G(a, b)\end{aligned}$$

$$= F_1(G(a, b), H(\lim(a_n, b))) \cdot G_1(a, b) \qquad \text{since } H \text{ is continuous}$$

$$= F_1(G(a, b), H(a, b)) \cdot G_1(a, b),$$

and

$$\lim\left(\frac{F(G(a, b), H(a_n, b)) - F(G(a, b), H(a, b))}{a_n - a}\right)$$

$$= \lim\left(\frac{d F_2(H(a_n, b)) - d F_2(H(a, b))}{a_n - a}\right) \qquad \text{where } d = G(a, b)$$

$$= [_d F_2(_b H_1)]'(a) \qquad \text{since } [f(g)]'(a) = \lim\left(\frac{f(g(a_n)) - f(g(a))}{a_n - a}\right)$$

$$= [_d F_2]'(_b H_1(a)) \cdot (_b H_1)'(a)$$

$$= F_2(G(a, b), H(a, b)) \cdot H_1(a, b).$$

Thus $[F(G, H)]_1(a, b) = F_1(G(a, b), H(a, b)) \cdot G_1(a, b) + F_2(G(a, b), H(a, b)) \cdot H_1(a, b)$ whenever $(a, b) \in \mathcal{D}_{F(G,H)}$. Hence

$$[F(G, H)]_1 = \{((a, b), c) \mid c = F_1(G(a, b), H(a, b)) \cdot G_1(a, b)$$

$$+ F_2(G(a, b), H(a, b)) \cdot H_1(a, b)\}$$

$$= F_1(G, H) \cdot G_1 + F_2(G, H) \cdot H_1.$$

This establishes the first part of Theorem 6.5.9; the second part of the theorem can be established in the same way.

The following examples illustrate the use of the preceding six theorems in computing partial derivatives.

EXAMPLE 1. $[X + \sin(Y)]_1 = X_1 + [\sin(Y)]_1$ by Th. 6.5.5

$= 1 + [\cos(Y)] \cdot Y_1$ by Th. 6.5.4 and Th. 6.5.8

$= 1 + \cos(Y) \cdot 0$ by Th. 6.5.4

$= 1.$

EXAMPLE 2.

$[Y \cdot \tan(X \cdot Y)]_2 = Y \cdot [\tan(X \cdot Y)]_2 + Y_2 \cdot \tan(X \cdot Y)$ by Th. 6.5.6

$= Y \cdot \sec^2(X \cdot Y) \cdot [X \cdot Y]_2 + 1 \cdot \tan(X \cdot Y)$ by Th. 6.5.8 and Th. 6.5.4

$= X \cdot Y \cdot \sec^2(X \cdot Y) + \tan(X \cdot Y)$ by Th. 6.5.6 and Th. 6.5.4

EXAMPLE 3.

$$[[X \cdot Y^2](X \cdot \cos(Y), \log(X))]_1 = Y^2(X \cdot \cos(Y), \log(X)) \cdot \cos(Y)$$
$$+ (2 \cdot X \cdot Y)(X \cdot \cos(Y), \log(X)) \cdot 1/X,$$

by Theorem 6.5.9, since $[X \cdot Y^2]_1 = X \cdot [Y^2]_1 + X_1 \cdot Y^2 = 1 \cdot Y^2 = Y^2$ and

$$[X \cdot \cos(Y)]_1 = X \cdot [\cos(Y)]_1 + X_1 \cdot \cos(Y)$$
$$= X \cdot [-\sin(Y) \cdot Y_1] + 1 \cdot \cos(Y) = \cos(Y)$$

and $[X \cdot Y^2]_2 = X \cdot [Y^2]_2 + X_2 \cdot Y^2 = X \cdot (Y \cdot Y_2 + Y_2 \cdot Y) = 2 \cdot X \cdot Y$

and $[\log(X)]_1 = \dfrac{1}{x}(X) \cdot X_1 = \dfrac{1}{X} \cdot 1 = \dfrac{1}{X}.$

Thus

$$[[X \cdot Y^2](X \cdot \cos(Y), \log(X))]_1 = [\log(X)]^2 \cdot \cos(Y) + 2 \cdot [X \cdot \cos(Y)] \cdot \log(X) \cdot \frac{1}{X}$$
$$= [\log(X)]^2 \cdot \cos(Y) + 2 \cdot \cos(Y) \cdot \log(X).$$

As suggested by Example 3, many of the steps involved in computing partial derivatives can be carried out mentally; of course, this reduces the paper work and so speeds up the computation. Consider the following example, in which the first step is an application of Theorem 6.5.7 and the remaining steps have been worked out mentally. Can you recapture the missing steps?

EXAMPLE 4. $\left[\dfrac{\exp(X \cdot Y)}{X + Y}\right]_2 = \dfrac{(X + Y) \cdot \exp(X \cdot Y) \cdot X - \exp(X \cdot Y)}{(X + Y)^2}.$

In Theorems 6.5.5 through 6.5.9 we assumed that the partial derivatives of the functions involved possess the same domain as the functions themselves. Examining the proofs of these theorems, we find that these restrictions can be reduced considerably. Consider the following five theorems.

THEOREM 6.5.5'. $(a, b) \in \mathcal{D}_{(G+H)_1}$ iff $(a, b) \in \mathcal{D}_{G_1}$ and $(a, b) \in \mathcal{D}_{H_1}$; furthermore, $(G + H)_1(a, b) = (G_1 + H_1)(a, b)$. Also, $(a, b) \in \mathcal{D}_{(G+H)_2}$ iff $(a, b) \in \mathcal{D}_{G_2}$ and $(a, b) \in \mathcal{D}_{H_2}$; furthermore, $(G + H)_2(a, b) = (G_2 + H_2)(a, b)$.

THEOREM 6.5.6'. $(a, b) \in \mathcal{D}_{(G \cdot H)_1}$ iff $(a, b) \in \mathcal{D}_{G_1}$ and $(a, b) \in \mathcal{D}_{H_1}$; furthermore, $(G \cdot H)_1(a, b) = (G \cdot H_1 + G_1 \cdot H)(a, b)$. Also $(a, b) \in \mathcal{D}_{(G \cdot H)_2}$ iff $(a, b) \in \mathcal{D}_{G_2}$ and $(a, b) \in \mathcal{D}_{H_2}$; furthermore, $(G \cdot H)_2(a, b) = (G \cdot H_2 + G_2 \cdot H)(a, b)$.

THEOREM 6.5.7'. $(a, b) \in \mathcal{D}_{(G/H)_1}$ iff $(a, b) \in \mathcal{D}_{G_1}$ and $(a, b) \in \mathcal{D}_{H_1}$; furthermore,
$$(G/H)_1(a, b) = \frac{H \cdot G_1 - H_1 \cdot G}{H^2}(a, b).$$ Also, $(a, b) \in \mathcal{D}_{(G/H)_2}$ iff $(a, b) \in \mathcal{D}_{G_2}$ and
$(a, b) \in \mathcal{D}_{H_2}$; furthermore, $(G/H)_2(a, b) = \dfrac{H \cdot G_2 - H_2 \cdot G}{H^2}(a, b)$.

THEOREM 6.5.8'. $(a, b) \in \mathcal{D}_{[h(G)]_1}$ iff $(a, b) \in \mathcal{D}_{G_1}$ and $G(a, b) \in \mathcal{D}_{h'}$; furthermore, $[h(G)]_1(a, b) = [h'(G) \cdot G_1](a, b)$. Also, $(a, b) \in \mathcal{D}_{[h(G)]_2}$ iff $(a, b) \in \mathcal{D}_{G_2}$ and $G(a, b) \in \mathcal{D}_{h'}$; furthermore, $[h(G)]_2(a, b) = [h'(G) \cdot G_2](a, b)$.

THEOREM 6.5.9'. $(a, b) \in \mathcal{D}_{[F(G, H)]_1}$ if $(a, b) \in \mathcal{D}_{G_1}$, $(a, b) \in \mathcal{D}_{H_1}$, $(G(a, b)$, $H(a, b)) \in \mathcal{D}_{F_1}$, $(G(a, b), H(a, b)) \in \mathcal{D}_{F_2}$, and F_1 and F_2 are continuous; furthermore, $[F(G, H)]_1(a, b) = [F_1(G, H) \cdot G_1 + F_2(G, H) \cdot H_1](a, b)$. Also, $(a, b) \in$ $\mathcal{D}_{[F(G, H)]_2}$ if $(a, b) \in \mathcal{D}_{G_2}$, $(a, b) \in \mathcal{D}_{H_2}$, $(G(a, b), H(a, b)) \in \mathcal{D}_{F_1}$, $(G(a, b), H(a, b)) \in$ $\mathcal{D}_{F_2}$, and F_1 and F_2 are continuous; furthermore, $[F(G, H)]_2(a, b) = [F_1(G, H) \cdot G_2 + F_2(G, H) \cdot H_2](a, b)$.

We now want to prove that F_1 and F_2 are elementary functions whenever F is an elementary function. We shall make use of Metatheorem 6.3.1, which we now restate.

METATHEOREM 6.3.1. Each elementary function with two arguments has property P if

(1) each atomic elementary function has property P,
(2) $G + H$ and $G \cdot H$ each has property P whenever G and H are elementary functions with property P,
(3) $h(G)$ has property P whenever G is an elementary function with two arguments which possesses property P, and h is an elementary function with one argument.

We now prove the following theorem.

THEOREM 6.5.10. F_1 and F_2 are elementary functions whenever F is an elementary function.

Proof: 1. By Theorem 6.5.4, $X_1 = Y_2 = 1$, $X_2 = Y_1 = 0$, and $k_1 = k_2 = 0$ whenever k is a real number; hence each atomic elementary function has the stated property.

2. Assume that G and H are elementary functions with the stated property, i.e., G_1, G_2, H_1, and H_2 are elementary functions. Then, by Theorem 6.5.5', $(G + H)_1 = G_1 + H_1$ and $(G + H)_2 = G_2 + H_2$; hence $G + H$ has the required property. Also, by Theorem 6.5.6', $(G \cdot H)_1 = G \cdot H_1 + G_1 \cdot H$ and $(G \cdot H)_2 = G \cdot H_2 + G_2 \cdot H$; hence $G \cdot H$ has the required property.

3. Assume that G is an elementary function with two arguments possessing the stated property, and that h is any elementary function with one argument. Then, by Theorem 6.5.8', $[h(G)]_1 = h'(G) \cdot G_1$ and $[h(G)]_2 = h'(G) \cdot G_2$. Since h' is an elementary function with one argument, it follows that $[h(G)]_1$ and $[h(G)]_2$ are elementary functions with two arguments. This establishes Theorem 6.5.10.

Using Metatheorem 6.3.1, we shall establish one more result in this section. But first, some notation. Suppose that F is a function with two arguments; then the partial derivatives of F—F_1 and F_2—are functions with two arguments. Again, the partial derivatives of F_1 and F_2—$(F_1)_1, (F_1)_2, (F_2)_1$, and $(F_2)_2$—are functions with two arguments. Similarly, $((F_2)_1)_1$ and $((F_2)_1)_2$ are the partial derivatives of $(F_2)_1$. Notice how the parentheses are piling up. Clearly, a parentheses-omitting convention is called for. Let us agree to denote $(F_1)_1, (F_1)_2, (F_2)_1, (F_2)_2$ by writing "$F_{1,1}$," "$F_{1,2}$", "$F_{2,1}$," "$F_{2,2}$", respectively. Thus each pair of parentheses is replaced by a single comma. In the same way we agree to denote $((F_2)_1)_1$ and $((F_2)_1)_2$ by writing "$F_{2,1,1}$" and "$F_{2,1,2}$", respectively. One more example should suffice to illustrate this parentheses-omitting convention: $((((F_1)_2)_2)_1)_2$ is denoted by "$F_{1,2,2,1,2}$". As a further abbreviation we shall sometimes omit commas; for example, we shall denote $F_{2,1}$ by writing "F_{21}".

Now consider the function $X^3 \cdot Y^2 + 5X \cdot \sin(X \cdot Y^3)$, which we shall denote by "F". Then

$$F_1 = 3X^2 \cdot Y^2 + 5\sin(X \cdot Y^3) + 5X \cdot Y^3 \cdot \cos(X \cdot Y^3),$$

$$F_{1,2} = 6X^2 \cdot Y + 15X \cdot Y^2 \cdot \cos(X \cdot Y^3) + 15X \cdot Y^2 \cdot \cos(X \cdot Y^3)$$
$$- 15X^2 \cdot Y^5 \cdot \sin(X \cdot Y^3),$$

$$F_2 = 2X^3 \cdot Y + 15X^2 \cdot Y^2 \cdot \cos(X \cdot Y^3),$$

$$F_{2,1} = 6X^2 \cdot Y + 30X \cdot Y^2 \cdot \cos(X \cdot Y^3) - 15X^2 \cdot Y^5 \cdot \sin(X \cdot Y^3).$$

We see that $F_{1,2} = F_{2,1}$; no doubt the reader has already observed that the order of partial differentiation is immaterial. This result is important and warrants a precise statement and proof.

THEOREM 6.5.11. $F_{1,2} = F_{2,1}$ whenever F is an elementary function with two arguments.

Proof: We apply Metatheorem 6.3.1.

1. $X_{1,2} = 1_2 = 0$ and $X_{2,1} = 0_1 = 0$, $Y_{1,2} = 0_2 = 0$, and $Y_{2,1} = 1_1 = 0$; furthermore, $k_{1,2} = 0_2 = 0$ and $k_{2,1} = 0_1 = 0$ whenever k is a real number. Thus each atomic elementary function has the stated property.

2. Assume that G and H are elementary functions with the stated property, i.e., $G_{1,2} = G_{2,1}$ and $H_{1,2} = H_{2,1}$. Then

$$(G + H)_{1,2} = (G_1 + H_1)_2 = G_{1,2} + H_{1,2} \qquad \text{by Th. 6.5.5'}$$

$$(G + H)_{2,1} = (G_2 + H_2)_1 = G_{2,1} + H_{2,1} \qquad \text{by Th. 6.5.5'}$$

$$= G_{1,2} + H_{1,2} \qquad \text{by assumption.}$$

Hence $G + H$ has the stated property. Also,

$$(G \cdot H)_{1,2} = (G \cdot H_1 + G_1 \cdot H)_2 \qquad \text{by Th. 6.5.6'}$$

$$= (G \cdot H_1)_2 + (G_1 \cdot H)_2 \qquad \text{by Th. 6.5.5'}$$

$$= G \cdot H_{1,2} + G_2 \cdot H_1 + G_1 \cdot H_2 + G_{1,2} \cdot H \qquad \text{by Th. 6.5.6',}$$

and

$$(G \cdot H)_{2,1} = (G \cdot H_2 + G_2 \cdot H)_1 \qquad \text{by Th. 6.5.6'}$$

$$= (G \cdot H_2)_1 + (G_2 \cdot H)_1 \qquad \text{by Th. 6.5.5'}$$

$$= G \cdot H_{2,1} + G_1 \cdot H_2 + G_2 \cdot H_1 + G_{2,1} \cdot H \qquad \text{by Th. 6.5.6' .}$$

$$= G \cdot H_{1,2} + G_1 \cdot H_2 + G_2 \cdot H_1 + G_{1,2} \cdot H \qquad \text{by assumption.}$$

Hence $G \cdot H$ has the stated property.

3. Assume that G is an elementary function with two arguments such that $G_{1,2} = G_{2,1}$, and that h is any elementary function with one argument. Then

$$[h(G)]_{1,2} = [h'(G) \cdot G_1]_2 \qquad \text{by Th. 6.5.8'}$$

$$= h'(G) \cdot G_{1,2} + [h'(G)]_2 \cdot G_1 \qquad \text{by Th. 6.5.6'}$$

$$= h'(G) \cdot G_{1,2} + h^{(2)}(G) \cdot G_2 \cdot G_1 \qquad \text{by Th. 6.5.8',}$$

and $\qquad [h(G)]_{2,1} = [h'(G) \cdot G_2]_1 \qquad \text{by Th. 6.5.8'}$

$$= h'(G) \cdot G_{2,1} + [h'(G)]_1 \cdot G_2 \qquad \text{by Th. 6.5.6'}$$

$$= h'(G) \cdot G_{2,1} + h^{(2)}(G) \cdot G_1 \cdot G_2 \qquad \text{by Th. 6.5.8'}$$

$$= h'(G) \cdot G_{1,2} + h^{(2)}(G) \cdot G_1 \cdot G_2 \qquad \text{by assumption.}$$

Hence $h(G)$ has the stated property.

By applying Metatheorem 6.3.1, Theorem 6.5.11 is established.

It is convenient to use partial derivatives to characterize the tangent plane to a surface at a point on the surface.

THEOREM 6.5.12. Suppose that $[a - h, a + h] \times [b - k, b + k]$ is a subset of both $\mathscr{D}_{F_1}$ and $\mathscr{D}_{F_2}$, and suppose that there is a tangent plane to the graph of F at (a, b, c), where $c = F(a, b)$. Then this tangent plane is

$$\{(x, y, z) \mid F_1(a, b)(x - a) + F_2(a, b)(y - b) - (z - c) = 0.\}$$

Proof: See Section 6.4.

EXERCISES

Compute the following:

1. $_0(X \cdot Y^2)_1$.
2. $_3(X^2 \cdot Y + Y^3)_1$.
3. $(X^2 \cdot Y + Y^3)_1$.
4. $_7(X + 5Y)_2$.
5. $(X + 5Y)_2$.

6. $_a(3X \cdot Y^2 - 7X^3)_2$.
7. $(3X \cdot Y^2 - 7X^3)_2$.
8. $[\sin(X^2 \cdot Y^2)]_1$.
9. $\sin([X^2 \cdot Y^2]_1)$.
10. $(\sin[(X^2 \cdot Y^2)_1])_2$.

11. Let F be any function with two arguments such that $(a, b) \in \mathscr{D}_{F_2}$; suppose (b_n) is any sequence such that $\lim(b_n) = b$, $b_n \neq b$, and $(a, b_n) \in \mathscr{D}_F$ for each n. Prove that $\lim(F(a, b_n)) = F(a, b)$.

12. Prove that $(G \cdot H)_2 = G \cdot H_2 + G_2 \cdot H$ provided $\mathscr{D}_{G_2} = \mathscr{D}_G$ and $\mathscr{D}_{H_2} = \mathscr{D}_H$.

Use Theorems 6.5.4 through 6.5.9 to compute the following:

13. $[X \cdot Y + \sin(X \cdot Y)]_1$.
14. $[X \cdot Y + \cos(X + Y)]_2$.
15. $[\log(X^2 + 3Y + 5Y^3)]_2$.
16. $[X \cdot \exp(X^3 + X^2 \cdot Y)]_1$.
17. $[(X^2 \cdot Y)(\sin(X), \cos(X \cdot Y))]_2$.
18. $[\sin^2(X) \cdot \cos(X \cdot Y)]_2$.

19. Given that G and H are elementary functions, prove that

$$[F(G, H)]_1 = F_1(G, H) \cdot G_1 + F_2(G, H) \cdot H_1$$

whenever F is an elementary function. Use Metatheorem 6.3.1.

20. Given that G and H are elementary functions, prove that

$$[F(G, H)]_2 = F_1(G, H) \cdot G_2 + F_2(G, H) \cdot H_2$$

whenever F is an elementary function. Use Metatheorem 6.5.1.

21. Given that $F_1 = 8X^3 \cdot Y$ and $_0F_2 = \{(b, c)\,|\,c = 3b\}$, find F.   *(Answer: $F = 2X^4 \cdot Y + 3Y$)*
22. Given that $F_2 = X^2 \cdot \cos(X^2 \cdot Y)$ and $_1F_1 = \{(a, c)\,|\,c = a^2 \cos a^2 + a^2\}$, find F.
(Answer: $F = \sin(X^2 \cdot Y) + X^2$)
23. Given that $F_1 = 4X \cdot Y$ and $F_2 = 2X^2 + 12Y^2$, find F.   *(Answer: $F = 2X^2 \cdot Y + 4Y^3$)*

6.6   The Fundamental Theorem of Partial Derivatives

In this section we shall establish a basic result about functions with several arguments which corresponds to the Mean Value Theorem for functions with one argument, and in fact relies upon the Mean Value Theorem. The proof of our result centers around the process for reducing a function with two arguments to a function with one argument (see Definition 6.5.1 and Definition 6.5.3).

The notion of an *interval*, which is useful in the study of functions with one argument, is easily extended to the notion of a *2-interval* or *rectangle*.

> **DEFINITION 6.6.1.**   Let $\mathscr{I}_1$ and $\mathscr{I}_2$ be any intervals; then we shall say that $\mathscr{I}_1 \times \mathscr{I}_2$ is a *2-interval* or *rectangular*.

For example, R is an interval; therefore R_2 is a 2-interval. Again, $[2, 4]$ and $[3, 7]$ are intervals; therefore $[2, 4] \times [3, 7]$ is a 2-interval. Similarly, we see that $(2, 4) \times (3, 7)$, namely $\{(a, b)\,|\,2 < a < 4$ and $3 < b < 7\}$, is a 2-interval. More generally, if h and k are positive real numbers and if a and b are real numbers, then $[a - h, a + h] \times [b - k, b + k]$ is a 2-interval.

We need two preliminary results.

> **THEOREM 6.6.1.**   Suppose that the 2-interval $\mathscr{I}_1 \times \mathscr{I}_2$ is a subset of $\mathscr{D}_{F_1}$; then $_bF_1$ is differentiable throughout the interval $\mathscr{I}_1$ (i.e. $\mathscr{I}_1 \subset \mathscr{D}_{(_bF_1)'}$).
> *Proof:*   Apply Definition 6.5.2.

> **THEOREM 6.6.2.**   Suppose that the 2-interval $\mathscr{I}_1 \times \mathscr{I}_2$ is a subset of $\mathscr{D}_{F_2}$; then $_aF_2$ is differentiable throughout the interval $\mathscr{I}_2$ (i.e. $\mathscr{I}_2 \subset \mathscr{D}_{(_aF_2)'}$).
> *Proof:*   Apply Definition 6.5.4.

We are now in a position to consider our basic result.

> **FUNDAMENTAL THEOREM OF PARTIAL DERIVATIVES.**   Suppose that $[a - h, a + h] \times [b - k, b + k]$ is a subset of $\mathscr{D}_{F_1}$ and of $\mathscr{D}_{F_2}$, suppose that $((a_n, b_n))$ is any $[F, (a, b)]$-sequence whose terms are members of the given 2-interval, and suppose that F_1 and F_2 are continuous at (a, b). Then corresponding to each natural number n there are real numbers s_n and t_n such that $F(a_n, b_n) - F(a, b) = (a_n - a)[F_1(a, b) + s_n] + (b_n - b)[F_2(a, b) + t_n]$; furthermore, $\lim(s_n) = \lim(t_n) = 0$.

Proof: Let n be any natural number; then

$$F(a_n, b_n) - F(a, b) = F(a_n, b_n) - F(a, b_n) + F(a, b_n) - F(a, b)$$

$$= {}_{b_n}F_1(a_n) - {}_{b_n}F_1(a) + {}_aF_2(b_n) - {}_aF_2(b)$$

$$= (a_n - a)({}_{b_n}F_1)'(c_n) + (b_n - b)({}_aF_2)'(d_n) \qquad \text{by the Mean Value Theorem, where } c_n \text{ is between } a \text{ and } a_n, \text{ and } d_n \text{ is between } b \text{ and } b_n$$

$$= (a_n - a)F_1(c_n, b_n) + (b_n - b)F_2(a, d_n)$$

$$= (a_n - a)[F_1(a, b) + s_n] + (b_n - b)[F_2(a, b) + t_n]$$

where $s_n = F_1(c_n, b_n) - F_1(a, b)$ and $t_n = F_2(a, d_n) - F_2(a, b)$. Moreover, since F_1 is continuous at (a, b),

$$\lim(F_1(c_n, b_n)) = F_1(\lim(c_n), \lim(b_n)) = F_1(a, b),$$

i.e., $\lim(F_1(a, b) + s_n) = F_1(a, b)$. Thus $\lim(s_n) = 0$. Similarly, since F_2 is continuous at (a, b), it follows that $\lim(t_n) = 0$. This establishes our theorem.

The Fundamental Theorem of Partial Derivatives is the basis of a technique for proving the theorems of Section 6.5. For example, we present the following alternative proof.

Alternative Proof of Theorem 6.5.9: Let (a, b) be any member of the domain of $F(G, H)$ and let (a_n, b) be an $[F(G, H), (a, b)]$-sequence. Then

$$\lim\left(\frac{F(G, H)(a_n, b) - F(G, H)(a, b)}{a_n - a}\right) = \lim\left(\frac{F(G(a_n, b), H(a_n, b)) - F(G(a, b), H(a, b))}{a_n - a}\right)$$

$$= \lim\left(\frac{[G(a_n, b) - G(a, b)][F_1(G(a, b), H(a, b)) + s_n] + [H(a_n, b) - H(a, b)][F_2(G(a, b), H(a, b)) + t_n]}{a_n - a}\right)$$

by the Fundamental Theorem, where $\lim(s_n) = \lim(t_n) = 0$

$$= G_1(a, b) \lim(F_1(G, H)(a, b) + s_n) + H_1(a, b) \lim(F_2(G, H)(a, b) + t_n)$$

$$= [F_1(G, H) \cdot G_1](a, b) + [F_2(G, H) \cdot H_1](a, b).$$

Therefore

$$[F(G, H)]_1 = \{((a, b), c) \mid c = [F_1(G, H) \cdot G_1 + F_2(G, H) \cdot H_1](a, b)\}$$

$$= F_1(G, H) \cdot G_1 + F_2(G, H) \cdot H_1.$$

The second part of the theorem can be established in a similar way.

We now introduce a useful method of constructing a function with one argument from a function with two arguments, say H, and two functions with one argument, say f and g.

DEFINITION 6.6.2. $H(f, g) = \{(a, b) \mid b = H(f(a), g(a))\}$.

Notice that this is an extension of the idea of a composite function. For example, $[X^2 \cdot Y](\sin, 1/x) = \{(a, b) \mid b = (\sin^2 a)/a\} = \sin^2/x$; indeed, $[X^2 \cdot Y](f, g) = f^2 \cdot g$ whenever f and g are functions with one argument. Note that $[X^2/Y](\sin, 1/x) = x \sin^2 R \; \mathcal{D}_{1/x}$.

We now use our Fundamental Theorem of Partial Derivatives to establish the following generalization of the Chain Rule.

THEOREM 6.6.3. $[H(f, g)]' = H_1(f, g) \cdot f' + H_2(f, g) \cdot g'$ provided that $\mathcal{D}_{H_1} = \mathcal{D}_{H_2} = \mathcal{D}_H$, $\mathcal{D}_{f'} = \mathcal{D}_f$, and $\mathcal{D}_{g'} = \mathcal{D}_g$.

Proof: Let $a \in \mathcal{D}_{H(f,g)}$ and let (a_n) be any $(H(f, g), a)$-sequence. Then

$$\lim\left(\frac{H(f, g)(a_n) - H(f, g)(a)}{a_n - a}\right) = \lim\left(\frac{H(f(a_n), g(a_n)) - H(f(a), g(a))}{a_n - a}\right)$$

$$= \lim\left(\frac{[f(a_n) - f(a)][H_1(f(a), g(a)) + s_n] + [g(a_n) - g(a)][H_2(f(a), g(a)) + t_n]}{a_n - a}\right)$$

$$= H_1(f(a), g(a)) \cdot f'(a) + H_2(f(a), g(a)) \cdot g'(a) + f'(a) \cdot \lim(s_n) + g'(a) \cdot \lim(t_n)$$

$$= [H_1(f, g) \cdot f' + H_2(f, g) \cdot g'](a),$$

since $\lim(s_n) = \lim(t_n) = 0$. Hence $[H(f, g)]'(a) = [H_1(f, g) \cdot f' + H_2(f, g) \cdot g'](a)$ whenever $a \in \mathcal{D}_{H(f,g)}$; therefore

$$[H(f, g)]' = \{(a, b) \mid b = [H_1(f, g) \cdot f' + H_2(f, g) \cdot g'](a)\} = H_1(f, g) \cdot f' + H_2(f, g) \cdot g'.$$

This establishes Theorem 6.6.3.

From the proof of Theorem 6.6.3 it is easy to establish the following theorem.

THEOREM 6.6.4. $[H(f, g)]'(a) = H_1(f(a), g(a)) \cdot f'(a) + H_2(f(a), g(a)) \cdot g'(a)$ if

(i) $a \in \mathcal{D}_{f'} \cap \mathcal{D}_{g'}$,

(ii) $(f(a), g(a)) \in \mathcal{D}_{H_1} \cap \mathcal{D}_{H_2}$.

EXAMPLE 1.   Compute $[H(f, g)]'$, where $H = X^2 + Y^3$, $f = x \sin$, and $g = \cos$.
Solution: Here, $H_1 = 2X$, $H_2 = 3Y^2$, $f' = x \cos + \sin$, and $g' = -\sin$; therefore

$$[H(f, g)]' = 2X(f, g) \cdot [x \cos + \sin] + 3Y^2(f, g) \cdot [-\sin]$$

$$= 2f \cdot [x \cos + \sin] + 3g^2 \cdot [-\sin]$$

$$= 2x \sin \cdot [x \cos + \sin] + 3 \cos^2 \cdot [-\sin]$$

$$= 2x^2 \sin \cdot \cos + 2x \sin^2 - 3 \cos^2 \cdot \sin.$$

THEOREM 6.6.5.   Let f and H be functions such that $\mathcal{D}_f$ is an interval, $\mathcal{D}_{H_1} = \mathcal{D}_{H_2} = \mathcal{D}_H$, and $H(t, f(t)) = k$ whenever $t \in \mathcal{D}_f$; then $f' = -H_1(x, f)/H_2(x, f)$.

Proof: Clearly, $H(x, f) = k \ \mathrm{R} \ \mathcal{D}_f$. Since $\mathcal{D}_f$ is an interval, $[H(x, f)]' = 0 \ \mathrm{R} \ \mathcal{D}_f$. Therefore $H_1(x, f) + H_2(x, f) \cdot f' = 0 \ \mathrm{R} \ \mathcal{D}_f$. Thus $f' = -H_1(x, f)/H_2(x, f)$. This establishes our result.

EXAMPLE 2.   Determine f', given that $\mathcal{D}_f = [-r, r]$ and that $t^2 + f^2(t) = r^2$ whenever $t \in \mathcal{D}_f$.

Solution: The conditions of Theorem 6.6.5 are satisfied, where $H = X^2 + Y^2$; therefore $f' = -2X(x, f)/2Y(x, f) = -x/f$.

E X E R C I S E S

1. Show that $\{(a, b) \mid 2 \leq a < 4 \text{ and } 3 < b \leq 7\}$ is a 2-interval.

2. Prove Theorem 6.6.1.

3. Prove Theorem 6.6.2.

4. Prove that $H(f, g)$ is continuous, given that H, f, and g are continuous.

5. Use the Fundamental Theorem of Partial Derivatives to prove the second part of Theorem 6.5.9.

6. Use the Fundamental Theorem of Partial Derivatives to prove Theorem 6.5.6.

7. Let $H = X \cdot Y$.
   a. Simplify $H(f, g)$.
   b. Use Theorem 6.6.3 to obtain $[H(f, g)]'$.

8. Obtain $[H(f, g)]'$, given the following.
   a. $H = 2XY^2, f = \log, g = x^2$.
   b. $H = \tan(XY), f = 1 + x^2, g = 1/x$.
   c. $H = \exp(X + 2Y^3), f = \sec^2, g = \arctan$.

9. Use Theorem 6.6.5 to determine f', given the following.
   a. $\mathcal{D}_f = R$ and $t^3 + tf(t) = 0$ whenever $t \in R$.
   b. $\mathcal{D}_f = [1, 2]$ and $1/t + t/f(t) = 0$ whenever $t \in [1, 2]$.
   c. $\mathcal{D}_f = R$ and $\log|t| + \exp(f(t)) = 10$ whenever $t \in R$.

6.7 Functions with Three Arguments

The ideas discussed in this chapter can be extended to functions with more than two arguments. In particular, we shall consider the case of functions with three arguments. By a function with three arguments we mean any mapping of a subset of R_3 into R. We have agreed to use small letters for functions with one argument, and capital letters for functions with two arguments. Rather than introduce additional symbols, let us agree to use capital letters for functions with three arguments; we shall rely on the context to avoid ambiguity. Again, we shall say that the empty set $\emptyset$ is a function with three arguments, the vacuous function. Consider the following definitions.

DEFINITION 6.7.1. $X = \{((a, b, c), a) \mid (a. b, c) \in R_3\}$.

DEFINITION 6.7.2. $Y = \{((a, b, c), b) \mid (a, b, c) \in R_3\}$.

DEFINITION 6.7.3. $Z = \{((a, b, c), c) \mid (a, b, c) \in R_3\}$.

DEFINITION 6.7.4. $k = \{((a, b, c), k) \mid (a, b, c) \in R_3\}$ whenever $k \in R$.

DEFINITION 6.7.5. $h(F) = \{((a, b, c), d) \mid d = h(F(a, b, c))\}$ whenever h is a function with one argument and F is a function with three arguments.

DEFINITION   6.7.6. $K(F, G, H) = \{((a, b, c), d) \mid d = K(F(a, b, c), \quad G(a, b, c), H(a, b, c))\}$ whenever $F, G, H,$ and K are functions with three arguments.

A function with one argument can be constructed from one function with three arguments and from three functions with one argument.

DEFINITION 6.7.7. $K(f, g, h) = \{(a, b) \mid b = K(f(a), g(a), h(a))\}$ whenever K is a function with three arguments and $f, g,$ and h are functions with one argument.

Moreover, a function with three arguments can be reduced to a function with one argument, as follows.

DEFINITION 6.7.8. $_{b,c}F_1 = \{(a, d) \mid d = F(a, b, c)\}$ whenever F is a function with three arguments.

DEFINITION 6.7.9. $_{a,c}F_2 = \{(b, d) \mid d = F(a, b, c)\}$ whenever F is a function with three arguments.

DEFINITION 6.7.10. $_{a,b}F_3 = \{(c, d) \mid d = F(a, b, c)\}$ whenever F is a function with three arguments.

The partial derivatives of a function with three arguments are defined as follows.

DEFINITION 6.7.11. $F_1 = \{((a, b, c), d) \mid d = (_{b,c}F_1)'(a)\}$ whenever F is a function with three arguments.

DEFINITION 6.7.12. $F_2 = \{((a, b, c), d) \mid d = (_{a,c}F_2)'(b)\}$ whenever F is a function with three arguments.

DEFINITION 6.7.13. $F_3 = \{((a, b, c), d) \mid d = ({}_{a,b}F_3)'(c)\}$ whenever F is a function with three arguments.

We need the notion of an $[F, (a, b, c)]$-sequence.

DEFINITION 6.7.14. $((a_n, b_n, c_n))$ is said to be an $[F, (a, b, c)]$-sequence iff

(i) $\lim(a_n, b_n, c_n) = (a, b, c)$,

(ii) $(a_n, b_n, c_n) \in \mathscr{D}_F$ whenever $n \in N$,

(iii) $(a_n, b_n, c_n) \neq (a, b, c)$ whenever $n \in N$.

DEFINITION 6.7.15. $\lim_{(a,b,c)} F = L$ iff

(i) $\lim(F(a_n, b_n, c_n)) = L$ whenever $((a_n, b_n, c_n))$ is an $[F, (a, b, c)]$-sequence,

(ii) an $[F, (a, b, c)]$-sequence exists.

DEFINITION 6.7.16. F is said to be *continuous* at (a, b, c) iff $\lim_{(a,b,c)} F = F(a, b, c)$.

The following theorems are useful.

THEOREM 6.7.1.   Let $(a, b, c) \in \mathscr{D}_{F_1}$ and let $((a_n, b, c))$ be an $[F, (a, b, c)]$-sequence;

then $$F_1(a, b, c) = \lim\left(\frac{F(a_n, b, c) - F(a, b, c)}{a_n - a}\right).$$

Proof: Apply Definition 6.7.11.

THEOREM 6.7.2.   Let $(a, b, c) \in \mathscr{D}_{F_2}$ and let $((a, b_n, c))$ be an $[F, (a, b, c)]$-sequence; then

$$F_2(a, b, c) = \lim\left(\frac{F(a, b_n, c) - F(a, b, c)}{b_n - b}\right).$$

Proof: Apply Definition 6.7.12.

THEOREM 6.7.3.   Let $(a, b, c) \in \mathscr{D}_{F_3}$ and let $((a, b, c_n))$ be an $[F, (a, b, c)]$-sequence; then

$$F_3(a, b, c) = \lim\left(\frac{F(a, b, c_n) - F(a, b, c)}{c_n - c}\right).$$

202   Calculus

Proof: Apply Definition 6.7.13.

Corresponding to our Fundamental Theorem of Partial Derivatives, we have the following theorem.

THEOREM 6.7.4.   Suppose that $((a_n, b_n, c_n))$ is any $[F, (a, b, c)]$-sequence and that F_1, F_2, and F_3 are continuous at (a, b, c). Then corresponding to each natural number n there are real numbers s_n, t_n, and u_n such that

$$F(a_n, b_n, c_n) - F(a, b, c) = (a_n - a)[F_1(a, b, c) + s_n] + (b_n - b)[F_2(a, b, c) + t_n]$$
$$+ (c_n - c)[F_3(a, b, c) + u_n].$$

Furthermore, $\lim(s_n) = \lim(t_n) = \lim(u_n) = 0$.

Proof: First, note that $F(a_n, b_n, c_n) - F(a, b, c) = F(a_n, b_n, c_n) - F(a, b_n, c_n) + F(a, b_n, c_n) - F(a, b, c_n) + F(a, b, c_n) - F(a, b, c)$; next, apply the Mean Value Theorem.

Corresponding to Theorem 6.6.3, we have the following theorem.

THEOREM 6.7.5. $[K(f, g, h)]' = K_1(f, g, h) \cdot f' + K_2(f, g, h) \cdot g' + K_3(f, g, h) \cdot h'$ provided that $\mathscr{D}_{K_1} = \mathscr{D}_{K_2} = \mathscr{D}_{K_3} = \mathscr{D}_K$, $\mathscr{D}_{f'} = \mathscr{D}_f$, $\mathscr{D}_{g'} = \mathscr{D}_g$, and $\mathscr{D}_{h'} = \mathscr{D}_h$.
Proof: Apply Theorem 6.7.4.

THEOREM 6.7.6.   Let K be any continuous function with three arguments and let F, G, and H be any continuous functions with three arguments; then

$$[K(F, G, H)]_1 = K_1(F, G, H) \cdot F_1 + K_2(F, G, H) \cdot G_1 + K_3(F, G, H) \cdot H_1,$$
$$[K(F, G, H)]_2 = K_1(F, G, H) \cdot F_2 + K_2(F, G, H) \cdot G_2 + K_3(F, G, H) \cdot H_2,$$
$$[K(F, G, H)]_3 = K_1(F, G, H) \cdot F_3 + K_2(F, G, H) \cdot G_3 + K_3(F, G, H) \cdot H_3.$$
Proof: Let (a_n, b, c) be a $[K(F, G, H), (a, b, c)]$-sequence; then

$$\lim\left(\frac{K(F, G, H)(a_n, b, c) - K(F, G, H)(a, b, c)}{a_n - a}\right)$$
$$= \lim\left(\frac{[F(a_n, b, c) - F(a, b, c)][K_1(F, G, H)(a, b, c) + s_n]}{a_n - a}\right)$$
$$+ \lim\left(\frac{[G(a_n, b, c) - G(a, b, c)][K_2(F, G, H)(a, b, c) + t_n]}{a_n - a}\right)$$
$$+ \lim\left(\frac{[H(a_n, b, c) - H(a, b, c)][K_3(F, G, H)(a, b, c) + u_n]}{a_n - a}\right) \quad \text{by Th. 6.7.4}$$
$$= [K_1(F, G, H) \cdot F_1 + K_2(F, G, H) \cdot G_1 + K_3(F, G, H) \cdot H_1](a, b, c).$$

Therefore, by Theorem 6.7.1,

$$[K(F, G, H)]_1(a, b, c) = [K_1(F, G, H) \cdot F_1 + K_2(F, G, H) \cdot G_1$$

$$+ K_3(F, G, H) \cdot H_1](a, b, c);$$

hence $[K(F, G, H)]_1 = K_1(F, G, H) \cdot F_1 + K_2(F, G, H) \cdot G_1 + K_3(F, G, H) \cdot H_1$. This establishes the first part of our theorem; the remainder of the theorem can be demonstrated in a similar fashion.

THEOREM 6.7.7. Let F be any function with two arguments whose domain is rectangular, and let K be any function with three arguments such that $K(X, Y, F) = 0 \text{ R } \mathscr{D}_F$. Then $F_1 = -K_1(X, Y, F)/K_3(X, Y, F)$ and $F_2 = -K_2(X, Y, F)/K_3(X, Y, F)$.

Proof: Since $K(X, Y, F) = 0 \text{ R } \mathscr{D}_F$, it follows that $[K(X, Y, F)]_1 = 0 \text{ R } \mathscr{D}_F$.
Clearly, $[K(X, Y, F)]_1 = K_1(X, Y, F) + K_3(X, Y, F) \cdot F_1$. Therefore $K_1(X, Y, F) + K_3(X, Y, F) \cdot F_1 = 0 \text{ R } \mathscr{D}_F$; hence $F_1 = -K_1(X, Y, F)/K_3(X, Y, F)$. Similarly, it is easy to prove that $F_2 = -K_2(X, Y, F)/K_3(X, Y, F)$.

EXAMPLE 1. Compute F_1, given that $\mathscr{D}_F$ is a 2-interval and that $X \cdot Y^2 + X \cdot F - F^2 = 0 \text{ R } \mathscr{D}_F$.

Solution: Here, $K = XY^2 + XZ - Z^2$; thus $K_1 = Y^2 + Z$ and $K_3 = X - 2Z$. Therefore, by Theorem 6.7.7, $F_1 = -K_1(X, Y, F)/K_3(X, Y, F) = -(Y^2 + F)/(X - 2F)$.

As another application of Theorem 6.7.7, we present a symmetric method of representing the tangent plane to the graph of a function.

THEOREM 6.7.8. Suppose that F is a function with two arguments such that $[a - h, a + h] \times [b - k, b + k]$ is a subset of both $\mathscr{D}_{F_1}$ and $\mathscr{D}_{F_2}$, let K be a function with three arguments such that $K(X, Y, F) = 0 \text{ R } \mathscr{D}_F$, and suppose there is a tangent plane to the graph of F at (a, b, c), where $c = F(a, b)$. Then this tangent plane is

$$\{(x, y, z) \mid K_1(a, b, c)(x - a) + K_2(a, b, c)(y - b) + K_3(a, b, c)(z - c) = 0\}.$$

Proof: By Theorem 6.5.12, the required tangent plane is

$$\{(x, y, z) \mid F_1(a, b)(x - a) + F_2(a, b)(y - b) - (z - c) = 0\}.$$

In view of Theorem 6.7.7, $F_1(a, b) = -K_1(a, b, c)/K_3(a, b, c)$ and $F_2(a, b) = -K_2(a, b, c)/K_3(a, b, c)$; therefore the required tangent plane is

$$\{(x, y, z) \mid K_1(a, b, c)(x - a) + K_2(a, b, c)(y - b) + K_3(a, b, c)(z - c) = 0\}.$$

This establishes Theorem 6.7.8.

EXAMPLE 2. Determine the tangent plane to the graph of F at $(2, 0, 8)$, given that $\mathscr{D}_{F_1} = \mathscr{D}_{F_2} = R_2$ and $X^2 Y + X^3 - F + YF^2 = 0$.

Solution 1: Here, $K = X^2 Y + X^3 - Z + YZ^2$; therefore $K_1 = 2XY + 3X^2$, $K_2 = X^2 + Z^2$, and $K_3 = -1 + 2YZ$; so $K_1(2, 0, 8) = 12$, $K_2(2, 0, 8) = 68$, and $K_3(2, 0, 8) = -1$. Thus, by Theorem 6.7.8, the required tangent plane is $\{(x, y, z) \mid 12(x - 2) + 68y - (z - 8) = 0\}$.

We present another solution which bypasses Theorem 6.7.8.

Solution 2: Since $X^2 Y + X^3 - F + YF^2 = 0$, it follows that $2XY + 3X^2 - F_1 + 2YFF_1 = 0$ and $X^2 - F_2 + F^2 + 2YFF_2 = 0$. Therefore $F_1 = (2XY + 3X^2)/(1 - 2YF)$ and $F_2 = (X^2 + F^2)/(1 - 2YF)$. Hence $F_1(2, 0) = 12$ and $F_2(2, 0) = 68$. Thus, by Theorem 6.5.12, the required tangent plane is $\{(x, y, z) \mid 12(x - 2) + 68y - (z - 8) = 0\}$.

EXERCISES

Simplify the following.

1. $X(F, G, H)$.

2. $Y(F, G, H)$.

3. $Z(F, G, H)$.

4. $[XY](Z, Y, X)$.

5. $Z^2(F, G, H)$.

6. $_{b,c}[XZ]_1$.

7. $_{b,c}[XY]_1$.

8. $_{a,c}[XY]_2$.

9. $_{b,b}[XY]_2$.

10. $_{a,b}[\sin(Z)]_3$.

11. $_{a,b}[X^2 \cdot \sin(Z)]_3$.

12. $_{c,a}[X^2 \cdot \sin(Z)]_3$.

13. $[X^2 \cdot \sin(Z)]_1$.

14. $[XYZ^2]_3$.

15. $[XYZ^2]_2$.

16. Prove Theorem 6.7.1.

17. Prove Theorem 6.7.2.

18. Prove Theorem 6.7.3.

19. Prove Theorem 6.7.4.

20. Prove Theorem 6.7.5.

6.8 Directional Derivatives

We return now to the problem of Section 6.4; we want to prove that the plane $\{(x, y, z) \mid F_1(a, b)(x - a) + F_2(a, b)(y - b) - (z - c) = 0\}$ contains the tangent at (a, b, c) to the curve of intersection of the graph of F and the plane $\mathscr{P}$ whenever $\mathscr{P}$ is a plane through (a, b, c) which is perpendicular to the XY-plane. In the following we shall assume that F possesses continuous partial derivatives.

First, we note that $\mathscr{P}$ is characterized by its trace in the XY-plane, namely the line of intersection of these two planes. (See Figure 6.8.1.) In turn, this line, say L, is characterized by the angle θ which it forms with the X-axis. To be precise, θ is found as follows: if L does not intersect the X-axis, then $\theta = 0$; otherwise, consider the unit circle whose center is the point of intersection of the X-axis and L; then θ is the length of the arc of this circle which is between the X-axis and L, measured counterclockwise (viewed from the positive Z-axis) from the X-axis. Clearly, $L = \{(a + t \cos \theta, b + t \sin \theta, 0) \mid t \in R\}$ and $\mathscr{P} = \{(x, y, z) \mid (x - a) \sin \theta - (y - b) \cos \theta = 0\}$. Let $\mathscr{C}$ be the curve of intersection of the graph of F and the plane $\mathscr{P}$; then $\mathscr{C} = \{(a + t \cos \theta, b + t \sin \theta, F(a + t \cos \theta, b + t \sin \theta)) \mid t \in R\}$. Our problem is to determine the tangent to $\mathscr{C}$ at (a, b, c). We simplify the geometry by imposing a coordinate system on the plane $\mathscr{P}$. For H we take the line L, directed from $(a, b, 0)$ to $(a + \cos \theta, b +$ $\sin \theta, 0)$, and for V we take the line through $(a, b, 0)$ which is perpendicular to L and is in the plane $\mathscr{P}$, namely $\{(a, b, t) \mid t \in R\}$; further-more, we direct V so that it has the same direction as the Z-axis. The origin of this coordinate system is the point $(a, b, 0)$. We have achieved a simple way of representing the curve $\mathscr{C}$. For in our coordinate system $\mathscr{C}$ is the graph of a function with one argument, namely f, where $f = F(a + x \cos \theta, b + x \sin \theta)$. Now, the tangent to $\mathscr{C}$ at $(0, c)$ has slope $f'(0)$; but, by Theorem 6.6.3, $f' = F_1(a + x \cos \theta, b + x \sin \theta) \cdot \cos \theta + F_2(a + x \cos \theta, b + x \sin \theta) \cdot \sin \theta$. Thus

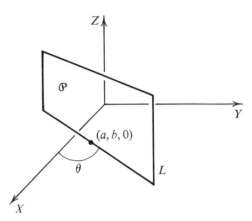

Figure 6.8.1

$$(1) \qquad f'(0) = F_1(a, b) \cdot \cos \theta + F_2(a, b) \cdot \sin \theta.$$

Now, in the HV-coordinate system the point $(1, c + f'(0))$ is on the tangent to $\mathscr{C}$. Thus in the XYZ-coordinate system the point $(a + \cos \theta, b + \sin \theta, c + f'(0))$ is on the tangent to $\mathscr{C}$. This means that in the XYZ-coordinate system our tangent has direction $(\cos \theta, \sin \theta, f'(0))$; hence the tangent to $\mathscr{C}$ is $\{(a + t \cos \theta, b + t \sin \theta, c + tf'(0)) \mid t \in R\}$. We must show that this line is contained in the plane

$$\{(x, y, z) \mid F_1(a, b)(x - a) + F_2(a, b)(y - b) - (z - c) = 0\}.$$

But, for each t,

$$F_1(a, b)[t \cos \theta] + F_2(a, b)[t \sin \theta] - tf'(0)) = t[F_1(a, b) \cos \theta + F_2(a, b) \sin \theta - f'(0)] = 0.$$

This demonstrates that the tangent plane to the graph of F at (a, b, c), where $c = F(a, b)$, is

$$\{(x, y, z) \mid F_1(a, b)(x - a) + F_2(a, b)(y - b) - (z - c) = 0\}.$$

The curve $\mathscr{C}$ discussed here is of some significance; in particular, the slope of the tangent to $\mathscr{C}$ at $(a, b, F(a, b))$ is important. We have already introduced a notation for the function involved, namely the notation "$H(f, g)$"; we need a specific notation for the derivative of $F(a + x \cos \theta, b + x \sin \theta)$. We introduce the notion of a *directional derivative*.

DEFINITION 6.8.1.   Let H be any function with two arguments such that H_1 and H_2 are continuous, and suppose that $0 \le \theta < 2\pi$; then by "$D_\theta H$" (read "the directional derivative of H in the direction θ") we mean the function $H_1 \cos \theta + H_2 \sin \theta$, i.e., $D_\theta H = H_1 \cos \theta + H_2 \sin \theta$.

Notice that $D_\theta H$ is a linear combination of the functions H_1 and H_2.

Referring to (1), we see that $f'(0) = D_\theta F(a, b)$. Thus the number that $D_\theta F$ associates with (a, b) is the slope of the tangent to the graph of $F(a + x \cos \theta, b + x \sin \theta)$ at $(a, b, F(a, b))$. In this way the directional derivative gives us the slope of the tangent to the trace of the surface in a plane perpendicular to the XY-plane.

It is worthwhile to state explicitly our result concerning the tangent line to the curve of intersection of a surface and a plane which is perpendicular to the XY-plane.

THEOREM 6.8.1.   Suppose that F_1 and F_2 are continuous; let $\mathscr{C}$ be the curve of intersection of the graph of F and the plane

$$\{(x, y, z) \mid (x - a) \sin \theta - (y - b) \cos \theta = 0\}.$$

Then the tangent to $\mathscr{C}$ at $(a, b, F(a, b))$ is the line through $(a, b, F(a, b))$ with direction $(\cos \theta, \sin \theta, D_\theta F(a, b))$, i.e., the line $\{(a + t \cos \theta, b + t \sin \theta, F(a, b) + tD_\theta F(a, b)) \mid t \in R\}$.

Clearly, the directional derivative is really a family of functions, one for each θ between 0 and 2π. In other words, $D_\theta F$ is a function whenever $0 \le \theta < 2\pi$. This family of functions contains the partial derivatives F_1 and F_2 as members, for $D_0 F = F_1$ and $D_{\pi/2} F = F_2$. Notice that $D_\pi F = -F_1$ and $D_{3\pi/2} F = -F_2$.

We now illustrate these ideas.

EXAMPLE 1.   Compute $D_{\pi/4} F$, where $F = X^3 - 2XY$.

Solution: $F_1 = 3X^2 - 2Y$ and $F_2 = -2X$; therefore

$$D_{\pi/4} F = [3X^2 - 2Y] \cos \frac{\pi}{4} - 2X \sin \frac{\pi}{4} = \frac{1}{\sqrt{2}} (3X^2 - 2Y - 2X).$$

EXAMPLE 2.   Find the tangent to the curve of intersection of the graph of $X^3 - 2XY$ and the plane $\{(x, y, z) \mid x + \sqrt{3}y - 1 - 2\sqrt{3} = 0\}$ at the point $(1, 2, -3)$.

Solution: The given plane is $\{(x, y, z) \mid (x - 1) \sin \theta - (y - 2) \cos \theta = 0\}$, where $\theta = 5\pi/6$. Therefore, by Theorem 6.8.1, the required tangent is the line through $(1, 2, -3)$ with direction $(-\sqrt{3}/2, 1/2, D_{5\pi/6}[X^3 - 2XY](1, 2))$. Now, $D_{5\pi/6}[X^3 - 2XY] = [3X^2 - 2Y](-\sqrt{3}/2) - 2X(1/2) = [-3\sqrt{3}/2] X^2 + Y\sqrt{3} - X$. Thus $D_{5\pi/6}[X^3 - 2XY](1, 2) = -3\sqrt{3}/2 + 2\sqrt{3} - 1 = \sqrt{3}/2 - 1$. Hence the required tangent line is $\{(1 - \sqrt{3}t/2, 2 + t/2, -3 + t(\sqrt{3}/2 - 1)) \mid t \in R\}$.

EXAMPLE 3.   Find θ such that $D_\theta F(2, -4)$ is a minimum, where $F = 2XY + Y^2$.

Solution: Here, $F_1 = 2Y$ and $F_2 = 2X + 2Y$; therefore $D_\theta F(2, -4) = -8 \cos \theta - 4 \sin \theta$. We are required to minimize the function $-8 \cos - 4 \sin$. By the Second Derivative Test, this function has its minimum value at arctan $\frac{1}{2}$. Therefore $D_\theta F(2, -4)$ is a minimum when $\theta = $ arctan $\frac{1}{2}$.

EXAMPLE 4. Find θ such that $D_\theta F(2, -4)$ is a maximum, where $F = 2XY + Y^2$.

Solution: Here, $F_1 = 2Y$ and $F_2 = 2X + 2Y$; therefore $D_\theta F(2, -4) = -8 \cos \theta - 4 \sin \theta$. We are required to maximize the function $-8 \cos - 4 \sin$. By the Second Derivative Test, this function has its maximum value at $\pi + \arctan \frac{1}{2}$. Therefore $D_\theta F(2, -4)$ is a maximum when $\theta = \pi + \arctan \frac{1}{2}$.

We have used the notion of a directional derivative to prove that

$$\{(x, y, z) \mid F_1(a, b)(x - a) + F_2(a, b)(y - b) - (z - c) = 0\}$$

is the tangent plane to the graph of F at (a, b, c) where $c = F(a, b)$. This fact provides us with an easy way of determining the tangent to our curve $\mathscr{C}$ at the point (a, b, c) where $\mathscr{C}$ is the curve of intersection of the graph of F and the plane $\{(x, y, z) \mid A(x - a) + B(y - b) = 0\}$; here, A and B are given numbers. Since the tangent plane at (a, b, c) contains the tangent to $\mathscr{C}$ at (a, b, c), it follows that the required tangent is the line of intersection of the planes $\{(x, y, z) \mid F_1(a, b)(x - a) + F_2(a,b)(y - b) - (z - c) = 0\}$ and $\{(x, y, z) \mid A(x - a) + B(y - b) = 0\}$. Of course, it is easy to find the line of intersection of two planes. Notice that this method avoids determining the trace of the given plane in the XY-plane and the value of the parameter θ. To illustrate this technique, we solve the problem of Example 2.

EXAMPLE 5. Find the tangent to the curve of intersection of the graph of $X^3 - 2XY$ and the plane $\{(x, y, z) \mid x + \sqrt{3}y - 1 - 2\sqrt{3} = 0\}$ at the point $(1, 2, -3)$.

Solution: Let $F = X^3 - 2XY$; then $F_1 = 3X^2 - 2Y$ and $F_2 = -2X$. Therefore the tangent plane to the graph of F at $(1, 2, -3)$ is

$$\{(x, y, z) \mid -(x - 1) - 2(y - 2) - (z + 3) = 0\}, \text{ i.e., } \{(x, y, z) \mid x + 2y + z - 2 = 0\}.$$

Now, a direction perpendicular to both $(1, 2, 1)$ and $(1, \sqrt{3}, 0)$ is $(-\sqrt{3}, 1, \sqrt{3} - 2)$. Therefore the line of intersection of the tangent plane and the given plane is $\{(1 - t\sqrt{3}, 2 + t, -3 + t(\sqrt{3} - 2)) \mid t \in R\}$. Hence this line is the required tangent.

EXAMPLE 6. Find the tangent to the curve of intersection of the graphs of $-X^2$ and $X \cdot Y$ at the point $(2, -2, -4)$.

Solution: The tangent plane to the graph of $-X^2$ at $(2, -2, -4)$ is $\{(x, y, z) \mid -4(x - 2) - (z + 4) = 0\}$. The tangent plane to the graph of $X \cdot Y$ at $(2, -2, -4)$ is $\{(x, y, z) \mid -2(x - 2) + 2(y + 2) - (z + 4) = 0\}$. The line of intersection of these planes is $\{(2 - t, -2 + t, -4 + 4t) \mid t \in R\}$. Therefore this line is the required tangent line.

Note: Since the intersection of the given graphs is the curve $\{(t, -t, -t^2) \mid t \in R\}$, we see that the tangent to this curve at the point $(s, -s, -s^2)$ has direction $(1, -1, -2s)$. For the given point, $s = 2$; therefore the required tangent line has direction $(1, -1, -4)$. This verifies our result.

Here is another, more direct method of establishing our result. Consider the graph of F and the point (a, b, c) on the graph. Suppose that the curve $\{(f(t), g(t), h(t)) \mid t \in R\}$ is contained in the given surface and passes through the given point; indeed, let $(f(t_0),$

$g(t_0), h(t_0)) = (a, b, c)$. Then, for each t, $h(t) = F(f(t), g(t))$, and so $h = F(f, g)$; thus $h' = F_1(f, g) \cdot f' + F_2(f, g) \cdot g'$. Now, the tangent to the curve at (a, b, c) has direction $(f'(t_0), g'(t_0), h'(t_0))$. Thus the tangent to the curve at (a, b, c) is $\{(a + tf'(t_0), b + tg'(t_0), c + th'(t_0)) \mid t \in R\}$. We now show that for each t the point $(a + tf'(t_0), b + tg'(t_0), c + th'(t_0))$, which is on the tangent line, is also on the plane $\{(x, y, z) \mid F_1(a, b)(x - a) + F_2(a, b)(y - b) - (z - c) = 0\}$. Now,

$$F_1(a, b)tf'(t_0) + F_2(a, b)tg'(t_0) - th'(t_0) = t[F_1(a, b)f'(t_0) + F_2(a, b)g'(t_0) - h'(t_0)] = 0,$$

since
$$h'(t_0) = F_1(f(t_0), g(t_0))f'(t_0) + F_2(f(t_0), g(t_0))g'(t_0)$$

$$= F_1(a, b)f'(t_0) + F_2(a, b)g'(t_0).$$

This establishes our result.

EXERCISES

1. Determine $D_\theta H$, given the following.
   a. $H = X^2 Y$ and $\theta = \pi/4$.
   b. $H = Y^2 \sin(X)$ and $\theta = \pi/6$.
   c. $H = X$ and $\theta = \pi/3$.
2. Determine the tangent to the curve of intersection of the graph of $X^2 + 3X^3 Y$ and the plane $\{(x, y, z) \mid x \sin \pi/5 - (y - 3) \cos \pi/5 = 0\}$ at the point $(0, 3, 0)$.
3. Determine the tangent to the curve of intersection of the graph of $X \cdot \exp(Y)$ and the plane $\{(x, y, z) \mid x/2 - (\sqrt{3}/2)(y + 2) = 0\}$ at the point $(0, -2, 0)$.
4. Find θ such that $D_\theta F(1, -1)$ is a maximum, where $F = XY^2$.
5. Find θ such that $D_\theta XY^2(0, 1)$ is a maximum.
6. Determine the tangent to the curve of intersection of the graph of $X^2 Y + 2XY$ and the plane $\{(x, y, z) \mid x + y + z = 1\}$ at the point $(0, 1, 0)$.
7. Determine the tangent to the curve of intersection of the graphs of $XY^2 - X^2 Y$ and $X^2 + Y^2 - 2X$ at the point $(1, 1, 0)$.

6.9   The Partial Derivatives Test; "Max-Min" Problems

Here, we shall consider the problem of finding the relative maxima and the relative minima of a function with two arguments. An ordered pair, say (a, b), is said to be a *relative maximum* of F iff (a, b) is an interior point of some 2-interval, contained in the domain of F, over which the values of F nowhere exceed $F(a, b)$. Similarly, (a, b) is said to be a *relative minimum* of F iff (a, b) is an interior point of some 2-interval, contained in the domain of F, over which the values of F everywhere exceed or equal $F(a, b)$. Moreover, the ordered pair (a, b) is said to be an *extremum* of F iff (a, b) is a relative maximum of F or (a, b) is a relative minimum of F.

Clearly, if (a, b) is an extremum of F, then the tangent plane to the graph of F at $(a, b, F(a, b))$ is parallel to the XY-plane. Therefore $F_1(a, b) = F_2(a, b) = 0$ whenever (a, b) is an extremum of F. Thus the vanishing of the partial derivatives is a necessary condition for an extremum. However, this is not a sufficient condition for an extremum.

To see whether (a, b) is an extremum of F, we must investigate the behavior of F in the immediate vicinity of (a, b). We want to compare the numbers $F(a, b)$ and $F(a + h, b + k)$, where h and k are not both zero [from an intuitive viewpoint, we want $(a + h, b + k)$ to be a member of $\mathcal{D}_F$ which is close to (a, b); i.e., we want h and k to be small]. We get a grip on the situation by considering $\mathcal{C}$, the curve of intersection of the graph of F and the plane perpendicular to the XY-plane whose trace in the XY-plane is the line through $(a, b, 0)$ and $(a + h, b + k, 0)$. As we have seen in Section 6.8, $\mathcal{C}$ is the graph of f, where $f = F(a + x \cos \theta, b + x \sin \theta)$ (see Figure 6.9.1). Clearly,

$$f' = [F_1 \cos \theta + F_2 \sin \theta](a + x \cos \theta, b + x \sin \theta)$$

and

$$f^{(2)} = [F_{11} \cos^2 \theta + 2F_{12} \cos \theta \sin \theta + F_{22} \sin^2 \theta](a + x \cos \theta, b + x \sin \theta).$$

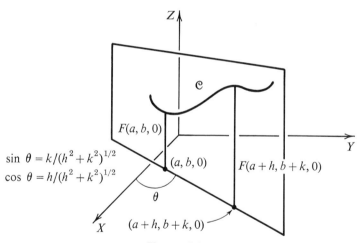

Figure 6.9.1

Now, by Taylor's Theorem, given t, there is a real number c between 0 and t, such that

(1) $$f(t) = f(0) + tf'(0) + \frac{t^2}{2} f^{(2)}(c).$$

Let t be the distance between $(a, b, 0)$ and $(a + h, b + k, 0)$, i.e., $t = (h^2 + k^2)^{1/2}$; then from (1) we obtain

(2) $F(a + h, b + k) = F(a, b) + hF_1(a, b) + kF_2(a, b)$
$$+ \tfrac{1}{2}[h^2 F_{11} + 2hk F_{12} + k^2 F_{22}](a + sh, b + sk),$$

where $0 < s < 1$. Next, suppose that $F_1(a, b) = F_2(a, b) = 0$; then from (2)

(3) $F(a + h, b + k) - F(a, b) = \frac{1}{2}[h^2 F_{11} + 2hk F_{12} + k^2 F_{22}](a + sh, b + sk)$.

Clearly, h and k are not both zero. Suppose $h \neq 0$; then there is a real number u such that $k = uh$. Thus

$$[h^2 F_{11} + 2hk F_{12} + k^2 F_{22}](a, b) = h^2[F_{11} + 2u F_{12} + u^2 F_{22}](a, b).$$

Let D be the discriminant of the quadratic $u^2 F_{22}(a, b) + 2u F_{12}(a, b) + F_{11}(a, b)$; then $D = 4[(F_{12})^2 - F_{22}F_{11}](a, b)$. If $D < 0$, then $[u^2 F_{22} + 2u F_{12} + F_{11}](a, b)$ has the same algebraic sign regardless of the value of u. Therefore, for each u,

$$[u^2 F_{22} + 2u F_{12} + F_{11}](a, b)$$

has the same algebraic sign as does $F_{11}(a, b)$. Thus, by continuity, $\frac{1}{2}[h^2 F_{11} + 2hk F_{12} + k^2 F_{22}](a + sh, b + sk)$ has the same algebraic sign as does $F_{11}(a, b)$ provided that h and k are small enough. Examining (3), we find that this means that (a, b) is a relative maximum of F if $F_{11}(a, b) < 0$, whereas (a, b) is a relative minimum of F if $F_{11}(a, b) > 0$.

Next, suppose that $[(F_{12})^2 - F_{11}F_{22}](a, b) > 0$; then there are real numbers u_1 and u_2 such that $[F_{11} + 2u_1 F_{12} + u_1^2 F_{22}](a, b) > 0$, whereas $[F_{11} + 2u_2 F_{12} + u_2^2 F_{22}](a, b) < 0$. Therefore, corresponding to any natural number q, there are points $(a + h_1, b + u_1 h_1)$ and $(a + h_2, b + u_2 h_2)$ of the rectangular region $[a - 10^{-q}, a + 10^{-q}] \times [b - 10^{-q}, b + 10^{-q}]$, found by choosing h_1 and h_2 sufficiently small, such that

$$F(a + h_2, b + u_2 h_2) < F(a, b) < F(a + h_1, b + u_1 h_1).$$

This means that (a, b) is *not* an extremum of F. We have established the following result.

THE PARTIAL DERIVATIVES TEST.   Let F_{11}, F_{22}, and F_{12} be continuous throughout a rectangular region T, and let $F_1(a, b) = F_2(a, b) = 0$, where (a, b) is an interior point of T.

1. Suppose $[(F_{12})^2 - F_{11}F_{22}](a, b) < 0$;

      (i) if $F_{11}(a, b) < 0$, then (a, b) is a relative maximum of F;
      (ii) if $F_{11}(a, b) > 0$, then (a, b) is a relative minimum of F.
2. Suppose $[(F_{12})^2 - F_{11}F_{22}](a, b) > 0$; then (a, b) is not an extremum of F.

Notice that our result leads to a positive conclusion in case

$$[(F_{12})^2 - F_{11}F_{22}](a, b) \neq 0.$$

If $[(F_{12})^2 - F_{11}F_{22}](a, b) = 0$, our theorem does *not* answer the question: is (a, b) an extremum of F? In this case we must try a direct approach.

We shall say that F is *critical* at (a, b) iff $F_1(a, b) = F_2(a, b) = 0$. For convenience, we list the steps involved in determining the extrema of F.

1. Determine the ordered pairs at which F is critical and which are interior points of some rectangular region over which F_{11}, F_{22}, and F_{12} are continuous.
2. Compute the algebraic sign of $[(F_{12})^2 - F_{11}F_{22}](a, b)$ for each (a, b) given by step 1.
3. If $[(F_{12})^2 - F_{11}F_{22}](a, b) < 0$, determine the algebraic sign of $F_{11}(a, b)$.
4. If $[(F_{12})^2 - F_{11}F_{22}](a, b) = 0$, test the values of F over a rectangular region containing (a, b).

EXAMPLE 1.   Find the extrema of $X^2 + 2Y^3 - 6Y$.

Solution: Let $F = X^2 + 2Y^3 - 6Y$; then $F_1 = 2X$, $F_2 = 6Y^2 - 6$, $F_{12} = 0$, $F_{11} = 2$, and $F_{22} = 12Y$. Clearly, F is critical at (a, b) iff $2a = 0$ and $6b^2 - 6 = 0$; therefore F is critical at $(0, 1)$ and $(0, -1)$. Now, $(F_{12})^2 - F_{11}F_{22} = -24Y$. Note that $-24Y(0, 1) < 0$, whereas $-24Y(0, -1) > 0$. Hence $(0, 1)$ is the only extremum of F. Moreover, $F_{11}(0, 1) = 2$; therefore F is a relative minimum at $(0, 1)$.

EXAMPLE 2.   Find the extrema of F where $F = 2X^2 - 4XY + Y^2$.

Solution: Here, $F_1 = 4X - 4Y$, $F_2 = -4X + 2Y$, $F_{12} = -4$, $F_{11} = 4$, and $F_{22} = 2$. Clearly, F is critical at (a, b) iff $4a - 4b = 0$ and $-4a + 2b = 0$; thus $(0, 0)$ is the only critical point of F. But $[(F_{12})^2 - F_{11}F_{22}](0, 0) = 8$; hence, by the Partial Derivatives Test, $(0, 0)$ is not an extremum of F. We conclude that F has no extremum.

EXAMPLE 3.   Compute the distance between the point $(1, -2, 3)$ and the line of intersection of the planes $\{(x, y, z) \mid x - y = 2\}$ and $\{(x, y, z) \mid 2x + y - z = 0\}$.

Solution: Let (a, b, c) be any point on the given line. The square of the distance between $(1, -2, 3)$ and (a, b, c) is $(a - 1)^2 + (b + 2)^2 + (c - 3)^2$. But (a, b, c) is on both planes; therefore $a - b = 2$ and $2a + b - c = 0$. Thus we want to minimize the function with one argument,

$$(x - 1)^2 + x^2 + (2x + x - 2 - 3)^2,$$

i.e., $11x^2 - 32x + 26$. This function is critical at $16/11$; applying the Second Derivative Test, we conclude that $11x^2 - 32x + 26$ is minimum at $16/11$. Therefore the point on the given line which is closest to $(1, -2, 3)$ is $(16/11, -6/11, 26/11)$. Thus the required distance is $\sqrt{(5/11)^2 + (16/11)^2 + (7/11)^2}$, namely $(1/11)\sqrt{330}$.

EXAMPLE 4.   Compute the distance between the point $(2, 5, -1)$ and the plane $\{(x, y, z) \mid 3x - y + z - 1 = 0\}$.

Solution: It is easy to solve this problem by using our analytic geometry; indeed, by Corollary 5.3.1, the required distance is $|6 - 5 - 1 - 1|/11^{1/2}$, i.e., $1/\sqrt{11}$. Let us solve this problem by calculus methods. Let (a, b, c) be any point on the plane; then $3a - b + c - 1 = 0$. The square of the distance between $(2, 5, -1)$ and (a, b, c) is $(a - 2)^2 + (b - 5)^2 + (c + 1)^2$. Since $c = 1 - 3a + b$, we want to minimize $(a - 2)^2 + (b - 5)^2 + (2 - 3a + b)^2$. Consider the function F, where $F = (X - 2)^2 + (Y - 5)^2 + (2 - 3X + Y)^2$; then

$$F_1 = 2(X - 2) - 6(2 - 3X + Y) = 20X - 6Y - 16,$$

$$F_2 = 2(Y - 5) + 2(2 - 3X + Y) = -6X + 4Y - 6,$$

$$F_{12} = -6, \; F_{11} = 20, \text{ and } F_{22} = 4.$$

Clearly, F is critical at (s, t) iff $10s - 3t = 8$ and $3s - 2t = -3$; therefore F is critical at $(25/11, 54/11)$. Now, $[(F_{12})^2 - F_{11}F_{22}](25/11, 54/11) = -44$. Since $F_{11}(25/11, 54/11) > 0$, we conclude by the Partial Derivatives Test that F is a minimum at $(25/11, 54/11)$. Thus the point of the given plane which is closest to $(2, 5, -1)$ is $(25/11, 54/11, -10/11)$. Hence the required distance is $\sqrt{(3/11)^2 + (1/11)^2 + (1/11)^2}$, namely $1/\sqrt{11}$.

EXAMPLE 5.   Compute the minimum distance between the lines

$$\{(t + 1, -t, 2t + 2) \mid t \in R\} \quad \text{and} \quad \{(3t, 1, 1 - t) \mid t \in R\}.$$

Solution: Let $(t + 1, -t, 2t + 2)$ and $(3s, 1, 1 - s)$ be any two points, one from each of the given lines. The square of the distance between these points is $(t - 3s + 1)^2 + (-t - 1)^2 + (2t + s + 1)^2$. We are involved with the function F, where $F = (X - 3Y + 1)^2 + (X + 1)^2 + (2X + Y + 1)^2$. Let us minimize F; now,

$$F_1 = 2(X - 3Y + 1) + 2(X + 1) + 4(2X + Y + 1) = 12X - 2Y + 8,$$

$$F_2 = -6(X - 3Y + 1) + 2(2X + Y + 1) = -2X + 20Y - 4,$$

$$F_{12} = -2, \ F_{11} = 12, \text{ and } F_{22} = 20.$$

Clearly, F is critical at (a, b) iff $6a - b = -4$ and $a - 10b = -2$; therefore F is critical at $(-38/59, 8/59)$ only. Now, $[(F_{12})^2 - F_{11}F_{22}](-38/59, 8/59) = -236 < 0$; thus $(-38/59, 8/59)$ is an extremum of F. Moreover, $F_{11}(-38/59, 8/59) = 12 > 0$; therefore F is a minimum at $(-38/59, 8/59)$. We conclude that the minimum distance between the given lines is $[F(-38/59, 8/59)]^{1/2}$, namely $\sqrt{531}/59$.

EXAMPLE 6.   Determine the dimensions of the rectangular parallelepiped of maximum volume that can be inscribed in the ellipsoid $\{(x, y, z) \mid 4x^2 + 9y^2 + z^2 = 1\}$, given that the faces of the parallelepiped are parallel to the coordinate planes.

Solution: Let the rectangular parallelepiped with dimensions $2a \times 2b \times 2c$ be inscribed in the given ellipsoid; then $4a^2 + 9b^2 + c^2 = 1$ and the volume of the parallelepiped is $8abc$. Therefore we want to maximize the function $8XYG$, where $4X^2 + 9Y^2 + G^2 = 1$. Now, $8X + 2GG_1 = 0$, so $G_1 = -4X/G$; also $18Y + 2GG_2 = 0$, so $G_2 = -9Y/G$. Let $F = 8XYG$; then

$$F_1 = 8YG + 8XYG_1 = 8YG - 32X^2Y/G,$$

$$F_2 = 8XG + 8XYG_2 = 8XG - 72XY^2/G.$$

Thus F is critical at (s, t) iff $tG(s, t) = 4s^2t/G(s, t)$ and $sG(s, t) = 9st^2/G(s, t)$; hence, if $G(s, t) \neq 0$, then $t[G^2(s, t) - 4s^2] = 0$ and $s[G(s, t) - 9t^2] = 0$, where $G^2(s, t) = 1 - 4s^2 - 9t^2$. Thus $t[1 - 8s^2 - 9t^2] = 0$ and $s[1 - 4s^2 - 18t^2] = 0$; clearly, $s \neq 0$ and $t \neq 0$, and so $1 - 8s^2 - 9t^2 = 0$ and $1 - 4s^2 - 18t^2 = 0$. Thus $4s^2 = 9t^2$, i.e., $s = 3t/2$.

This result enables us to reduce our problem by one dimension by eliminating s. We want to maximize the expression $8stG(s, t)$; since $s = 3t/2$, this expression reduces to $12t^2(1 - 18t^2)^{1/2}$. Accordingly, let $f = x^4(1 - 18x^2)$; to maximize f, we apply the Second Derivative Test. Now, $f' = 4x^3 - 108x^5$ and $f^{(2)} = 12x^2 - 540x^4$; thus f is critical at $1/3\sqrt{3}$ and at $-1/3\sqrt{3}$. Since $f^{(2)}(1/3\sqrt{3}) < 0$, we conclude that f is a maximum at $1/3\sqrt{3}$.

Returning to our function F, we find that this result suggests we test the critical point $(1/2\sqrt{3}, 1/3\sqrt{3})$. Now, $F_{12} = 8G - (8/G)[9Y^2 + 4X^2 + 36X^2Y^2]$, $F_{11} = (-32XY/G)[3 + 4X^2/G^2]$, and $F_{22} = (-72XY/G)[3 + 9Y^2/G^2]$. Hence $F_{12}(1/2\sqrt{3}, 1/3\sqrt{3}) = -16/\sqrt{3}$, $F_{11}(1/2\sqrt{3}, 1/3\sqrt{3}) = -64\sqrt{3}/9$, and $F_{22}(1/2\sqrt{3}, 1/3\sqrt{3}) = -16\sqrt{3}$. Thus $[(F_{12})^2 - F_{11}F_{22}](1/2\sqrt{3}, 1/3\sqrt{3}) = -256 < 0$. Since $F_{11}(1/2\sqrt{3}, 1/3\sqrt{3}) < 0$, we conclude that F is a relative maximum at $(1/2\sqrt{3}, 1/3\sqrt{3})$. Thus the required rectangular parallelepiped has dimensions $1/2\sqrt{3} \times 1/3\sqrt{3} \times 1/\sqrt{3}$.

EXAMPLE 7. Compute the minimum distance between the circle $\{(\cos t, \sin t, 0)\,|\,t \in R\}$ and the line $\{(t, 2t, -t)\,|\,t \in R\}$.

Solution: Let $(\cos s, \sin s, 0)$ and $(t, 2t, -t)$ be any two points, one on each of the given curves. The square of the distance between these points is $(t - \cos s)^2 + (2t - \sin s)^2 + t^2$. Therefore we want to minimize the function F, where $F = (X - \cos Y)^2 + (2X - \sin Y)^2 + X^2$. Now,

$$F_1 = 2(X - \cos Y) + 4(2X - \sin Y) + 2X = 12X - 2\cos Y - 4\sin Y,$$

$$F_2 = 2(X - \cos Y)\sin Y - 2(2X - \sin Y)\cos Y = 2X\sin Y - 4X\cos Y,$$

$$F_{12} = 2\sin Y - 4\cos Y,$$

$$F_{11} = 12,$$

$$F_{22} = 2X\cos Y + 4X\sin Y.$$

Thus F is critical at (a, b) iff $6a - \cos b - 2\sin b = 0$ and $a(\sin b - 2\cos b) = 0$. If $a = 0$, then $\tan b = -1/2$; therefore $[(F_{12})^2 - F_{11}F_{22}](0, b) = (-2/\sqrt{5} - 8/\sqrt{5})^2 > 0$. Hence $(0, b)$ is not an extremum of F. If $a \neq 0$, then $\sin b = 2\cos b$, and so $\tan b = 2$. Therefore $b = k\pi + \arctan 2$, where k is an integer, and $a = (1/6)(\cos b + 2\sin b)$. This leads to two critical ordered pairs $(\sqrt{5}/6, \arctan 2)$ and $(-\sqrt{5}/6, \pi + \arctan 2)$. Now, $[(F_{12})^2 - F_{11}F_{22}](\sqrt{5}/6, \arctan 2) = -12(1/3 + 4/3) = -20$. Also, $[(F_{12})^2 - F_{11}F_{22}](-\sqrt{5}/6, \pi + \arctan 2) = -12(1/3 + 4/3) = -20$. Thus $(\sqrt{5}/6, \arctan 2)$ and $(-\sqrt{5}/6, \pi + \arctan 2)$ are extrema of F. Since $F_{11} = 12$, we see that F is a relative minimum at both extrema. Now,

$$\sqrt{F(\sqrt{5}/6, \arctan 2)} = \sqrt{(\sqrt{5}/6 - 1/\sqrt{5})^2 + (\sqrt{5}/3 - 2/\sqrt{5})^2 + 5/36}$$

$$= \sqrt{(5/36 + 1/5 - 1/3) + (5/9 + 4/5 - 4/3) + 5/36}$$

$$= 1/\sqrt{6}.$$

The other extremum leads us to the same result. Thus the minimum distance between the given curves is $1/\sqrt{6}$.

EXERCISES

1. Find the ordered pairs at which F is critical, given the following.
   a. $F = X^2 + Y^2$.
   b. $F = X^2 + 4Y^2 - 2X$.
   c. $F = X^2 - 2XY - 4Y + 4Y^2$.

2. Find a function F such that F is critical at $(0, 0)$ and yet $(0, 0)$ is *not* an extremum of F.

3. Find the extrema of F, given the following.
    a. $F = X^2 - 2X + Y^3$.
    b. $F = X^2 - 6Y + Y^2 - 2X$.
    c. $F = X^3 + Y^3 - 3XY$.
    d. $F = X^2 - 2XY - 4Y + 4Y^2$.

4. Use the Partial Derivatives Test to compute the distance between the origin and the plane $\{(x, y, z) \mid 3x - 2y - 2z + 4 = 0\}$. Check your answer by solving this problem geometrically.

5. Use the Partial Derivatives Test to compute the distance between the point $(-1, 0, 2)$ and the plane $\{(x, y, z) \mid x + y + z = 3\}$. Check your answer by solving this problem geometrically.

6. Use the Partial Derivatives Test to compute the minimum distance between the lines $\{(t, -t, 3t) \mid t \in R\}$ and $\{(1 + t, 1-t, 0) \mid t \in R\}$. Check your answer by solving this problem geometrically.

7. Determine the dimensions of the rectangular parallelepiped of maximum volume that can be inscribed in the ellipsoid $\{(x, y, z) \mid x^2 + y^2 + 4z^2 = 1\}$, given that the faces of the parallelepiped are parallel to the coordinate planes.

8. Compute the minimum distance between the circle $\{(\cos t, \sin t, 0) \mid t \in R\}$ and the line $\{(2t, -t, -t) \mid t \in R\}$.

9. Compute the minimum distance between the circle $\{(\cos t, \sin t, 2) \mid t \in R\}$ and the curve $\{(t, t, t^2) \mid t \in R\}$.

10. Compute the minimum distance between the line $\{(1 + t, -t, 2t - 1) \mid t \in R\}$ and the curve $\{(t, 0, t^2) \mid t \in R\}$.

11. Compute the minimum distance between the curves $\{(1, t, t^2) \mid t \in R\}$ and $\{(t, -t^2, 0) \mid t \in R\}$.

12. Find the points on the surface $\{(x, y, z) \mid x^2 - yz = 1\}$ which are closest to the origin.

13. A rectangular box without a top is to have a given volume. What dimensions will require the least material?

14. Compute the minimum distance from the origin to the curve of intersection of the surfaces $\{(x, y, z) \mid x^2 + y^2 = 1\}$ and $\{(x, y, z) \mid x^2 + y^2 - z^2 - xy = 1\}$.

6.10 The Gradient*

Let H be a function with three arguments such that H_1, H_2, and H_3 are continuous. Let $(a, b, c) \in \mathcal{D}_H$; we develop some insight into the behavior of H near (a, b, c) by determining the rate of change of H at (a, b, c) with respect to a particular direction, say α, where α is the unit vector (a_1, a_2, a_3). To this purpose let us restrict the domain of H to the line $\{(a, b, c) + t\alpha \mid t \in R\}$. Clearly, this reduces H to a function with one argument; it is easy to compute the rate of change of this function with one argument. The function that we are talking about is $H(a + a_1x, b + a_2x, c + a_3x)$; we denote this function by "f". Then

$$f' = a_1 H_1(a + a_1x, b + a_2x, c + a_3x) + a_2 H_2(a + a_1x, b + a_2x, c + a_3x)$$

$$+ a_3 H_3(a + a_1x, b + a_2x, c + a_3x).$$

So

(1) $$f'(0) = a_1 H_1(a, b, c) + a_2 H_2(a, b, c) + a_3 H_3(a, b, c).$$

Thus the rate of change of H at (a, b, c) in the direction of the unit vector (a_1, a_2, a_3) is $a_1 H_1(a, b, c) + a_2 H_2(a, b, c) + a_3 H_3(a, b, c)$. Notice that we have developed a *directional derivative* (in three dimensions rather than two dimensions); accordingly, we shall denote the function $a_1 H_1 + a_2 H_2 + a_3 H_3$ by "$D_\alpha H$", where $\alpha = (a_1, a_2, a_3)$. The mapping that associates the vector $(H_1(a, b, c), H_2(a, b, c), H_3(a, b, c))$ with the vector (a, b, c) is called the *gradient of H* and is denoted by "∇H" or by "grad H"; any mapping of a set of vectors into a set of vectors is called a *vector field*.

DEFINITION 6.10.1.   grad H associates the vector $(H_1(a, b, c), H_2(a, b, c), H_3(a, b, c))$ with (a, b, c) whenever $(a, b, c) \in \mathscr{D}_{H_1} \cap \mathscr{D}_{H_2} \cap \mathscr{D}_{H_3}$.

We need a convenient method of representing vector fields.

DEFINITION 6.10.2.   Let F, G, and H be any functions with three arguments; then the vector field that associates the vector $(F(a, b, c), G(a, b, c), H(a, b, c))$ with the vector (a, b, c) whenever $(a, b, c) \in \mathscr{D}_F \cap \mathscr{D}_G \cap \mathscr{D}_H$ is denoted by "(F, G, H)".

In other words, $\{(F(a, b, c), G(a, b, c), H(a, b, c)) \mid (a, b, c) \in \mathscr{D}_F \cap \mathscr{D}_G \cap \mathscr{D}_H\}$ is denoted by "(F, G, H)". In particular, grad $H = (H_1, H_2, H_3)$ whenever H is a function with three arguments. For example, grad$[X^2 - 3XY + XZ^3]$ is $(2X - 3Y + Z^3, -3X, 3XZ^2)$.
    Now, let $(a, b, c) \in \mathscr{D}_H$, where H is any function with three arguments; from (1) the rate of change of H at (a, b, c) in the direction α is given by the inner product [grad H]$(a, b, c) \cdot \alpha$.

EXAMPLE 1.   Find $D_\alpha H$, given that $H = X^2 - 3XY + XZ^3$ and $\alpha = (\tfrac{1}{3}, \tfrac{2}{3}, -\tfrac{2}{3})$.

Solution: $D_\alpha H = \tfrac{1}{3}H_1 + \tfrac{2}{3}H_2 - \tfrac{2}{3}H_3 = \tfrac{1}{3}[2X - 3Y + Z^3 - 6X - 6XZ^2]$

$\qquad\qquad = \tfrac{1}{3}[-4X - 3Y + Z^3 - 6XZ^2].$

EXAMPLE 2.   Compute the rate of change of $X^2 - 3XY + XZ^3$ at $(2, 0, 1)$ in the direction $(2, -1, 1)$.
    Solution: Let $\alpha = (2/\sqrt{6}, -1/\sqrt{6}, 1/\sqrt{6})$; then

$$D_\alpha[X^2 - 3XY + XZ^3] = \frac{1}{\sqrt{6}}[4X - 6Y + 2Z^3 + 3X + 3XZ^2] = \frac{1}{\sqrt{6}}[7X - 6Y + 2Z^3 + 3XZ^2].$$

Therefore $D_\alpha[X^2 - 3XY + XZ^3](2, 0, 1) = \dfrac{1}{\sqrt{6}}(14 + 2 + 6) = 22/\sqrt{6}.$

Next, we consider the problem of finding a direction α which will maximize the rate of change of H at a given point (a, b, c); i.e., we want to find a unit vector α such that [grad H]$(a, b, c) \cdot \alpha$ is maximum. We are involved with an inner product. Let θ be the angle between α and [grad H](a, b, c); then $\cos \theta = \alpha \cdot$ [grad H]$(a, b, c)/\|$[grad H]$(a, b, c)\|$, so that $\alpha \cdot$ [grad H]$(a, b, c) = \|$[grad H]$(a, b, c)\| \cos \theta$. Therefore [grad H]$(a, b, c) \cdot \alpha$ is maximum when the angle between these vectors is zero, i.e., when $H(a, b, c)$ and α are vectors with the same direction. In other words, we maximize the rate of change of H at (a, b, c) by choosing the direction [grad H](a, b, c), namely $(H_1(a, b, c), H_2(a, b, c), H_3(a, b, c))$. Thus the direction of the maximum rate of increase of the function H is given by the vector field grad H. Similarly, the direction of the maximum rate of decrease of H is given by the vector field $-$grad H.

Next, let

$$\alpha = \frac{[\text{grad } H](a, b, c)}{\|[\text{grad } H](a, b, c)\|}$$

[i.e., let α be a unit vector with the same direction as [grad H](a, b, c)]. As we have seen, the rate of change of H at (a, b, c) in the direction α is $\alpha \cdot$ [grad H](a, b, c); but

$$\alpha \cdot [\text{grad } H](a, b, c) = \|[\text{grad } H](a, b, c)\| \cos 0 = \|[\text{grad } H](a, b, c)\|.$$

In other words, the maximum rate of increase of H at (a, b, c) is the length of the vector [grad H](a, b, c).

EXAMPLE 3. Find the direction of the maximum rate of increase of $X^2 - 3XY + XZ^3$ at $(2, 0, 1)$.

Solution: grad$[X^3 - 3XY + XZ^3] = (3X^2 - 3Y + Z^3, -3X, 3XZ^2)$; hence (grad$[X^3 - 3XY + XZ^3])(2, 0, 1) = (13, -6, 6)$. Therefore the required direction is $(13, -6, 6)$.

EXAMPLE 4. Find the maximum rate of increase of $X^2 - 3XY + XZ^3$ at $(2, 0, 1)$.

Solution: Since $\|$[grad H]$(a, b, c)\|$ is the maximum rate of increase of H at (a, b, c), it follows from Example 3 that $\|(13, -6, 6)\|$ is the maximum rate of increase of the given function at $(2, 0, 1)$. Thus $\sqrt{241}$ is the maximum rate of increase.

We present one final point regarding the significance of the vector field grad H. Suppose that F is a function with two arguments such that $H(X, Y, F) = k$; then, by Theorem 6.7.8, the tangent plane to the graph of F at (a, b, c), where $c = F(a, b)$, is $\{(x, y, z) \mid H_1(a, b, c)(x - a) + H_2(a, b, c)(y - b) + H_3(a, b, c)(z - c) = 0\}$ provided [grad H]$(a, b, c) \neq \mathbf{0}$ and H_1, H_2, and H_3 are continuous. Thus the vector [grad H] (a, b, c) is a direction of the normal to the graph of F at (a, b, c).

EXAMPLE 5. Find the normal to the graph of F at $(3, 0, -2)$, given that $X^2 - 3XY + 4F = 1$.

Solution: Let $H = X^2 - 3XY + 4Z$; then the required normal has direction [grad H] $(3, 0, -2)$. But grad $H = (2X - 3Y, -3X, 4)$; therefore our normal has direction $(6, -9, 4)$. Thus the required normal is $\{(3 + 6t, -9t, -2 + 4t) \mid t \in R\}$.

E X E R C I S E S

1. Find $D_\alpha H$, where $H = XYZ$ and $\alpha = (\frac{2}{7}, -\frac{3}{7}, \frac{6}{7})$.

2. Show that $D_{(1,0,0)}H = H_1$, $D_{(0,1,0)}H = H_2$, and $D_{(0,0,1)}H = H_3$.

3. Compute the rate of change of XYZ at $(3, -1, 2)$ in the direction $(1, -2, 2)$.

4. Find the direction of the maximum rate of increase of XYZ at $(3, -1, 2)$.

5. Find the direction of the maximum rate of decrease of XYZ at $(3, -1, 2)$.

6. Find the maximum rate of increase of $XZ^2 - 3X^2Y$ at $(0, 0, 0)$.

7. Find the maximum rate of increase of $X \sin Y + Y \cos Z$ at $(0, 0, 0)$.

8. Find the normal to the surface $\{(x, y, z) \mid x^2 + 2yz = 0\}$ at $(2, 1, -2)$.

9. Prove that each normal to a sphere passes through the center of the sphere.

10. Determine the gradient of each of the following functions.
   a. $XY + YZ + ZX$.
   b. $X^2 + Y^2 + Z^2$.
   c. $X + Y + Z$.
   d. $\sin(XYZ)$.

6.11   Vector Calculus*

In the preceding sections of this chapter we have, for the most part, carefully displayed the arguments of our functions. In an introduction to partial derivatives this is important. Now that we have grasped the nature of a partial derivative and are experienced in handling functions with several arguments, we are in a position to appreciate a more sophisticated approach to this subject; incidentally, we shall see that this approach simplifies the notation and provides us with a birds'-eye view of our theory.

The idea is to regard a function with several arguments as a function with one argument. This sounds paradoxical! However, the domain of a function with t arguments, $t > 1$, is a subset of R_t, the set of all ordered t-tuples of real numbers; therefore a function with t arguments is a mapping of a set of t-vectors into R. Moreover, we shall say that the empty set $\varnothing$ is a function with t arguments whenever $t \in N$.

Let F be any function with t arguments, $t > 1$; let α be any t-vector, say $(a_1, a_2, \cdots, a_t)$, in the domain of F. Now, $F(a_1, a_2, \cdots, a_t)$ is a real number; hence substituting "α" for "$(a_1, a_2, \cdots, a_t)$", we have that $F\alpha$ is a real number. This is our first economy of notation; we write "$F\alpha$" instead of "$F(a_1, a_2, \cdots, a_t)$". Nonetheless, it is sometimes convenient to write "$F(\alpha)$" for "$F\alpha$".

In presenting the theory, we develop our notation as follows.

> DEFINITION 6.11.1. Let α be any t-vector; then "α^i" denotes the ith term of α whenever $1 \leq i \leq t$.

For example, $(3, 5, 7, 2)^3 = 7$; in general, $(a_1, \cdots, a_i, \cdots, a_t)^i = a_i$.

DEFINITION 6.11.2.   Let α be any t-vector; then "α^i" denotes the $(t-1)$-vector obtained from α by deleting its ith term, whenever $1 \le i \le t$.

For example, $(3, 5, 7, 2)^{\hat{3}} = (3, 5, 2)$ and $(2, -1, 3, 7, 8)^{\hat{2}} = (2, 3, 7, 8)$.

Next, we consider the elementary functions with t arguments, where $t > 1$. First, we have the *constant* functions $\{(\alpha, k) \mid \alpha \in R_t\}$, where k is any real number. We have t *identity* functions $\{(\alpha, \alpha^i) \mid \alpha \in R_t\}$, $1 \le i \le t$. If G and H are any elementary functions with t arguments and if f is any elementary function with one argument, then the following are elementary functions with t arguments:

$$G + H = \{(\alpha, b) \mid b = G\alpha + H\alpha\},$$

$$G \cdot H = \{(\alpha, b) \mid b = [G\alpha][H\alpha]\},$$

$$f(H) = \{(\alpha, b) \mid b = f(H\alpha)\}.$$

By a *vector field* we mean any mapping of a set of vectors into a set of vectors. Let $\mathscr{F}$ be any vector field which associates an m-vector with a given t-vector, and let H be any function with m arguments. Then $\{(\alpha, b) \mid b = H(\mathscr{F}\alpha)\}$ is a function with t arguments; this function is denoted by "$H(\mathscr{F})$" or by "$H\mathscr{F}$". Now, a vector field $\mathscr{F}$ which associates an m-vector with a given t-vector can be represented by an ordered m-tuple of functions which have t arguments. For example, let $\mathscr{F}$ be the mapping that associates $(\alpha^1, (\alpha^2)^2, \alpha^1 + \alpha^2)$ with α whenever $\alpha \in R_2$; then $\mathscr{F}$ is represented by the ordered triple $(X, Y^2, X + Y)$. Later we shall want to refer to the functions that make up the vector field $\mathscr{F}$. Since the vector field $\mathscr{F}$ is given by an ordered m-tuple, we shall use our code for naming the ith term of an ordered m-tuple. Thus "$\mathscr{F}^i$" denotes the ith term of $\mathscr{F}$, whenever $1 \le i \le m$. For example, $(X, Y^2, X + Y)^3 = X + Y$.

Next, we need the notion of the *limit* of a sequence of t-vectors. For each natural number n, let $\alpha_n = (a_{1n}, a_{2n}, \cdots, a_{tn})$, and suppose that the sequences (a_{1n}), (a_{2n}), $\cdots$, (a_{tn}) converge. Then we say that $\lim(\alpha_n) = (\lim(a_{1n}), \lim(a_{2n}), \cdots, \lim(a_{tn}))$. Thus the limit of a sequence of t-vectors is a t-vector.

DEFINITION 6.11.3.   Let F be any function with t arguments; we shall say that (α_n) is an (F, α)-sequence iff

(i) $\lim(\alpha_n) = \alpha$,

(ii) $\alpha_n \in \mathscr{D}_F$ whenever $n \in N$,

(iii) $\alpha_n \ne \alpha$ whenever $n \in N$.

Using this notion, we define the limit of a function at a vector.

DEFINITION 6.11.4.   Let F be any function with t arguments and let α be any t-vector; then $\lim\limits_{\alpha} F = L$ iff

(i) $\lim(F\alpha_n) = L$ whenever (α_n) is an (F, α)-sequence,

(ii) an (F, α)-sequence exists.

We shall say that F is *continuous at* α iff $\alpha \in \mathscr{D}_F$, $\lim_{\alpha} F$ exists, and $\lim_{\alpha} F = F\alpha$. We shall say that F is *continuous on* E iff F is continuous at each member of E. We shall say that F is *continuous* iff F is continuous on $\mathscr{D}_F$.

Consider, now, the *partial derivatives* of F, a function with t arguments. First, we must reduce F to a function with one argument.

DEFINITION 6.11.5.   Let $1 \leq i \leq t$ and let α be any $(t-1)$-vector; then ${}_\alpha F_i = \{(a, b) \mid \text{there is a } t\text{-vector } \beta \text{ such that } a = \beta^i, \beta_{\hat{\imath}} = \alpha, \text{ and } b = F\beta\}$.

In particular, ${}_\alpha F_1 = \{(a, b) \mid \text{there is a } t\text{-vector } \beta \text{ such that } a = \beta^1, \beta^{\hat{1}} = \alpha, \text{ and } b = F\beta\}$.
Now we can define the t partial derivatives of F.

DEFINITION 6.11.6.   Let $1 \leq i \leq t$; then $F_i = \{(\alpha, b) \mid a = \alpha^i \text{ and } b = ({}_{\alpha\hat{\imath}}F_i)'(a)\}$.

In particular, $F_1 = \{(\alpha, b) \mid a = \alpha^1 \text{ and } b = ({}_{\alpha\hat{1}}F_1)'(a)\}$.
The following theorem is useful for working out partial derivatives.

THEOREM 6.11.1.   Let F be any function with t arguments, let $\alpha \in \mathscr{D}_F$, let $1 \leq i \leq t$, and let (α_n) be any (F, α)-sequence such that $\alpha_n^{\hat{\imath}} = \alpha^{\hat{\imath}}$ for each n. Then

$$F_i(\alpha) = \lim\left(\frac{F\alpha_n - F\alpha}{\alpha_n^i - \alpha^i}\right).$$

Proof: By Definition 6.11.6, $F_i(\alpha) = ({}_{\alpha\hat{\imath}}F_i)'(\alpha^i)$. Therefore

$$F_i(\alpha) = \lim\left(\frac{{}_{\alpha\hat{\imath}}F_i(\alpha_n^i) - {}_{\alpha\hat{\imath}}F_i(\alpha^i)}{\alpha_n^i - \alpha^i}\right) = \lim\left(\frac{F\alpha_n - F\alpha}{\alpha_n^i - \alpha^i}\right) \qquad \text{by Def. 6.11.5.}$$

We shall now establish our Fundamental Theorem of Partial Derivatives. First, we need to generalize the notion of an interval to t dimensions.

DEFINITION 6.11.7.   Let $\mathscr{I}_1, \mathscr{I}_2, \cdots, \mathscr{I}_t$ be any intervals; then $\mathscr{I}_1 \times \mathscr{I}_2 \times \cdots \times \mathscr{I}_t$ is said to be a *t-interval*.

For example, $\mathscr{I}_1 \times \mathscr{I}_2$ is a 2-interval and $\mathscr{I}_1 \times \mathscr{I}_2 \times \mathscr{I}_3$ is a 3-interval, provided $\mathscr{I}_1, \mathscr{I}_2$, and $\mathscr{I}_3$ are intervals.

Also, we need the notion of an *inner* vector of a set of t-vectors.

DEFINITION 6.11.8.   Let α be any t-vector and let S be any set of t-vectors; then α is said to be an *inner* vector of S iff there exists a natural number p such that $\{\beta \mid \beta \in R_t \text{ and } \|\beta - \alpha\| < 10^{-p}\} \subset S$.

The set $\{\beta \mid \beta \in R_t \text{ and } \|\beta - \alpha\| < 10^{-p}\}$ is said to be a *neighborhood* of α whenever $p \in N$.

THEOREM 6.11.2. Let $\mathscr{I}$ be a t-interval, say $\mathscr{I}_1 \times \mathscr{I}_2 \times \cdots \times \mathscr{I}_t$, suppose that $\mathscr{I} \subset \mathscr{D}_{F_i}$, and let α be an inner vector of $\mathscr{I}$; then $_\alpha F_i$ is differentiable throughout $\mathscr{I}_i$, where $1 \leq i \leq t$.

Proof: Apply Definition 6.11.6.
We come now to our Fundamental Theorem of Partial Derivatives.

THEOREM 6.11.3 (Fundamental Theorem of Partial Derivatives). Let F be any function with t arguments, let $\mathscr{I}$ be a t-interval such that $\mathscr{I} \subset \mathscr{D}_F$, let α be an inner vector of $\mathscr{I}$, and suppose that each F_i is continuous at α. Let (α_n) be any (F, α)-sequence whose terms are members of $\mathscr{I}$; then there exists a sequence (β_n) such that, for each n, $F(\alpha_n) - F(\alpha) = (\alpha_n - \alpha) \cdot (\beta_n + [\text{grad } F]\alpha)$ and $\lim(\beta_n) = \mathbf{0}$.

Proof: First, note that our theorem asserts that for each natural number n, the real number $F(\alpha_n) - F(\alpha)$ is the inner product of the vectors $\alpha_n - \alpha$ and $\beta_n + [\text{grad } F]\alpha$. Let $\alpha_n = (a_{1n}, a_{2n}, \cdots, a_{tn})$ for each n, and let $\alpha = (a_1, a_2, \cdots, a_t)$. Then

$$F(\alpha_n) - F(\alpha) = [F(\alpha_n) - F(a_1, a_{2n}, \cdots, a_{tn})] + [F(a_1, a_{2n}, \cdots, a_{tn}) - F(a_1, a_2, a_{3n}, \cdots, a_{tn})]$$

$$+ \cdots + [F(a_1, \cdots, a_{t-1}, a_{tn}) - F(\alpha)]$$

$$= (a_{1n} - a_1)[b_{1n} + F_1(\alpha)] + (a_{2n} - a_2)[b_{2n} + F_2(\alpha)] + \cdots$$

$$+ (a_{tn} - a_t)[b_{tn} + F_t(\alpha)] \quad \text{by the Mean Value Theorem, where } b_{1n}, b_{2n},$$
$$\cdots, b_{tn} \text{ are real numbers which balance the equation}$$

$$= (\alpha_n - \alpha) \cdot (\beta_n + [\text{grad } F]\alpha),$$

where $\beta_n = (b_{1n}, b_{2n}, \cdots, b_{tn})$ for each n. Moreover, it follows that $\lim(\beta_n) = \mathbf{0}$ since F_i is continuous at α, $1 \leq i \leq t$. This completes our proof.

By using the Fundamental Theorem of Partial Derivatives, it is easy to establish the following theorems, where F and G are functions with t arguments.

THEOREM 6.11.4. Let $1 \leq i \leq t$; then $[F + G]_i = F_i + G_i$ provided that $\mathscr{D}_{F_i} = \mathscr{D}_F$ and $\mathscr{D}_{G_i} = \mathscr{D}_G$.

THEOREM 6.11.5. Let $1 \leq i \leq t$; then $[F \cdot G]_i = F \cdot G_i + F_i \cdot G$ provided that $\mathscr{D}_{F_i} = \mathscr{D}_F$ and $\mathscr{D}_{G_i} = \mathscr{D}_G$.

THEOREM 6.11.6. Let $1 \leq i \leq t$; then $[F/G]_i = (G \cdot F_i - F \cdot G_i)/G^2$ provided that $\mathscr{D}_{F_i} = \mathscr{D}_F$ and $\mathscr{D}_{G_i} = \mathscr{D}_G$.

We shall now prove the following generalizations of the Chain Rule.

THEOREM 6.11.7.   Let f be any function with one argument such that f' is continuous, and let H be any function with t arguments such that $\mathscr{D}_{H_i} = \mathscr{D}_H$ whenever $1 \leq i \leq t$; then $[f(H)]_i = f'(H) \cdot H_i$ whenever $1 \leq i \leq t$.

Proof: Let $\alpha \in \mathscr{D}_{f(H)}$ and let (α_n) be an $(f(H), \alpha)$-sequence such that $\alpha_n^i = \alpha^i$ for each n. Now,

$$\lim\left(\frac{[f(H)]\alpha_n - [f(H)]\alpha}{\alpha_n^i - \alpha^i}\right) = \lim\left(\frac{f(H\alpha_n) - f(H\alpha)}{\alpha_n^i - \alpha^i}\right)$$

$$= \lim\left(\frac{[H\alpha_n - H\alpha]f'(b_n)}{\alpha_n^i - \alpha^i}\right) \qquad \text{by the Mean Value Theorem,}$$
$$\text{where } b_n \text{ is between } H\alpha \text{ and} \cdot$$
$$H\alpha_n \text{ for each } n$$

$$= [H_i\alpha] \lim(f'(b_n)) \qquad \text{by Th. 6.11.1}$$

$$= [H_i\alpha] \cdot f'(\lim(b_n)) \qquad \text{since } f' \text{ is continuous}$$

$$= [H_i\alpha] \cdot f'(H\alpha) \qquad \text{since } \lim(b_n) = \lim(H\alpha_n)$$
$$= H\alpha.$$

We conclude that $[f(H)]_i\alpha = ([f'(H)] \cdot H_i)\alpha$; thus $[f(H)]_i = f'(H) \cdot H_i$.

THEOREM 6.11.8.   Let $\mathscr{F}$ be any vector field which associates an m-vector with a given t-vector, $t > 1$, let H be a function with m arguments, and let $1 \leq i \leq t$; then

$$[H\mathscr{F}]_i = [H_1\mathscr{F}] \cdot \mathscr{F}_i^1 + [H_2\mathscr{F}] \cdot \mathscr{F}_i^2 + \cdots + [H_m\mathscr{F}] \cdot \mathscr{F}_i^m$$

provided that $\mathscr{D}_{Hj} = \mathscr{D}_H$ and $\mathscr{D}_{\mathscr{F}_i j} = \mathscr{D}_{\mathscr{F}j}$ whenever $1 \leq j \leq m$.

Proof: Let $\alpha \in \mathscr{D}_{H\mathscr{F}}$ and let (α_n) be any $(H\mathscr{F}, \alpha)$-sequence such that $\alpha_n^i = \alpha^i$ for each n; then

$$[H\mathscr{F}]_i\alpha = \lim\left(\frac{[H\mathscr{F}]\alpha_n - H[\mathscr{F}]\alpha}{\alpha_n^i - \alpha^i}\right) = \lim\left(\frac{H(\mathscr{F}\alpha_n) - H(\mathscr{F}\alpha)}{\alpha_n^i - \alpha^i}\right)$$

$$= \lim\left(\frac{(\mathscr{F}\alpha_n - \mathscr{F}\alpha) \cdot (\beta_n + [\text{grad } H]\mathscr{F}\alpha)}{\alpha_n^i - \alpha^i}\right) \qquad \text{by the Fundamental Theorem of}$$
$$\text{Partial Derivatives}$$

$$= \lim\left(\frac{\mathscr{F}^1\alpha_n - \mathscr{F}^1\alpha}{\alpha_n^i - \alpha^i} [\beta_n + [\text{grad } H]\mathscr{F}\alpha]^1\right) + \cdots$$

$$+ \lim\left(\frac{\mathscr{F}^m\alpha_n - \mathscr{F}^m\alpha}{\alpha_n^i - \alpha^i} [\beta_n + [\text{grad } H]\mathscr{F}\alpha]^m\right)$$

$$= \mathscr{F}_i^1\alpha \lim(\beta_n + [\text{grad } H]\mathscr{F}\alpha)^1 + \cdots + \mathscr{F}_i^m\alpha \lim(\beta_n + [\text{grad } H]\mathscr{F}\alpha)^m$$

$$= H_1(\mathscr{F}\alpha)\mathscr{F}_i^1\alpha + \cdots + H_m(\mathscr{F}\alpha)\mathscr{F}_i^m\alpha$$

$$= ([H_1\mathscr{F}]\mathscr{F}_i^1 + \cdots + [H_m\mathscr{F}]\mathscr{F}_i^m)\alpha.$$

Therefore $[H\mathcal{F}]_i = [H_1\mathcal{F}] \cdot \mathcal{F}_i^1 + [H_2\mathcal{F}] \cdot \mathcal{F}_i^2 + \cdots + [H_m\mathcal{F}] \cdot \mathcal{F}_i^m$. This completes our proof.

In particular, let H be a function with four arguments, let F, G, K, L be functions with three arguments, and let $\mathcal{F}$ be the vector field (F, G, K, L). Then, if $1 \le i \le 4$, $[H\mathcal{F}]_i = [H_1\mathcal{F}]F_i + [H_2\mathcal{F}]G_i + [H_3\mathcal{F}]K_i + [H_4\mathcal{F}]L_i$ provided that $\mathcal{D}_{H_j} = \mathcal{D}_H$ and $\mathcal{D}_{\mathcal{F}_{ij}} = \mathcal{D}_{\mathcal{F}_j}$ whenever $1 \le j \le 4$.

DEFINITION 6.11.9.   Let $f_1, f_2, \cdots, f_m$ be functions with one argument and let H be a function with m arguments; then "$H(f_1, f_2, \cdots, f_m)$" denotes the function with one argument $\{(a, b) | b = H(f_1(a), f_2(a), \cdots, f_m(a))\}$.

THEOREM 6.11.9.   Let $f_1, f_2, \cdots, f_m$ be functions with one argument, let $\mathcal{F} = (f_1, f_2, \cdots, f_m)$, and let H be a function with m arguments. Then $[H\mathcal{F}]' = [H_1\mathcal{F}]f_1' + [H_2\mathcal{F}]f_2' + \cdots + [H_m\mathcal{F}]f_m'$ provided that $\mathcal{D}_{H_j} = \mathcal{D}_H$ and $\mathcal{D}_{f'_j} = \mathcal{D}_f$ whenever $1 \le j \le m$.

Proof: Let $a \in \mathcal{D}_{H\mathcal{F}}$ and let (a_n) be any $(H\mathcal{F}, a)$-sequence. Now,

$$\lim\left(\frac{[H\mathcal{F}](a_n) - [H\mathcal{F}](a)}{a_n - a}\right) = \lim\left(\frac{H(\mathcal{F}a_n) - H(\mathcal{F}a)}{a_n - a}\right)$$

$$= \lim\left(\frac{(\mathcal{F}a_n - \mathcal{F}a) \cdot (\beta_n + [\text{grad } H]\mathcal{F}a)}{a_n - a}\right) \qquad \text{by the Fundamental Theorem of Partial Derivatives, where } \lim(\beta_n) = \mathbf{0}$$

$$= \lim\left(\frac{f_1(a_n) - f_1(a)}{a_n - a} [\beta_n^1 + H_1(\mathcal{F}a)]\right) + \cdots$$

$$+ \lim\left(\frac{f_m(a_n) - f_m(a)}{a_n - a} [\beta_n^m + H_m(\mathcal{F}a)]\right)$$

$$= H_1(\mathcal{F}a)f_1'(a) + \cdots + H_m(\mathcal{F}a)f_m'(a) \qquad \text{since } \lim(\beta_n^k) = 0,\ 1 \le k \le m$$

$$= ([H_1\mathcal{F}]f_1' + \cdots + [H_m\mathcal{F}]f_m')(a).$$

Therefore $[H\mathcal{F}]'(a) = ([H_1\mathcal{F}]f_1' + \cdots + [H_m\mathcal{F}]f_m')(a)$; hence

$$[H\mathcal{F}]' = [H_1\mathcal{F}]f_1' + \cdots + [H_m\mathcal{F}]f_m'.$$

EXERCISES

1. Prove the following metatheorem: let $t > 1$; then each elementary function with t arguments has property P if
   (i) the identity and constant functions with t arguments have property P;

(ii) $G + H$ and $G \cdot H$ each has property P whenever G and H are elementary functions with t arguments which possess property P;

(iii) $f(H)$ has property P whenever H is an elementary function with t arguments which has property P, and f is an elementary function with one argument.

2. Prove that each elementary function with t arguments is continuous.

3. Let $\mathscr{F}$ be a vector field represented by an ordered m-tuple whose terms are elementary functions with t arguments. Prove that $H\mathscr{F}$ is an elementary function with t arguments whenever H is an elementary function with m arguments.

4. Prove that if F is an elementary function with t arguments, then one of the following is true:
   (1) F is an identity function or a constant function with t arguments.
   (2) There are elementary functions with t arguments, say G and H, such that $F = G + H$ or $F = G \cdot H$.
   (3) There is an elementary function with one argument, say h, and an elementary function with t arguments, say G, such that $F = h(G)$.

5. Given that (α_n) and (β_n) are sequences of t-vectors which converge, prove that $(\alpha_n + \beta_n)$ converges and

$$\lim(\alpha_n + \beta_n) = \lim(\alpha_n) + \lim(\beta_n).$$

6. Given that $\lim_\alpha F$ and $\lim_\alpha G$ both exist, prove the following.
   a. $\lim_\alpha(F + G)$ exists and $\lim_\alpha(F + G) = \lim_\alpha F + \lim_\alpha G$.
   b. $\lim_\alpha(F \cdot G)$ exists and $\lim_\alpha(F \cdot G) = [\lim_\alpha F] \cdot [\lim_\alpha G]$.

7. Prove Theorem 6.11.4.

8. Prove Theorem 6.11.5.

9. Prove Theorem 6.11.6.

Chapter 7

Multiple Integrals

7.1 · Properties of Continuous Functions

In this chapter we shall develop the concept of the integral of a function with several arguments over a region. First, we shall consider functions with two arguments and regions of 2-space. The development parallels the case of a function with one argument; indeed, it is merely a matter of adding one dimension throughout. In the case of functions with one argument, the basic theorem asserts that f is integrable over an interval provided that f is continuous on the interval. Stepping up the dimension by one, we shall prove that F is integrable over a 2-interval provided F is continuous on the 2-interval. In the case of functions with one argument, we require certain properties of continuous functions in order to establish that f is integrable. For functions with two arguments the situation is similar. We shall now establish the properties of continuous functions that we shall need.

THEOREM 7.1.1.   Let (α_n) be a sequence of 2-vectors, and let α be a 2-vector; then $\lim(\alpha_n) = \alpha$ iff $\lim(\|\alpha_n - \alpha\|) = 0$.

Proof: 1. Assume $\lim(\alpha_n) = \alpha$. Let $\alpha_n = (a_n, b_n)$ whenever $n \in N$, and let $\alpha = (a,b)$. Then $\lim(a_n) = a$ and $\lim(b_n) = b$; so $\lim(a_n - a) = 0$ and $\lim(b_n - b) = 0$. Hence $\lim([a_n - a]^2 + [b_n - b]^2) = 0$; thus $\lim(\sqrt{(a_n - a)^2 + (b_n - b)^2}) = 0$, i.e., $\lim(\|\alpha_n - \alpha\|) = 0$.

2. Assume $\lim(\|\alpha_n - \alpha\|) = 0$. Again, let $\alpha_n = (a_n, b_n)$ whenever $n \in N$, and let $\alpha = (a, b)$. Then $\lim(\sqrt{(a_n - a)^2 + (b_n - b)^2}) = 0$; thus $\lim([a_n - a]^2 + [b_n - b]^2) = 0$. But $0 \le (a_n - a)^2 \le (a_n - a)^2 + (b_n - b)^2$ whenever $n \in N$; thus

$$0 \le \lim([a_n - a]^2) \le \lim([a_n - a]^2 + [b_n - b]^2) = 0,$$

i.e., $\lim([a_n - a]^2) = 0$, and so $\lim(a_n - a) = 0$. Similarly, it is easy to show that $\lim(b_n - b) = 0$. This establishes our result.

THEOREM 7.1.2. $\lim_{\alpha} F = L$ iff

(i) given any natural number p, there is a natural number q such that $|F\beta - L| < 10^{-p}$ whenever $\beta \in \mathcal{D}_F$ and $0 < \|\beta - \alpha\| < 10^{-q}$;

(ii) there is at least one (F, α)-sequence.

Proof: The proof is in two parts.

1. Assume $\lim_\alpha F = L$; we must prove that given any natural number p, there is a natural number q such that $|F\beta - L| < 10^{-p}$ whenever $\beta \in \mathcal{D}_F$ and $0 < \|\beta - \alpha\| < 10^{-q}$. Suppose that this is false; then there is a natural number t such that corresponding to each natural number q, there is a member of $\mathcal{D}_F$, say β, such that $0 < \|\beta - \alpha\| < 10^{-q}$ and $|F\beta - L| \geq 10^{-t}$. In particular, there are members of $\mathcal{D}_F$, say $\beta_1, \beta_2, \beta_3, \cdots$, such that

$$0 < \|\beta_1 - \alpha\| < 10^{-1} \quad \text{and} \quad |F\beta_1 - L| \geq 10^{-t}$$

$$0 < \|\beta_2 - \alpha\| < 10^{-2} \quad \text{and} \quad |F\beta_2 - L| \geq 10^{-t}$$

$$0 < \|\beta_3 - \alpha\| < 10^{-3} \quad \text{and} \quad |F\beta_3 - L| \geq 10^{-t}$$

and so on. Consider the sequence (β_n). By construction, $\lim(\beta_n) = \alpha$; moreover, $\beta_n \neq \alpha$ whenever $n \in N$. Thus (β_n) is an (F, α)-sequence. But $|F\beta_n - L| \geq 10^{-t}$ whenever $n \in N$; hence $\lim(F\beta_n) \neq L$. Since (β_n) is an (F, α)-sequence, $L = \lim_\alpha F = \lim(F\beta_n)$. This contradiction establishes our result.

2. Assume (i) and (ii). We must prove that $\lim_\alpha F = L$. Let (α_n) be any (F, α)-sequence; we shall show that $\lim(F\alpha_n) = L$, i.e., given any natural number p, there is a natural number t such that $|F\alpha_n - L| < 10^{-p}$ whenever $n > t$. By (i), corresponding to p there is a natural number q such that $|F\alpha_n - L| < 10^{-p}$ whenever $0 < \|\alpha_n - \alpha\| < 10^{-q}$. But $\lim(\alpha_n) = \alpha$; so $\lim(\|\alpha_n - \alpha\|) = 0$. Hence there is a natural number t such that $0 < \|\alpha_n - \alpha\| < 10^{-q}$ whenever $n > t$. Thus, if $n > t$, then $0 < \|\alpha_n - \alpha\| < 10^{-q}$; therefore $|F\alpha_n - L| < 10^{-p}$. We have shown that corresponding to a given natural number p there is a natural number t such that $|F\alpha_n - L| < 10^{-p}$ whenever $n > t$. Thus $\lim(F\alpha_n) = L$. This proves that $\lim_\alpha F = L$. We have established Theorem 7.1.2.

COROLLARY 7.1.1. F is continuous at α iff

(i) given any natural number p, there is a natural number q such that $|F\beta - F\alpha| < 10^{-p}$ whenever $\beta \in \mathcal{D}_F$ and $\|\beta - \alpha\| < 10^{-q}$;
(ii) there is at least one (F, α)-sequence.

Proof: Apply Theorem 7.1.2.

We shall need the following notions.

DEFINITION 7.1.1.   We shall say that F is *bounded above* on S iff there is a real number K such that $K \geq F\alpha$ whenever $\alpha \in S$. We shall say that F is *bounded below* on S iff there is a real number L such that $L \leq F\alpha$ whenever $\alpha \in S$. We shall say that F is *bounded* on S iff F is bounded above on S and F is bounded below on S.

We also need the notion of a *closed* 2-interval.

DEFINITION 7.1.2.   Let $\mathscr{I}$ be any 2-interval, say $\mathscr{I} = \mathscr{I}_1 \times \mathscr{I}_2$ where $\mathscr{I}_1$ and $\mathscr{I}_2$ are intervals; then $\bar{\mathscr{I}}_1 \times \bar{\mathscr{I}}_2$ is said to be the *closure* of $\mathscr{I}$ and is denoted by "$\bar{\mathscr{I}}$".

Note: If $\mathscr{J}$ is an interval, then $\bar{\mathscr{J}} = \mathscr{J} \cup \{t | t$ is an endpoint of $\mathscr{J}\}$. Here, $\bar{\mathscr{J}}$ is called the closure of $\mathscr{J}$.

For example, the closure of $(1, 3) \times [2, 5)$ is $[1, 3] \times [2, 5]$.

DEFINITION 7.1.3.   Let $\mathscr{I}$ be any 2-interval; then $\mathscr{I}$ is said to be closed iff $\mathscr{I} = \bar{\mathscr{I}}$.

For example, $[1, 3] \times [2, 5]$ is closed, whereas $(1, 3) \times [2, 5)$ is not closed.

THEOREM 7.1.3. F is bounded above on $\mathscr{I}$ provided (i) $\mathscr{I}$ is a closed 2-interval, (ii) F is continuous on $\mathscr{I}$.

Proof: We shall prove the theorem for the closed 2-interval $[0, 1] \times [0, 1]$; the following proof is easily extended to *any* closed 2-interval. Suppose that F is *not* bounded above on $[0, 1] \times [0, 1]$; we propose to construct a 2-vector α and a sequence (α_n) such that $\lim(\alpha_n) = \alpha$, yet $\lim(F\alpha_n) \neq F\alpha$. We begin by dividing the interval $[0, 1]$ into ten subintervals of equal length; the cross partition of this set with itself subdivides $[0, 1] \times [0, 1]$ into 100 2-intervals. Clearly, there is at least one of these 2-intervals on which F is not bounded above; we choose one of these 2-intervals and select one of its members, say α_1, such that $F\alpha_1 > 1$. Notice that this subinterval provides us with the first digit of both terms of α; e.g., if our subinterval is $[.2, .3] \times [.6, .7]$, then $\alpha = (.2 \cdots, .6 \cdots)$. We continue this procedure; i.e., we subdivide the 2-interval we have just chosen into 100 2-intervals, select one of these 2-intervals on which F is not bounded above, and choose one of its members, α_2, such that $F\alpha_2 > 2$. In this way we obtain the second digit of both terms of α. Continuing, we see that we simultaneously obtain the kth term of the sequence (α_n) and the kth digit of both terms of α. But $\lim(\alpha_n) = \alpha$ by construction, and $\lim(F\alpha_n) \neq F\alpha$ since $F\alpha_n > n$ whenever $n \in N$. This completes our proof.

THEOREM 7.1.4. F has a maximum value on $\mathscr{I}$ provided (i) $\mathscr{I}$ is a closed 2-interval, (ii) F is continuous on $\mathscr{I}$.

Proof: Let "V" denote the set of values of F over $\mathscr{I}$, i.e., $V = \{F\alpha \,|\, \alpha \in \mathscr{I}\}$. We want to show that V has a largest member. By Theorem 7.1.3, F is bounded above on $\mathscr{I}$; but any nonempty set of real numbers which is bounded above has a least upper bound. Therefore there is a real number M such that $M = $ l.u.b. V. We shall prove that $M \in V$. Suppose that $M \bar{\in} V$, i.e., $F\alpha \neq M$ whenever $\alpha \in \mathscr{I}$. Then $M - F\alpha \neq 0$ whenever $\alpha \in \mathscr{I}$; hence $1/(M - F)$ is continuous on $\mathscr{I}$. Thus, by Theorem 7.1.3, $1/(M - F)$ is bounded above on $\mathscr{I}$. But $M = $ l.u.b V; thus, given p, we can find a member of $\mathscr{I}$, say α, such that $0 < M - F\alpha \leq 10^{-p}$. Hence $1/(M - F\alpha) \geq 10^p$. This means that $1/(M - F)$ is *not* bounded above on $\mathscr{I}$. This contradiction establishes that $M \in V$. Thus our proof is complete.

THEOREM 7.1.5. F has a minimum value on $\mathscr{I}$ provided (i) $\mathscr{I}$ is a closed 2-interval, (ii) F is continuous on $\mathscr{I}$.

Proof: Consider the function $-F$ and apply Theorem 7.1.4.

We need the following fact to establish the Intermediate Value Theorem.

THEOREM 7.1.6.   Let F be continuous on $\mathscr{I}_1 \times \mathscr{I}_2$, let $a \in \mathscr{I}_1$, and let $b \in \mathscr{I}_2$; then $_bF_1$ is continuous on $\mathscr{I}_1$, and $_aF_2$ is continuous on $\mathscr{I}_2$.

Proof: The proof is obvious.

THEOREM 7.1.7 (Intermediate Value Theorem).   Let F be continuous on $\mathscr{I} = \mathscr{I}_1 \times \mathscr{I}_2$ and let $\alpha \in \mathscr{I}$, $\beta \in \mathscr{I}$; then corresponding to any real number K such that $F\alpha \leq K \leq F\beta$, there is a member of $\mathscr{I}$, say γ, such that $F\gamma = K$.

Proof: Let $\alpha = (a, b)$ and let $\beta = (c, d)$. Consider the function $_bF_1$; by Theorem 7.1.6, $_bF_1$ is continuous on $\mathscr{I}_1$. If there is a member of $\mathscr{I}_1$, say t, such that $_bF_1(t) \geq K$, then by the intermediate value theorem for functions with one argument, we shall have our result. Suppose, then, that $_bF_1(t) < K$ whenever $t \in \mathscr{I}_1$; we consider the function $_cF_2$. Now, $_cF_2(b) = _bF_1(c)$ and so $_cF_2(b) < K$. Hence $_cF_2(b) < K < _cF_2(d)$, where $b \in \mathscr{I}_2$ and $d \in \mathscr{I}_2$; moreover, $_cF_2$ is continuous on $\mathscr{I}_2$. Hence, by the intermediate value theorem for functions with one argument, there is a real number, say s, between b and d such that $_cF_2(s) = K$. Thus $F(c, s) = K$. This establishes Theorem 7.1.7.

We now introduce the concept of *uniform* continuity.

DEFINITION 7.1.4. F is said to be *uniformly* continuous on $\mathscr{I}$, where $\mathscr{I}$ is a 2-interval, iff

(i) given any natural number p, there is a natural number q such that $|F\beta - F\alpha| < 10^{-p}$ whenever $\|\beta - \alpha\| < 10^{-q}$, $\alpha \in \mathscr{I}$, and $\beta \in \mathscr{I}$;

(ii) $\mathscr{I} \subset \mathscr{D}_F$.

THEOREM 7.1.8 (Uniform Continuity). F is uniformly continuous on $\mathscr{I}$ provided (i) $\mathscr{I}$ is a closed 2-interval, (ii) F is continuous on $\mathscr{I}$.

Proof: The proof follows the pattern of the proof for the case of a function with one argument. The details are left as an exercise.

The Intermediate Value Theorem can be extended by relaxing the requirement that $\mathscr{I}$ be a 2-interval. We introduce the notion of a *simple* region.

DEFINITION 7.1.5.   Let f and g be continuous functions such that $f(t) \leq g(t)$ whenever $t \in [c, d]$; then the following regions of the XY-plane are said to be *simple* (see Figures 7.1.1 and 7.1.2):

(1) $\{(a, b) \,|\, c \leq a \leq d$ and $f(a) \leq b \leq g(a)\}$,

(2) $\{(b, a) \,|\, c \leq a \leq d$ and $f(a) \leq b \leq g(a)\}$.

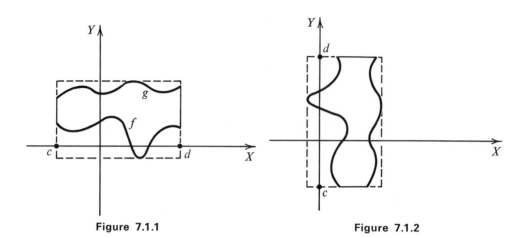

Figure 7.1.1   Figure 7.1.2

With each simple region S we shall associate the smallest closed 2-interval which contains S; e.g., if $S = \{(a, b) \mid c \le a \le d$ and $f(a) \le b \le g(a)\}$, then the required 2-interval is $[c, d] \times [u, v]$, where $u = \min\{f(t) \mid t \in [c, d]\}$ and $v = \max\{g(t) \mid t \in [c, d]\}$; whereas if $S = \{(b, a) \mid c \le a \le d$ and $f(a) \le b \le g(a)\}$, then the required 2-interval is $[u, v] \times [c, d]$.

We need the following result.

THEOREM 7.1.9.   Let F be a function with two arguments such that $\mathcal{D}_F = S$, where S is simple, and let F be continuous on S; then F can be extended to a function which is continuous on the smallest closed 2-interval which contains S.

Proof: We shall suppose that S is a simple region of the type illustrated in Figure 7.1.1; an argument similar to the following argument establishes our result for the case of a simple region of the type illustrated in Figure 7.1.2. Let $\mathscr{I}$ be the smallest closed 2-interval which contains S. We shall extend F to a function G as follows: let $(a, b) \in \mathscr{I}$; then

$$G(a, b) = \begin{cases} F(a, b) \text{ if } f(a) \le b \le g(a) \\ F(a, g(a)) \text{ if } b > g(a) \\ F(a, f(a)) \text{ if } b < f(a). \end{cases}$$

We shall now prove that G is continuous on $\mathscr{I}$. Let $(a, b) \in \mathscr{I}$. Now, F is continuous at $(a, g(a))$; therefore, given p, q_1 exists such that if α is a member of both S and the circle with center $(a, g(a))$ and radius 10^{-q_1}, then $|F(a, g(a)) - F\alpha| < 10^{-p}$. This circle contains within its boundary a portion of the graph of g; we are interested only in the domain of this set. By definition, $[c, d] \subset \mathcal{D}_g$; therefore the domain of the subset of g whose graph is contained within the circle is a closed interval, say $[t_1, t_2]$. Moreover, q_2 exists such that if β is a member of both S and the circle with center $(a, f(a))$ and radius 10^{-q_2}, then $|F(a, f(a)) - F\beta| < 10^{-p}$. Let $[s_1, s_2]$ be the domain of the portion of the graph of f which is contained within this circle. Finally, we construct the circle with center (a, b) and radius chosen so that the first term of each ordered pair which is in $\mathscr{I}$ and which is also inside the circle is a member of both $[t_1, t_2]$ and $[s_1, s_2]$ (see Figure 7.1.3). By construction, then, $|G(a, b) - G\gamma| < 10^{-p}$ whenever γ is a member of this circle. This establishes that G is continuous on $\mathcal{I}$.

We can now extend the Intermediate Value Theorem.

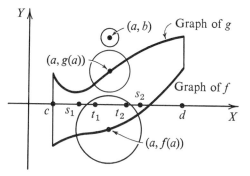

Figure 7.1.3

THEOREM 7.1.10.   Let F be continuous on the simple region S and let $\alpha \in S$ and $\beta \in S$; then corresponding to each real number K such that $F\alpha \leq K \leq F\beta$ there is a member of S, say γ, such that $F\gamma = K$.

Proof: Let $\alpha \in S$, let $\beta \in S$, and let $F\alpha \leq K \leq F\beta$. Let $\mathcal{I}$ be the smallest closed 2-interval which contains S and let G be the function constructed from S as in the proof of Theorem 7.1.9. Then G is continuous on $\mathcal{I}$. Thus, by the Intermediate Value Theorem, there is a member of $\mathcal{I}$, say γ, such that $G\gamma = K$. If $\gamma \in S$, then $G\gamma = F\gamma$. Otherwise, let $\gamma = (a, b)$. If $b > g(a)$, then $G\gamma = F(a, g(a))$; if $b < f(a)$, then $G\gamma = F(a, f(a))$. This establishes Theorem 7.1.10.

Moreover, we can extend Theorem 7.1.8, which asserts that a function which is continuous on a closed 2-interval is uniformly continuous on the 2-interval.

THEOREM 7.1.11. F is uniformly continuous on S provided (i) S is a simple region, (ii) F is continuous on S.

Proof: Let $\mathcal{I}$ be the smallest closed 2-interval which contains S. By the proof of Theorem 7.1.9, we can construct a function, say G, such that G is continuous on $\mathcal{I}$ and $G\alpha = F\alpha$ whenever $\alpha \in S$. By Theorem 7.1.8, G is uniformly continuous on $\mathcal{I}$; therefore G is uniformly continuous on S. Thus F is uniformly continuous on S. This establishes our result.

7.2   The Volume of a Region of 3-space

Consider the region of 3-space under the graph of the function X^2, above the XY-plane, and bounded by the cylinder on the boundary of the 2-interval D, where $D = [1,12] \times [2, 4]$, namely $\{(\alpha, c) \mid \alpha \in [1, 2] \times [2, 4]$ and $0 \leq c \leq X^2\alpha\}$ (see Figure 7.2.1). We shall compute the volume of this region, assuming that it possesses a volume. The idea, which goes back to the Greek mathematicians of the classical era, is to partition D into a large number of small 2-intervals. Each of these rectangles will form the base of a parallelepiped whose height is the number that the given function X^2 asssociates with some member of the 2-interval (or a boundary point of the 2-interval). The volume of each of the resulting parallelepipeds is the product of its height and the area of its base; thus we obtain an approximation to the volume of the given region.

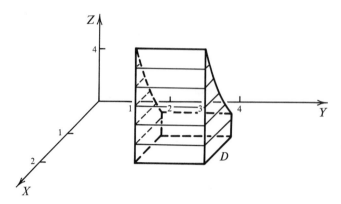

Figure 7.2.1

We shall run through this procedure twice. First, we shall construct each of our parallelepipeds so that it *contains* the portion of the given region which is bounded by the cylinder on the base of the parallelepiped; thus the total volume of these parallelepipeds is not less than the volume of the given region. Next, we shall construct each of our parallelepipeds so that it is *contained in* the portion of the given region bounded by the cylinder on the base of the parallelepiped; thus the total volume of these parallelepipeds is not greater than the volume of the given region. We thereby get a grip on the volume of the given region, provided it possesses a volume.

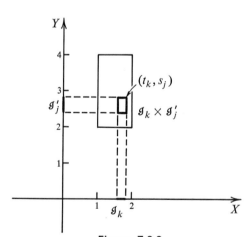

Figure 7.2.2

We must fix our attention on the 2-interval D; notice that our procedure centers around D. Our first goal is systematically to subdivide D into smaller 2-intervals, so that the distance between any two members of one 2-interval is small. This can be achieved as follows. Let $(\{(\mathscr{I}_1, t_1), (\mathscr{I}_2, t_2), \cdots, (\mathscr{I}_n, t_n)\})$ be a [1, 2]-sequence where, for each k, t_k is the right-hand endpoint of $\mathscr{I}_k$, and $|\mathscr{I}_k| = 1/n$ whenever $1 \le k \le n$. Let $(\{(\mathscr{I}'_1, s_1), (\mathscr{I}'_2, s_2), \cdots, (\mathscr{I}'_n, s_n)\})$ be a [2, 4]-sequence where, for each j, s_j is the right-hand endpoint of $\mathscr{I}'_j$, and $|\mathscr{I}'_j| = 2/n$ whenever $1 \le j \le n$. We shall represent the given [1, 2]-sequence by $((P_n, Q_n))$, where $P_n = \{\mathscr{I}_1, \mathscr{I}_2, \cdots, \mathscr{I}_n\}$ and $Q_n = \{t_1, t_2, \cdots, t_n\}$. Similarly, we shall represent the given [2, 4]-sequence by $((P'_n, Q'_n))$, where $P'_n = \{\mathscr{I}'_1, \mathscr{I}'_2, \cdots, \mathscr{I}'_n\}$ and $Q'_n = \{s_1, s_2, \cdots, s_n\}$ for each $n \in N$. Corresponding to each natural number n, we obtain a partition of D by forming the cross partition of P_n and P'_n; e.g., $\mathscr{I}_k \times \mathscr{I}'_j$ is a member of this partition of D whenever $\mathscr{I}_k \in P_n$ and $\mathscr{I}'_j \in P'_n$. Now, t_k is associated with $\mathscr{I}_k$ and s_j is associated with $\mathscr{I}'_j$; so we shall associate (t_k, s_j) with $\mathscr{I}_k \times \mathscr{I}'_j$ (see Figure 7.2.2).

Next, consider the parallelepiped with base $\mathscr{I}_k \times \mathscr{I}'_j$ and height $X^2(t_k, s_j)$; the area of the base is $|\mathscr{I}_k| \, |\mathscr{I}'_j|$ and the height is t_k^2. Thus the volume of this parallelepiped is $2t_k^2/n^2$. We shall add the volumes of our parallelepipeds by columns; i.e., we shall consider all parallelepipeds with base $\mathscr{I}_1$, then all parallelepipeds with base $\mathscr{I}_2, \cdots$, and finally all parallelepipeds with base $\mathscr{I}_n$. Note that there are n parallelepipeds per column. Let "U_n" denote the volume of all these parallelepipeds; then

$$U_n = (2/n^2)[n(1 + 1/n)^2 + n(1 + 2/n)^2 + \cdots + n(1 + n/n)^2]$$

$$= (2/n)[n + 2(1 + 2 + \cdots + n)/n + (1^2 + 2^2 + \cdots + n^2)/n^2]$$

$$= (2/n)[n + (n + 1) + (n + 1)(2n + 1)/6n]$$

$$= (2n + 1)(7n + 1)/3n^2.$$

Using left-hand endpoints to obtain the heights of our parallelepipeds, we build up a region of space which is contained in the given region. Let "L_n" denote the volume of these parallelepipeds; then, as above, we see that $L_n = (2n - 1)(7n - 1)/3n^2$.

Assuming that the given region possesses a volume, let "V" denote its volume; then $L_n \leq V \leq U_n$ whenever $n \in N$. Thus $\lim(L_n) \leq V \leq \lim(U_n)$; but $\lim(L_n) = 14/3$ and $\lim(U_n) = 14/3$. We conclude that $V = 14/3$. Thus the volume of the given region is $14/3$, provided it possesses a volume.

Examining the procedure of this example, we see that the basic idea is to approximate the given region of 3-space by parallelepipeds; then the total volume of the parallelepipeds approximates the volume of the given region. The base of each parallelepiped is a 2-interval which is contained in the given 2-interval D; the height of each parallelepiped is the distance from some member of the 2-interval or its boundary to the graph of the function involved.

Our first job is to describe this procedure mathematically. To be specific, we consider the region of 3-space which is bounded by the graph of a function with two arguments, say F, the XY-plane, and the cylinder on the boundary of D, a given 2-interval; we shall assume that F is continuous and nonnegative on $\bar{D}$. Here, the 2-interval D plays a key role, for this set provides us with the base of each of our parallelepipeds. To obtain our parallelepipeds, we first partition D into n 2-intervals, say $\mathscr{I}_1, \mathscr{I}_2, \cdots, \mathscr{I}_n$. Next, we associate with each of these 2-intervals one of its members (or possibly a member of its boundary). Indeed, we shall actually pair with each 2-interval the 2-vector which is associated with it. For example, suppose that α_k is associated with $\mathscr{I}_k$ (so that $\alpha_k \in \mathscr{I}_k$ or α_k is a member of the boundary of $\mathscr{I}_k$) whenever $1 \leq k \leq n$; then we form the set of ordered pairs $\{(\mathscr{I}_1, \alpha_1), (\mathscr{I}_2, \alpha_2), \cdots, (\mathscr{I}_n, \alpha_n)\}$, which we shall call a *parallelepiped-builder*. The first terms of members of this set provide us with the bases of our parallelepipeds the second terms lead us, via the given function F, to the height of each of our parallelepipeds. For example, from the ordered pair $(\mathscr{I}_k, \alpha_k)$ we obtain the parallelepiped with base $\mathscr{I}_k$ and height $F(\alpha_k)$. The volume of this parallelepiped is the product of the area of its base and its height. If $\mathscr{I}_k = \mathscr{I} \times \mathscr{J}$, where $\mathscr{I}$ and $\mathscr{J}$ are intervals, then the area of $\mathscr{I}_k$ is $|\mathscr{I}| \, |\mathscr{J}|$. It is convenient to denote the area of $\mathscr{I}_k$ by "$|\mathscr{I}_k|$". Thus the volume of our parallelepiped is $F(\alpha_k)|\mathscr{I}_k|$. So the parallelepiped-builder $\{(\mathscr{I}_1, \alpha_1), (\mathscr{I}_2, \alpha_2), \cdots,$

$(\mathscr{I}_n, \alpha_n)\}$ serves to approximate the given region by parallelepipeds; therefore the *volume* of the given region is approximated by the sum of the volumes of these parallelepipeds, namely $\sum_{k=1}^{n} F(\alpha_k)|\mathscr{I}_k|$.

Let us formalize the notion of a parallelepiped-builder.

> DEFINITION 7.2.1.   Let D be any 2-interval; then $\{(\mathscr{I}_1, \alpha_1), (\mathscr{I}_2, \alpha_2), \cdots,$ $(\mathscr{I}_n, \alpha_n)\}$ is said to be a *parallelepiped-builder over D* iff
>
>> (i) $\{\mathscr{I}_1, \mathscr{I}_2, \cdots, \mathscr{I}_n\}$ is a partition of D whose members are 2-intervals;
>> (ii) $\mathscr{I}_j \neq \mathscr{I}_k$ whenever $j \neq k$, $1 \leq j \leq n$, and $1 \leq k \leq n$;
>> (iii) $\alpha_k \in \bar{\mathscr{I}}_k$ whenever $1 \leq k \leq n$.

We want to ensure that our procedure for approximating the volume of a given region can be carried out to *any* desired accuracy. To achieve this goal, we shall insist that the bases of our parallelepipeds be sufficiently small. This involves us with a *sequence* of parallelepiped-builders, say $(\{(\mathscr{I}_1, \alpha_1), (\mathscr{I}_2, \alpha_2), \cdots, (\mathscr{I}_m, \alpha_m)\})$; the nth term of this sequence is the parallelepiped-builder $\{(\mathscr{I}_1, \alpha_1), (\mathscr{I}_2, \alpha_2), \cdots, (\mathscr{I}_m, \alpha_m)\}$, where m depends upon n. At first sight we might think that we have only to require that the maximum area of the 2-intervals $\mathscr{I}_1, \mathscr{I}_2, \cdots, \mathscr{I}_m$ be small; however, in view of uniform continuity, what we need is the requirement that the maximum distance between any two members of one 2-interval be small.

> DEFINITION 7.2.2.   Let S be any set of 2-vectors; by the *diameter* of S we mean the least upper bound of $\{\|\alpha - \beta\| \mid \alpha \in S \text{ and } \beta \in S\}$.

We shall require that the maximum diameter of the 2-intervals $\mathscr{I}_1, \mathscr{I}_2, \cdots, \mathscr{I}_m$ be small provided that m is large. Concentrate on the partition $\{\mathscr{I}_1, \mathscr{I}_2, \cdots, \mathscr{I}_m\}$, which is obtained from the nth term of our sequence. Consider the largest of the real numbers:

$$\text{diameter of } \mathscr{I}_1, \text{ diameter of } \mathscr{I}_2, \cdots, \text{ diameter of } \mathscr{I}_m;$$

this real number is called the *mesh* or the *norm* of the partition $\{\mathscr{I}_1, \mathscr{I}_2, \cdots, \mathscr{I}_m\}$ and is denoted by " $\|\{\mathscr{I}_1, \mathscr{I}_2, \cdots, \mathscr{I}_m\}\|$ ". To guarantee that the bases of our parallelepipeds are sufficiently small, we shall restrict ourselves to a sequence of parallelpiped-builders, say $(\{(\mathscr{I}_1, \alpha_1), (\mathscr{I}_2, \alpha_2), \cdots, (\mathscr{I}_m, \alpha_m)\})$, such that $\lim (\|\{\mathscr{I}_1, \mathscr{I}_2, \cdots, \mathscr{I}_m\}\|) = 0$.

Accordingly, we introduce the notion of a *D-sequence*, where D is any 2-interval.

> DEFINITION 7.2.3.   Let D be any 2-interval; then the sequence $(\{(\mathscr{I}_1, \alpha_1),$ $(\mathscr{I}_2, \alpha_2), \dots, (\mathscr{I}_m, \alpha_m)\})$, where m depends upon n, is said to be a *D-sequence* iff
>
>> (i)   each term of the sequence is a parallelepiped-builder over D,
>>
>> (ii) $\lim(\|\{\mathscr{I}_1, \mathscr{I}_2, \cdots, \mathscr{I}_m\}\|) = 0$.

We emphasize that each term of a D-sequence represents a family of parallelepipeds which approximate the given region of 3-space. Thus a D-sequence represents a *sequence* of families of parallelepipeds which approximate, as closely as desired, the given region. We are now in a position to define the concept of the *volume* of a region of 3-space.

DEFINITION 7.2.4. Let D be a closed 2-interval and let F be continuous and nonnegative on $\bar{D}$. Then V is said to be the *volume* of the region bounded by the graph of F, the XY-plane, and the cylinder on the boundary of D, provided that $\lim\left(\sum_{k=1}^{m} F(\alpha_k)|\mathscr{I}_k|\right) = V$ whenever $(\{(\mathscr{I}_1, \alpha_1), (\mathscr{I}_2, \alpha_2), \cdots, (\mathscr{I}_m, \alpha_m)\})$ is a D-sequence.

We point out that the volume of the region bounded by the graph of F, the XY-plane, and the cylinder on the boundary of D is the common limit of a family of sequences. Notice that this region is $\{(\alpha, c) \mid \alpha \in D \text{ and } 0 \le c \le F(\alpha)\}$.

7.3   The Double Integral

We shall now generalize the notion of volume discussed in Section 7.2. There, we saw how to associate a real number with the region of 3-space bounded by the graph of a function with two arguments, the XY-plane, and the cylinder on the boundary of a 2-interval. Essentially, we are associating a real number with a function and a 2-interval. Let D be a closed 2-interval and suppose that $D \subset \mathscr{D}_F$; then the real number associated with F and D is called *the integral of F over D* and is denoted by "$\int_D F$". Generalizing the discussion of Section 7.2, we shall not insist that F be either continuous or nonnegative on D; however, we shall insist that $D \subset \mathscr{D}_F$.

DEFINITION 7.3.1   Let the closed 2-interval D be a subset of $\mathscr{D}_F$; then F is said to be *integrable over D* iff there is a real number L such that $\lim\left(\sum_{k=1}^{m} F(\alpha_k)|\mathscr{I}_k|\right) = L$ whenever $(\{(\mathscr{I}_1, \alpha_1), (\mathscr{I}_2, \alpha_2), \cdots, (\mathscr{I}_m, \alpha_m)\})$ is a D-sequence; L is called *the integral of F over D* and is denoted by "$\int_D F$".

Note: The expression "$\int_D F$" is said to be a double integral.

EXAMPLE 1.   Compute $\int_D 5$, where $D = [0, 3] \times [-2, -1]$.

Solution: Let $(\{(\mathscr{I}_1, \alpha_1), (\mathscr{I}_2, \alpha_2), \cdots, (\mathscr{I}_m, \alpha_m)\})$ be any D-sequence. Then

$$\lim\left(\sum_{k=1}^{m} 5(\alpha_k)|\mathscr{I}_k|\right) = \lim\left(5\sum_{k=1}^{m}|\mathscr{I}_k|\right) = \lim(15) = 15$$

since $\sum_{k=1}^{m} |\mathscr{I}_k|$ is the area of the rectangle $[0, 3] \times [-2, -1]$. We conclude that 5 is integrable over D and that $\int_D 5 = 15$.

We now state an important existence theorem.

THEOREM 7.3.1 (The Fundamental Theorem).   Let D be any closed 2-interval and let F be any function with two arguments. Then F is integrable over D if F is continuous on D.

This theorem asserts the existence of the real number $\int_D F$ provided that F is continuous on the closed 2-interval D. Once we know that $\int_D F$ exists, then we have a chance of computing this real number. It is evident that Theorem 7.3.1 is a key result in the development of the properties of the double integral. For this reason we call this theorem the *Fundamental Theorem*. For a proof of this theorem, see Section 7.4.

As an immediate application, we have the following result.

THEOREM 7.3.2. $\int_D F$ is the volume of $\{(\alpha, c) \,|\, \alpha \in D \text{ and } 0 \le c \le F\alpha\}$ provided (i) D is a closed 2-interval, (ii) F is continuous and nonnegative on D.
Proof: Consider Definitions 7.2.4 and 7.3.1.

We want to extend our notion of a double integral by modifying the requirement that D be a closed 2-interval; this condition is too restrictive. First, let us show that we can live with 2-intervals to a limited extent.

EXAMPLE 2.   Express as a double integral the volume of the region of 3-space which is bounded by the XY-plane and the graph of $(I - X^2 - Y^2)^{1/2}$.

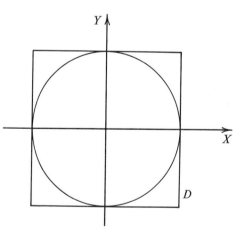

Solution: The given surface intersects the XY-plane in the circle with center at the origin and radius 1. Thus on the set $\{(a, b) \,|\, a^2 + b^2 = 1\}$ the given function takes the value 0; i.e., $Fa = 0$ if $\|\alpha\| = 1$, where $F = (I - X^2 - Y^2)^{1/2}$. Now, consider the 2-interval D where $D = [-1, 1] \times [-1, 1]$. Clearly, $\{(a, b) \,|\, a^2 + b^2 \le 1\} \subset D$, i.e., D contains both the circle and the interior of the circle. The problem is that F is not defined at those points of D which are outside of the circle (see Figure 7.3.1). This difficulty is easily overcome by extending the given function F to a function, say G, which is defined as follows:

$$G\alpha = \begin{cases} F\alpha & \text{if } \alpha \in \mathscr{D}_F \\ 0 & \text{otherwise.} \end{cases}$$

Figure 7.3.1

Clearly, G is continuous and nonnegative on D. By the Fundamental Theorem, G is integrable over D, and, by Theorem 7.3.2, $\int_D G$ is the volume of $\{(\alpha, c) \,|\, \alpha \in D \text{ and } 0 \le c \le G\alpha\}$. Since this region consists of the given region together with a portion of the XY-plane, at an intuitive level it is clear that both regions have the same volume (i.e., intuitively, we see that the *volume* of a two-dimensional region is zero, just as the *area* of a one-dimensional region is zero). Therefore $\int_D G$ is the volume of the given region.

To make sense out of Example 2, we need to know what is meant by the *volume* of a region of the type considered. We shall now remedy this gap. Our purpose in presenting this example is to bring out the intuitive idea behind the following extension of the notion of volume.

DEFINITION 7.3.2.   Let S be any simple region, let F be a function with two arguments which is continuous and nonnegative on S and is zero on the boundary of S, let D be the smallest closed 2-interval which contains S, and let G be con-structed from S as follows:

$$G\alpha = \begin{cases} F\alpha \text{ whenever } \alpha \in S \\ 0 \text{ otherwise.} \end{cases}$$

Then $\int_D G$ is said to be the volume of $\{(\alpha, c) \mid \alpha \in S \text{ and } 0 \le c \le F\alpha\}$.

Our definition contains an unnecessary restriction on the region S, namely the re-quirement that $F\alpha = 0$ whenever α is on the boundary of S. We insert this condition because it ensures that G is continuous on D; this enables us to apply the Fundamental Theorem. However, just as in the case of the definite integral, it is possible to relax the continuity requirement slightly. Consider the following fact.

THEOREM 7.3.3.   Let D be any closed 2-interval and let F be any function which is defined throughout D and is bounded on D; then F is integrable over D if the set of points of D at which F is discontinuous has area zero.

Discussion: We shall not prove this theorem; indeed, a proof is beyond the level of this book. However, we shall consider the intuitive ideas that are involved. When we say that a subset of D, say E, has area zero, we mean the following. Let $\{\mathcal{I}_1, \mathcal{I}_2, \cdots, \mathcal{I}_m\}$ be the partition of D involved in the nth term of a given D-sequence. Let P_m be the subset of $\{\mathcal{I}_1, \mathcal{I}_2, \cdots, \mathcal{I}_m\}$ whose members are not disjoint with E. Let A_m be the sum of the areas of the members of P_m. Then we require that $\lim(A_m) = 0$. In other words, if $E \subset D$, then E has area zero iff each D-sequence provides us with a sequence of 2-intervals which contain E, and yet the sequence of sums of the areas of the 2-intervals involved has limit zero. Accordingly, we can contain, i.e., isolate, the points of discontinuity of F within 2-intervals whose total area is less than any preassigned positive number. Since F is bounded on D, it follows that the total volume of parallelepipeds erected on these 2-intervals is less than any preassigned positive number; thus we can neglect these par-allelepipeds when considering $\sum_{k=1}^{m} F(\alpha_k)|\mathcal{I}_k|$. It follows from this that $\lim\left(\sum_{k=1}^{m} F(\alpha_k)|\mathcal{I}_k|\right)$

is independent of the particular D-sequence involved. Thus, by Definition 7.3.1, F is integrable over D.

Assuming that the boundary of a simple region has area zero, it follows from Theorem 7.3.3 that we can extend our notion of the volume of a region of 3-space as follows.

DEFINITION 7.3.3.   Let S be any simple region, let F be continuous and non-negative on S, let D be the smallest closed 2-interval which contains S, and let G be the function constructed from F as follows:

$$G\alpha = \begin{cases} F\alpha \text{ whenever } \alpha \in S \\ 0 \text{ otherwise.} \end{cases}$$

Then $\int_D G$ is said to be the *volume* of $\{(\alpha, c) \mid \alpha \in S \text{ and } 0 \le c \le F\alpha\}$.

The point is that G is integrable over D even if $F\alpha \ne 0$ for some α on the boundary of S. Moreover, this notion of the volume of a region of 3-space is in accord with our intuition. To be specific, let us consider a particular D-sequence. We observe that each 2-interval which lies outside of S contributes zero to the sum $\sum_{k=1}^{m} G(\alpha_k)|\mathcal{I}_k|$; moreover, those 2-intervals that contain a boundary point of S can be ignored since their total contribution is negligible. Thus a given D-sequence leads us, essentially, to a sequence of families of parallelepipeds which approximate the given region of 3-space, namely $\{(\alpha, c) \mid \alpha \in S \text{ and } 0 \le c \le F\alpha\}$.

We have extended our concept of the volume of a region of 3-space; let us extend the notion of a double integral in a similar fashion.

DEFINITION 7.3.4.   Let S be any simple region and let D be the smallest closed 2-interval which contains S. Let $(\{(\mathcal{I}_1, \alpha_1), (\mathcal{I}_2, \alpha_2), \cdots, (\mathcal{I}_m, \alpha_m)\})$ be any D-sequence; then by an S-*sequence* we mean the sequence obtained from the given D-sequence by deleting each 2-interval which is not a subset of S.

DEFINITION 7.3.5.   Let S be a simple region and let F be defined throughout S. Then F is said to be integrable over S iff there is a real number L such that $\lim \left(\sum_{k=1}^{m} F(\alpha_k)|\mathcal{I}_k| \right) = L$ whenever $(\{(\mathcal{I}_1, \alpha_1), (\mathcal{I}_2, \alpha_2), \cdots, (\mathcal{I}_m, \alpha_m)\})$ is an S-sequence; L is called the *integral of F over S* and is denoted by " $\int_S F$ ".

The following existence theorem is a consequence of Theorem 7.3.3.

THEOREM 7.3.4.   Let S be any simple region whose boundary has area zero and let F be continuous on S. Then F is integrable over S; moreover, $\int_S F = \int_D G$, where D is the smallest closed 2-interval which contains S, and G is the function constructed from F as in Definition 7.3.3.

Proof: First, we observe that, by Theorem 7.3.3, G is integrable over D, i.e., $\int_D G$ exists. Next, consider any D-sequence and the corresponding sequence of sums of products. In particular, we fix our attention on the nth term of this sequence. We consider the contribution to the total sum of a particular 2-interval, say $\mathscr{I}_k$. If $\bar{\mathscr{I}}_k$ is disjoint with S, then $G\alpha_k = 0$; if $\bar{\mathscr{I}}_k$ straddles the boundary of S (i.e., $\bar{\mathscr{I}}_k$ is disjoint with neither S nor $D - S$), then $G(\alpha_k)|\mathscr{I}_k|$ is small since the boundary of S has area zero. The idea is to classify the nonzero terms appearing in our sum into two groups: those associated with intervals which are contained in S, and those terms associated with intervals which straddle S. Hence the limit of our sequence can be represented as the sum of the limits of two sequences. Since the boundary of S has area zero, one of these sequences has limit zero, whereas the remaining sequence is the expression involved in Definition 7.3.5. Accordingly, the limit of this sequence is $\int_D G$. This completes our proof.

The following result follows immediately from Theorem 7.3.4.

THEOREM 7.3.5 $\int_S F$ is the volume of $\{(\alpha, c) \mid \alpha \in S \text{ and } 0 \leq c \leq F\alpha\}$ if (i) S is a simple region whose boundary has area zero, (ii) F is continuous and nonnegative on S.

7.4   Proof of the Fundamental Theorem*

In this section we shall establish Theorem 7.3.1.

Let F be continuous on D, a closed 2-interval, and let P be a partition of D into n 2-intervals, say $\{\mathscr{I}_1, \mathscr{I}_2, \cdots, \mathscr{I}_n\}$. In view of Theorem 7.1.5, there is a member of $\bar{\mathscr{I}}_k$, say α_k, such that $F(\alpha_k)$ is the smallest value of F over $\bar{\mathscr{I}}_k$ whenever $1 \leq k \leq n$. Similarly, by Theorem 7.1.4, there is a member of $\bar{\mathscr{I}}_k$, say β_k, such that $F(\beta_k)$ is the largest value of F over $\bar{\mathscr{I}}_k$ whenever $1 \leq k \leq n$. Consider the sums $\sum_{k=1}^{n} F(\alpha_k)|\mathscr{I}_k|$ and $\sum_{k=1}^{n} F(\beta_k)|\mathscr{I}_k|$, which we shall denote by "$L[P]$" (read "the lower sum of P") and by "$U[P]$" (read "the upper sum of P"), respectively; i.e., $L[P] = \sum_{k=1}^{n} F(\alpha_k)|\mathscr{I}_k|$ and $U[P] = \sum_{k=1}^{n} F(\beta_k)|\mathscr{I}_k|$.

THEOREM 7.4.1. $L[P] \leq U[P]$ whenever P is a partition of D into a finite number of 2-intervals.

Proof: The proof is obvious.

Next, let P^* be the partition of D obtained from a given partition of D, say P, by partitioning one member of P into two 2-intervals. It is clear that the lower sum is not decreased and that the upper sum is not increased, for the minimum value of F over a portion of a 2-interval is not less than the minimum value of F over the entire 2-interval, and the maximum value of F over a portion of a 2-interval is not greater than the maximum value of F over the entire 2-interval. This observation establishes the following fact.

THEOREM 7.4.2. $L[P] \leq L[P^*]$ and $U[P^*] \leq U[P]$ whenever P is a partition of D into a finite number of 2-intervals, and P^* is obtained from P by subdividing one member of P into two 2-intervals.

This result is easily extended as follows.

THEOREM 7.4.3. $L[P] \leq L[P^*]$ and $U[P^*] \leq U[P]$ whenever P is a partition of D into a finite number of 2-intervals, and P^* is obtained from P by subdividing one member of P into a finite number of 2-intervals.

We shall want to partition several members of P into a finite number of 2-intervals.

DEFINITION 7.4.1.   Let P' be a partition of D obtained from a given partition of D, say P, by subdividing one or more members of P into a finite number of 2-intervals. Then P' is said to be a *refinement* of P.

Notice that if P' is a refinement of P, then each member of P is a member of P' or is the union of a finite number of members of P'. Moreover, if P' is a refinement of P, then there is a chain of partitions of D, say $P_1, P_2, \cdots, P_t$, such that $P_1 = P$, $P_t = P'$, and P_{k+1} is obtained from P_k by partitioning one member of P_k into a finite number of 2-intervals, whenever $1 \leq k < t$. In view of this, we readily establish the following result by appealing to Theorem 7.4.3.

COROLLARY 7.4.1. $L[P] \leq L[P']$ and $U[P'] \leq U[P]$ whenever P' is a refinement of P.

THEOREM 7.4.4.   Let P_1 and P_2 be partitions of D into a finite number of 2-intervals; then $L[P_1] \leq U[P_2]$.

Proof: Let P' be a refinement of both P_1 and P_2 (e.g., let P' be the cross partition of P_1 and P_2). Then, by Corollary 7.4.1, $L[P_1] \leq L[P']$ and $U[P'] \leq U[P_2]$; but $L[P'] \leq U[P']$, by Theorem 7.4.1. Thus $L[P_1] \leq L[P'] \leq U[P'] \leq U[P_2]$, i.e., $L[P_1] \leq U[P_2]$. This establishes our result.

THEOREM 7.4.5.   The sequence $(L[P_n])$ converges whenever (P_n) is a sequence of partitions of D such that (i) $P_1 = \{D\}$, (ii) P_{n+1} is a refinement of P_n whenever $n \in N$.

Proof: By Theorem 7.4.4, $U[P_1]$ is an upper bound of $\{L[P_n] \mid n \in N\}$. Moreover, by Corollary 7.4.1, $(L[P_n])$ is monotonically increasing. Therefore $(L[P_n])$ converges.

It is convenient to represent the parallelepiped-builder $\{(\mathscr{I}_1, \alpha_1), (\mathscr{I}_2, \alpha_2), \cdots, (\mathscr{I}_m, \alpha_m)\}$ by "$[P, Q]$", where "P" denotes the partition $\{\mathscr{I}_1, \mathscr{I}_2, \cdots, \mathscr{I}_m\}$ and "Q" gives us the 2-vectors at which F is evaluated, namely $\{\alpha_1, \alpha_2, \cdots, \alpha_m\}$. This means that we can denote a D-sequence, say $(\{(\mathscr{I}_1, \alpha_1), (\mathscr{I}_2, \alpha_2), \cdots, (\mathscr{I}_m, \alpha_m)\})$, by writing

"$([P_n, Q_n])$", since the nth term of the D-sequence is represented by "$[P_n, Q_n]$" for each n. Furthermore, we shall denote the sum of products $\sum_{k=1}^{m} F(\alpha_k)|\mathscr{I}_k|$ associated with the parallelepiped-builder $\{(\mathscr{I}_1, \alpha_1), (\mathscr{I}_2, \alpha_2), \cdots, (\mathscr{I}_m, \alpha_m)\}$ by "$S[F, P, Q]$".

THEOREM 7.4.6.   Let $([P_n, Q_n])$ and $([P_n, Q_n'])$ be D-sequences and let F be continuous on D. Then corresponding to each natural number p there is a natural number q such that $|S[F, P_n, Q_n] - S[F, P_n, Q_n']| \leq 10^{-p}$ whenever $\|P_n\| < 10^{-q}$.

Proof: Let $Q_n = \{\alpha_1, \alpha_2, \cdots, \alpha_m\}$ and let $Q_n' = \{\beta_1, \beta_2, \cdots, \beta_m\}$. By Theorem 7.1.8, F is uniformly continuous on D; therefore, given p, we can choose q such that $|F\alpha - F\beta| < 10^{-p}/|D|$ whenever $\|\alpha - \beta\| < 10^{-q}$. Hence, if $\|P_n\| < 10^{-q}$, then

$$|S[F, P_n, Q_n] - S[F, P_n, Q_n']| \leq \sum_{k=1}^{m} |F(\alpha_k) - F(\beta_k)| \, |\mathscr{I}_k| < (10^{-p}/|D|) \sum_{k=1}^{m} |\mathscr{I}_k| = 10^{-p}.$$

This establishes our result.

COROLLARY 7.4.2.   Let F be continuous on D; then the sequences $(S[F, P_n, Q_n])$ and $(S[F, P_n, Q_n'])$ have the same limit, or both sequences diverge.

Proof: The proof is obvious.

THEOREM 7.4.7.   Let (P_n) and (P_n^*) be sequences of partitions of the closed 2-interval D, each with mesh zero, and let F be continuous on D. Then $(L[P_n])$ and $(L[P_n^*])$ have the same limit, or both sequences diverge.

Proof: For each n, let R_n be a refinement of both P_n and P_n^*. By uniform continuity, it is easy to prove that corresponding to each natural number p there is a natural number q such that $L[R_n] - L[P_n] < 10^{-p}$ whenever $\|P_n\| < 10^{-q}$. Therefore $(L[P_n])$ and $(L[R_n])$ have the same limit, or both sequences diverge. Similarly, by uniform continuity, corresponding to each natural number p there is a natural number q such that $L[R_n] - L[P_n^*] < 10^{-p}$ whenever $\|P_n^*\| < 10^{-q}$. Therefore $(L[P_n^*])$ and $(L[R_n])$ have the same limit, or both sequences diverge. We conclude that $(L[P_n])$ and $(L[P_n^*])$ have the same limit, or both sequences diverge.

THEOREM 7.4.8.   Let (P_n) be any sequence of partitions of the closed 2-interval D with mesh zero, and let F be continuous on D. Then $(L[P_n])$ converges.

Proof: Apply Theorems 7.4.7 and 7.4.5.

THEOREM 7.4.9.   Let F be continuous on the closed 2-interval D, and let $([P_n, Q_n])$ be any D-sequence; then $\lim(S[F, P_n, Q_n]) = \lim(L[P_n])$.

Proof: Apply Theorem 7.4.8 and Corollary 7.4.2.

THEOREM 7.4.10. Let F be continuous on the closed 2-interval D, and let $([P_n, Q_n])$ and $([P_n^*, Q_n^*])$ be any D-sequences; then $\lim(S[F, P_n, Q_n]) = \lim(S[F, P_n^*, Q_n^*])$.

Proof: $\lim(S[F, P_n, Q_n]) = \lim(L[P_n])$ by Th. 7.4.9

$\lim(S[F, P_n^*, Q_n^*]) = \lim(L[P_n^*])$ by Th. 7.4.9

$\lim(L[P_n]) = \lim(L[P_n^*])$ by Th. 7.4.7 and Th. 7.4.8.

Therefore $\lim(S[F, P_n, Q_n]) = \lim(S[F, P_n^*, Q_n^*])$.

COROLLARY 7.4.3. If F is continuous on the closed 2-interval D, then F is integrable over D.

7.5   Properties of the Double Integral

We shall now establish some of the properties of the double integral.

THEOREM 7.5.1. $F + G$ is integrable over S and $\int_S (F + G) = \int_S F + \int_S G$ if (i) S is a simple region whose boundary has area zero, (ii) F and G are integrable over S.

Proof: Let $([P_n, Q_n])$ be any S-sequence; clearly, for each n,

$$S[F + G, P_n, Q_n] = S[F, P_n, Q_n] + S[G, P_n, Q_n].$$

Therefore $\lim(S[F + G, P_n, Q_n]) = \lim(S[F, P_n, Q_n]) + \lim(S[G, P_n, Q_n])$

$$= \int_S F + \int_S G.$$

We conclude that $F + G$ is integrable over S and that $\int_S (F + G) = \int_S F + \int_S G$.

THEOREM 7.5.2. Let $k \in R$; then kF is integrable over S and $\int_S kF = k \int_S F$ if (i) S is a simple region whose boundary has area zero, (ii) F is integrable over S.
Proof: Let $([P_n, Q_n])$ be any S-sequence. Then, for each n, $S[kF, P_n, Q_n] = kS[F, P_n, Q_n]$. Therefore $\lim(S[kF, P_n, Q_n]) = k \lim(S[F, P_n, Q_n]) = k \int_S F$. We conclude that kF is integrable over S and that $\int_S kF = k \int_S F$.

Since we shall be working with simple regions whose boundaries have area zero, it is convenient to introduce the following term.

DEFINITION 7.5.1. A region of the XY-plane, say S, is said to be a *standard region* iff (i) S is simple, (ii) the boundary of S has area zero.

THEOREM 7.5.3.   Let S_1 and S_2 be standard regions such that (i) S_1 and S_2 intersect only at their boundaries, and (ii) $S_1 \cup S_2$ is a standard region, and let F be continuous on $S_1 \cup S_2$. Then $\int_{S_1 \cup S_2} F = \int_{S_1} F + \int_{S_2} F$.

Proof: By Theorem 7.3.4, F is integrable over $S_1 \cup S_2$, S_1, and S_2. Let $([P_n, Q_n])$ be any $S_1 \cup S_2$-sequence; then $\int_{S_1 \cup S_2} F = \lim(S[F, P_n, Q_n])$. Consider the nth term of the given $S_1 \cup S_2$-sequence, namely $[P_n, Q_n]$, and in particular consider the partition P_n. The 2-intervals which occur in P_n can be classified in three ways:

(1) subsets of S_1,

(2) subsets of S_2,

(3) contain members of S_1 and S_2.

But any 2-interval which is in category (3) of necessity contains boundary points of S_1; since the boundary of S_1 has area zero, it follows that these terms can be neglected when computing sums. Moreover, the 2-intervals in category (1) give rise to an S_1-sequence, and the 2-intervals in category (2) give rise to an S_2-sequence. By forming sums and taking the limit, it follows that $\int_{S_1 \cup S_2} F = \int_{S_1} F + \int_{S_2} F$.

THE MEAN VALUE THEOREM FOR DOUBLE INTEGRALS.   Let S be any standard region and suppose F is continuous on S; then there is a member of S, say γ, such that $\int_S F = A \cdot F\gamma$, where A is the area of S.

Proof: Let $\mathcal{I}$ be the smallest closed 2-interval which contains S, and let G be the continuous function constructed from F as in the proof of Theorem 7.1.9. Now, by Theorems 7.1.4 and 7.1.5, G has a maximum value on $\mathcal{I}$ and a minimum value on $\mathcal{I}$. In view of the manner in which G is constructed from F, it follows that F has a maximum value on S and a minimum value on S, say M and m, respectively. By Theorem 7.3.4, $\int_S F$ exists; considering Definition 7.3.5, we see that $Am \leq \int_S F \leq AM$, i.e., $m \leq (1/A) \int_S F \leq M$. But there are members of S, say α and β, such that $m = F\alpha$ and $M = F\beta$; therefore, by Theorem 7.1.10, there is a member of S, say γ, such that $F\gamma = (1/A) \int_S F$. Hence $\int_S F = A \cdot F\gamma$. This completes our proof.

We shall now prove that the double integral can be obtained by partitioning the region involved into *standard* regions.

THEOREM 7.5.4.   Let S be a standard region and let F be continuous on S; then $\int_S F$ can be computed as follows:

1. partition S into standard regions;
2. evaluate F at some member of each region, and multiply by the area of the region;

3. form the sum of the products obtained in step 2;
4. consider a sequence of partitions obtained in step 1, such that the limit of the sequence of meshes is zero; compute step 3 for each partition of the sequence;
5. take the limit of the resulting sequence of sums.

Proof: Recall that the *mesh* of a finite partition is the largest of the diameters of the members of the partition; the *diameter* of a region is the least upper bound of the set of distances between any two points of the region. Now, let P be a partition of S into n standard regions, say $S_1, S_2, \cdots, S_n$. Then

$$\int_S F = \int_{S_1} F + \int_{S_2} F + \cdots + \int_{S_n} F \qquad \text{by Th. 7.5.3}$$

$$= A(S_1)F(\gamma_1) + A(S_2)F(\gamma_2) + \cdots + A(S_n)F(\gamma_n),$$

by the Mean Value Theorem, where "$A(S_i)$" denotes the area of S_i. Let $\alpha_1, \alpha_2, \cdots, \alpha_n$ be any members of $S_1, S_2, \cdots, S_n$, respectively. We want to show that given any natural number p, we can restrict the mesh of our partition so that

(1) $|[A(S_1)F(\gamma_1) + \cdots + A(S_n)F(\gamma_n)] - [A(S_1)F(\alpha_1) + \cdots + A(S_n)F(\alpha_n)]| < 10^{-p}.$

This means that we can evaluate F at the α's instead of the γ's; moreover, using the α's, we have $\int_S F$ as our sum. Thus the resulting sequence of sums has limit $\int_S F$. We shall now establish (1). Since F is continuous on S and S is a closed region, it follows that F is uniformly continuous on S. Therefore there is a natural number q such that $|F\alpha - F\beta| < 10^{-p}/A(S)$ whenever $\|\alpha - \beta\| < 10^{-q}$. Suppose that the mesh of our partition is less than 10^{-q}. In particular,

$$\|\gamma_1 - \alpha_1\| < 10^{-q}, \quad \|\gamma_2 - \alpha_2\| < 10^{-q}, \quad \cdots, \quad \|\gamma_n - \alpha_n\| < 10^{-q}.$$

Thus $|F(\gamma_1) - F(\alpha_1)| < 10^{-p}/A(S), \quad |F(\gamma_2) - F(\alpha_2)| < 10^{-p}/A(S), \quad \cdots, \quad |F(\gamma_n) - F(\alpha_n)|$

$$< 10^{-p}/A(S).$$

We concentrate on the left-hand side of (1):

$|A(S_1)[F(\gamma_1) - F(\alpha_1)] + \cdots + A(S_n)[F(\gamma_n) - F(\alpha_n)]|$

$$\leq A(S_1)|F(\gamma_1) - F(\alpha_1)| + \cdots + A(S_n)|F(\gamma_n) - F(\alpha_n)|$$

$$< [A(S_1) + \cdots + A(S_n)]10^{-p}/A(S)$$

$$= A(S)10^{-p}/A(S)$$

$$= 10^{-p}.$$

This completes our proof.

7.6 Evaluating Double Integrals

At last we shall consider the problem of actually computing a double integral; i.e., we want to develop a technique for *computing* the integral of a function over a region. Obviously, it is impractical to work directly from Definition 7.3.1; fortunately, it is possible to compute a double integral by working out two definite integrals.

THEOREM 7.6.1.   Let F be continuous on the 2-interval D, where $D = [a, b] \times [c, d]$, and let $f(t) = \int_c^d {}_t F_2$, whenever $t \in [a, b]$; then $\int_D F = \int_a^b f$.

Proof: By the Fundamental Theorem, F is integrable over D; therefore we can evaluate $\int_D F$ by considering a particular D-sequence. Let $([P_n, Q_n])$ be a D-sequence such that, for each n, (1) the members of Q_n are obtained by choosing the upper right-hand point of each rectangle in P_n (see Figure 7.6.1), (2) any two rectangles in P_n have the same dimensions. As we proceed, we shall specify further the D-sequence that we are constructing. Of course, this D-sequence need not be unique; indeed, there are many D-sequences that have the properties we need. We must keep an eye on the sequence $(S[F, P_n, Q_n])$; our purpose is to demonstrate that $\lim (S[F, P_n, Q_n]) = \int_a^b f$. Let p be any natural number; we shall construct a parallelepiped-builder, say $[P_m, Q_m]$, such that $\left| S[F, P_m, Q_m] - \int_a^b f \right| < 10^{-p}$. First, we partition $[a, b]$ into s intervals of equal length,

say $\mathscr{I}_1, \mathscr{I}_2, \cdots, \mathscr{I}_s$; let t_k be the right-hand endpoint of $\mathscr{I}_k$ whenever $1 \le k \le s$. We can choose s so that $\left| \sum_{k=1}^{s} f(t_k) |\mathscr{I}_k| - \int_a^b f \right| < 10^{-(p+1)}$. This means that our parallelepiped builder $[P_m, Q_m]$ is obtained by first dividing $[a, b]$, the base of D, into s intervals each of length $(b - a)/s$. On each of these intervals we shall erect a column of 2-intervals by dividing the interval $[c, d]$ into r intervals, each of length $(d - c)/r$, say the intervals $\mathscr{J}_1, \mathscr{J}_2, \cdots, \mathscr{J}_r$; let b_i be the right-hand endpoint of $\mathscr{J}_i$ whenever $1 \le i \le r$.

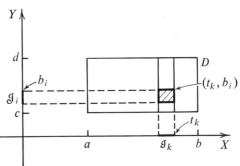

Figure 7.6.1

Now consider $S[F, P_m, Q_m]$; we shall take subtotals by columns and then sum the subtotals. For example, consider the column erected on the interval $\mathscr{I}_k$ (see Figure 7.6.1); this column of 2-intervals has for its sum $\sum_{i=1}^{r} {}_{t_k} F_2(b_i) |\mathscr{J}_i|$. But we can choose r so that

(1)
$$\left| \sum_{i=1}^{r} {}_{t_k} F_2(b_i) |\mathscr{J}_i| - \int_c^d {}_{t_k} F_2 \right| < 10^{-(p+1)}/(b - a).$$

Indeed, since there are only s columns, we can choose r so large that the inequality (1) is maintained whenever $1 \le k \le s$. Let $\sum_{i=1}^{r} {}_{t_k} F_2(b_i) |\mathscr{J}_i| - \int_c^d {}_{t_k} F_2 = \varepsilon_k$ whenever $1 \le k \le s$.

Then

$$S[F, P_m, Q_m] = \sum_{k=1}^{s} \left(\sum_{i=1}^{r} {}_{t_k}F_2(b_i)|\mathscr{I}_i| \right)|\mathscr{I}_k|$$

$$= \sum_{k=1}^{s} \left(\varepsilon_k + \int_{c}^{d} {}_{t_k}F_2 \right)|\mathscr{I}_k|$$

$$= \sum_{k=1}^{s} |\mathscr{I}_k| \int_{c}^{d} {}_{t_k}F_2 + \frac{b-a}{s} \sum_{k=1}^{s} \varepsilon_k$$

$$= \sum_{k=1}^{s} f(t_k)|\mathscr{I}_k| + \frac{b-a}{s} \sum_{k=1}^{s} \varepsilon_k .$$

Thus

$$\left| S[F, P_m, Q_m] - \int_{a}^{b} f \right| = \left| \sum_{k=1}^{s} f(t_k)|\mathscr{I}_k| - \int_{a}^{b} f + \frac{b-a}{s} \sum_{k=1}^{s} \varepsilon_k \right|$$

$$\leq \left| \sum_{k=1}^{s} f(t_k)|\mathscr{I}_k| - \int_{a}^{b} f \right| + \frac{b-a}{s} \sum_{k=1}^{s} |\varepsilon_k|$$

$$< 10^{-(p+1)} + \frac{b-a}{s} \times \frac{s10^{-(p+1)}}{b-a}$$

$$= 10^{-(p+1)} + 10^{-(p+1)}$$

$$< 10^{-p}.$$

We have achieved our goal! We have constructed a parallelepiped-builder, namely $[P_m, Q_m]$, such that $\left| S[F, P_m, Q_m] - \int_{a}^{b} f \right| < 10^{-p}$. In the same way we can construct the next term of our D-sequence, namely $[P_{m+1}, Q_{m+1}]$, so that $\left| S[F, P_{m+1}, Q_{m+1}] - \int_{a}^{b} f \right| < 10^{-(p+1)}$. Continuing in this fashion, we obtain a D-sequence, say $([P_1, Q_1], [P_2, Q_2], \cdots, [P_m, Q_m], \cdots)$, such that $\lim(S[F, P_n, Q_n]) = \int_{a}^{b} f$. This completes our proof.

THEOREM 7.6.2.   Let F be continuous on the 2-interval D, where $D = [a, b] \times [c, d]$, and let $g(t) = \int_{a}^{b} {}_{t}F_1$ whenever $t \in [c, d]$; then $\int_{D} F = \int_{c}^{d} g$.

Proof: Apply the procedure of the proof of Theorem 7.6.1, working with rows rather than columns.

EXAMPLE 1.   Compute $\int_{D} X^2 Y$, where $D = [-1, 2] \times [2, 7]$.

Solution: We shall apply Theorem 7.6.1. Let $t \in [-1, 2]$; then

$$f(t) = \int_{2}^{7} t^2 x = t^2 x^2/2 \Big]_{2}^{7} = 45t^2/2. \text{ Thus } \int_{D} F = \int_{-1}^{2} 45x^2/2 = 15x^3/2 \Big]_{-1}^{2} = 67.5.$$

Using Theorem 7.6.1 or Theorem 7.6.2, it is a simple matter to evaluate the integral of a function over a 2-interval. We must extend our technique so that we can compute the integral of a function over a *standard* region. This is the purpose of the following theorems.

THEOREM 7.6.3. Let F be continuous on the standard region S, where $S = \{(a, b) \mid c \leq a \leq d \text{ and } f(a) \leq b \leq g(a)\}$; let $h(t) = \int_{f(t)}^{g(t)} {}_t F_2$ whenever $c \leq t \leq d$.

Then $\int_S F = \int_c^d h$.

Proof: Let G be the function constructed from F as follows:

$$G\alpha = \begin{cases} F\alpha & \text{whenever } \alpha \in S \\ 0 & \text{otherwise,} \end{cases}$$

and let D be the smallest closed 2-interval which contains S, i.e., $D = [c, d] \times [r, s]$, where $r = \min\{f(t) \mid t \in [c, d]\}$ and $s = \max\{g(t) \mid t \in [c, d]\}$. Then, by Theorems 7.6.1 and 7.3.4, $\int_S F = \int_D G = \int_c^d m$, where $m(t) = \int_r^s {}_t G_2$ whenever $t \in [c, d]$. But for each t,

$$\int_r^s {}_t G_2 = \int_r^{f(t)} {}_t G_2 + \int_{f(t)}^{g(t)} {}_t G_2 + \int_{g(t)}^s {}_t G_2$$

$$= \int_{f(t)}^{g(t)} {}_t G_2 \qquad \text{since } {}_t G_2(u) = 0 \text{ whenever } r < u < f(t) \text{ or } g(t) < u < s$$

$$= \int_{f(t)}^{g(t)} {}_t F_2 \qquad \text{since } {}_t G_2(u) = {}_t F_2(u) \text{ whenever } f(t) \leq u \leq g(t)$$

$$= h(t).$$

Thus $\int_S F = \int_c^d h$. This completes our proof.

Similarly, using Theorem 7.6.2 in place of Theorem 7.6.1, it is easy to establish the following result.

THEOREM 7.6.4. Let F be continuous on the standard region S, where $S = \{(b, a) \mid c \leq a \leq d \text{ and } f(a) \leq b \leq g(a)\}$; let $h(t) = \int_{f(t)}^{g(t)} {}_t F_1$ whenever $c \leq t \leq d$. Then $\int_S F = \int_c^d h$.

EXAMPLE 2. Compute $\int_S X^2 Y$, where $S = \{(a, b) \mid -1 \leq a \leq 2 \text{ and } a^2 \leq b \leq 5 + a\}$.

Solution: First, we sketch the region S; note that S is a standard region (see Figure 7.6.2).

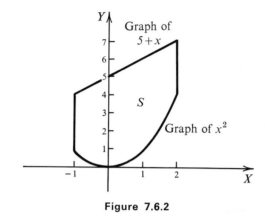

Figure 7.6.2

We shall apply Theorem 7.6.3. Let $t \in [-1, 2]$; then

$$h(t) = \int_{t^2}^{5+t} t^2 x = t^2 x^2/2 \Big]_{t^2}^{5+t}$$

$$= (t^2/2)([5 + t]^2 - t^4)$$

$$= (t^2/2)(25 + 10t + t^2 - t^4);$$

thus $h = .5x^3(25x^2 + 10x^3 + x^4 - x^6)$. Therefore, by Theorem 7.6.3,

$$\int_S X^2 Y = \tfrac{1}{2} \int_{-1}^{2} (25x^2 + 10x^3 + x^4 - x^6)$$

$$= \tfrac{1}{2} \Big[25x^3/3 + 5x^4/2 + x^5/5 - x^7/7 \Big]_{-1}^{2} \approx 68.8.$$

EXAMPLE 3. Compute $\int_S X^2 Y$, where $S = \{(b, a) \mid 0 \leq a \leq \pi \text{ and } -2 \leq b \leq \sin a\}$.

Solution: First, we sketch the region S; note that S is a standard region (see Figure 7.6.3).

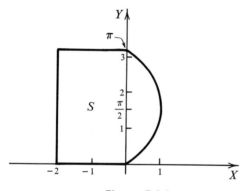

Figure 7.6.3

We shall apply Theorem 7.6.4. Let $t \in [0, \pi]$; then

$$h(t) = t \int_{-2}^{\sin t} x^2 = tx^3/3 \Big]_{-2}^{\sin t} = (t/3)(\sin^3 t + 8);$$

thus $h = (1/3)(8x + x \sin^3)$. Therefore, by Theorem 7.6.4,

$$\int_S X^2 Y = \tfrac{1}{3} \int_0^{\pi} (8x + x \sin^3) = \tfrac{8}{3} \int_0^{\pi} x +$$

$$\tfrac{1}{3} \int_0^{\pi} x \sin^3 = 4\pi^2/3 + \tfrac{1}{3} \int_0^{\pi} x \sin^3.$$

Now, $\int_0^{\pi} x \sin^3$ is easy to compute by applying elementary integration technique. Perhaps it is worthwhile to present the details so as to review the fundamental technique. The idea is to integrate by parts, as follows:

$$\int_0^{\pi} x \sin^3 = -x \sin^2 \cdot \cos \Big]_0^{\pi} + \int_0^{\pi} \cos \cdot (\sin^2 + 2x \sin \cdot \cos)$$

$$= \int_0^{\pi} \cos \cdot \sin^2 + 2 \int_0^{\pi} x \sin \cdot (1 - \sin^2)$$

$$= \sin^3/3 \Big]_0^{\pi} + 2 \int_0^{\pi} x \sin - 2 \int_0^{\pi} x \sin^3.$$

Thus

$$\int_0^{\pi} x \sin^3 = \tfrac{2}{3} \int_0^{\pi} x \sin = -(2/3)x \cos \Big]_0^{\pi} + \tfrac{2}{3} \int_0^{\pi} \cos = 2\pi/3.$$

Hence $\int_S X^2 Y = 4\pi^2/3 + 2\pi/9$.

Theorem 7.5.4 has an important impli-
cation: we are free to subdivide a given
region of 2-space into standard regions
which are not necessarily 2-intervals. It is
sometimes helpful to break down a given
region into standard regions which are
bounded by line segments and by arcs of
circles (see Figure 7.6.4). By taking subtotals appropriately, it is possible to make
use of two definite integrals, just as in
Theorems 7.6.1 and 7.6.2. The following
example will illustrate the idea.

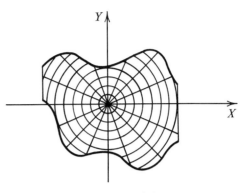

Figure 7.6.4

EXAMPLE 4.   Compute $\int_S (X^2 + Y^2)^{1/2}$, where $S = \{(a, b) \mid 0 \le a \le 2 \text{ and } 0 \le b \le (4 - a^2)^{1/2}\}$.

Solution: We shall partition S by means of a network of circles with center at the origin and
lines through the origin (see Figure 7.6.5). The resulting partition of S consists of standard

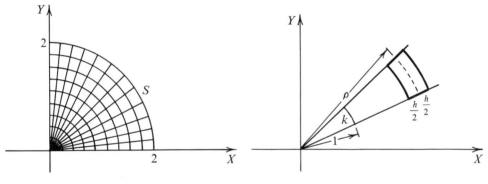

Figure 7.6.5   **Figure 7.6.6**

regions bounded by two circular arcs and two lines through the origin. We need the area of each
of these regions. This can be expressed in terms of the radius, say ρ, of the circle midway between
the two circles involved, the difference between the radii of the two circles, say h, and the length
of the arc of the unit circle cut off by the two given lines, say k (i.e., k is the *angle* between the
given lines). From elementary calculus or directly from the geometry involved, it is easy to establish that the area of this region is $\rho h k$ (see Figure 7.6.6). It is convenient to evaluate the given
function $(X^2 + Y^2)^{1/2}$ at a point on the circle midway between the given circles and on the lower
boundary of the region. Clearly, the number that the function $(X^2 + Y^2)^{1/2}$ associates with a
given point is the distance of the point from the origin; thus $(X^2 + Y^2)^{1/2}$ associates ρ with
our point. Therefore the contribution of this member of our partition to our sum is $\rho^2 h k$. We
shall take subtotals for regions lying between two given lines and then total the subtotals.
Consider the regions lying between the line with slope α and the line with slope $\alpha + k$ (see
Figure 7.6.7). To work out our subtotal, concentrate on the portion of the graph of $x \tan \alpha$
which lies inside the region S. We can represent this line segment by the interval $[0, 2]$. The arcs
of circles displayed in Figure 7.6.7 mark out a partition of our line segment into s intervals

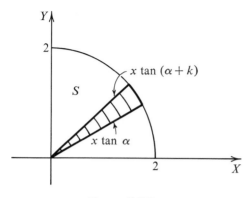

Figure 7.6.7

each of length h. Moreover, we are evaluating the function $(X^2 + Y^2)^{1/2}$ at the midpoint of each of our intervals. Thus the contribution of the regions displayed in Figure 7.6.7 is $\sum_{j=1}^{8} f(t_j)|\mathscr{I}_j|$, where $f = kx^2$ and $|\mathscr{I}_j| = h$ whenever $1 \leq j \leq s$. Thus our subtotal is approximated by $k \int_0^2 x^2$, namely $8k/3$; moreover, the error in the approximation for each of our subtotals can be made as small as we wish by taking s large enough. Finally, we must total our subtotals. Again, this leads us to a definite integral; suppose there are r subtotals, so that $k = \pi/2r$. Then our grand total is

$\sum_{i=1}^{r} 8k/3$. Notice that this sum can be obtained by partitioning the interval $[0, \pi/2]$ into r intervals each of length k, evaluating the function $8/3$ at the right-hand endpoint of each interval, multiplying by the length of each interval, and finally summing these products. Hence $\sum_{i=1}^{r} 8k/3 =$

$\sum_{j=1}^{r} f(t_j)|\mathscr{I}_j|$, where $f = 8/3$. Thus our sum is approximated by $\int_0^{\pi/2} 8/3$, namely $4\pi/3$. We conclude that $\int_S (X^2 + Y^2)^{1/2} = 4\pi/3$.

Note: The above argument can be made rigorous by the method of the proof of Theorem 7.6.1.

EXAMPLE 5. Determine the volume of the region under the graph of $X^2 Y$, above the XY-plane, and bounded by the cylinder on the boundary of S, where $S = \{(a, b) \mid 0 \leq a \leq 1$ and $0 \leq b \leq (1 - a^2)^{1/2}\}$.

Solution: First, we sketch the region S; next we subdivide this region by means of a family of concentric circles with center at the origin, and a family of lines through the origin (see Figure 7.6.8). By Theorem 7.3.5, the required volume is $\int_S X^2 Y$. We shall now evaluate this

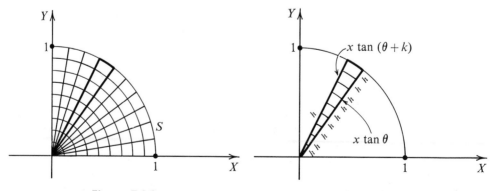

Figure 7.6.8   **Figure 7.6.9**

double integral. By Theorem 7.5.4, we are entitled to use a sequence of partitions of S of the type displayed in Figure 7.6.8. The area of each of these standard regions is easily obtained (see Example 4); it remains to evaluate $X^2 Y$ at a point of each region, multiply by the area of the region, and sum. Let (a, b) be a member of S whose distance from the origin is ρ, and such that the line through (a, b) and the origin makes an angle of θ with the line X. Then the number that $X^2 Y$ associates with (a, b) is $(\rho \cos \theta)^2 \rho \sin \theta$, i.e., $\rho^3 \cos^2 \theta \sin \theta$.

Next, consider the portion of the graph of $x \tan \theta$ which is displayed in Figure 7.6.9; we partition this line segment into s intervals each of length h. Clearly, the contribution of the corresponding regions (see Figure 7.6.9) is $\sum_{j=1}^{s} f(t_j)|\mathscr{I}_j|$, where $f = (\cos^2 \theta \sin \theta x^3) k x$ and $|\mathscr{I}_j| = h$ whenever $1 \leq j \leq s$. Thus our subtotal is approximated by $k \cos^2 \theta \sin \theta \int_0^1 x^4$, i.e., $k/5 \cos^2 \theta \sin \theta$. Finally, we sum these subtotals; suppose there are r subtotals, so that $k = \pi/2r$. Then our sum is

(1) $\quad \dfrac{k}{5} \cos^2 0 \sin 0 + \dfrac{k}{5} \cos^2 k \sin k + \dfrac{k}{5} \cos^2 2k \sin 2k + \cdots + \dfrac{k}{5} \cos^2(\pi/2 - k) \sin(\pi/2 - k).$

Notice that this sum can be obtained by partitioning the interval $[0, \pi/2]$ into r intervals each of length k, evaluating the function $(1/5) \cos^2 \cdot \sin$ at the left-hand endpoint of each of these intervals, multiplying by the length of each interval, and summing. In other words, (1) can be represented by $\sum_{j=1}^{r} f(t_j)|\mathscr{I}_j|$, where $f = (1/5) \cos^2 \cdot \sin$. Hence this sum is approximated by $\frac{1}{5} \int_0^{\pi/2} \cos^2 \cdot \sin$.

We conclude that the required volume is

$$\frac{1}{5} \int_0^{\pi/2} \cos^2 \cdot \sin = -\frac{1}{15} \cos^3 \Big]_0^{\pi/2} = \frac{1}{15}.$$

Now that we have discussed the intuitive ideas, we are in a position to formalize the steps involved in computing a double integral by the method of Examples 4 and 5. Consider the following theorem.

THEOREM 7.6.5. Let F be continuous on S, where S is the region bounded by the graphs of $x \tan \alpha$, $x \tan \beta$, $\rho_1 \cos * \rho_1 \sin$, and $\rho_2 \cos * \rho_2 \sin$, where $\alpha < \beta$ and $\rho_1(\theta) \leq \rho_2(\theta)$ whenever $\alpha \leq \theta \leq \beta$ (see Figure 7.6.10). Moreover, let $h(\theta) = \int_{\rho_1(\theta)}^{\rho_2(\theta)} x[F(x \cos \theta, x \sin \theta)]$ whenever $\alpha \leq \theta \leq \beta$; then $\int_S F = \int_\alpha^\beta h$.

Proof: First, we sketch the region S (see Figure 7.6.10). We subdivide S by means of a family of circles with center at the origin and a family of lines through the origin. We must multiply the area of each region by the value of F at some point of the region, and then add. First, consider the regions between the graphs of $x \tan \theta$ and $x \tan(\theta + k)$, where $k > 0$. The total contribution of these regions is approximated by $\int_{\rho_1(\theta)}^{\rho_2(\theta)} xF(x \cos \theta,$ $x \sin \theta)$, namely $h(\theta)$ [for an explanation of the notation " $F(f, g)$ ", see Definition 6.11.9]. Totaling the subtotals, we are led to the definite integral $\int_\alpha^\beta h$. Following the procedure

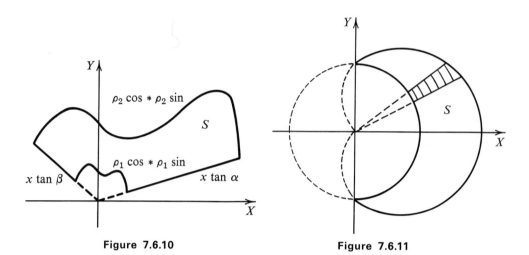

Figure 7.6.10   **Figure 7.6.11**

of the proof of Theorem 7.6.1, it is a simple matter to present the above argument rigorously.

We now illustrate Theorem 7.6.5.

EXAMPLE 6. Compute $\int_S Y$, where S is the region which lies outside the unit circle with center at the origin and inside the graph of $(1 + \cos) \cdot \cos * (1 + \cos) \cdot \sin$.

Solution: First, we sketch S (see Figure 7.6.11). We shall apply Theorem 7.6.5; here, $\alpha = -\pi/2$, $\beta = \pi/2$, $\rho_1 = 1$, and $\rho_2 = 1 + \cos$. The conditions of the theorem are met. Let, $\theta \in [-\pi/2, \pi/2]$; then

$$h(\theta) = \int_1^{1+\cos\theta} x[Y(x\cos\theta, x\sin\theta)]$$

$$= \int_1^{1+\cos\theta} x^2 \sin\theta$$

$$= \tfrac{1}{3}\sin\theta[(1+\cos\theta)^3 - 1];$$

hence $h = (1/3)\sin \cdot [(1+\cos)^3 - 1]$. Thus

$$\int_S Y = \frac{1}{3}\int_{-\pi/2}^{\pi/2} \sin \cdot [(1+\cos)^3 - 1] = \left[\frac{-1}{12}(1+\cos)^4 + \frac{1}{3}\cos\right]_{-\pi/2}^{\pi/2} = 0.$$

Note: It may have been clear from the outset that $\int_S Y = 0$; in any case we have proven that this is so.

The theorems of this section have a direct bearing on the technique for computing *definite* integrals; this is paradoxical since we use definite integrals to compute double integrals. The idea is brought out by the following examples.

EXAMPLE 7. Compute $\int_0^1 h$, where $h(t) = \int_t^1 \exp x^2$ whenever $t \in [0, 1]$.

Solution: By Theorem 7.6.4, $\int_0^1 h = \int_S \exp(X^2)$, where S is the region of the XY-plane displayed in Figure 7.6.12. But, by Theorem 7.6.3, $\int_S \exp(X^2) = \int_0^1 g$, where $g(t) = \exp t^2 \int_0^t 1 = t \exp t^2$ whenever $t \in [0, 1]$. Thus $g = x \exp x^2$, and so

$$\int_S \exp(X^2) = \int_0^1 x \exp x^2$$

$$= (1/2) \exp x^2 \Big]_0^1$$

$$= \tfrac{1}{2}(\exp 1 - \exp 0)$$

$$= (e - 1)/2.$$

We conclude that $\int_0^1 h = (e - 1)/2$.

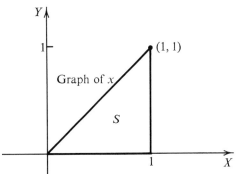

Figure 7.6.12

EXAMPLE 8. Compute $\int_0^2 h$, where $h(t) =$
$t \int_4^{(4-t^2)^{1/2}} (x^2 + t^2)^{1/2}$ whenever $t \in [0, 2]$.

Solution: By Theorem 7.6.4, $\int_0^2 h = \int_S Y(X^2 + Y^2)^{1/2}$, where S is the region of the XY-plane displayed in Figure 7.6.13. But, by Theorem 7.6.5, $\int_S Y(X^2 + Y^2)^{1/2} = \int_0^{\pi/2} g$, where $g(\theta) = \sin \theta \int_0^2 x^3 = 4 \sin \theta$ whenever $\theta \in [0, \pi/2]$, i.e., $g = 4 \sin$. Thus $\int_S Y(X^2 + Y^2)^{1/2} = \int_0^{\pi/2} 4 \sin = 4$. Hence $\int_0^2 h = 4$.

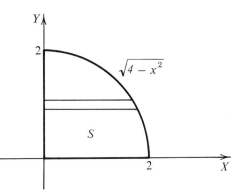

Figure 7.6.13

EXAMPLE 9. Compute $\mathscr{I} \int_0^\infty \exp(-x^2)$.

Solution: Let (a_n) be any sequence such that $\lim(1/a_n) = 0$ and $a_n > 0$ whenever $n \in N$. Then $\mathscr{I} \int_0^\infty \exp(-x^2) = \lim\left(\int_0^{a_n} \exp(-x^2)\right)$. Let $L_n = \int_0^{a_n} \exp(-x^2)$ whenever $n \in N$. Let " S_n" denote the region of the XY-plane displayed in Figure 7.6.14. Now, by Theorem 7.6.1,

$$\int_{S_n} \exp(-X^2 - Y^2) = \int_0^{a_n} f,$$

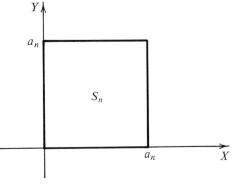

Figure 7.6.14

where $f(t) = \exp(-t^2) \int_0^{a_n} \exp(-x^2) = L_n \exp(-t^2)$ whenever $t \in [0, a_n]$; thus $f = L_n \exp(-x^2)$. Hence $\int_{S_n} \exp(-X^2 - Y^2) = L_n \int_0^{a_n} \exp(-x^2) = L_n^2$ whenever $n \in N$. Thus we have reduced our problem to that of computing $\lim\left(\int_{S_n} \exp(-X^2 - Y^2)\right)$. Now, each rectangle S_n is caught between two quarter-circles, one with radius a_n and the other with radius a_{n+q}, provided q is sufficiently large (see Figure 7.6.15); it follows that $\left(\int_{S_n} \exp(-X^2 - Y^2)\right)$ converges iff

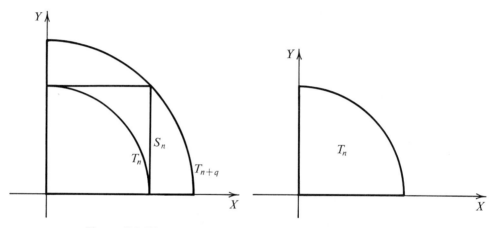

Figure 7.6.15   **Figure 7.6.16**

$\left(\int_{T_n} \exp(-X^2 - Y^2)\right)$ converges, where the region T_n is the portion of the XY-plane bounded by the circle with radius a_n and center at the origin, the positive half of the X-axis, and the positive half of the Y-axis (see Figure 7.6.16). But $\int_{T_n} \exp(-X^2 - Y^2) = \int_0^{\pi/2} g$, where

$$g(\theta) = \int_0^{a_n} x \exp(-x^2) = -\left.(1/2) \exp(-x^2)\right]_0^{a_n}$$

$$= \tfrac{1}{2}[1 - \exp(-a_n^2)] \quad \text{whenever } \theta \in [0, \pi/2].$$

So $\int_{T_n} \exp(-X^2 - Y^2) = \tfrac{1}{2} \int_0^{\pi/2} [1 - \exp(-a_n^2)] = \pi[1 - \exp(-a_n^2)]/4$. Thus

$$\lim\left(\int_{T_n} \exp(-X^2 - Y^2)\right) = (\pi/4) \lim(1 - \exp(-a_n^2)) = \pi/4 - (\pi/4) \lim(\exp(-a_n^2)) = \pi/4.$$

We conclude that $\left(\int_{S_n} \exp(-X^2 - Y^2)\right)$ converges and $\lim\left(\int_{S_n} \exp(-X^2 - Y^2)\right) = \pi/4$. Since $\int_{S_n} \exp(-X^2 - Y^2) = L_n^2$, we have that $\lim(L_n^2) = \pi/4$; so $\lim(L_n) = \sqrt{\pi}/2$. This establishes that $\mathscr{I} \int_0^\infty \exp(-x^2) = \sqrt{\pi}/2$.

E X E R C I S E S

1. Compute $\int_D Y^2$, where $D = [2, 5] \times [-1, 1]$.

2. Compute $\int_D Y \sin(X)$, where $D = [3, 5] \times [1, 7]$.

3. Compute $\int_S (X^2 + Y^2)^{3/2}$, where $S = \{(a, b) \,|\, a^2 + b^2 \leq 1\}$.

4. Compute $\int_S (X^2 + Y^2)^{1/2}$, where S is the region of the XY-plane bounded by the X-axis and the graphs of $\{(a, a) \,|\, a \geq 0\}$ and $\{(a, b) \,|\, a^2 + b^2 = 9, \ a \geq 0, \text{ and } b \geq 0\}$.

5. Compute $\int_S [(X - 1)^2 + (Y - 2)^2]$, where $S = \{(a, b) \,|\, (a - 1)^2 + (b - a)^2 \leq 16\}$.

6. Compute $\int_S XY^2$, where $S = \{(a, b) \,|\, -1 \leq a \leq 3 \text{ and } (a - 1)^2 \leq b \leq 7 + a\}$.

7. Compute $\int_S 1$, where S is the region of the XY-plane bounded by the graphs of $x + 2$ and x^2.

8. Compute $\int_S 1$, where S is the region of the XY-plane bounded by the graphs of $2x - x^2$ and $2x^3 - x^2$.

9. Compute $\int_S XY^2$, where $S = \{(a, b) \,|\, 0 \leq a \leq \pi \text{ and } 0 \leq b \leq \sin a\}$.   *(Answer: $2\pi/9$)*

10. Compute $\int_S XY$, where $S = \{(a, b) \,|\, 0 \leq a \leq 1 \text{ and } 0 \leq b \leq \exp a\}$.

(Answer: $(1 + e^2)/8$)

11. Compute $\int_S \sin(X^2)$, where $S = \{(a, b) \,|\, 0 \leq a \leq 1 \text{ and } 0 \leq b \leq a\}$.

(Answer: $(1 - \cos 1)/2$)

12. Compute $\int_S (X^2 + Y^2)^{-1/2}$, where $S = \{(a, b) \,|\, 0 \leq a \leq 4 \text{ and } a \leq b \leq 4\}$.

(Answer: $4 \log(1 + \sqrt{2})$)

13. Compute $\int_0^1 h$, given that $h(t) = \int_t^1 \sin x^2$ whenever $t \in [0, 1]$.   *(Answer: $(1 - \cos 1)/2$)*

14. Compute $\int_0^3 h$, given that $h(t) = \int_0^{(9-t^2)^{1/2}} (x^2 + t^2)^{1/2}$ whenever $t \in [0, 3]$.

(Answer: $9\pi/2$)

15. Compute $\int_0^{\pi/2} h$, given that $h(t) = \int_t^{\pi/2} \sin/x$ whenever $t \in [0, \pi/2]$.   *(Answer: 1)*

16. Compute $\int_0^\pi h$, given that $h(t) = \int_{2t}^{\pi/2} \sin/x$ whenever $t \in [0, \pi/2]$.   *(Answer: 2)*

17. Compute $\int_S [1/X^2] \sin(X)$, where $S = \{(a, b) \,|\, 0 \leq a \leq \pi/2 \text{ and } 0 \leq b \leq a^2\}$.

(Answer: 1)

18. Compute $\int_S [Y/X] \sin(X)$, where $S = \{(a, b) \,|\, 0 \leq a \leq \pi/2 \text{ and } 0 \leq b \leq a\}$.

(Answer: 1/2)

19. Compute $\int_S X^2$, where $S = \{(a, b) \,|\, -1 \leq a \leq 1 \text{ and } 0 \leq b \leq (1 - a^2)^{1/2}\}$.

(Answer: $\pi/8$)

7.7 Applications of the Double Integral

As we have seen, the theory of the double integral follows closely the theory of the definite integral. Indeed, the difference between the two theories is merely the dimension; the definite integral involves 1-intervals and functions with one argument, whereas the double integral involves 2-intervals and functions with two arguments. The applications of the definite integral sometimes lead to sums that involve the values of two functions at distinct members of each interval of a particular partition. The limit of a sequence of sums of this sort is expressed by a definite integral, in view of the Theorem of Bliss. The situation with regard to double integrals is quite the same.

THEOREM 7.7.1 (Theorem of Bliss)   Let S be any standard region of 2-space, let $(\{(\mathscr{I}_1, \alpha_1), (\mathscr{I}_2, \alpha_2), \cdots, (\mathscr{I}_m, \alpha_m)\})$ and $(\{(\mathscr{I}_1, \beta_1), (\mathscr{I}_2, \beta_2), \cdots, (\mathscr{I}_m, \beta_m)\})$ be S-sequences, and let F and G be continuous on S. Then

$$\lim \left(\sum_{j=1}^{m} F(\alpha_j) G(\beta_j) |\mathscr{I}_j| \right) = \int_S F \cdot G.$$

Proof: The proof differs from the Theorem of Bliss for definite integrals only as to the dimension of the intervals involved. For the details, see Volume I.

There are many applications of the double integral. We have already seen that if F is continuous and nonnegative on a standard region S, then the volume of the region bounded by the graph of F, the XY-plane, and the cylinder on the boundary of S, i.e., $\{(\alpha, c) \mid \alpha \in S \text{ and } 0 \le c \le F\alpha\}$, is $\int_S F$.

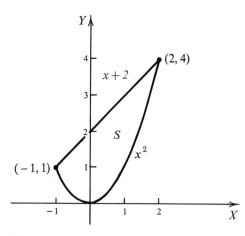

Figure 7.7.1

EXAMPLE 1.   Compute the volume of the region bounded by the graph of X^2, the XY-plane, and the cylinder on the boundary of S, where $S = \{(a, b) \mid -1 \le a \le 2 \text{ and } a^2 \le b \le a + 2\}$.

Solution: First, we sketch S (see Figure 7.7.1). The required volume is $\int_S X^2 = \int_{-1}^{2} h$, where $h(t) = t^2 \int_{t^2}^{t+2} 1 = t^2(t + 2 - t^2)$ whenever $t \in [-1, 2]$; hence $h = x^3 + 2x^2 - x^4$.

Thus
$$\int_S X^2 = \int_{-1}^{2} (x^3 + 2x^2 - x^4)$$

$$= \left[x^4/4 + 2x^3/3 - x^5/5 \right]_{-1}^{2}$$

$$= 3.15.$$

As another application of the double integral, we point out that the *area* of a standard region S is given by the double integral $\int_S 1$.

EXAMPLE 2.   Compute the area of the region of the XY-plane bounded by the graph of $\rho \cos * \rho \sin$, where $\rho = 2 \cos 3x$.

Solution: By symmetry, one-sixth of the required area is given by S, the shaded region of Figure 7.7.2. This region lies between the graphs of $x \tan 0$ and $x \tan \pi/6$. Therefore, by Theorem 7.6.5, $\int_S 1 = \int_0^{\pi/6} h$, where $h(\theta) = \int_0^{2\cos 3\theta} x = 2 \cos^2 3\theta$ whenever $\theta \in [0, \pi/6]$. This means that $h = 2 \cos^2 3x$. Thus

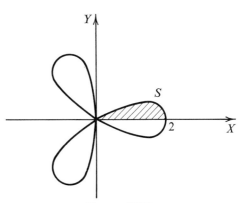

$$\int_S 1 = \int_0^{\pi/6} 2 \cos^2 3x = \int_0^{\pi/6} (1 + \cos 6x) =$$

$$\left[x + \frac{1}{6} \sin 6x \right]_0^{\pi/6} = \pi/6.$$

Since the area of S is one-sixth of the area of the given region, we conclude that π is the area of the given region.

Figure 7.7.2

Next, consider a plane lamina such that the density at each point of the lamina is given by a continuous function, say F; i.e., $F\alpha$ is the density of the lamina at α. Using the notion of the double integral, it is easy to see that the mass of the lamina is given by $\int_S F$, where S is the region of the XY-plane occupied by the lamina.

EXAMPLE 3.   Compute the mass of the plane lamina which has the form of a disc of radius 1, given that the density of the lamina at each point is the square of the distance of the point from the center of the disc.

Solution: The region of the XY-plane covered by the lamina is S, where $S = \{(a, b) \,|\, a^2 + b^2 \leq 1\}$. The density of the lamina at α is $\|\alpha\|^2$; thus the density of the lamina is given by the function $X^2 + Y^2$. Hence the mass of the lamina is $\int_S (X^2 + Y^2) = \int_0^{2\pi} h$, where $h(\theta) = \int_0^1 x^3 = 1/4$ whenever $0 \leq \theta \leq 2\pi$. Thus the mass of the lamina is $\int_0^{2\pi} 1/4 = \pi/2$.

Consider a lamina which occupies the region S of the XY-plane, and suppose that the density of the lamina at each point of S is given by the continuous function F. Then the *moment* of S about the X-axis is given by the double integral $\int_S Y \cdot F$, and the moment of S about the Y-axis is given by the double integral $\int_S X \cdot F$. Now, the centroid $(\bar{x}, \bar{y})$ of the lamina is the balancing point of the lamina; i.e., the particle which acts at the point $(\bar{x}, \bar{y})$ and whose mass is that of the lamina has the same moments about the X-axis and the Y-axis as has the lamina. Thus

$$\bar{x} \int_S F = \int_S X \cdot F \quad \text{and} \quad \bar{y} \int_S F = \int_S Y \cdot F.$$

EXAMPLE 4.   Determine the centroid of the lamina of Example 3.

Solution: The moment of the lamina about the X-axis is $\int_S Y \cdot (X^2 + Y^2) = \int_0^{2\pi} h$, where $h(\theta) = \int_0^1 x^4 \sin \theta = \frac{1}{5} \sin \theta$ whenever $\theta \in [0, 2\pi]$; thus $h = (1/5) \sin$.   Hence the moment about the X-axis is $\int_0^{2\pi} (1/5) \sin = -(1/5) \cos \Big|_0^{2\pi} = 0$. Since $\bar{x} \int_S (X^2 + Y^2) = 0$, we see that $\bar{x} = 0$. The moment of the lamina about the Y-axis is $\int_S X \cdot (X^2 + Y^2) = \int_0^{2\pi} g$, where $g(\theta) = \int_0^1 x^4 \cos \theta = \frac{1}{5} \cos \theta$ whenever $\theta \in [0, 2\pi]$. Thus $g = (1/5) \cos$. Hence the moment about the Y-axis is $\int_0^{2\pi} (1/5) \cos = (1/5) \sin \Big|_0^{2\pi} = 0$. Thus $\bar{y} = 0$. We conclude that the centroid of this lamina is the center of the disc.

The moment of inertia about the X-axis of the lamina which covers a region S of the XY-plane is given by $\int_S Y^2 \cdot F$, where F represents the density of the lamina at each point of S. Similarly, the moment of inertia about the Y-axis of this lamina is given by $\int_S X^2 \cdot F$; the moment of inertia about the Z-axis (which is called the *polar moment of inertia*) is given by $\int_S (X^2 + Y^2) \cdot F$.

EXAMPLE 5.   Determine the moments of inertia of the lamina of Example 3 about the three coordinate axes.

Solution: It is customary to denote the moments of a lamina about the X-axis, Y-axis, and Z-axis by "I_X", "I_Y", "I_Z", respectively. Here, $I_X = \int_S Y^2 \cdot (X^2 + Y^2) = \int_0^{2\pi} h$, where $h(\theta) = \int_0^1 x^5 \sin^2 \theta = \frac{1}{6} \sin^2 \theta$ whenever $\theta \in [0, 2\pi]$; thus $h = (1/6) \sin^2$. Hence

$$I_X = \frac{1}{6} \int_0^{2\pi} \sin^2 = \frac{1}{12} \int_0^{2\pi} (1 - \cos 2x) = \frac{1}{12} \left[x - \frac{1}{2} \sin 2x \right]_0^{2\pi} = \pi/6.$$

Also, $I_Y = \int_S X^2 \cdot (X^2 + Y^2) = \int_0^{2\pi} g$, where $g(\theta) = \int_0^1 x^5 \cos^2 \theta = \frac{1}{6} \cos^2 \theta$ whenever $\theta \in [0, 2\pi]$; thus $g = (1/6) \cos^2$. Hence

$$I_Y = \frac{1}{6} \int_0^{2\pi} \cos^2 = \frac{1}{12} \int_0^{2\pi} (1 + \cos 2x) = \frac{1}{12} \left[x + \frac{1}{2} \sin 2x \right]_0^{2\pi} = \pi/6.$$

Also, $I_Z = I_X + I_Y = \pi/3$.

As a final application of the double integral, we shall work out an expression for the *area* of a surface in three-dimensional space. Let S be a standard region of the XY-plane and let F be continuous on S. The graph of F is a surface. We want to determine the area of the part of this surface which is bounded by the cylinder on the boundary of S; i.e., we want the area of the part of the surface which lies above the region S. We must consider what we mean by the *area* of a surface. Just as a curve in a plane is approximated by line segments which are constructed using tangents to the curve, so a surface is approximated by portions of planes, namely the tangent planes to the surface. Intuitively, we see that the tangent plane at a point on the surface approximates a small region of the surface around the point in question. Accordingly, we consider an S-sequence, say $(\{(\mathscr{I}_1, \alpha_1), (\mathscr{I}_2, \alpha_2), \cdots, (\mathscr{I}_m, \alpha_m)\})$. Now, the 2-interval $\mathscr{I}_k$ and the associated 2-vector α_k lead us to the tangent plane to the surface at $(\alpha_k, F\alpha_k)$. In particular, we want the portion of this tangent plane which lies above $\mathscr{I}_k$; this is called the *projection* of $\mathscr{I}_k$ into the tangent plane at $(\alpha_k, F\alpha_k)$; see Figure 7.7.3. By Theorem 5.5.2, the area of this region of the tangent plane is $|\mathscr{I}_k|\sqrt{l^2 + m^2 + n^2}/|n|$, where (l, m, n) is a direction of a normal to the tangent plane at $(\alpha_k, F\alpha_k)$.

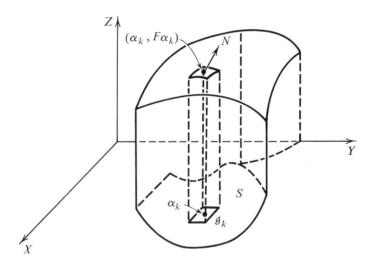

Figure 7.7.3

In Section 6.7 we proved that a normal to the graph of F at $(a, b, F(a, b))$ has direction $(F_1(a, b), F_2(a, b), -1)$. Thus the area of our region of the tangent plane is

$$\sqrt{1 + F_1^2 + F_2^2}\, (\alpha_k) \cdot |\mathscr{I}_k|.$$

Summing over each member of the partition, we obtain

$$\sum_{k=1}^{m} \sqrt{1 + F_1^2 + F_2^2}\, (\alpha_k) \cdot |\mathscr{I}_k|.$$

But

$$\lim \left(\sum_{k=1}^{m} \sqrt{1 + F_1^2 + F_2^2}(\alpha_k) \cdot |\mathscr{I}_k| \right) = \int_S \sqrt{1 + F_1^2 + F_2^2}.$$

We conclude that $\int_S \sqrt{1 + F_1^2 + F_2^2}$ is the required surface area.

EXAMPLE 6. Find the surface area of the portion of the graph of $\sqrt{X^2 + Y^2}$ which lies inside the cylinder on the boundary of S, where $S = \{(a, b)\,|\, a^2 + (b-1)^2 \leq 1\}$.

Solution: First, we sketch S, the region of the XY-plane which limits our surface (see Figure 7.7.4). In view of the preceding theory, we must compute F_1 and F_2, where $F = \sqrt{X^2 + Y^2}$.

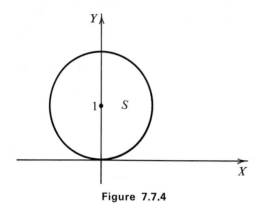

Figure 7.7.4

Now, $F_1 = X/F$ and $F_2 = Y/F$. Thus

$$\sqrt{1 + F_1^2 + F_2^2} = \sqrt{1 + X^2/F^2 + Y^2/F^2} = 2^{1/2}.$$

Hence the required surface area is $\int_S 2^{1/2}$. This double integral can be evaluated by applying Theorem 7.6.5; more directly, we can compute $\int_S 2^{1/2}$ by observing that this double integral is the volume of a circular cylinder whose height is $2^{1/2}$ and whose base is a disc of radius 1; thus $\int_S 2^{1/2} = \pi\sqrt{2}$.

EXERCISES

1. Prove Theorem 7.7.1.

2. Compute the volume of the region bounded by the graph of Y^2, the XY-plane, and the cylinder on the boundary of $\{(a, b)\,|\,2 \le a \le 3 \text{ and } a \le b \le 2a\}$.   (*Answer:* 455/12)

3. Compute the volume of the region bounded by the graph of $X\sin(X)$, the XY-plane, and the cylinder on the boundary of $\{(a, b)\,|\,0 \le a \le \pi/2 \text{ and } a \le b \le 2a\}$.
                (*Answer:* $\pi - 2$)

4. Compute the volume of the region bounded by the graph of $Y\sin(X)$, the XY-plane, and the cylinder on the boundary of $\{(a, b)\,|\,0 \le a \le \pi/2 \text{ and } a \le b \le 2a\}$.
                (*Answer:* $3\pi/2 - 3$)

5. Compute the volume of the region bounded by the graph of $X\sin(X)$, the XY-plane, and the cylinder on the boundary of $\{(a, b)\,|\,0 \le a \le \pi \text{ and } a \le b \le 2a\}$.   (*Answer:* $\pi^2 - 4$)

6. Compute the volume of the region bounded by the graph of $X \cdot Y$, the XY-plane, and the cylinder on $\{(a, b)\,|\,(a - 1)^2 + b^2 = 1 \text{ and } b \ge 0\}$.   (*Answer:* 2/3)

7. Compute the volume of the region bounded by the graph of $4 - Y$, the XY-plane, and the cylinder on $\{(a, b)\,|\,a^2 + b^2 = 9\}$.   (*Answer:* 36π)

8. Compute the volume of the region bounded by the graph of $(1/2)(X^2 + Y^2)$, the XY-plane, and the cylinder on $\{(a, b)\,|\,a^2 + b^2 = 4b\}$.   (*Answer:* 12π)

9. Compute the mass of the plane lamina which has the form of a disc of radius 2, given that the density of the lamina at each point is the cube of the distance of the point from the center of the disc.   (*Answer:* $64\pi/5$)

10. Determine the centroid of the region $\{(a, b)\,|\,0 \le a \le 5 \text{ and } a \le b \le 6a - a^2\}$.
                (*Answer:* (5/2, 5))

11. Determine the centroid of the region $\{(a, b)\,|\,-1 \le b \le 2 \text{ and } b^2 - 1 \le a \le 1 + b\}$.
                (*Answer:* $(\frac{3}{5}, \frac{1}{2})$)

12. Find the mass of the plane lamina which covers the region $\{(a, b)\,|\,0 \le a \le \pi/2$ and $0 \le b \le \sin a\}$, given that the density of the lamina at (a, b) is ab whenever (a, b) is a member of the region. *(Answer: $\tfrac{1}{4}$)*

13. For the lamina of Exercise 12, compute the following.
    a. The moment of inertia about the X-axis.
    b. The moment of inertia about the Y-axis.
    c. The moment of inertia about the Z-axis.

14. Find the surface area of the portion of the graph of $(4X - Y^2)^{1/2}$ which lies above $\{(a, b)\,|\,0 \le a \le 3$ and $-\sqrt{a} \le b \le \sqrt{a}\}$. *(Answer: $28\pi/9$)*

7.8 The Triple Integral

The ideas centering around the double integral are easily generalized to any number of dimensions. In this section we shall step up the dimension by one; this means that we shall discuss the *triple* integral. The idea is to associate a real number with a given function and a given 3-interval. Let D be a closed 3-interval and let H be a function with three arguments such that $D \subset \mathscr{D}_H$; then the real number associated with H and D is called the *integral of H over D* and is denoted by "$\int_D H$".

First, we need the notion of a 4-interval-builder.

> **DEFINITION 7.8.1.** Let D be any 3-interval; then $\{(\mathscr{I}_1, \alpha_1), (\mathscr{I}_2, \alpha_2), \cdots, (\mathscr{I}_n, \alpha_n)\}$ is said to be a 4-interval-builder over D iff
>
> (i) $\{\mathscr{I}_1, \mathscr{I}_2, \cdots, \mathscr{I}_n\}$ is a partition of D whose members are 3-intervals;
> (ii) $\mathscr{I}_j \ne \mathscr{I}_k$ whenever $j \ne k$, $1 \le j \le n$, and $1 \le k \le n$;
> (iii) $\alpha_k \in \bar{\mathscr{I}}_k$ whenever $1 \le k \le n$.

Next, we need the concept of the *mesh* or *norm* of a partition.

> **DEFINITION 7.8.2.** By the *mesh* or *norm* of the partition $\{\mathscr{I}_1, \mathscr{I}_2, \cdots, \mathscr{I}_n\}$ we mean the largest of the diameters of the 3-intervals $\mathscr{I}_1, \mathscr{I}_2, \cdots, \mathscr{I}_n$. This real number is denoted by "$\|\{\mathscr{I}_1, \mathscr{I}_2, \cdots, \mathscr{I}_n\}\|$".

Finally, we introduce the notion of a D-sequence.

> **DEFINITION 7.8.3.** Let D be any 3-interval; the sequence $(\{(\mathscr{I}_1, \alpha_1), (\mathscr{I}_2, \alpha_2), \cdots, (\mathscr{I}_m, \alpha_m)\})$, where m depends upon n, is said to be a *D-sequence* iff
>
> (i) each term of the sequence is a 4-interval-builder over D,
> (ii) $\lim(\|\{\mathscr{I}_1, \mathscr{I}_2, \cdots, \mathscr{I}_m\}\|) = 0$.

We are now in a position to define a triple integral.

DEFINITION 7.8.4.   Let H be a function with three arguments and let D be a closed 3-interval such that $D \subset \mathscr{D}_H$; then H is said to be *integrable over* D iff there is a real number L such that $\lim\left(\sum_{k=1}^{m} H(\alpha_k)|\mathscr{I}_k|\right) = L$ whenever $(\{(\mathscr{I}_1, \alpha_1), (\mathscr{I}_2, \alpha_2), \cdots, (\mathscr{I}_m, \alpha_m)\})$ is a D-sequence; L is called the *integral of H over* D and is denoted by "$\int_D H$".

Notice that $\int_D H$, if it exists, is the common limit of a family of sequences.

EXAMPLE 1.   Compute $\int_D 5$, where $D = [0, 3] \times [-2, -1] \times [2, 4]$.

Solution: Let $(\{(\mathscr{I}_1, \alpha_1), (\mathscr{I}_2, \alpha_2), \cdots, (\mathscr{I}_m, \alpha_m)\})$ be any D-sequence. Then $\lim\left(\sum_{k=1}^{m} 5(\alpha_k)|\mathscr{I}_k|\right)$

$= \lim\left(5\sum_{k=1}^{m} |\mathscr{I}_k|\right) = 5 \lim\left(\sum_{k=1}^{m} |\mathscr{I}_k|\right) = 30$ since $\sum_{k=1}^{m} |\mathscr{I}_k|$ is the volume of the 3-interval $[0, 3] \times$

$[-2, -1] \times [2, 4]$, namely 6. We conclude that 5 is integrable over D and that $\int_D 5 = 30$.

Consider the following *existence* theorem.

THEOREM 7.8.1.   Let D be any closed 3-interval and let H be any function with three arguments. Then H is integrable over D if H is continuous on D.

Proof: A proof of this theorem is easily obtained by following through the development of Section 7.4. The details are left as an exercise.

Next, we extend our notion of a triple integral by relaxing the requirement that D be a 3-interval.

DEFINITION 7.8.5.   Let f and g be continuous functions with one argument such that $f(t) \leq g(t)$ whenever $t \in [c, d]$, and let F and G be continuous functions with two arguments such that $F\alpha \leq G\alpha$ whenever $\alpha \in D$, where D is the 2-interval $[c, d] \times [\min_{[c,d]} f, \max_{[c, d]} g]$. Then the following region of 3-space is said to be a *simple region*:

$$\{(x, y, z) \mid c \leq x \leq d, f(x) \leq y \leq g(x), \text{ and } F(x, y) \leq z \leq G(x, y)\}.$$

THEOREM 7.8.2.   Let S be any simple region of 3-space, and let H be continuous on S and zero on the boundary of S. Let D be the smallest closed 3-interval which contains S, and let K be the function with three arguments constructed from H as follows:

$$K\alpha = \begin{cases} H\alpha \text{ whenever } \alpha \in S \\ 0 \text{ otherwise.} \end{cases}$$

Then K is integrable over D.

Proof: It is easy to show that K is continuous on D; therefore, by Theorem 7.8.1, K is integrable over D.

In view of Theorem 7.8.2, it makes sense to extend our notion of a triple integral as follows.

DEFINITION 7.8.6. Let H and K be the functions described in Theorem 7.8.2, and let S and D be the regions described in Theorem 7.8.2; then we shall say that H *is integrable over* S and that $\int_S H = \int_D K$.

It is possible to throw out the requirement that H take the value zero on the boundary of S. This follows from the observation that we can relax the continuity requirement of our basic existence theorem. Just as in the case of the double integral, a proof of the following theorem is beyond the scope of this book.

THEOREM 7.8.3. Let D be any closed 3-interval and let F be any function which is defined throughout D and is bounded on D; then F is integrable over D if the set of points of D at which F is discontinuous has volume zero.

THEOREM 7.8.4. Let S be any simple region whose boundary has volume zero, and let H be continuous on S. Let D be the smallest closed 3-interval which contains S, and let K be constructed from H as in Theorem 7.8.2. Then K is integrable over D.

Proof: Apply Theorem 7.8.3.

We want to extend our notion of a triple integral to simple regions rather than merely 3-intervals. Moreover, in case H and S meet the conditions of Theorem 7.8.4, we want the integral of H over S to be $\int_D K$. This is achieved by first introducing the notion of an *S-sequence.*

DEFINITION 7.8.7. Let S be any simple region and let D be the smallest closed 3-interval which contains S. Let $(\{(\mathcal{I}_1, \alpha_1), (\mathcal{I}_2, \alpha_2), \cdots, (\mathcal{I}_m, \alpha_m)\})$ be any D-sequence; then by an *S-sequence* we mean the sequence obtained from the given D-sequence by deleting each 3-interval which is not a subset of S.

DEFINITION 7.8.8. Let S be any simple region and let H be defined throughout S. Then H is said to be *integrable* over S iff there is a real number L such that $\lim\left(\sum_{k=1}^{m} H(\alpha_k)|\mathcal{I}_k|\right) = L$ whenever $(\{(\mathcal{I}_1, \alpha_1), (\mathcal{I}_2, \alpha_2), \cdots, (\mathcal{I}_m, \alpha_m)\})$ is an S-sequence; L is called the *integral of H over S* and is denoted by " $\int_S H$ ".

DEFINITION 7.8.9.   A region of 3-space, say S, is said to be a *standard* region iff (i) S is a simple region, (ii) the boundary of S has volume zero.

The following *existence* theorem is a consequence of Theorem 7.8.3.

THEOREM 7.8.5.   Let S be any standard region and let H be continuous on S. Then H is integrable over S; moreover, $\int_S H = \int_D K$, where D is the smallest closed 3-interval which contains S, and K is the function constructed from H as in Theorem 7.8.2.

Proof: Follow the pattern of the proof of Theorem 7.3.4. The details are left as an exercise.

EXERCISES

1. Prove Theorem 7.8.1.
2. Prove Theorem 7.8.2.
3. Prove Theorem 7.8.4.
4. Prove Theorem 7.8.5.

7.9   Evaluating Triple Integrals

We shall now develop a technique for computing triple integrals.

THEOREM 7.9.1.   Let H be continuous on the 3-interval D, where $D = [a, b] \times [c, d] \times [e, f]$, and let $F\alpha = \int_e^f {}_\alpha H_3$ whenever $\alpha \in [a, b] \times [c, d]$; then $\int_D H = \int_{D_1} F$, where $D_1 = [a, b] \times [c, d]$.

Proof: By Theorem 7.8.1, H is integrable over D; therefore we can compute $\int_D H$ by considering a particular D-sequence. Let $([P_n, Q_n])$ be a D-sequence such that for each natural number n (i) the members of Q_n consist of the top right-hand vertex of each 3-interval in P_n, (ii) any two 3-intervals in P_n have the same dimensions.

As we proceed, we shall specify further the D-sequence that we are constructing. We must keep an eye on the sequence $(S[H, P_n, Q_n])$; our purpose is to prove that $\lim(S[H, P_n, Q_n]) = \int_{D_1} F$. Let p be any natural number; we shall construct a 4-interval-builder, say $[P_m, Q_m]$, such that $\left| S[H, P_m, Q_m] - \int_{D_1} F \right| < 10^{-p}$. First, we partition $[a, b] \times [c, d]$ into s 2-intervals of equal area, say $\mathscr{I}_1, \mathscr{I}_2, \cdots, \mathscr{I}_s$. Let α_k be the upper right-hand endpoint of $\mathscr{I}_k$ whenever $1 \le k \le s$. We can choose s so that $\left| \sum_{k=1}^{s} F(\alpha_k)|\mathscr{I}_k| - \int_{D_1} F \right| < 10^{-(p+1)}$. This means that our 4-interval-builder $[P_m, Q_m]$ is obtained by first dividing

$[a, b] \times [c, d]$, the base of D, into s 2-intervals each of area $(b - a)(d - c)/s$. On each of these 2-intervals we shall erect a column of 3-intervals by dividing the interval $[e, f]$ into r intervals each of length $(f - e)/r$, say the intervals $\mathscr{I}_1, \mathscr{I}_2, \cdots, \mathscr{I}_r$; let b_i be the right-hand endpoint of $\mathscr{I}_i$ whenever $1 \le i \le r$. Now, consider $S[H, P_m, Q_m]$; we shall take subtotals by columns and then total the subtotals. For example, consider the column erected on the 2-interval $\mathscr{I}_k$; this column of 3-intervals has for its sum $\sum\limits_{i=1}^{r} {}_{\alpha_k}H_3(b_i)|\mathscr{I}_i|$.

But we can choose r so that

(1)
$$\left| \sum_{i=1}^{r} {}_{\alpha_k}H_3(b_i)|\mathscr{I}_i| - \int_e^f {}_{\alpha_k}H_3 \right| < 10^{-(p+1)}/(b - a)(d - c).$$

Indeed, since there are only s columns, we can choose r so large that the inequality (1) is maintained whenever $1 \le k \le s$.

Let $\sum\limits_{i=1}^{r} {}_{\alpha_k}H_3(b_i)|\mathscr{I}_i| - \int_e^f {}_{\alpha_k}H_3 = \varepsilon_k$ whenever $1 \le k \le s$; then

$$S[H, P_m, Q_m] = \sum_{k=1}^{s} \left(\sum_{i=1}^{r} {}_{\alpha_k}H_3(b_i)|\mathscr{I}_i| \right)|\mathscr{I}_k|$$

$$= \sum_{k=1}^{s} \left(\varepsilon_k + \int_e^f {}_{\alpha_k}H_3 \right)|\mathscr{I}_k|$$

$$= \sum_{k=1}^{s} |\mathscr{I}_k| \int_e^f {}_{\alpha_k}H_3 + \frac{(b - a)(d - c)}{s} \sum_{k=1}^{s} \varepsilon_k$$

$$= \sum_{k=1}^{s} F(\alpha_k)|\mathscr{I}_k| + \frac{(b - a)(d - c)}{s} \sum_{k=1}^{s} \varepsilon_k.$$

Thus
$$\left| S[H, P_m, Q_m] - \int_{D_1} F \right| = \left| \sum_{k=1}^{s} F(\alpha_k)|\mathscr{I}_k| - \int_{D_1} F + \frac{(b - a)(d - c)}{s} \sum_{k=1}^{s} \varepsilon_k \right|$$

$$\le \left| \sum_{k=1}^{s} F(\alpha_k)|\mathscr{I}_k| - \int_{D_1} F \right| + \frac{(b - a)(d - c)}{s} \sum_{k=1}^{s} |\varepsilon_k|$$

$$< 10^{-(p+1)} + \frac{(b - a)(d - c)}{s} \sum_{k=1}^{s} |\varepsilon_k|$$

$$< 10^{-(p+1)} + \frac{(b - a)(d - c)}{s} \times \frac{10^{-(p+1)}s}{(b - a)(d - c)}$$

$$= 2 \times 10^{-(p+1)} < 10^{-p}.$$

We have achieved our goal! We have constructed a 4-interval-builder, namely $[P_m, Q_m]$, such that $\left| S[H, P_m, Q_m] - \int_{D_1} F \right| < 10^{-p}$. In the same way we can construct the next term of our D-sequence, namely $[P_{m+1}, Q_{m+1}]$, so that $\left| S[H, P_{m+1}, Q_{m+1}] - \int_{D_1} F \right|$ $< 10^{-(p+1)}$. Continuing in this fashion, we obtain a D-sequence, say $([P_1, Q_1], [P_2, Q_2],$ $\cdots, [P_m, Q_m], \cdots)$ such that $\lim(S[H, P_m, Q_m]) = \int_{D_1} F$. This completes our proof.

COROLLARY 7.9.1. Let H be continuous on the 3-interval D, where $D = [a, b] \times [c, d] \times [e, f]$, let $F\alpha = \int_e^f {}_\alpha H_3$ whenever $\alpha \in [a, b] \times [c, d]$, and let $g(t) = \int_c^d {}_t F_2$ whenever $t \in [a, b]$. Then $\int_D H = \int_a^b g$.

Proof: Theorems 7.9.1 and 7.6.1.

EXAMPLE 1. Compute $\int_D X^2 YZ$, where $D = [-1, 2] \times [3, 5] \times [-4, -2]$.

Solution: Let $H = X^2 YZ$; then $F\alpha = (X^2 Y)\alpha \int_{-4}^{-2} x = -6(X^2 Y)\alpha$ whenever $\alpha \in [-1, 2] \times [3, 5]$; thus $F = -6X^2 Y$. Therefore $g(t) = -6t^2 \int_3^5 x = -48t^2$ whenever $t \in [-1, 2]$; thus $g = -48x^2$. Hence $\int_D H = \int_{-1}^2 -48x^2 = -16x^3 \Big]_{-1}^2 = -144$.

COROLLARY 7.9.2. Let H be continuous on the 3-interval D, where $D = [a, b] \times [c, d] \times [e, f]$, let $F\alpha = \int_e^f {}_\alpha H_3$ whenever $\alpha \in [a, b] \times [c, d]$, and let $h(t) = \int_a^b {}_t F_1$ whenever $t \in [c, d]$. Then $\int_D H = \int_c^d h$.

Proof: Theorems 7.9.1 and 7.6.2.

We now rework Example 1.

EXAMPLE 2. Compute $\int_D X^2 YZ$, where $D = [-1, 2] \times [3, 5] \times [-4, -2]$.

Solution: Let $H = X^2 YZ$; as in Example 1, $F = -6X^2 Y$. Thus $h(t) = -6t \int_{-1}^2 x^2 = -2tx^3 \Big]_{-1}^2$ $= -18t$ whenever $t \in [3, 5]$; so $h = -18x$. Therefore $\int_D H = \int_3^5 -18x = -9x^2 \Big]_3^5 = -144$.

We have developed a technique for evaluating $\int_S H$ in case S is a 3-interval. In the following theorem we extend this technique to *standard* regions.

THEOREM 7.9.2. Let $S = \{(a_1, a_2) \mid c \leq a_1 \leq d$ and $f(a_1) \leq a_2 \leq g(a_1)\}$ be a standard region, let $\mathscr{S} = \{(\alpha, a_3) \mid \alpha \in S$ and $F\alpha \leq a_3 \leq G\alpha\}$ be a standard region, let H be continuous on $\mathscr{S}$, and let $L\alpha = \int_{F\alpha}^{G\alpha} {}_\alpha H_3$ whenever $\alpha \in S$. Then $\int_{\mathscr{S}} H = \int_S L$.

Proof: Let K be the function constructed from H as follows:

$$K\alpha = \begin{cases} H\alpha & \text{if } \alpha \in \mathscr{S} \\ 0 & \text{otherwise,} \end{cases}$$

and let D be the smallest closed 3-interval which contains $\mathscr{S}$, i.e., $D = [c, d] \times [\min_{[c, d]} f, \max_{[c, d]} g]$ $\times [\min_S F, \max_S G]$. Let $r = \min_S F$ and let $s = \max_S G$. Then, by Theorems 7.9.1 and 7.8.5,

$\int_{\mathscr{S}} H = \int_D K = \int_{D_1} M$, where $M\alpha = \int_r^s {}_\alpha K_3$ whenever $\alpha \in [c, d] \times [\min f, \max g] = D_1$.

Now, $M\alpha = \int_r^s {}_\alpha K_3 = \int_r^{F\alpha} {}_\alpha K_3 + \int_{F\alpha}^{G\alpha} {}_\alpha K_3 + \int_{G\alpha}^s {}_\alpha K_3 = \int_{F\alpha}^{G\alpha} {}_\alpha K_3$. If $\alpha \bar{\in} S$, then $(\alpha, a_3) \bar{\in} \mathscr{S}$

for each a_3; thus ${}_\alpha K_3 = 0$ and $\int_{F\alpha}^{G\alpha} {}_\alpha K_3 = 0$. Hence, $M\alpha = 0$ if $\alpha \bar{\in} S$. If $\alpha \in S$, then ${}_\alpha K_3(a_3) = H(\alpha, a_3)$ whenever $F\alpha \le a_3 \le G\alpha$; thus $M\alpha = \int_{F\alpha}^{G\alpha} {}_\alpha H_3 = L\alpha$. So

$$\int_{\mathscr{S}} H = \int_{D_1} M = \int_S L \qquad \text{by Th. 7.3.4,}$$

since D_1 is the smallest closed 2-interval which contains S, and M is the function constructed from L as in Definition 7.3.4. This establishes our result.

Notice that Theorem 7.9.2 reduces the problem of evaluating a triple integral to that of evaluating a double integral. Thus the technique of Section 7.6 can be brought to bear on the problem of evaluating a triple integral.

EXAMPLE 3. Compute $\int_{\mathscr{S}} X$, where $\mathscr{S} = \{(\alpha, c) \mid \alpha \in S$ and $0 \le c \le (X^2 + Y)\alpha\}$ and $S = \{(a, b) \mid -1 \le a \le 2$ and $0 \le b \le 3 + a\}$.

Solution: First, note that ${}_\alpha X_3$ is the constant function $X(\alpha)$. Let $L\alpha = \int_0^{(X^2 + Y)\alpha} {}_\alpha X_3 = \int_0^{(X^2+Y)\alpha} X\alpha = [X(X^2 + Y)]\alpha$ whenever $\alpha \in S$; then $L = X(X^2 + Y)$. Hence, by Theorem 7.9.2, $\int_{\mathscr{S}} X = \int_S (X^3 + XY)$. We shall now evaluate the double integral $\int_S (X^3 + XY)$ by applying Theorem 7.6.3. First, we sketch S (see Figure 7.9.1). Next, let $t \in [-1, 2]$; then

$h(t) = \int_0^{3+t} (t^3 + tx) = \left[t^3 x + tx^2/2 \right]_0^{3+t}$

$= 7t^3/2 + t^4 + 3t^2 + 9t/2;$

thus $h = 7x^3/2 + x^4 + 3x^2 + 9x/2$. So by Theorem 7.6.3,

$\int_S (X^3 + XY) = \int_{-1}^2 h =$

$\int_{-1}^2 (7x^3/2 + x^4 + 3x^2 + 9x/2) =$

$\left[7x^4/8 + x^5/5 + x^3 + 9x^2/4 \right]_{-1}^2$

$= 35\dfrac{19}{40}.$

We conclude that $\int_{\mathscr{S}} X = 35\frac{19}{40}.$

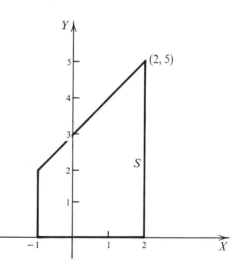

Figure 7.9.1

EXAMPLE 4. Compute $\int_{\mathscr{S}} Z$, where $\mathscr{S} = \{(\alpha, c) \mid \alpha \in S$ and $0 \leq c \leq \sqrt{16 - (X^2 + Y^2)}(\alpha)\}$ and $S = \{(a, b) \mid 0 \leq a \leq 1$ and $0 \leq b \leq \sqrt{1 - a^2}\}$.

Solution: Let $L\alpha = \int_0^{\sqrt{16 - (X^2 + Y^2)}(\alpha)} x = [8 - (1/2)(X^2 + Y^2)](\alpha)$ whenever $\alpha \in S$; then

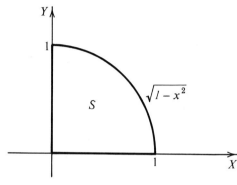

$L = 8 - (1/2)(X^2 + Y^2)$. Hence, by Theorem 7.9.2, $\int_{\mathscr{S}} Z = \int_S [8 - (1/2)(X^2 + Y^2)]$. To evaluate this double integral, we apply Theorem 7.6.5. First, we sketch S (see Figure 7.9.2). Note that $\sqrt{1 - x^2} = \cos * \sin$, and so $\rho_2 = 1$; moreover, $\rho_1 = 0$. Let $\theta \in [0, \pi/2]$; then $h(\theta) = \int_0^1 x(8 - x^2/2) = \left[4x^2 - x^4/8\right]_0^1 = 31/8$; thus $h = 31/8$. So, by Theorem 7.6.5, $\int_S [8 - (1/2)(X^2 + Y^2)] = \int_0^{\pi/2} 31/8 = 31\pi/16$. We conclude that $\int_{\mathscr{S}} Z = 31\pi/16$.

Figure 7.9.2

E X E R C I S E S

Compute the following triple integrals.

1. $\int_{\mathscr{S}} XYZ$, where $\mathscr{S} = [1, 2] \times [0, 3] \times [-3, -1]$.   *(Answer: −27)*

2. $\int_{\mathscr{S}} Z^2$, where $\mathscr{S} = [0, 1] \times [0, 1] \times [0, 1]$.   *(Answer: 1/3)*

3. $\int_{\mathscr{S}} XZ$, where $\mathscr{S} = [0, 1] \times [0, 2] \times [0, 3]$.   *(Answer: 9/2)*

4. $\int_{\mathscr{S}} X \sin(Z)$, where $\mathscr{S} = [0, \pi/2] \times [0, \pi/2] \times [0, \pi/2]$.   *(Answer: $\pi^3/16$)*

5. $\int_{\mathscr{S}} Y$, where $\mathscr{S} = \{(\alpha, c) \mid \alpha \in S$ and $0 \leq c \leq X^2\alpha\}$ and $S = \{(a, b) \mid 1 \leq a \leq 2$ and $0 \leq b \leq 2a\}$.   *(Answer: 62/5)*

6. $\int_{\mathscr{S}} Z$, where $\mathscr{S} = \{(\alpha, c) \mid \alpha \in S$ and $0 \leq c \leq Y^{1/2}\alpha\}$ and $S = \{(a, b) \mid 0 \leq a \leq 2$ and $a \leq b \leq a^2 + a\}$.   *(Answer: 18/5)*

7. $\int_{\mathscr{S}} YZ$, where $\mathscr{S} = \{(\alpha, c) \mid \alpha \in S$ and $0 \leq c \leq X\alpha\}$ and $S = \{(a, b) \mid 1 \leq a \leq 2$ and $0 \leq b \leq 1 + a\}$.   *(Answer: 481/120)*

8. $\int_{\mathscr{S}} \exp(X)$, where $\mathscr{S} = \{(\alpha, c) \mid \alpha \in S$ and $0 \leq c \leq Y\alpha\}$ and $S = \{(a, b) \mid 0 \leq a \leq 1$ and $0 \leq b \leq a\}$.   *(Answer: 1/2)*

9. $\int_{\mathscr{S}} Z$, where $\mathscr{S} = \{(\alpha, c) \mid \alpha \in S$ and $(Y - 1)\alpha \leq c \leq (Y + 1)\alpha\}$ and $S = \{(a, b) \mid 0 \leq a \leq 1$ and $a^2 \leq b \leq a\}$.   *(Answer: 2/15)*

10. $\int_{\mathscr{S}} X$, where $\mathscr{S} = \{(\alpha, c) \mid \alpha \in S$ and $(Y - 1)\alpha \leq c \leq (Y + 1)\alpha\}$ and $S = \{(a, b) \mid 0 \leq a \leq 1$ and $a^2 \leq b \leq a\}$.   *(Answer: 1/6)*

11. $\int_{\mathscr{S}} XZ$, where $\mathscr{S} = \{(\alpha, c) \mid \alpha \in S \text{ and } (Y - 1)\alpha \le c \le (Y + 1)\alpha\}$ and $S = \{(a, b) \mid 0 \le a \le 1$ and $a^2 \le b \le a\}$.   (*Answer:* 1/12)

12. $\int_{\mathscr{S}} \sin(Y)$, where $\mathscr{S} = \{(\alpha, c) \mid \alpha \in S \text{ and } 0 \le c \le Y\alpha\}$ and $S = \{(a, b) \mid 0 \le a \le 1$ and $0 \le b \le \pi/2\}$.   (*Answer:* 1)

13. $\int_{\mathscr{S}} Z$, where $\mathscr{S} = \{(\alpha, c) \mid \alpha \in S \text{ and } 0 \le c \le \sqrt{1 - (X^2 + Y^2)}(\alpha)\}$ and $S = \{(a, b) \mid 0 \le a \le 1$ and $0 \le b \le \sqrt{1 - a^2}\}$.   (*Answer:* $\pi/16$)

14. $\int_{\mathscr{S}} 1$, where $\mathscr{S} = \{(\alpha, c) \mid \alpha \in S \text{ and } 0 \le c \le \sqrt{X^2 + Y^2}(\alpha)\}$ and $S = \{(a, b) \mid 0 \le a \le 3$ and $0 \le b \le \sqrt{9 - a^2}\}$.   (*Answer:* $9\pi/2$)

15. $\int_{\mathscr{S}} (X^2 + Y^2)^{-1/2}$, where $\mathscr{S} = \{(\alpha, c) \mid \alpha \in S \text{ and } 0 \le c \le \sqrt{1 - X^2 - Y^2}(\alpha)\}$ and $S = \{(a, b) \mid 0 \le a \le 1$ and $0 \le b \le \sqrt{1 - a^2}\}$.   (*Answer:* $\pi^2/8$)

16. $\int_{\mathscr{S}} (X^2 + Y^2)^{-1/2}$, where $\mathscr{S} = \{(\alpha, c) \mid \alpha \in S \text{ and } 0 \le c \le \sqrt{1 - X^2 - Y^2}(\alpha)\}$ and $S = \{(a, b) \mid 0 \le a \le 4$ and $0 \le b \le \sqrt{16 - a^2}\}$.   (*Answer:* $2\pi^2$)

17. $\int_{\mathscr{S}} (2Z + 1)$, where $\mathscr{S} = \{(\alpha, c) \mid \alpha \in S \text{ and } 2 \le c \le 5\}$ and $S = \{\alpha \mid \|\alpha\| \le 3\}$. (*Answer:* 216π)

18. $\int_{\mathscr{S}} Z(X^2 + Y^2)^{-1/2}$, where $\mathscr{S} = \{(\alpha, c) \mid \alpha \in S \text{ and } 0 \le c \le 1\}$ and $S = \{(a, b) \mid 0 \le a \le 1$ and $0 \le b \le a\}$.   (*Answer:* $\frac{1}{2}\log(1 + \sqrt{2})$)

19. $\int_{\mathscr{S}} (X^2 + Y^2)^{1/2}$, where $\mathscr{S} = \{(\alpha, c) \mid \alpha \in S \text{ and } 0 \le c \le 6\}$ and $S = \{(a, b) \mid 0 \le a \le 1$ and $0 \le b \le a\}$.   (*Answer:* $\sqrt{2} + \log(1 + \sqrt{2})$)

20. $\int_{\mathscr{S}} (X^2 + Y^2)^{1/2}$, where $\mathscr{S} = \{(\alpha, c) \mid \alpha \in S \text{ and } 0 \le c \le 6\}$ and $S = \{(a, b) \mid 0 \le a \le 1$ and $a \le b \le 1\}$.   (*Answer:* $\sqrt{2} + \log(1 + \sqrt{2})$)

21. $\int_{\mathscr{S}} (X^2 + Y^2)^{1/2}$, where $\mathscr{S} = \{(\alpha, c) \mid \alpha \in S \text{ and } 0 \le c \le 6\}$ and $S = [0, 1] \times [0, 1]$.   (*Answer:* $2^{3/2} + \log(3 + 2^{3/2})$)

7.10 Applications of the Triple Integral

The applications of the triple integral follow the pattern of the double integral. First, we note that the triple integral gives us the *measure* of a region of 4-space, just as the double integral gives us the measure of a region of 3-space. To be precise, let $\mathscr{S}$ be a standard region of 3-space and let H be a function which is continuous and nonnegative on $\mathscr{S}$. Then $\int_{\mathscr{S}} H$ is the measure, or 4-volume, of $\{(\alpha, b) \mid \alpha \in \mathscr{S}$ and $0 \le b \le H\alpha\}$, a region of 4-space. It may be helpful to point out that we have already used integrals to measure regions of 2-space and of 3-space in precisely this way. To see the pattern more clearly, let $\mathscr{I} = [c, d]$ and let us agree to denote the definite integral $\int_c^d f$ by "$\int_{\mathscr{I}} f$". Then we have the following result: if f is continuous and nonnegative on $\mathscr{I}$, then $\int_{\mathscr{I}} f$ is the area, or 2-volume, of $\{(\alpha, b) \mid \alpha \in \mathscr{I}$ and $0 \le b \le f\alpha\}$, a region of 2-space. Moreover, if S is a standard region of 2-space and F is continuous and nonnegative on S, then $\int_S F$ is the volume, or 3-volume, of $\{(\alpha, b) \mid \alpha \in S \text{ and } 0 \le b \le F\alpha\}$, a region of 3-space. Finally, as we have now observed, if $\mathscr{S}$ is a standard region of 3-space and H is continuous and nonnegative on $\mathscr{S}$, then $\int_{\mathscr{S}} H$ is the 4-volume of $\{(\alpha, b) \mid \alpha \in \mathscr{S} \text{ and } 0 \le b \le H\alpha\}$, a region of 4-space.

EXAMPLE 1. Compute the 4-volume of $\{(\alpha, b) \mid \alpha \in \mathscr{S} \text{ and } 0 \le b \le (YZ)\alpha\}$, where $\mathscr{S} = \{(\alpha, b) \mid \alpha \in [0, 1] \times [0, 2] \text{ and } X\alpha \le b \le (X + Y)\alpha\}$.

Solution: The required 4-volume is $\int_{\mathscr{S}} YZ$. Let $\alpha \in [0, 1] \times [0, 2] = S$; then $L\alpha = Y\alpha \int_{X\alpha}^{(X+Y)\alpha} x$

$= ((Y/2)[(X + Y)^2 - X^2])\alpha$; thus $L = (Y/2)[Y^2 + 2XY]$. Hence $\int_{\mathscr{S}} YZ = \int_S (Y^3/2 + XY^2)$. Let

$t \in [0, 1]$; then $h(t) = \frac{1}{2} \int_0^2 (x^3 + 2tx^2) = \frac{1}{2}\left[x^4/4 + 2tx^3/3\right]_0^2 = 2 + 8t/3$; so $h = 2 + 8x/3$. Therefore

$\int_{\mathscr{S}} YZ = \int_0^1 (2 + 8x/3) = \left[2x + 4x^2/3\right]_0^1 = 10/3$. We conclude that the 4-volume of the given region is 10/3.

EXAMPLE 2. Compute the 4-volume of the 4-sphere $\{\alpha \mid \alpha \in R_4 \text{ and } \|\alpha\| \le r\}$.

Solution: The required 4-volume is $2 \int_{\mathscr{S}} \sqrt{r^2 - X^2 - Y^2 - Z^2}$, where $\mathscr{S} = \{\alpha \mid \alpha \in R_3 \text{ and } \|\alpha\| \le r\}$. Now, $\mathscr{S} = \{(\alpha, b) \mid \alpha \in S \text{ and } |b| \le \sqrt{r^2 - \|\alpha\|^2}\}$, where $S = \{(a, b) \mid -r \le a \le r \text{ and } |b| \le \sqrt{r^2 - a^2}\}$. Let $\alpha \in S$; then

$$L = 2 \int_{-\sqrt{r^2 - (X^2 + Y^2)\alpha}}^{\sqrt{r^2 - (X^2 + Y^2)\alpha}} \sqrt{r^2 - (X^2 + Y^2)\alpha - x^2} = \pi[r^2 - (X^2 + Y^2)](\alpha).$$

Thus $L = \pi(r^2 - X^2 - Y^2)$.   Hence $2 \int_{\mathscr{S}} \sqrt{r^2 - X^2 - Y^2 - Z^2} = \pi \int_S (r^2 - X^2 - Y^2)$.   Let

$\theta \in [0, 2\pi]$;   then $h(\theta) = \int_0^r \pi x(r^2 - x^2) = \pi\left[r^2x^2/2 - x^4/4\right]_0^r = \pi r^4/2$;   thus $h = \pi r^4/2$.   So

$\pi \int_S (r^2 - X^2 - Y^2) = \int_0^{2\pi} \pi r^4/2 = \pi^2 r^4 = (\pi r^2)^2$. We conclude that $(\pi r^2)^2$ is the 4-volume of the 4-sphere with radius r.

As usual, the Theorem of Bliss has a bearing on applications of the triple integral.

THEOREM 7.10.1. (Theorem of Bliss).   Let $\mathscr{S}$ be any standard region of 3-space, let $(\{(\mathscr{S}_1, \alpha_1), (\mathscr{S}_2, \alpha_2), \cdots, (\mathscr{S}_m, \alpha_m)\})$ and $(\{(\mathscr{S}_1, \beta_1), (\mathscr{S}_2, \beta_2), \cdots, (\mathscr{S}_m, \beta_m)\})$ be $\mathscr{S}$-sequences, and let F and G be continuous on $\mathscr{S}$. Then $\lim\left(\sum_{j=1}^{m} F(\alpha_j)G(\beta_j)|\mathscr{S}_j|\right) =$ $\int_{\mathscr{S}} F \cdot G$.

Proof: A proof of this theorem can be patterned on the proof in the case of the definite integral. For the details, see Volume I.

As another application of the triple integral, consider a solid whose density is given by a continuous function H; i.e., $H\alpha$ is the density of the solid at α whenever α is a member of the region occupied by the solid. Then the solid has mass $\int_{\mathscr{S}} H$, where $\mathscr{S}$ is the region of 3-space occupied by the solid.

EXAMPLE 3.   Compute the mass of the solid which occupies the region $\mathscr{S}$, where $\mathscr{S}$ is $\{(\alpha, b) \mid \alpha \in S$ and $X\alpha \leq b \leq (XY)\alpha\}$ and $S = [0, 2] \times [1, 2]$, and the density of the solid is given by the function YZ.

Solution: The required mass is $\int_{\mathscr{S}} YZ$. Let $\alpha \in S$; then $L\alpha = Y\alpha \int_{X\alpha}^{(XY)\alpha} x = [(Y/2)(X^2 Y^2 - X^2)](\alpha)$; thus $L = X^2 Y^3/2 - X^2 Y/2$. Hence the required mass is $\int_S (X^2 Y^3/2 - X^2 Y/2)$. Let $t \in [0, 2]$; then $h(t) = \frac{1}{2} \int_1^2 (t^2 x^3 - t^2 x) = \left[t^2 x^4/8 - t^2 x^2/4 \right]_1^2 = 9t^2/8$; thus $h = 9x^2/8$. Hence the required mass is $\int_0^2 9x^2/8 = 3x^3/8 \Big|_0^2 = 3$.

The moment of a particle about a plane is defined to be the product of the mass of the particle and the directed distance from the particle to the plane. It follows that the moment of a homogeneous solid of unit density about the XY-plane is $\int_{\mathscr{S}} Z$, where $\mathscr{S}$ is the region of 3-space occupied by the solid. Similarly, the moment of this solid about the YZ-plane is $\int_{\mathscr{S}} X$, and the moment of this solid about the ZX-plane is $\int_{\mathscr{S}} Y$. It is easy to see that the center of mass of our solid is $(\bar{x}, \bar{y}, \bar{z})$, where $M\bar{x} = \int_{\mathscr{S}} X$, $M\bar{y} = \int_{\mathscr{S}} Y$, and $M\bar{z} = \int_{\mathscr{S}} Z$, assuming that M is the mass of the solid, i.e., $M = \int_{\mathscr{S}} 1$. In particular, the *centroid* of $\mathscr{S}$, a region of 3-space, is $(\bar{x}, \bar{y}, \bar{z})$, where $V\bar{x} = \int_{\mathscr{S}} X$, $V\bar{y} = \int_{\mathscr{S}} Y$, and $V\bar{z} = \int_{\mathscr{S}} Z$, assuming that V is the volume of $\mathscr{S}$, i.e., $V = \int_{\mathscr{S}} 1$.

The moment of inertia of a particle with respect to a line is defined as the product of the mass of the particle and the square of the distance between the particle and the line. Thus the moment of a homogeneous solid of unit density about the X-axis is $I_X = \int_{\mathscr{S}} (Y^2 + Z^2)$, where $\mathscr{S}$ is the region of 3-space occupied by the solid. Similarly, the moments of inertia of the given solid about the remaining coordinate axes are $I_Y = \int_{\mathscr{S}} (Z^2 + X^2)$ and $I_Z = \int_{\mathscr{S}} (X^2 + Y^2)$.

In case the density of the solid is given by a continuous function H, the moments of inertia about the coordinate axes are

$$I_X = \int_{\mathscr{S}} (Y^2 + Z^2)H, \quad I_Y = \int_{\mathscr{S}} (Z^2 + X^2)H, \quad I_Z = \int_{\mathscr{S}} (X^2 + Y^2)H.$$

EXAMPLE 4.   Find the centroid of $\{(\alpha, b) \mid \alpha \in S$ and $X\alpha \leq b \leq (XY)\alpha\}$, where $S = [0, 2] \times [1, 2]$.

Solution: The volume of the given region of 3-space is $\int_{\mathscr{S}} 1$. Let $\alpha \in S$; then $L\alpha = \int_{X\alpha}^{(XY)\alpha} 1 = (XY - X)\alpha$; thus $L = XY - X$. Hence $\int_{\mathscr{S}} 1 = \int_S (XY - X)$. Let $t \in [0, 2]$; then $h(t) = \int_1^2 (tx - t) = \left[tx^2/2 - tx \right]_1^2 = t/2$; so $h = x/2$. Thus $\int_{\mathscr{S}} 1 = \int_0^2 x/2 = x^2/4 \Big|_0^2 = 1$. We conclude that the given region has unit volume. Thus the centroid of the given region is $(\bar{x}, \bar{y}, \bar{z})$, where $\bar{x} = \int_{\mathscr{S}} X$,

$\bar{y} = \int_{\mathscr{S}} Y$, and $\bar{z} = \int_{\mathscr{S}} Z$. We compute $\int_{\mathscr{S}} X$. Let $\alpha \in S$; then $L\alpha = X\alpha \int_{X\alpha}^{(XY)\alpha} 1 = [X(XY - X)]\alpha$;

thus $L = X^2 Y - X^2$. Let $t \in [0, 2]$; then $h(t) = \int_1^2 (t^2 x - t^2) = \left[t^2 x^2/2 - t^2 x\right]_1^2 = t^2/2$; so $h = x^2/2$.

Thus $\bar{x} = \int_{\mathscr{S}} X = \int_0^2 x^2/2 = x^3/6 \Big]_0^2 = 4/3$. We now compute $\int_{\mathscr{S}} Y$. Let $\alpha \in S$; then $L\alpha = Y\alpha \int_{X\alpha}^{(XY)\alpha} 1$

$= Y(XY - X)\alpha$; thus $L = XY^2 - XY$. Let $t \in [0, 2]$; then $h(t) = \int_1^2 (tx^2 - tx) = \left[tx^3/3 - tx^2/2\right]_1^2$

$= 4t/3$; so $h = 4x/3$. Hence $\bar{y} = \int_{\mathscr{S}} Y = \int_0^2 4x/3 = 2x^2/3 \Big]_0^2 = 8/3$. Finally, we compute $\int_{\mathscr{S}} Z$.

Let $\alpha \in S$; then $L\alpha = \int_{X\alpha}^{(XY)\alpha} x = (1/2)(X^2 Y^2 - X^2)\alpha$; thus $L = (1/2)(X^2 Y^2 - X^2)$. Let $t \in [0, 2]$; then

$h(t) = \frac{1}{2}\int_1^2 (t^2 x^2 - t^2) = \frac{1}{2}\left[t^2 x^3/3 - t^2 x\right]_1^2 = 2t^2/3$; hence $h = 2x^2/3$. Thus $\bar{z} = \int_{\mathscr{S}} Z = \int_0^2 2x^2/3 =$

$2x^3/9 \Big]_0^2 = 16/9$. We conclude that $(4/3, 8/3, 16/9)$ is the centroid of $\mathscr{S}$.

E X E R C I S E S

1. Compute the 4-volume of $\{(\alpha, b) \mid \alpha \in \mathscr{S}$ and $0 \le b \le (XZ)\alpha\}$, where $\mathscr{S} = \{(\alpha, b) \mid \alpha \in [0, 1] \times [0, 2]$ and $X\alpha \le b \le (X + Y)\alpha\}$.

2. Compute the 4-volume of $\{(\alpha, b) \mid \alpha \in \mathscr{S}$ and $0 \le b \le Z\alpha\}$, where $\mathscr{S} = \{(\alpha, b) \mid \alpha \in [0, 1] \times [0, 2]$ and $0 \le b \le (XY)^{1/2}\alpha\}$.

3. Compute the 4-volume of $\{(\alpha, b) \mid \alpha \in \mathscr{S}$ and $0 \le b \le (XY)\alpha\}$, where $\mathscr{S} = \{(\alpha, b) \mid \alpha \in S$ and $3 \le b \le (2X + 3Y)\alpha\}$ and $S = \{(a, b) \mid 1 \le a \le 3$ and $a \le b \le a^2\}$.

4. Compute the 4-volume of $\{(\alpha, b) \mid \alpha \in \mathscr{S}$ and $0 \le b \le X\alpha\}$, where $\mathscr{S} = \{(\alpha, b) \mid \alpha \in S$ and $1 \le b \le 5\}$ and $S = \{(a, b) \mid 0 \le a \le 1$ and $0 \le a^2 + b^2 \le 1\}$.

5. Compute the 4-volume of $\{(\alpha, b) \mid \alpha \in \mathscr{S}$ and $0 \le b \le Z\alpha\}$, where $\mathscr{S} = \{(\alpha, b) \mid \alpha \in S$ and $1 \le b \le 5\}$ and $S = \{(a, b) \mid 0 \le a \le 1$ and $0 \le a^2 + b^2 \le 1\}$.

6. Compute the 4-volume of $\{(\alpha, b) \mid \alpha \in \mathscr{S}$ and $0 \le b \le Y\alpha\}$, where $\mathscr{S} = \{(\alpha, b) \mid \alpha \in S$ and $0 \le b \le (X + Y)\alpha\}$ and $S = \{(a, b) \mid 0 \le a \le 1$ and $0 \le a^2 + b^2 \le 1\}$.

7. Compute the mass of the solid which occupies the region $\mathscr{S} = \{(\alpha, b) \mid \alpha \in S$ and $0 \le b \le (X + Y)\alpha\}$, where $S = \{(a, b) \mid 0 \le a \le 1$ and $0 \le a^2 + b^2 \le 1\}$; the density of the solid is given by the function Z.

8. Compute the mass of the solid which occupies the region $\mathscr{S} = \{(\alpha, b) \mid \alpha \in S$ and $0 \le b \le (X + Y)\alpha\}$, where $S = \{(a, b) \mid 2 \le a \le 3$ and $4 \le a^2 + b^2 \le 9\}$; the density of the solid is given by the function $(X^2 + Y^2)^{-1/2}$.

9. Compute the moment about the XY-plane of the homogeneous solid that occupies the region $\mathscr{S} = \{(\alpha, b) \mid \alpha \in S$ and $0 \le b \le (X + Y)\alpha\}$, where $S = \{(a, b) \mid 0 \le a \le 1$ and $0 \le b \le a\}$.

10. Compute the moment about the YZ-plane of the homogeneous solid that occupies the region $\mathscr{S} = \{(\alpha, b) \mid \alpha \in S$ and $0 \le b \le (X + Y)\alpha\}$, where $S = \{(a, b) \mid 0 \le a \le 1$ and $0 \le b \le a\}$.

11. Compute I_Z for the homogeneous solid that occupies the region $\mathscr{S} = \{(\alpha, b) \mid \alpha \in S$ and $0 \le b \le \sqrt{16 - (X^2 + Y^2)}(\alpha)\}$, where $S = \{(a, b) \mid 0 \le a \le 1$ and $0 \le b \le \sqrt{1 - a^2}\}$.

12. Find the centroid of $\{(\alpha, b) \mid \alpha \in S$ and $X\alpha \le b \le (XY)\alpha\}$, where $S = \{(a, b) \mid 0 \le a \le 2$ and $a + 1 \le b \le 2a + 1\}$.

13. Find the centroid of $\{(\alpha, b) \mid \alpha \in S$ and $0 \le b \le (X + Y)\alpha\}$, where $S = \{(a, b) \mid 0 \le b \le 1$ and $b \le a \le 2 - b\}$.

PART
IV
Differential Equations

Chapter 8

First-Order Differential Equations

8.1 Introduction

The problem of finding an antiderivative of a given function is closely studied in introductory calculus courses because a knowledge of antiderivatives is helpful in evaluating definite integrals. The problem of finding $\boldsymbol{\mathsf{A}}\, g$, where g is a given function with one argument, can be expressed as follows: find f such that $f' = g$ and $\mathscr{D}_f = \mathscr{D}_g$. Here we shall consider the more general problem illustrated by the following examples.

(1) Find f such that $f' = f^2$.

(2) Find f such that $f^{(2)} = f$.

(3) Find f such that $f^{(2)} = 3f'$.

(4) Find f such that $f^{(4)} - 4f^{(2)} - 5f = -5 \sin 2x$.

(5) Find f such that $xf^{(3)} + f^{(2)} + (f')^2 + (4 - 2 \cos) \cdot f = \sin^2 + 2 \cos$.

It is easy to verify that $-1/x$ satisfies (1), that exp satisfies (2), that $\exp(3x)$ satisfies (3), that $\sin 2x - 3 \cos$ satisfies (4), and that $x \sin$ satisfies (5).

The equations which appear in (1), (2), (3), (4), and (5) are called *ordinary differential equations*. An equation is said to be an ordinary differential equation provided that the equation involves only an unknown function with one argument, certain derivatives of the unknown function, and certain given functions. From (3) we see that the unknown function itself need not appear in the equation. There are also *partial differential equations*. These are equations which connect an unknown function which has several arguments, certain of its partial derivatives, and certain given functions. For example, $F_{11} + F_{22} = 0$ is a partial differential equation; here, the problem is to find a function with two arguments, say F, such that $F_{11} + F_{22} = 0$.

In these chapters we shall restrict ourselves to *ordinary* differential equations, since a technique for handling ordinary differential equations is basic to a discussion of partial differential equations. Accordingly, we shall freely drop the adjective *ordinary* when referring to an ordinary differential equation.

It is convenient to classify differential equations according to the highest derivative of the unknown function which appears in the equation. Thus we have the notion of the *order* of a differential equation.

DEFINITION 8.1.1.   A differential equation is said to have *order n* iff n is the largest natural number such that $f^{(n)}$ occurs in the differential equation.

For example, the differential equation $x + f^{(2)} + (f')^3 = 0$ has order 2.

In this chapter we shall concentrate on differential equations of order 1. We already possess a highly developed technique for handling a certain class of differential equations of the first order, namely those differential equations in which f itself does not occur. To solve the differential equation $f' = g$, where g is a given function, we have only to compute an antiderivative of g. For example, sin is a solution of the differential equation $f' = \cos$; indeed, if k is a constant function, then $k + \sin$ is a solution of this differential equation.

Certain differential equations of the first order are easy to solve even though f appears in the equation.

EXAMPLE 1.   Find a function f such that $f' = xf$.

Solution: We rewrite the given differential equation as follows: $f'/f = x$; thus $\int f'/f = \int x$, i.e., $\log|f| \equiv x^2/2$. Hence we may choose f so that $\log|f| = x^2/2$; thus $f = \exp(x^2/2)$. We note that $-\exp(x^2/2)$ is another solution of the given differential equation; indeed, $k \exp(x^2/2)$ is a solution whenever k is a constant function.

Our aim, given a differential equation of the first order, is to characterize the family of *all* solutions of the differential equation; i.e., we want to find all solutions of the differential equation. This is achieved by smuggling a parameter into one solution so that each solution is obtained by substituting a real number for the parameter. We say, then, that we have obtained a *complete*, or *general*, solution of the given differential equation.

For the moment, let us consider first-order differential equations of the form $f' = H(x, f)$, where H is a function with two arguments. We state the following *unique-existence* theorem without proof (a *unique-existence* theorem asserts the existence of a unique object which possesses a given property; on the other hand, an *existence* theorem asserts the existence of at least one object which possesses a given property).

THEOREM 8.1.1.   Let D be a region such that both H and H_2 are continuous on D and let $(a, b) \in D$. Then there is an open interval $\mathscr{I}$ which contains a, and there is exactly one function, say f, such that $f' = H(x, f), f(a) = b$, and $\mathscr{D}_f = \mathscr{I}$.

In a moment we shall point out the connection between Theorem 8.1.1 and our problem of finding a complete solution of a given differential equation. First, consider the following illustration.

EXAMPLE 2.   Find a complete solution of $f' = f$.

Solution: Clearly, exp is a particular solution of this differential equation; indeed, k exp is a particular solution whenever k is a constant function. We want to prove that this differential equation has no other solution. To this purpose we use Theorem 8.1.1. Here, the function H is Y, since $Y(x, f) = f$. Now, $Y_2 = 1$; moreover, Y and 1 are continuous on R_2. Since the conditions of Theorem 8.1.1 are met, we know that there is exactly one solution of $f' = f$ of which

(a, b) is a member. But it is easy to choose k so that $(a, b) \in k$ exp, namely $k = be^{-a}$. Thus be^{-a} exp is a solution of $f = f'$ of which (a, b) is a member. By Theorem 8.1.1, there is no other solution of $f' = f$ of which (a, b) is a member. Therefore the family of solutions of $f' = f$ is given by $\{k \exp \mid k \in R\}$. We conclude that $f = k$ exp provides us with a complete solution of the differential equation $f' = f$.

The connection between Theorem 8.1.1 and the problem of characterizing the solutions of the differential equation $f' = H(x, f)$ is now clear. If by some method we have found that g is a solution of the given differential equation and if $(a, g(a))$ is a member of a region on which both H and H_2 are continuous, then g is the only solution of the given differential equation through $(a, g(a))$ which has domain $\mathscr{D}_g$. We hasten to point out that if $\mathscr{I}$ is a proper subset of $\mathscr{D}_g$, then $g \, \mathsf{R} \, \mathscr{I}$ is also a solution of the given differential equation. In a real sense, however, we regard this solution as being contained in, or given by, the solution g.

EXAMPLE 3.   Find a complete solution of $f' = xf$.

Solution: In Example 1 we pointed out that $k \exp(x^2/2)$ is a solution of this differential equation whenever $k \in R$. We want to prove that there are no other solutions of $f' = xf$, except for functions which are subsets of these solutions. We apply Theorem 8.1.1. Here, $H = XY$, and so $H_2 = X$; clearly, both H and H_2 are continuous on R_2. Let $(a, b) \in R_2$; by Theorem 8.1.1, there is an open interval $\mathscr{I}$ such that there is exactly one function which satisfies the differential equation, has domain $\mathscr{I}$, and contains (a, b). But the function $k \exp(x^2/2) \, \mathsf{R} \mathscr{I}$ has these properties provided $k = b \exp(-a^2/2)$. We conclude that $f = k \exp(x^2/2)$ provides us with a complete solution of the differential equation $f' = xf$.

In the preceding examples we have exhibited a complete solution of a given differential equation by expressing one solution in terms of a parameter; i.e., instead of writing "$\{k \exp(-x^2/2) \mid k \in R\}$", we have written "$f = k \exp(-x^2/2)$". More generally, we shall find it convenient to express a complete solution of a differential equation by means of an equation which exhibits a relation between the unknown function and certain other functions. For example, we shall regard "$\log|f| = k + x^2/2$" as expressing a complete solution of the differential equation $f' = xf$. The point is that we cannot always exhibit a solution of a differential equation in explicit terms, but must be content with presenting a solution implicitly. For example, a solution of the differential equation $f' = 2x/(2f \cdot \cos f^2 - 1)$ is given implicitly by $\sin f^2 = x^2 + f$.

We hasten to point out that there are differential equations which have no solution. Consider, for example, the differential equation $f'/x = (2 + x)$ exp. At first glance, we might think that x^2 exp is a solution since $(x^2 \exp)' = (2x + x^2)$ exp; however, this observation is misleading. To see that there is no function f such that $f'/x = (2 + x)$ exp, we have only to examine the domains of the functions f'/x and $(2 + x)$ exp. Clearly, $0 \bar{\in} \mathscr{D}_{f'/x}$, yet 0 is a member of the domain of $(2 + x)$ exp. Thus, no matter how we choose f, the functions f'/x and $(2 + x)$ exp have different domains, and therefore cannot be the same function.

Perhaps you consider this to be a technicality and feel that the differential equation $f'/x = (2 + x)$ exp really has a solution, namely x^2 exp. The thing to do is to rewrite the differential equation so as to avoid a conflict in domains. How about putting both sides of the equation together on one side, e.g., writing "$f'/x - (2 + x) \exp = 0$"? Unfortunately, this does not help; we still have a function to the right of the equals sign, namely the constant function 0, and this function has domain R. What we must do is *restrict* the function on the right to the domain of the function on the left. Thus we write "$f'/x = (2 + x) \exp \mathsf{R} E$", where E is the domain of f'/x, i.e., $E = \{t \mid t \in \mathscr{D}_{f'} \text{ and } t \neq 0\}$.

We shall follow this prescription whenever there is a genuine possibility that the two sides of a given differential equation are functions with different domains. Thus we shall introduce "$\mathsf{R} E$" on one side of a differential equation, where E is the domain of the function which appears on the other side of the equation. We shall not always spell out the members of E. Therefore our convention is this: if E is not specified, then E is assumed to be the domain of the function which constitutes the other side of the equation.

EXERCISES

1. Verify the following statements.
   a. $f^{(2)} = -f$ if $f = \sin$.
   b. $f' = 3f$ if $f = \exp(3x)$.
   c. If $f' = 3f$, then there is a constant function k such that $f = k \exp(3x)$.
   d. $f' = 1 + f^2$ if $f = \tan$.
   e. If $f' = 1 + f^2$, then there is a constant function k such that $f = \tan(x + k)$.
   f. $f' = f^2$ if $f = -1/x$.
   g. If $f' = f^2$, then there is a constant function k such that $f = -1/(k + x)$.
   h. $f' = -x \exp(f)$ if $f = \log(2/x^2)$.
   i. If $f' = -x \exp(f)$, then there is a constant function k such that $f = \log 2 - \log(k + x^2)$.

2. Find a solution of each of the following differential equations.
   a. $f' = -f$. **d.** $f' = 1 + f^2$.
   b. $f^{(2)} = x^3$. **e.** $f' = \tan \cdot f$.
   c. $f^{(2)} + f' = 2$. **f.** $f' = xf^2$.

3. Find a complete solution of the differential equation $f' = xf^2$.

8.2   Separating the Variables

Consider a differential equation of the form $f' = g \cdot h(f)$, where g and h are given functions with one argument. Suppose that f is a solution of this differential equation (we use the same letter "f" as appears in the differential equation in order to economize on our notation); then $f'/h(f) = g \mathsf{R} E$, where $E = \{t \mid t \in \mathscr{D}_{h(f)} \cap \mathscr{D}_{f'} \text{ and } h(f(t)) \neq 0\}$. Thus $\mathsf{A} f'/h(f) \equiv \mathsf{A} g \mathsf{R} E$. With luck we may be able to compute these antiderivatives; suppose that $z' = f'/h(f)$ and that $w' = g \mathsf{R} E$; then $z \equiv w$, and so $z = k + w$ whenever $k \in R$. Since our argument is reversible, we conclude that $z = k + w$ is a complete solution of the given differential equation. Note that generally z is a function of f; thus $z = k + w$ gives f implicitly.

EXAMPLE 1.   Find a complete solution of $f' = xf^3$.

Solution: If f is a solution of the given differential equation, then $f'/f^3 = x$ R E, where $E = \{t \mid t \in \mathcal{D}_f \cap \mathcal{D}_{f'}$ and $f^3(t) \neq 0\}$. Thus $\displaystyle\bigwedge f'/f^3 \equiv \bigwedge x$ R E, i.e., $f^{-2}/-2 \equiv x^2/2$ R E, and so $f^{-2} = k - x^2$ R E. We conclude that $f = (k + x^2)^{-1/2}$ is a complete solution of the given differential equation.

EXAMPLE 2.   Find a complete solution of $f' = (1 + f) \cdot \cos$.

Solution: If f is a solution of the given differential equation, then $f'/(1 + f) = \cos$ R E, where $E = \{t \mid t \in \mathcal{D}_f \cap \mathcal{D}_{f'}$ and $f(t) \neq -1\}$. Thus $\displaystyle\bigwedge f'/(1 + f) \equiv \bigwedge \cos$ R E, i.e., $\log|1 + f| \equiv \sin$ R E, and so $\log|1 + f| = k + \sin$ R E is a complete solution. This gives f implicitly; it is not difficult to obtain f explicitly, as follows: $1 + f = c \exp(\sin)$, and so $f = -1 + c \exp(\sin)$ is our complete solution where c is a parameter.

EXERCISES

Find a complete solution of each of the following differential equations.

1. $f' = xf^4$.
2. $f' = x(1 + f)$.
3. $f' = \cos \cdot \exp(f)$.
4. $f' = (1 - f^2)^{1/2}$.
5. $f' = x(1 - f^2)^{1/2}$.

6. $f' = x^2 f$.
7. $f' = x^2/f^2$.
8. $f' \cdot \cos(f) = 1 + 3x^2$.
9. $f' = 1 + x^2 + f^2 + x^2 f^2$.
10. $f' = x \cos^2(f)$.

11. Find a function f such that $f' = 1 + f^2$ and $f(0) = 1$.   (*Answer:* $\tan(\pi/4 + x)$)
12. Find a function f such that $f' = 5f$ and $f(0) = 2$.   (*Answer:* $2 \exp(5x)$)
13. Find a function f such that $f' = -x/f$ and $f(1) = 0$.   (*Answer:* $(1 - x^2)^{1/2}$)
14. Find a function f such that $f' = f/x - x^3/f$ and $f(0) = 0$.   (*Answer:* $x(1 - x^2)^{1/2}$)

8.3   Exact Differential Equations

Consider a differential equation of the form $f' = -M(x, f)/N(x, f)$, where M and N are continuous functions with two arguments. This differential equation can be solved provided that there is a continuous function with two arguments, say G, such that $G_1 = M$ and $G_2 = N$. Under this circumstance the differential equation $f' = -M(x, f)/N(x, f)$ is said to be *exact*.

It is a fact that any exact differential equation can be solved easily. To see this, we recall Theorem 6.6.5.

THEOREM 6.6.5.   Let f and H be functions such that $\mathcal{D}_f$ is an interval, $\mathcal{D}_{H_1} = \mathcal{D}_{H_2} = \mathcal{D}_H$, and $H(t, f(t)) = k$ whenever $t \in \mathcal{D}_f$; then $f' = -H_1(x, f)/H_2(x, f)$.

In view of this result, if F is continuous, then $F(x, f) = k$ is a complete solution of the differential equation $f' = -F_1(x, f)/F_2(x, f)$ since this differential equation is exact. Notice that f is given implicitly by this solution.

EXAMPLE 1.   Find a complete solution of $f' = -(2f + 6xf)/(2x + 3x^2 + 2f)$.

Solution: Here, $M = 2Y + 6XY$ and $N = 2X + 3X^2 + 2Y$. Let $F = Y^2 + 2XY + 3X^2Y$; then $F_1 = 2Y + 6XY = M$ and $F_2 = 2Y + 2X + 3X^2 = N$. Therefore the given differential equation is exact and a complete solution is $f^2 + 2xf + 3x^2f = k$.

We now consider some theorems about exact differential equations.

THEOREM 8.3.1.   If $f' = -M(x, f)/N(x, f)$ is exact, then $M_2 = N_1$.

Proof: If $f' = -M(x, f)/N(x, f)$ is exact, then there is a continuous function F such that $F_1 = M$ and $F_2 = N$. Since $F_{12} = F_{21}$, we see that $M_2 = N_1$. Thus "$M_2 = N_1$" is a *necessary* condition for exactness.

Next, we establish a *sufficient* condition for exactness.

THEOREM 8.3.2. $f' = -M(x, f)/N(x, f)$ is exact if M and N are continuous and $M_2 = N_1$.

Proof: We want to show that the given differential equation is exact if $M_2 = N_1$. Since M is continuous, we can find a continuous function G such that $G_1 = M$. We look for a continuous function with one argument, say h, such that $[G + h(Y)]_2 = N$; this will establish exactness. By assumption, $N_1 = M_2 = G_{12} = G_{21}$, i.e., $N_1 = G_{21}$; hence G_2 differs from N by a function which is independent of X; i.e., $N - G_2$ is a function of Y alone. Let h be a function with one argument such that $[h(Y)]_2 = N - G_2$; then $[G + h(Y)]_2 = G_2 + N - G_2 = N$. Thus $[G + h(Y)]_1 = M$ and $[G + h(Y)]_2 = N$. This proves that the differential equation $f' = -M(x, f)/N(x, f)$ is exact if M and N are continuous and $M_2 = N_1$.

COROLLARY 8.3.1. $f' = -M(x, f)/N(x, f)$ is exact iff M and N are continuous and $M_2 = N_1$.

EXAMPLE 2.   Find a complete solution of $\sinh \cdot \sinh(f) \cdot f' = -\cosh \cdot \cosh(f)$.

Solution: Here, $M = \cosh(X) \cdot \cosh(Y)$ and $N = \sinh(X) \cdot \sinh(Y)$; therefore $M_2 = \cosh(X) \cdot \sinh(Y)$ and $N_1 = \cosh(X) \cdot \sinh(Y)$. Since $M_2 = N_1$, we conclude that the given differential equation is exact. Here $F = \sinh(X) \cdot \cosh(Y)$; so $\sinh \cdot \cosh(f) = k$ is a complete solution of the given differential equation.

The proof of Theorem 8.3.2 provides us with a simple technique for solving an exact differential equation. To find a complete solution of the exact differential equation $f' = -M(x, f)/N(x, f)$, we proceed as follows. First write down M and N; next, find G such that $G_1 = M$ (this is achieved by antidifferentiating); finally, look for a function h such that $[G + h(Y)]_2 = N$ (again, this is achieved by antidifferentiating). Then $G(x, f) + h(f) = k$ is a complete solution of the given differential equation.

EXAMPLE 3. Find a complete solution of $f' = -(\cos + 2xf)/(x^2 + \sec^2(f))$.

Solution: Here, $M = \cos(X) + 2XY$ and $N = X^2 + \sec^2(Y)$. Noting that $M_2 = N_1$, we proceed as follows. Let $G = \sin(X) + X^2 Y$; then $G_1 = M$ and $G_2 = X^2$; so $N - G_2 = \sec^2(Y)$. We conclude that $h = \tan$; thus $h(Y) = \tan(Y)$. So we obtain the function $\sin(X) + X^2 Y + \tan(Y)$. Note that $[\sin(X) + X^2 Y + \tan(Y)]_1 = M$ and that $[\sin(X) + X^2 Y + \tan(Y)]_2 = N$. We conclude that $\sin + x^2 f + \tan(f) = k$ is a complete solution of the given differential equation.

E X E R C I S E S

Find a complete solution of each of the following differential equations, provided it is exact.

1. $f' = -2xf/(x^2 + 2f)$.   *(Answer: $x^2 f + f^2 = k$)*

2. $f' = -2xf/(x^2 + f)$.

3. $f' = -(\cos + \cos f)/-x \sin f$.   *(Answer: $\sin + x \cos f = k$)*

4. $f' = -(\exp f)/(x \exp f)$.   *(Answer: $x \exp f = k$)*

5. $f' = -(2xf + \cos)/(1 + x^2)$.   *(Answer: $x^2 f + f + \sin = k$)*

6. $f' = -(x^2 + f^2)/(x + f)$.

7. $f' = -\sec^2/(\tan f \cdot \sec f)$.   *(Answer: $\tan + \sec f = k$)*

8. $xf^2 \cdot (1 + f^2) \cdot f' = \arctan f - f$.   *(Answer: $x \arctan f - xf = k$)*

9. Find a complete solution of $f' = -(ax^2 f + 2f^2)/(x^3 + 4xf)$, where a is chosen so that this differential equation is exact.   *(Answer: $x^3 f + 2xf^2 = k$)*

8.4   Integrating Factors

We have seen that the differential equation $f' = -M(x,f)/N(x,f)$ is exact iff $M_2 = N_1$; moreover, it is easy to obtain a complete solution of an exact differential equation. In this section we shall consider differential equations of the form

$$M(x,f) + f' \cdot N(x,f) = 0$$

which are *not* exact. The idea is to transform a differential equation which possesses the above form into an exact differential equation by multiplying through by a suitable function. Any function which transforms a differential equation into an *exact* differential equation in this manner is said to be an *integrating factor* of the differential equation. To be specific, let $H(x,f)$ be an integrating factor of the differential equation $M(x,f) + f' \cdot N(x,f) = 0$. Then

$$H(x,f) \cdot M(x,f) + f' \cdot H(x,f) \cdot N(x,f) = 0$$

is exact. Therefore $[H \cdot M]_2 = [H \cdot N]_1$, i.e., $H \cdot M_2 + H_2 \cdot M = H \cdot N_1 + H_1 \cdot N$; thus

(1) $$H_2 \cdot M - H_1 \cdot N = H \cdot [N_1 - M_2].$$

We are faced with a partial differential equation in the unknown function H; unless we are especially lucky, we may not be able to find a particular solution. To simplify our problem, let us suppose that $H_2 = 0$ (i.e. H is a function of X alone). Following a well-established convention, we shall denote the integrating factor $H(x, f)$ by "μ". Therefore let $\mu = H(x, f)$; then $\mu' = H_1(x, f)$. Thus, from (1), $-\mu' \cdot N(x, f) = \mu \cdot [N_1 - M_2](x, f)$, and so

$$\mu'/\mu = \frac{M_2 - N_1}{N}(x, f).$$

Since μ'/μ is free of f, it follows that $\dfrac{M_2 - N_1}{N}(x, f)$ is free of f as well. Moreover,

$$\log|\mu| \equiv A\frac{M_2 - N_1}{N}(x, f);$$

thus

$$\mu \equiv \exp\left(A\frac{M_2 - N_1}{N}(x, f)\right).$$

We have found our integrating factor! This establishes the following theorem.

THEOREM 8.4.1.   The differential equation $M(x, f) + f' \cdot N(x, f) = 0$ has an integrating factor provided that $(M_2 - N_1)/N$ is free of Y; if so, then $\exp\left(A\dfrac{M_2 - N_1}{N}(x, f)\right)$ is an integrating factor.

EXAMPLE 1.   Find a complete solution of $f + \log - xf' = 0$.

Solution: Here, $M = Y + \log(X)$ and $N = -X$; thus $(M_2 - N_1)/N = -2/X$. Now, $A - 2/x \equiv \log(1/x^2)$; so $1/x^2$ is an integrating factor of the given differential equation. Thus $(f + \log)/x^2 - f'/x = 0$ is exact, and it follows that $f/x + 1/x + \log/x = k$ is a complete solution of the given differential equation. We conclude that $f = kx - 1 - \log$ is a complete solution.

E X E R C I S E S

Find a complete solution of each of the following.

1. $(1 + x)f + xf' = 0$.   (*Answer:* $f = k/(x \exp)$)

2. $(3 + 2x)f + 3xf' = 0$.   (*Answer:* $f = k \exp(-2x/3)/x$)

3. $(f - f/x^2) + (x + 1/x) \cdot f' = 0$.   (*Answer:* $f = kx/(1 + x^2)$)

4. $(x^3 \cos + 2f^2) - 2xf \cdot f' = 0$.

(*Answer:* $x^4 \sin + 4x^3 \cos - 12x^2 \sin - 24x \cos + 24 \sin + x^2 f^2 = k$)

5. $2 \cos f - xf' \cdot \sin f = 0$.   (*Answer:* $x^2 \cos f = k$)

6. $\sin f - xf' \cdot \cos f = 0$.   (*Answer:* $\sin f = kx$)

7. $2 \tan f + 3xf + x(\sec^2 f + x) \cdot f' = 0.$ (*Answer:* $x^2 \tan f + x^3 f = k$)

8. $f^2 + xf^2 \cdot \tan + \sec + 2xf \cdot f' = 0.$ (*Answer:* $x \sec \cdot f^2 + \tan = k$)

9. Given that $\mu = H(x,f)$ is an integrating factor of $M(x,f) + N(x,f) \cdot f' = 0$, and that $H_1 = 0$, show that:

   a. $(N_1 - M_2)/M$ is free of X

   b. $\mu'/\mu = \dfrac{N_1 - M_2}{M}(x,f) \cdot f'$

   c. if $h \equiv \mathbf{A} \dfrac{N_1 - M_2}{M}(x,x)$ then $h(f) \equiv \mathbf{A}\left[\dfrac{N_1 - M_2}{M}(x,f) \cdot f'\right]$

   d. $\log |\mu| \equiv h(f)$

   e. $\exp(h(f))$ is an integrating factor of the given differential equation.

   Find a complete solution of each of the following.

10. $1 + 2xf' = 0.$ (*Answer:* $x \exp(2f) = k$)

11. $1 + f' \cdot [x \tan f + \sec f] = 0.$ (*Answer:* $x \sec f + \tan f = k$)

12. $2xf - x^2 f' = 0.$ (*Answer:* $f = kx^2$)

13. $3x^2 f + f^2 + f' \cdot [2x^3 + 3xf] = 0.$ (*Answer:* $x^3 f^2 + xf^3 = k$)

14. $2x^2 f^2 + x^2 + 2x^3 f \cdot f' = 0.$ (*Answer:* $x^3(2f^2 + 1)\sqrt{1 + 2f^2} = k$)

8.5   Linear Differential Equations of the First Order

Let $n \in N$; by a linear differential equation of order n we mean $f^{(n)} + p_1 \cdot f^{(n-1)} + \cdots + p_{n-1} \cdot f' + p_n \cdot f = p_{n+1}$, where each p_i, $i = 1, \cdots, n + 1$, is a function with one argument. Here, we shall confine ourselves to linear differential equations of the first order, i.e., differential equations of the form $g \cdot f + f' = h$, where g and h are given functions with one argument. Writing this equation in the manner of Section 8.4, we have $(g \cdot f - h) + f' = 0$ R E. Here, $M = Y \cdot g(X) - h(X)$ and $N = 1$; so $(M_2 - N_1)/N = g(X)$. Therefore, by Theorem 8.4.1, $\exp\!\left(\mathbf{A} g\right)$ is an integrating factor. This means that the differential equation $(g \cdot f - h) \cdot \exp\!\left(\mathbf{A} g\right) + f' \cdot \exp\!\left(\mathbf{A} g\right) = 0$ R E is exact. We conclude that it is a simple matter to obtain a complete solution of any linear differential equation of the first order; the only difficulty is the technical problem of computing the anti-derivatives involved.

Since finding an integrating factor is the key to solving our differential equation, we state the above result as a theorem.

THEOREM 8.5.1. $\exp\!\left(\mathbf{A} g\right)$ is an integrating factor of $g \cdot f + f' = h$ R E, where g and h are any functions with one argument.

EXAMPLE 1. Find a complete solution of $f' + f/x = 3$ R E.

Solution: Here, $g = 1/x$. Therefore $\exp(\log|x|)$ is an integrating factor; i.e., $|x|$ is an integrating factor. To simplify the computations, we shall try x instead. Consider $f - 3x + xf' =$

---

0 R $\mathscr{D}_f$. This differential equation is exact; its complete solution is $xf - 3x^2/2 = k$. We conclude that $f = 3x/2 + k/x$ is a complete solution of the given differential equation.

EXAMPLE 2.   Find a complete solution of $f' = 2 - 2xf$.

Solution: Here, $g = 2x$. Thus $\exp\left(\mathbf{A} 2x\right)$ is an integrating factor; i.e., $\exp(x^2)$ is an integrating factor. Consider $(2xf - 2) \cdot \exp(x^2) + f' \cdot \exp(x^2) = 0$ R $\mathscr{D}_f$. Here, $M = [2XY - 2] \cdot [\exp(X^2)]$ and $N = \exp(X^2)$. Thus $f \cdot \exp(x^2) - \mathbf{A}\exp(x^2) = k$ is a complete solution, i.e., $f = \exp(-x^2) \cdot \left[k + \int_0^x \exp(x^2)\right]$ is a complete solution.

E X E R C I S E S

Find a complete solution of each of the following.

1. $x^2 + f/x + f' = 0$ R E.   (*Answer:* $f = (k - x^4/4)/x$)
2. $\tan \cdot f + f' = 0$ R E.   (*Answer:* $f = k \cos$)
3. $xf' + f = x \exp$.
4. $xf' + f = x \sin$.
5. $f' = f + x$.

8.6   Variation of Parameter

We now consider a second method of solving a linear differential equation of the first order; this method is valuable because it can be applied to a wider class of differential equations than can the method of Section 8.5.

Consider the differential equation $f' + g \cdot f = h$, where g and h are given functions with one argument. To solve this differential equation, we first solve the associated differential equation $f' + g \cdot f = 0$ R E. This differential equation is said to be the *reduced* form of $f' + g \cdot f = h$. Notice that $f' + g \cdot f = 0$ R E is easy to solve by separating the variables; indeed, $f'/f = -g$ R E, and so $\log |f| \equiv \mathbf{A} - g$; hence $f = k \exp\left(\mathbf{A} - g\right)$ is a complete solution of the reduced differential equation.

We point out that if f_1 is a solution of the given differential equation, then $f = k \exp\left(\mathbf{A} - g\right) + f_1$ is a complete solution of the given differential equation. Clearly, if $f = k \exp\left(\mathbf{A} - g\right) + f_1$, then $f' = -kg \exp\left(\mathbf{A} - g\right) + f_1'$; thus

$$f' + g \cdot f = -kg \exp\left(\mathbf{A} - g\right) + f_1' + kg \exp\left(\mathbf{A} - g\right) + g \cdot f_1$$

$$= f_1' + g \cdot f_1$$

$$= h$$

since f_1 is a particular solution of $f' + g \cdot f = h$.

Thus the problem of finding a *complete* solution of $f' + g \cdot f = h$ is reduced to the problem of finding a *particular* solution of this differential equation. Fortunately, we can find a particular solution of $f' + g \cdot f = h$ by considering a complete solution of the reduced differential equation, e.g., $f = k \exp\left(\bigwedge - g\right)$. We argue as follows. "Let's see if we can obtain a particular solution of the given differential equation by replacing the parameter k by a function". Thus we want a function with one argument, say v, such that $v \cdot \exp\left(\bigwedge - g\right)$ is a particular solution of $f' + g \cdot f = h$. Let $f_1 = v \cdot \exp\left(\bigwedge - g\right)$; then $f_1' = v' \cdot \exp\left(\bigwedge - g\right) - g \cdot v \cdot \exp\left(\bigwedge - g\right)$. So

$$f_1' + g_1 f_1 = v' \cdot \exp\left(\bigwedge - g\right) - g \cdot v \cdot \exp\left(\bigwedge - g\right) + g \cdot v \cdot \exp\left(\bigwedge - g\right)$$

$$= v' \cdot \exp\left(\bigwedge - g\right).$$

Hence we want to choose v so that $v' \cdot \exp\left(\bigwedge - g\right) = h$; this means that $v' \equiv h \cdot \exp\left(\bigwedge g\right)$, i.e., $v \equiv \bigwedge\left[h \cdot \exp\left(\bigwedge g\right)\right]$. Thus $v \cdot \exp\left(\bigwedge - g\right)$ is a particular solution of $f' + g \cdot f = h$ provided that $v \equiv \bigwedge\left[h \cdot \exp\left(\bigwedge g\right)\right]$.

Notice that the method breaks down into three steps, which we now summarize: (1) find a complete solution of the reduced differential equation; (2) find a particular solution of the given differential equation (this can be achieved by *varying* the parameter of the answer to step 1); (3) add the answers to steps 1 and 2.

The following example illustrates the method.

EXAMPLE 1.   Find a complete solution of $f' + f/x = x$ R E.

Solution: First, we find a complete solution of the reduced differential equation $f' + f/x = 0$ R E. Separating the variables, we obtain $f'/f = -1/x$, and so $\bigwedge f'/f \equiv \bigwedge -1/x$; thus $\log|f| \equiv \log|k/x|$. We conclude that $f = k/x$ is a complete solution of the reduced differential equation. Next, we find a particular solution of $f' + f/x = x$ R E. Let v be a function with one argument such that v/x is a solution; this means that $(xv' - v)/x^2 + v/x^2 = x$ R E. Hence $v' = x^2$ and $v = x^3/3$. Thus $x^2/3$ is a particular solution of the differential equation $f' + f/x = x$ R E (check that this is true). Finally, we conclude that $f = k/x + x^2/3$ is a complete solution of the given differential equation.

It is time that we explicitly mentioned a fact of elementary calculus that we have used in this example and have also used in several earlier examples (e.g., Example 1, Section 8.1), namely, if $\mathscr{I}$ is an interval and f and g are continuous functions with domain $\mathscr{I}$ such that $\log|f| = g$, then $f = \exp(g)$ or $f = -\exp(g)$. The proof is immediate: suppose there are members of $\mathscr{I}$, say a and b, such that $f(a) > 0$ and $f(b) < 0$; then, by the Intermediate Value Theorem, there is a real number c between a and b such that $f(c) = 0$. But $g = \log|f|$; therefore $c \equiv \mathscr{D}_g$. This contradiction establishes our result.

E X E R C I S E S

1. a. Find a complete solution of $f' - \cos \cdot f = 0$ R E.   *(Answer: $f = k \exp(\sin)$)*
   b. Using the method of this section, find a particular solution of $f' - \cos \cdot f = \cos$.
    (Answer: -1)
   c. Find a particular solution of $f' - \cos \cdot f = \exp(\sin)$.   *(Answer: $x \exp(\sin)$)*
   d. Find a particular solution of $f' - \cos \cdot f = 1 - x \cos$.   *(Answer: x)*
   e. Find a complete solution of $f' - \cos \cdot f = 1 - x \cos$.   *(Answer: $f = k \exp(\sin) + x$)*

2. a. Find a complete solution of $f' - 2xf = 0$ R E.   *(Answer: $f = k \exp(x^2)$)*
   b. Find a particular solution of $f' - 2xf = x$.   *(Answer: $-1/2$)*
   c. Find a particular solution of $f' - 2xf = 1 - 2x^2$.   *(Answer: x)*
   d. Find a particular solution of $f' - 2xf = \exp(x^2)$.   *(Answer: $x \exp(x^2)$)*
   e. Find a complete solution of $f' - 2xf = \exp(x^2)$.   *(Answer: $f = (k + x)\exp(x^2)$)*

3. a. Find a complete solution of $f' - \exp \cdot f = 0$ R E.   *(Answer: $f = k \exp(\exp)$)*
   b. Find a particular solution of $f' - \exp \cdot f = \exp(\exp)$.   *(Answer: $x \exp(\exp)$)*
   c. Find a particular solution of $f' - \exp \cdot f = \exp$.   *(Answer: -1)*
   d. Find a complete solution of $f' - \exp \cdot f = \exp$.   *(Answer: $f = k \exp(\exp) - 1$)*

4. Find a complete solution of $f' + x^2 f = 2x^2$ R E.   *(Answer: $f = k \exp(-x^3/3) + 2$)*

5. If $n \neq 0$ and $n \neq 1$, the differential equation $f' + g \cdot f = h \cdot f^n$, which is known as *Bernoulli's equation*, can be put into linear form by first dividing through by f^n and then introducing the unknown function u, where $u = f^{1-n}$. This produces the differential equation

$$u' + (1 - n)g \cdot u = (1 - n)h$$

which can be solved by the method of this section.
   a. Find a complete solution of $f' + f = f^3$ R E.   *(Answer: $f^{-2} = k \exp(2x) + 1$)*
   b. Find a complete solution of $f' - f = xf^2$ R E.

8.7 Homogeneous Differential Equations

Any differential equation which has the form

$$f' = g(f/x),$$

where g is a given function with one argument, is said to be *homogeneous*. For example, the following differential equations are homogeneous: $f' = f/x$ [here, $g = x$], $f' = f^2/x^2 + \sin(f/x)$ [here, $g = x^2 + \sin$], $f' = 3 - f^3/x^3 - \tan(x/f)$ [here $g = 3 - x^3 - \tan(1/x)$].

The fact is that any differential equation of this type can readily be solved. To see this, consider any homogeneous differential equation, say $f' = g(f/x)$, and suppose that $0 \bar{\in} \mathscr{D}_f$ (this simplifies our notation). Let $v = f/x$; then $f = x \cdot v$, and so $f' = v + x \cdot v'$.

Thus $v + x \cdot v' = g(v)$, and so $\dfrac{v'}{g(v) - v} = 1/x$. Notice that we have separated the variables.

Thus

$$\text{A}\frac{v'}{g(v) - v} \equiv \text{A}1/x, \quad \text{and so} \quad \int_a^x \frac{v'}{g(v) - v} = k + \log|x|.$$

Recalling that $v = f/x$, we see that this is a complete solution of the given differential equation $f' = g(f/x)$.

We now illustrate the above method with an example.

EXAMPLE 1.   Find a complete solution of $f' = f^2/x^2$.

Solution: Let $v = f/x$; then $f' = v + xv'$; so $v + xv' = v^2$ and $v'/(v^2 - v) = 1/x$. Thus

$$A\frac{v'}{v(v-1)} = A\,1/x, \quad \text{and so} \quad \log\left|\frac{v-1}{v}\right| = \log|kx|.$$

We conclude that $(v-1)/v = kx$; so $(f-x)/f = kx$. Therefore $f = x/(1-kx)$ is a complete solution of the given differential equation.

We need an easy way of recognizing that a given differential equation is homogeneous. To this purpose we introduce the notion of a *homogeneous function*.

DEFINITION 8.7.1.   Let H be any function with two arguments; then H is said to be *homogeneous of degree n* iff $H(ta, tb) = t^n H(a, b)$ whenever $t \in R$ and $(a, b) \in \mathcal{D}_H$.

For example, $X^3 - Y^3$ is a homogeneous function of degree 3; $\sin(X/Y) + (X^{3/2} - Y^{3/2})^{2/3}$ is a homogeneous function of degree 0.

THEOREM 8.7.1.   Let H be a homogeneous function of degree n; then there is a function with one argument, say g, such that $H(x, f) = x^n g(f/x)$.

Proof: Let $v = f/x$ and let $t \in \mathcal{D}_{H(x,f)}$; then

$$[H(x, f)](t) = H(t, f(t)) = H(t, tv(t)) = t^n H(1, v(t)) = t^n\,_1H_2(v(t)).$$

Let $g = {}_1H_2$, i.e., $g(t) = H(1, t)$ whenever $(1, t) \in \mathcal{D}_H$. Then $[H(x, f)](t) = t^n g(v(t))$, and so $H(x, f) = x^n g(v) = x^n g(f/x)$.

THEOREM 8.7.2.   The differential equation $M(x, f) + f' \cdot N(x, f) = 0$ R E is homogeneous provided that M and N are homogeneous functions of the same degree.

Proof: Let M and N be homogeneous functions of degree n. Then, by Theorem 8.7.1, there are functions g and h such that

$$M(x, f) = x^n g(f/x) \quad \text{and} \quad N(x, f) = x^n h(f/x).$$

Thus
$$f' = -\frac{M(x, f)}{N(x, f)} = -\frac{x^n g(f/x)}{x^n h(f/x)} = -\frac{g(f/x)}{h(f/x)} = -\frac{g}{h}(f/x).$$

We conclude that the given differential equation is homogeneous.

EXAMPLE 2.   Find a complete solution of $(x^2 + xf) + 2x^2f' = 0$ R E.

Solution: Here, $M = X^2 + XY$ and $N = 2X^2$; so M and N are homogeneous of degree 2. Let $v = f/x$; then $f' = v + xv'$; so $v + xv' = -(x^2 + xf)/2x^2 = -(x + f/2x) = -(x + xv)/2x = -(1 + v)/2$. Thus $xv' = -(1 + 3v)/2$, and $v'/(1 + 3v) = -1/2x$. Therefore $\displaystyle\int v'/(1 + 3v) = -\int 1/2x$; so $(1/3) \log|1 + 3v| = (-1/2) \log|kx|$. We conclude that $1 + 3v = (kx)^{-3/2}$; hence $f = -x/3 + cx^{-1/2}$ is a complete solution of the given differential equation.

E X E R C I S E S

Find a complete solution of each of the following.

1. $f' = f^2/x^2 + f/x$. (*Answer:* $f = -x/\log|kx|$)

2. $f' = f^2/x^2 + 2f/x$.

3. $f' = f^3/x^3$.

4. $f' = f^3/x^3 + f/x$.

5. $f' = f^3/x^3 + 2f/x$.

6. $f' = \cos(f/x) + f/x$.

7. $f^2 + 2xf - xf \cdot f' = 0$ R E. (*Answer:* $f = 2x \log|k/x|$)

8. $x^2f + f^3 - xf^2 - x^3f' = 0$ R E.

8.8   Clairaut's Differential Equation

We now present an example of a nonlinear first-order differential equation.

EXAMPLE 1.   Find a complete solution of $f = xf' + (f')^3$.

Solution: Let f be a function such that

$$f = xf' + (f')^3; \text{ then } f' = f' + xf^{(2)} + 3(f')^2 \cdot f^{(2)}$$

i.e., $f^{(2)} \cdot [x + 3(f')^2] = 0$ R E. Therefore $f^{(2)}(t)[t + 3(f'(t))^2] = 0$ if $t \in E$. If $f^{(2)} = 0$ R E, then $f' = k$ R E. Thus, from the given differential equation, $f = kx + k^3$. We have obtained a family of solutions of the given differential equation; however, this equation possesses still more solutions. Consider $x + 3(f')^2 = 0$ R E; using the given differential equation, we easily obtain the following two conditions:

(1) x R $E = -3(f')^2$ and $f = -3(f')^3 + (f')^3 = -2(f')^3$.

Notice that these solutions are expressed in terms of the parameter $f'(t)$; from (1) we see that our solutions of the given differential equation satisfy the parametric relation $-3x^2 * -2x^3$. We can write this relation explicitly: $f^2 = -4x^3/27$. To be specific, the functions $\{(a, b) | a < 0$ and $b = (-4a^3/27)^{1/2}\}$ and $\{(a, b) | a < 0$ and $b = -(-4a^3/27)^{1/2}\}$ are solutions of the given differential equation.

The differential equation of Example 1 is said to be *Clairaut's differential equation*; indeed, any differential equation of the form $f = xf' + g(f')$, where g is a given function with one argument, is called Clairaut's differential equation. A complete solution of such an equation can be obtained by the method of the example. We now present this method in its general setting. Consider the differential equation $f = xf' + g(f')$, and let f be any function which satisfies this equation. Then $f' = f' + xf^{(2)} + g'(f') \cdot f^{(2)}$; thus $f^{(2)} \cdot [x + g'(f')] = 0$ R E. If $f^{(2)} = 0$ R E, then $f' = k$ R E. Thus, from the given differential equation, $f = kx + g(k)$. This provides us with a family of solutions of the given differential equation, as is easily checked. The relation $x + g'(f') = 0$ R E provides us with additional solutions. Since x R E $= -g'(f')$, it follows from the given differential equation that $f = -f' \cdot g'(f') + g(f')$. Regarding $f'(t)$ as a parameter and observing that $-g'(f'(t)) = t$ whenever $t \in E$, we see that the parametric relation $-g' * (-xg' + g)$ provides us with more solutions.

The analysis presented here requires close study since the ideas involved are rather sophisticated. Clearly, the main problem centers around the particular solutions obtained from the parametric relation $-g' * (-xg' + g)$. We intend to show directly that each function contained in this parametric relation satisfies the given differential equation. The key to the situation is the hypothesis that the given function g and the particular solution f that we are after are such that

$$x + g'(f') = 0 \text{ R } E.$$

It is worth noting that this means that $-g'$ is an inverse of f' with respect to E. Here, E is the domain of the particular solution; i.e., E is a subset of the range of $-g'$. Assume that E has been chosen so that $[-g' * (-xg' + g)]$ R E is a function. Then the derivative of this function is $[-g' * x]$ R E [recall that $(u * v)' = u * v'/u'$]. We want to show that $-g'$ is an inverse of $-g' * x$ with respect to E, since this is our main hypothesis (otherwise, there is no point in proceeding). Clearly, $-g'(-g' * x) \subset x$; this demonstrates our point. Now, we can show directly that the function $[-g' * (-xg' + g)]$ R E is a particular solution of the given differential equation. Let $v = [-g' * (-xg' + g)]$ R E; then, $v' = -g' * x$. Observe that $(-g' * x) \circ -g' \subset x$, and so $-g' * x$ is an inverse of $-g'$; i.e. v' is an inverse of $-g'$. Hence

$$\begin{aligned}
v &= [-g' * (-xg' + g)] \text{ R } E \\
&= [(-xg' + g) \circ (-g')^{-1}] \text{ R } E \\
&= (-xg' + g) \circ v' \text{ R } E \\
&= -v' \cdot g'(v') + g(v') \text{ R } E \\
&= -xv' + g(v').
\end{aligned}$$

This v is a particular solution of the given differential equation.

EXAMPLE 2. Solve $f = xf' + \cos(f')$.

Solution: Clearly, $f = kx + \cos k$ is a family of solutions, i.e.; $kx + \cos k$ is a particular solution whenever $k \in R$. Moreover, the parametric relation $\sin * (x \sin + \cos)$ provides us with more solutions. For example, let $B = [-\pi/2, \pi/2]$; then $\sin R B * (x \sin + \cos)$ is a solution. We point out that this function is $(x \sin + \cos) \circ \arcsin$, namely $x \arcsin + \cos(\arcsin)$. Let us show that x arcsin $+ \cos(\arcsin)$ is a particular solution of the given differential equation. Clearly, $[x \arcsin + \cos(\arcsin)]' = \arcsin$; so

$$x[x \arcsin + \cos(\arcsin)]' + \cos \circ [x \arcsin + \cos(\arcsin)]' = x \arcsin + \cos(\arcsin).$$

Finally, we point out that the differential equations of the type considered in this section do not admit of a *unique-existence* theorem. Let us show that there are two particular solutions of the differential equation of Example 2 which contain $(0, 1)$. Now, the functions x arcsin $+ \cos(\arcsin)$ and I are both solutions of this differential equation. But $(0, 1) \in x$ arcsin $+ \cos(\arcsin)$, and $(0, 1) \in I$. This establishes our point.

E X E R C I S E S

Solve the following differential equations.

1. $f = xf' - 2(f')^2$.
2. $f = xf' + \exp(f')$.
3. $f = xf' + \sin(f')$.
4. $f = xf' + f' - (f')^2$.
5. Given that g and h are functions with one argument such that $g \cdot h = 0$ R E, does it follow that $g = 0$ R E or $h = 0$ R E?
6. Solve $2f' + 3(f')^2 - f = 0$ R E. (*Hint:* Regard f' as the unknown function and eliminate f from the given differential equation by differentiating. Once f' is found, it is easy to obtain f. It may be helpful to denote f' by "p".)
7. Solve $2xf' + f' - f = 0$ R E.

Chapter 9

Second-Order Differential Equations

9.1 Introduction

By a second-order differential equation we mean any equation of the form $F(x, f, f', f^{(2)}) = 0$ R E, where F is a given function with four arguments, and f is an unknown function. The problem is to find a function f which satisfies the equation.

For example,

(1) $$f^{(2)} + 6x = 0 \text{ R } E$$

is a second-order differential equation; here, $F = W + 6X$, where $W = \{(a, b, c, d, d) \mid (a, b, c, d) \in R_4\}$. This differential equation is easy to solve; antidifferentiating, we obtain

(2) $$f' + 3x^2 = k_1,$$

(3) $$f + x^3 = k_1 x + k_2,$$

where $k_1 \in R$ and $k_2 \in R$. So $f = -x^3 + k_1 x + k_2$; this means that $-x^3 + k_1 x + k_2$ is a solution of the given differential equation whenever k_1 and k_2 are real numbers. Let us find a solution of (1), say f, such that $f(1) = 2$ and $f'(1) = 5$. From (3), $f(1) + 1 = k_1 + k_2$, i.e., $k_1 + k_2 = 3$; and from (2), $f'(1) + 3 = k_1$, i.e., $k_1 = 8$. So $k_2 = -5$; thus the required function is $-x^3 + 8x - 5$, i.e., $f = -x^3 + 8x - 5$.

It is convenient to introduce the notion of a *neighborhood* of a real number.

> **DEFINITION 9.1.1.** Let $a \in R$ and let $\mathcal{N}$ be any open interval; then $\mathcal{N}$ is said to be a neighborhood of a iff $a \in \mathcal{N}$.

For example, (3, 7) is a neighborhood of 6, whereas (3, 7) is not a neighborhood of 7.

We now state without proof an important *unique-existence* theorem which guarantees the existence of a *unique* function which satisfies a given differential equation together with given boundary conditions.

> **THEOREM 9.1.1.** Let H be a function with three arguments such that H, H_2, and H_3 are continuous on D, where $D \subset R_3$, and let $(a, b, c) \in D$. Then there is a unique function f such that $f^{(2)} = H(x, f, f')$, $f(a) = b$, $f'(a) = c$, and $\mathcal{D}_f$ is a neighborhood of a.

289

EXAMPLE 1.   Find a complete solution of $f^{(2)} = f$.

Solution: Clearly, exp and exp($-x$) are particular solutions of the given differential equation; indeed, $k_1 \exp + k_2 \exp(-x)$ is a particular solution whenever $k_1 \in R$ and $k_2 \in R$. We want to prove that the given differential equation has no other solution. To this purpose we use Theorem 9.1.1. Here $H = Y$ since $Y(x, f, f') = f$. Now, $Y_2 = 1$ and $Y_3 = 0$; so Y, Y_2, and Y_3 are continuous on R_3. Therefore, given a, b, and c, there is exactly one function, say g, such that $g^{(2)} = g$, $g(a) = b$, and $g'(a) = c$. Let us choose k_1 and k_2 so that $g = k_1 \exp + k_2 \exp(-x)$. First, we need g'; $g' = k_1 \exp - k_2 \exp(-x)$. Thus

$$b = k_1 e^a + k_2 e^{-a} \quad \text{and} \quad c = k_1 e^a - k_2 e^{-a}.$$

Hence $k_1 = (b + c)/2e^a$ and $k_2 = (b - c)e^a/2$. We conclude that the family of solutions of the differential equation $f^{(2)} = f$ is given by $\{k_1 \exp + k_2 \exp(-x) \mid k_1 \in R$ and $k_2 \in R\}$. Thus $f = k_1 \exp + k_2 \exp(-x)$ provides us with a complete solution of the given differential equation.

The purpose of Example 1 is to bring out the role of Theorem 9.1.1 in characterizing the solutions of a differential equation of the type mentioned in the theorem. It might be helpful to read the example again from this point of view.

9.2   Reducible Second-Order Differential Equations

It is sometimes possible to reduce a given second-order differential equation to a first-order differential equation; if so, then we can use the technique of Chapter 8 in solving the given differential equation.

EXAMPLE 1.   Find a complete solution of $f^{(2)} = x + f'$.

Solution: Here, $f^{(2)} = H(x, f, f')$, where $H = X + Z$. Notice that $H_2 = 0$; i.e., f itself does not occur in the given differential equation. We can use this fact to good advantage. The idea is to solve the given differential equation for f' rather than for f. This means that we shall regard f' as the unknown function; from this point of view, the given differential equation has order one. To be systematic, let $p = f'$; then $p' = f^{(2)}$ and the given differential equation is $p' = x + p$. This is easy to solve by separating the variables: we obtain $p' - p = x$ R E. Noting that $\exp(-x)$ is an integrating factor, we readily find that $p = -x - 1 + k_1 \exp$. Thus $f' = -x - 1 + k_1 \exp$. It is now an easy matter to obtain f: $f \equiv \int (-x - 1 + k_1 \exp)$; so $f = -x^2/2 - x + k_1 \exp + k_2$. We have found a complete solution of the given differential equation. We note that our complete solution involves two parameters, k_1 and k_2. In general, the number of parameters in a complete solution is the *order* of the differential equation.

Any second-order differential equation which has the form $f^{(2)} = F(x, f')$ can be solved by setting $p = f'$ and solving the first-order differential equation $p' = F(x, p)$, where p is the unknown function. Once a complete solution of this differential equation has been found, it is easy to obtain a complete solution of the given differential equation. We emphasize that the differential equation $f^{(2)} = F(x, f')$ is a first-order differential equation in the unknown function f'.

Next, consider the second-order differential equation $f^{(2)} = H(f, f')$; notice that x does not appear on the right-hand side. Again, let $p = f'$. Suppose that the unknown function f possesses an inverse with respect to R, say f^*; then $f^*(f) = x$ and $p = p(x) = p(f^*(f)) = P(f)$, where $P = p(f^*)$. In short, we assume that $f' = P(f)$; i.e., we assume that the derivative of f is a function of f. Then

$$f^{(2)} = [P(f)]' = [P'(f)] \cdot f' = P'(f) \cdot P(f).$$

So $P'(f) \cdot P(f) = H(f, P(f))$. But if P is a function such that

(1) $$P' \cdot P = H(x, P),$$

then $[P' \cdot P](f) = [H(x, P)](f)$, i.e., $P'(f) \cdot P(f) = H(f, P(f))$. This means that the function f satisfies the given differential equation. Accordingly, we concentrate on solving (1); note that this is a differential equation of the first order in the unknown function P. If we can solve (1), then we easily obtain $P(f)$, which is f'. Once we know f', it is easy to find f.
The following example may clarify the method.

EXAMPLE 2. Find a complete solution of $f^{(2)} = f \cdot f'$.
Solution: Observe that the given differential equation has the form $f^{(2)} = H(f, f')$; here, $H = X \cdot Y$. We try the procedure outlined above. Let $f' = P(f)$; then $f^{(2)} = P'(f) \cdot P(f)$. Thus the given differential equation is $P'(f) \cdot P(f) = f \cdot P(f)$. We now solve the first-order differential equation $P' \cdot P = xP$ for the unknown function P. Here $P \cdot [P' - x] = 0$, and so $P = 0$ or $P' = x$ are obvious choices. From the condition $P' = x$ we obtain $P = x^2/2 + c_1$. Hence $P(f) = f^2/2 + c_1$, i.e., $f' = f^2/2 + c_1$. Thus

$$2f'/(f^2 + 2c_1) = 1 \qquad \text{and} \qquad x \equiv A \frac{2f'}{f^2 + 2c_1} \equiv \frac{2}{k_1} \arctan(f/k_1),$$

where $k_1{}^2 = 2c_1$. Therefore $x = (2/k_1) \arctan(f/k_1) + k_2$. From the condition $P = 0$, we obtain $P(f) = 0$, and so $f' = 0$ and $f = k$. We conclude that the solutions of the given differential equation are all constant functions together with all functions f such that $x = (2/k_1)\arctan(f/k_1) + k_2$.

E X E R C I S E S

Find a complete solution of each of the following.

1. $f^{(2)} = x^2 + f'$.   (*Answer:* $f = k_1 \exp - x^3/3 - x^2 - 2x + k_2$)
2. $f^{(2)} = x - f'/x$.   (*Answer:* $f = k_1 \log|x| + x^3/9 + k_2$)
3. $f^{(2)} = x - 2xf'$.   (*Answer:* $f = k_1 + x/2 + k_2 \int_0^x \exp(-x^2)$)
4. $xf^{(2)} + f' = 4x$ R E.   (*Answer:* $f = x^2 + k_1 \log|x| + k_2$)
5. $xf^{(2)} = (f')^3 + f'$.   (*Answer:* $k_1(x^2 + f^2) = 1 + k_2 f$)
6. $f^{(2)} + f \cdot f^{(2)} = (f')^2$. (*Answer:* $f = -1 + k_1 \exp$, or $f = k$)

7. $f^{(2)} = f'$.

8. $f^{(2)} = (f')^2$.

9. $f \cdot f^{(2)} + (f')^2 + 1 = 0$ R E.

10. $f^{(2)} = 3f \cdot (f')^3$.

11. $f^{(2)} = (f')^3 \cdot \exp(f)$.

12. $f^{(2)} = (f')^3 \cdot \cos(f)$.

(*Answer:* $f = k_1 + k_2 \exp$)

(*Answer:* $\exp(-f) = k_1 + k_2 x$)

(*Answer:* $f^2 = k_1{}^2 - (x - k_2)^2$)

(*Answer:* $f^3 + k_1 f = k_2 - 2x$)

(*Answer:* $k_1 f + \exp(f) = k_2 - x$)

(*Answer:* $k_1 f - \cos(f) = k_2 - x$)

9.3   An Existence Theorem for Linear Differential Equations; the Wronskian

By a *linear* differential equation of the second order we mean any differential equation of the form

(I) $$p_0 \cdot f^{(2)} + p_1 \cdot f' + p_2 \cdot f = p_3,$$

where p_0, p_1, p_2, and p_3 are given functions with one argument which are continuous on an interval $\mathscr{I}$.

In Section 9.4 we shall demonstrate that we can obtain a complete solution of (I) if we have a particular solution of the associated differential equation

(II) $$p_0 \cdot f^{(2)} + p_1 \cdot f' + p_2 \cdot f = 0 \text{ R } \mathscr{I}.$$

which is called the *reduced* equation of (I), or a *homogeneous* differential equation (note that the term *homogeneous* is not used here in the sense of Section 8.7).

Assuming that p_0 has no zeros in $\mathscr{I}$, we can normalize (II) by dividing through p_0. Thus we obtain

(III) $$f^{(2)} + p \cdot f' + q \cdot f = 0 \text{ R } \mathscr{I},$$

where $p = p_1/p_0$ and $q = p_2/p_0$.

Under certain conditions on the functions p and q, (III) possesses a solution. To express the required conditions on the coefficients, we need the notion of an *analytic* function.

> **DEFINITION 9.3.1.** A function, say g, is said to be *analytic in an interval* $\mathscr{I}$ iff corresponding to each member of $\mathscr{I}$, say a, there is a power series in $x - a$, say $\sum a_{n-1}(x - a)^{n-1}$, and a neighborhood of a, say $\mathscr{N}$, such that $g(t) = \sum a_{n-1}(t - a)^{n-1}$ whenever $t \in \mathscr{N}$.

For example, g is analytic in $\mathscr{I}$ if there are three members of $\mathscr{I}$, say a, b, and c, corresponding neighborhoods $\mathscr{N}_a$, $\mathscr{N}_b$, $\mathscr{N}_c$, and corresponding power series in $x - a$, $x - b$, $x - c$, say $\sum a_{n-1}(x - a)^{n-1}$, $\sum b_{n-1}(x - b)^{n-1}$, $\sum c_{n-1}(x - c)^{n-1}$, such that $\mathscr{I} \subset \mathscr{N}_a \cup \mathscr{N}_b \cup \mathscr{N}_c$ and

$$g(t) = \begin{cases} \sum a_{n-1}(t - a)^{n-1} & \text{if } t \in \mathscr{N}_a \\ \sum b_{n-1}(t - b)^{n-1} & \text{if } t \in \mathscr{N}_b \\ \sum c_{n-1}(t - c)^{n-1} & \text{if } t \in \mathscr{N}_c. \end{cases}$$

We can now state our *unique-existence* theorem.

THEOREM 9.3.1.   Let a, a_0, and a_1 be any real numbers, and let p and q be any functions with one argument which are analytic in $\mathcal{N}$, a neighborhood of a; then there is a unique function f such that $f^{(2)} + p \cdot f' + q \cdot f = 0$ R $\mathcal{N}$, $f(a) = a_0$, $f'(a) = a_1$, and $\mathcal{D}_f = \mathcal{N}$.

Our goal is to characterize a complete solution of (III); in this connection we need the notion of the *Wronskian* of two functions.

DEFINITION 9.3.2.   Let g and h be any functions; then $g \cdot h' - h \cdot g'$ is said to be the Wronskian of g and h and is denoted by " $W(g, h)$ ".

For example, $W(x^2, \sin) = x^2 \cos - 2x \sin$, $W(5x^3, \log) = 5x^2 - 15x^2 \log$, $W(\sin, \phi) = \sin \cdot \phi' - \phi \cdot \cos = \phi$, and $W(1, f) = f'$.

THEOREM 9.3.2.   Let g and h be any solutions of (III); then $W(g, h) = B \exp\left(-\int_b^x p\right)$, where $B = [g \cdot h' - h \cdot g'](b)$ and $b \in \mathcal{D}_p$.

Proof: Now, $W(g, h) = g \cdot h' - h \cdot g'$; so $[W(g, h)]' = g \cdot h^{(2)} - h \cdot g^{(2)}$. But $g^{(2)} + pg' + q \cdot g = 0$ R $\mathcal{I}$ and $h^{(2)} + p \cdot h' + q \cdot h = 0$ R $\mathcal{I}$; so $[W(g, h)]' = -g \cdot [p \cdot h' + q \cdot h] + h \cdot [p \cdot g' + q \cdot g] = -p \cdot g \cdot h' + p \cdot h \cdot g' = -p \cdot W(g, h)$. Thus $[W(g, h)]'/W(g, h) = -p$; so $\log|W(g, h)| \equiv$ $\bigwedge$ $- p$; thus $W(g, h) = k \exp\left(\int_b^x - p\right)$, where $k = [W(g, h)](b)$.

COROLLARY 9.3.1.   Let g and h be any solutions of (III); then the members of the range of $W(g, h)$ have the same algebraic sign.

Proof: Let $b \in \mathcal{D}_{W(g,h)}$; then each member of the range of $W(g, h)$ has the algebraic sign of $[W(g, h)](b)$ since $\mathcal{R}_{\exp} = \{t \mid t > 0\}$.

We also need the concepts of *linearly dependent functions* and *linearly independent functions*.

DEFINITION 9.3.3.   The functions $g_1, g_2, \cdots, g_n$ are said to be *linearly dependent* on $\mathcal{I}$ iff there are real numbers not all zero, say $k_1, k_2, \cdots, k_n$, such that $k_1 g_1 + k_2 g_2 + \cdots + k_n g_n$ R $\mathcal{I} = 0$ R $\mathcal{I}$.

DEFINITION 9.3.4.   The functions $g_1, g_2, \cdots, g_n$ are said to be *linearly independent* on $\mathcal{I}$ iff $g_1, g_2, \cdots, g_n$ are *not* linearly dependent on $\mathcal{I}$.

For example, cosh, exp, and $\exp(-x)$ are linearly dependent on R since $2 \cosh - \exp - \exp(-x) = 0$. Note that x and cos are linearly independent on R. To see this, suppose that $k_1 x + k_2 \cos = 0$; then $k_2 = 0$ (evaluate both sides of the equation at 0); thus $k_1 x = 0$, and so $k_1 = 0$ (evaluate both sides of this equation at 1). As another example, note that the functions x and $|x|$ are linearly dependent on $\{t \mid t \geq 0\}$ and are linearly dependent on $\{t \mid t < 0\}$; yet these functions are linearly independent on R.

THEOREM 9.3.3. Let g and h be linearly dependent on $\mathscr{I}$, where $\mathscr{I} = \mathscr{D}_{g'} \cap \mathscr{D}_{h'}$; then $W(g, h) = 0$ R $\mathscr{I}$.

Proof: Since g and h are linearly dependent on $\mathscr{I}$, it follows that each of g R $\mathscr{I}$ and h R $\mathscr{I}$ is a multiple of the other. In particular, h R $\mathscr{I} = kg$ R $\mathscr{I}$. Thus h' R $\mathscr{I} = kg'$ R $\mathscr{I}$; so $W(g, h) = g \cdot h' - h \cdot g' = kg \cdot g' - kg \cdot g'$ R $\mathscr{I} = 0$ R $\mathscr{I}$.

We now establish the converse of Theorem 9.3.3.

THEOREM 9.3.4. Let $\mathscr{D}_{g'} = \mathscr{D}_g = \mathscr{D}_{h'} = \mathscr{D}_h = \mathscr{I}$, where $\mathscr{I}$ is an interval, and let $W(g, h) = 0$ R $\mathscr{I}$; then g and h are linearly dependent on $\mathscr{I}$.

Proof: If $W(g, h) = 0$ R $\mathscr{I}$, then $g \cdot h' = h \cdot g'$. Thus $g'/g = h'/h$; so $\log|g| = \log|kh|$, where $k \neq 0$. Let $\log|g| = v$; then $g = \exp v$ or $g = -\exp v$, and $kh = \exp v$ or $kh = -\exp v$. Hence $g = kh$ or $g = -kh$. In either case g and h are linearly dependent on $\mathscr{I}$.

The preceding theorems provide us with an acid test for the linear dependence of particular solutions of (III).

COROLLARY 9.3.2. Let g and h be solutions of (III) such that $\mathscr{D}_{g'} = \mathscr{D}_g = \mathscr{D}_{h'} = \mathscr{D}_h = \mathscr{I}$, where $\mathscr{I}$ is an interval; then g and h are linearly dependent on $\mathscr{I}$ iff $W(g, h) = 0$ R $\mathscr{I}$.

Of course, this corollary provides us with a test for the linear independence of two solutions of (III). The fact is that a complete solution of (III) can be expressed in terms of any two linearly independent solutions of (III).

THEOREM 9.3.5. Let g_1 and g_2 be any linearly independent solutions of (III) such that $\mathscr{D}_{g_1'} = \mathscr{D}_{g_1} = \mathscr{D}_{g_2'} = \mathscr{D}_{g_2} = \mathscr{I}$, where $\mathscr{I}$ is an interval. Then $f = k_1 g_1 + k_2 g_2$ is a complete solution of (III).

Proof: It is easy to see that each linear combination of g_1 and g_2 is a solution of (III). We must show that each solution of (III) is a linear combination of g_1 and g_2. Let h be a solution of (III) and let $a \in \mathscr{D}_h \cap \mathscr{D}_{h'}$; let $h(a) = b$ and let $h'(a) = c$. We want to choose real numbers k_1 and k_2 so that

$$k_1 g_1(a) + k_2 g_2(a) = h(a) \quad \text{and} \quad k_1 g_1'(a) + k_2 g_2'(a) = h'(a).$$

But $W(g_1, g_2) \neq 0$ R $\mathscr{I}$; therefore

$$\begin{vmatrix} g_1(a) & g_2(a) \\ g_1'(a) & g_2'(a) \end{vmatrix} \neq 0;$$

so k_1 and k_2 exist as required. Thus $k_1 g_1 + k_2 g_2$ is a solution of (III) such that $[k_1 g_1 + k_2 g_2](a) = h(a)$ and $[k_1 g_1' + k_2 g_2'](a) = h'(a)$. Therefore, by Theorem 9.3.1, $k_1 g_1 + k_2 g_2 = h$. This completes our proof.

EXERCISES

1. Find a complete solution of each of the following.
   a. $f^{(2)} = \sec^2$. *(Answer: $f = k_1 + k_2 x + \log|\sec|$)*
   b. $f^{(2)} = x\exp$. *(Answer: $f = (x - 2)\exp + k_1 x + k_2$)*
   c. $f^{(2)} = x\sin$. *(Answer: $f = -x\sin - 2\cos + k_1 x + k_2$)*

2. Find a function, say f, such that $f^{(2)} = x^2\exp$, $f(0) = 2$, and $f'(0) = 3$.
   (Answer: $f = (x^2 - 4x + 6)\exp + x - 4$)

3. Find a function, say f, such that $f^{(2)} = x^2\exp$, $f(0) = 2$, and $f'(1) = e$.
   (Answer: $f = (x^2 - 4x + 6)\exp - 4$)

4. By considering $W(x, x^2)$, prove that x and x^2 are linearly independent on R.

5. Let n be any natural number. Prove that the functions $1, x, x^2, \cdots, x^n$ are linearly independent on R. (*Hint:* Note that if a is a zero of a polyonmial function, then $a \, x - $ is a factor of the polynomial.)

6. Show that the functions $\sinh$, $\exp$, and $\exp(-x)$ are linearly dependent on R.

7. Show that $\sin(2\arctan)$ and $x/(1 + x^2)$ are linearly dependent on R.

8. Let $f_1, f_2, \cdots, f_n$ be linearly dependent on $\mathscr{I}$, and let $\mathscr{I} \subset \mathscr{D}_{f_{n+1}}$. Prove that $f_1, f_2, \cdots, f_n, f_{n+1}$ are linearly dependent on $\mathscr{I}$. Prove that these functions are linearly independent on $\mathscr{I}$ if $\mathscr{I}$ is not a subset of $\mathscr{D}_{f_{n+1}}$.

9. a. If $\mathscr{D}_f \cap \mathscr{D}_g = \varnothing$, are f and g linearly independent on R? *(Answer: Yes)*
   b. If $\mathscr{I}$ is not a subset of $\mathscr{D}_f \cap \mathscr{D}_g$, are f and g linearly independent on $\mathscr{I}$?
   (Answer: Yes)

10. Given that g is a solution of (III) and that $W(g, h) = 0$ R $\mathscr{D}_g$, prove that h is a particular solution of (III).

9.4 Linear Differential Equations of the Second Order; Variation of Parameter

In this section we shall consider the problem of finding a complete solution of

(I) $$p_0 \cdot f^{(2)} + p_1 \cdot f' + p_2 \cdot f = p_3,$$

where p_0, p_1, p_2, and p_3 are given functions with one argument such that p_1/p_0 and p_2/p_0 are analytic in an interval $\mathscr{I}$.

Our method is based on the following two steps.

Step 1:   Find a complete solution of the *reduced* equation

(II) $$p_0 \cdot f^{(2)} + p_1 \cdot f' + p_2 \cdot f = 0 \text{ R } \mathscr{I}.$$

Step 2:   Find a particular solution of (I).

Imagine that steps 1 and 2 have been carried out; we shall show that this leads us to a complete solution of (I). By Theorem 9.3.5, there are functions g_1 and g_2 such that $f = k_1 g_1 + k_2 g_2$ is a complete solution of the reduced equation (II). Let g_3 be a particular solution of (I). We claim that $f = k_1 g_1 + k_2 g_2 + g_3$ is a complete solution of (I). To see this, we note that

$$p_0 \cdot (k_1 g_1 + k_2 g_2 + g_3)^{(2)} + p_1 \cdot (k_1 g_1 + k_2 g_2 + g_3)' + p_2 \cdot (k_1 g_1 + k_2 g_2 + g_3)$$
$$= p_0 \cdot (k_1 g_1^{(2)} + k_2 g_2^{(2)}) + p_1 \cdot (k_1 g_1' + k_2 g_2') + p_2 \cdot (k_1 g_1 + k_2 g_2)$$
$$+ (p_0 \cdot g_3^{(2)} + p_1 \cdot g_3' + p_2 \cdot g_3)$$
$$= p_3 .$$

Thus each member of our family is a particular solution of (I). It remains to show that if h is a particular solution of (I), then there exist real numbers k_1 and k_2 such that $h = k_1 g_1 + k_2 g_2 + g_3$. It is a simple matter to demonstrate this by considering the function $h - g_3$ and applying our unique-existence theorem, Theorem 9.3.1. We have now proved that we obtain a complete solution of (I) by combining a particular solution of (I) with a complete solution of the reduced equation (II).

It turns out that we can obtain a complete solution of (I) if we can find just one particular solution of (II); in other words, if we know a particular solution of (II), then we can work out a complete solution of (II) and we can work out a particular solution of (I). We have already observed in Section 9.3 that we can obtain a complete solution of (II) if we have two linearly independent solutions of (II). We need to establish that given a particular solution of (II), say g, we can compute another solution of (II), say h, such that g and h are linearly independent. We shall apply the idea of Section 8.6, i.e., variation of parameter. Since g is a solution of (II), so is kg whenever $k \in R$. We replace the parameter k by a function, say v; we want to determine v so that $v \cdot g$ is a solution of (II) and $v' \neq 0$. Now, $(v \cdot g)' = v' \cdot g + v \cdot g'$, and $(v \cdot g)^{(2)} = v^{(2)} \cdot g + 2v' \cdot g' + v \cdot g^{(2)}$. Therefore, if $v \cdot g$ is a solution of (II), then

$$p_0 \cdot [v^{(2)} \cdot g + 2v' \cdot g' + v \cdot g^{(2)}] + p_1 \cdot [v' \cdot g + v \cdot g'] + p_2 \cdot v \cdot g = 0 \ \text{R} \ \mathscr{I},$$

i.e., $v \cdot [p_0 \cdot g^{(2)} + p_1 \cdot g' + p_2 \cdot g] + p_0 \cdot [v^{(2)} \cdot g + 2v' \cdot g'] + p_1 \cdot v' \cdot g = 0 \ \text{R} \ \mathscr{I}$; hence

$$p_0 \cdot g \cdot v^{(2)} + v' \cdot [2p_0 \cdot g' + p_1 \cdot g] = 0 \ \text{R} \ \mathscr{I};$$

thus $\qquad\qquad\qquad v^{(2)}/v' = -2g'/g - p_1/p_0;$

so $\qquad\qquad\qquad \log|v'| \equiv -2 \log |g| - \int p_1/p_0.$

Now that we have v', it is an easy step to obtain v. Since our argument is reversible, i.e., since we can read *up* through the derivation as well as *down*, it follows that the function $v \cdot g$ is a solution of (II). To decide whether $v \cdot g$ and g are linearly independent, we have only to examine the Wronskian of these functions: we note that $W(g, v \cdot g) = v' \cdot g^2$.

We have said that one solution of (II) leads us to a complete solution of (I). It turns out that the technique used above provides us with a particular solution of (I), in terms of a solution of (II). To see this, let g be a particular solution of (II), and suppose that u is a function such that $u \cdot g$ is a particular solution of (I). Then

$$p_0 \cdot [u^{(2)} \cdot g + 2u' \cdot g' + u \cdot g^{(2)}] + p_1 \cdot [u' \cdot g + u \cdot g'] + p_2 \cdot u \cdot g = p_3;$$

so $$u \cdot [p_0 \cdot g^{(2)} + p_1 \cdot g' + p_2 \cdot g] + p_0 \cdot u^{(2)} \cdot g + 2p_0 \cdot u' \cdot g' + p_1 \cdot u' \cdot g = p_3;$$

thus $$p_0 \cdot g \cdot u^{(2)} + [2p_0 \cdot g' + p_1 \cdot g] \cdot u' = p_3;$$

so $$u^{(2)} + [2g'/g + p_1/p_0] \cdot u' = p_3/(p_0 \cdot g).$$

Note that this is a first-order differential equation in the unknown function u'; thus we can easily solve for u'. It is an easy step to obtain u once we have u'. Since the above argument is reversible, we conclude that the function $u \cdot g$ is a particular solution of (I). Of course, once we have a complete solution of (II) and a particular solution of (I), we can write down a complete solution of (I).

The following example illustrates the method.

EXAMPLE 1.   Find a complete solution of $xf^{(2)} + f' - 4f/x = 2x$ R E.

Solution: First, we observe that x^2 is a particular solution of the reduced equation $xf^{(2)} + f' - 4f/x = 0$ R E. We need another solution of the reduced equation which is linearly independent of x^2. Let v be a function such that $v \cdot x^2$ is a solution of the reduced equation. Then

$$x[v^{(2)} \cdot x^2 + 4xv' + 2v] + 2xv + x^2v' - 4xv = 0 \text{ R E};$$

i.e., $x^3v^{(2)} + v' \cdot (4x^2 + x^2) = 0$ R E; so $v^{(2)}/v' = -5/x$; thus $\log|v'| \equiv -5 \log|x|$; hence $v' = k_1x^{-5}$, and $v = -k_1x^{-4}/4 + k_2$. It is to our advantage to choose our v as simple as possible; we take $v = -x^{-4}/4$. We now see that $-x^{-2}/4$ is a solution of our reduced equation. Clearly, the functions x^2 and $-x^{-2}/4$ are linearly independent [if this is not obvious, then examine $W(x^2, -x^{-2}/4)$]. Thus $f = k_1x^2 + k_2x^{-2}$ is a complete solution of $xf^{(2)} + f' - 4f/x = 0$ R E. Next, we must determine a particular solution of the given differential equation. Let u be a function such that $u \cdot x^2$ is a solution of $xf^{(2)} + f' - 4f/x = 2x$ R E. Then $x[u^{(2)} \cdot x^2 + 4x \cdot u' + 2u] + 2u \cdot x + x^2 \cdot u' - 4u \cdot x = 2x$ R E, i.e., $x^3u^{(2)} + 5x^2u' = 2x$ R E; thus $u^{(2)} + 5u'/x = 2x^{-2}$. This is a linear differential equation of the first order in u'. Here, $\exp\left(\int 5/x\right)$ is an integrating factor; i.e., x^5 is an integrating factor. We obtain $(5x^4u' - 2x^3) + x^5u^{(2)} = 0$ R E, so $x^5u' - x^4/2 = 0$ R E; thus $u' = 1/(2x)$. Therefore $u \equiv (1/2)\log|x|$. Hence $(1/2)x^2 \log|x|$ is a particular solution of $xf^{(2)} + f' - 4f/x = 2x$ R E. We conclude that

$$f = k_1x^2 + k_2x^{-2} + (1/2)x^2 \log|x|$$

is a complete solution of the given differential equation.

There is a convenient method of working out a particular solution of our differential equation $p_0 \cdot f^{(2)} + p_1 \cdot f' + p_2 \cdot f = p_3$, once we have a complete solution of the reduced equation, say $f = k_1g + k_2h$, where g and h are linearly independent. Let u and v be functions with one argument such that $u \cdot g + v \cdot h$ is a solution of (I). Now, $(u \cdot g + v \cdot h)' = u' \cdot g + u \cdot g' + v' \cdot h + v \cdot h'$; let us assume that

(1) $$u' \cdot g + v' \cdot h = 0 \text{ R } E.$$

Then $(u \cdot g + v \cdot h)' = u \cdot g' + v \cdot h'$; hence $[u \cdot g + v \cdot h]^{(2)} = u \cdot g^{(2)} + u' \cdot g' + v \cdot h^{(2)} + v' \cdot h'$. Thus, from (I),

$$p_0 \cdot [u \cdot g^{(2)} + u' \cdot g' + v \cdot h^{(2)} + v' \cdot h'] + p_1 \cdot [u \cdot g' + v \cdot h'] + p_2 \cdot [u \cdot g + v \cdot h] = p_3,$$

i.e., $u \cdot [p_0 \cdot g^{(2)} + p_1 \cdot g' + p_2 \cdot g]$

$$+ v \cdot [p_0 \cdot h^{(2)} + p_1 \cdot h' + p_2 \cdot h] + p_0 \cdot [u' \cdot g' + v' \cdot h'] = p_3.$$

Thus $u' \cdot g' + v' \cdot h' = p_3/p_0$. Summarizing, we have shown that if the function $u \cdot g + v \cdot h$ is a solution of (I) such that $u' \cdot g + v' \cdot h = 0$ R E, then $u' \cdot g' + v' \cdot h' = p_3/p_0$. Moreover, it is clear from the above argument that the converse also holds; i.e., the function $u \cdot g + v \cdot h$ is a solution of (I) if $u' \cdot g + v' \cdot h = 0$ R E and if $u' \cdot g' + v' \cdot h' = p_3/p_0$. We are faced with a system of two equations in two unknowns; the unknowns are u' and v'. These equations are easy to solve. Since g and h are linearly independent, $W(g, h) \neq 0$; therefore, by Cramer's Rule,

$$u' = \frac{\begin{vmatrix} 0 & h \\ p_3/p_0 & h' \end{vmatrix}}{\begin{vmatrix} g & h \\ g' & h' \end{vmatrix}} \quad \text{and} \quad v' = \frac{\begin{vmatrix} g & 0 \\ g' & p_3/p_0 \end{vmatrix}}{\begin{vmatrix} g & h \\ g' & h' \end{vmatrix}}.$$

So $u' = -h \cdot p_3/(p_0 \cdot [g \cdot h' - g' \cdot h])$ and $v' = g \cdot p_3/(p_0 \cdot [g \cdot h' - g' \cdot h])$. Knowing u' and v', it is easy to obtain u and v. So we have a particular solution of (I), namely $u \cdot g + v \cdot h$. Using this method, we now rework Example 1.

EXAMPLE 2.   Find a complete solution of $xf^{(2)} + f' - 4f/x = 2x$ R E.

Solution: As in the solution of Example 1, we find that $f = k_1 x^2 + k_2 x^{-2}$ is a complete solution of the reduced equation. We can now compute a particular solution of the given differential equation. Consider $u \cdot x^2 + v \cdot x^{-2}$; now, $(u \cdot x^2 + v \cdot x^{-2})' = 2xu - 2x^{-3} \cdot v$ provided that $x^2 u' + x^{-2} \cdot v' = 0$ R E. Under this condition, $[u \cdot x^2 + v \cdot x^{-2}]^{(2)} = 2u + 2xu' + 6x^{-4} \cdot v - 2x^{-3} \cdot v'$. Thus $u \cdot x^2 + v \cdot x^{-2}$ is a particular solution of $xf^{(2)} + f' - 4f/x = 2x$ R E provided that $x^2 u' + x^{-2} \cdot v' = 0$ R E and $x[2u + 2xu' + 6x^{-4} \cdot v - 2x^{-3} \cdot v'] + [2xu - 2x^{-3} \cdot v] - 4u \cdot x - 4v \cdot x^{-3} = 2x$ R E. Simplifying, we find that these conditions become $x^2 u' + x^{-2} \cdot v' = 0$ R E and $xu' - x^{-3} \cdot v' = 1$ R E. We now solve for u' and v':

$$u' = \begin{vmatrix} 0 & x^{-2} \\ 1 & -x^{-3} \end{vmatrix} / W \quad \text{and} \quad v' = \begin{vmatrix} x^2 & 0 \\ x & 1 \end{vmatrix} / W,$$

where

$$W = \begin{vmatrix} x^2 & x^{-2} \\ x & -x^{-3} \end{vmatrix} = -1/x - 1/x = -2/x.$$

Hence $u' = 1/2x$ and $v' = -x^3/2$. Thus $u = (1/2) \log|x|$ and $v = -x^4/8$. We conclude that $(x^2/2) \log|x| - x^2/8$ is a particular solution of the given differential equation. Checking, we see that this is correct. Thus $f = k_1x^2 + k_2x^{-2} + (x^2/2) \log|x|$ is a complete solution of the given differential equation.

EXERCISES

1. a. Find a complete solution of $x^2f^{(2)} - 2xf' + 2f = 0$ R E, given that x is a particular solution of this differential equation.   *(Answer: $f = k_1x + k_2x^2$)*
  b. Find a particular solution of $x^2f^{(2)} - 2xf' + 2f = x^2$ R E.   *(Answer: $x^2 \log|x| - x^2$)*
  c. Find a complete solution of $x^2f^{(2)} - 2xf' + 2f = x^2$ R E.
          (Answer: $f = k_1x + k_2x^2 + x^2(-1 + \log|x|))$
2. a. Find a complete solution of $x^2f^{(2)} - xf' + f = 0$ R E, given that x is a particular solution of this differential equation.   *(Answer: $f = k_1x + k_2x \log|x|$)*
  b. Find a particular solution of $x^2f^{(2)} - xf' + f = x^3$ R E. What is E?
          (Answer: $x^3/4$; $E = R$)
  c. Find a complete solution of $x^2f^{(2)} - xf' + f = x^3$ R E. Determine E.
          (Answer: $f = k_1x + k_2x \log|x| + x^3/4$; $E = \{t \mid t \neq 0\}$)
3. a. Find a complete solution of $x^2f^{(2)} - 2f = 0$ R E, given that x^2 is a particular solution of this differential equation.   *(Answer: $f = k_1x^2 + k_2/x$)*
  b. Find a particular solution of $x^2f^{(2)} - 2f = x^3 \sin$ R E. Determine E.
          (Answer: $-x \sin - 2 \cos + 2 \sin/x$; $E = \{t \mid t \neq 0\}$)
  c. Find a complete solution of $x^2f^{(2)} - 2f = x^3 \sin$ R E. Determine E.
          (Answer: $f = k_1x^2 - x \sin - 2 \cos + (k_2 + 2 \sin)/x$; $E = \{t \mid t \neq 0\}$)
4. a. Find a complete solution of $\sin^2 \cdot f^{(2)} - (\sin 2x) \cdot f' + (1 + \cos^2) \cdot f = 0$ R E, given that $\sin$ is a particular solution of this differential equation.   *(Answer: $f = k_1 \sin + k_2x \sin$)*
  b. Find a particular solution of $\sin^2 \cdot f^{(2)} - (\sin 2x) \cdot f' + (1 + \cos^2) \cdot f = x \sin^3$ R E.
          (Answer: $x^3 \sin/6$)
  c. Find a complete solution of $\sin^2 \cdot f^{(2)} - (\sin 2x) \cdot f' + (1 + \cos^2) \cdot f = x \sin^3$ R E.
          (Answer: $f = k_1 \sin + k_2x \sin + x^3 \sin/6$)
5. a. Show that exp is a particular solution of $f^{(2)} - 2f' + f = 0$.
  b. Find a complete solution of $f^{(2)} - 2f' + f = 0$.   *(Answer: $f = k_1 \exp + k_2x \exp$)*
6. a. Show that $\exp(3x)$ is a particular solution of $f^{(2)} - 6f' + 9f = 0$.
  b. Find a complete solution of $f^{(2)} - 6f' + 9f = 0$.   *(Answer: $f = k_1 \exp(3x) + k_2x \exp(3x))$*
7. a. Show that exp is a particular solution of $f^{(2)} + f' - 2f = 0$.
  b. Find a complete solution of $f^{(2)} + f' - 2f = 0$.   *(Answer: $f = k_1 \exp + k_2 \exp(-2x))$*
8. a. Show that $\exp \cdot \sin$ is a particular solution of $f^{(2)} - 2f' + 2f = 0$.
  b. Find a complete solution of $f^{(2)} - 2f' + 2f = 0$. *(Answer: $f = k_1 \exp \cdot \sin + k_2 \exp \cdot \cos$)*

9.5 Linear Homogeneous Differential Equations with Constant Coefficients

We have seen that we can find a complete solution of the linear second-order differential equation $p_0 \cdot f^{(2)} + p_1 \cdot f' + p_2 \cdot f = p_3$ if we have a particular solution of the reduced equation $p_0 \cdot f^{(2)} + p_1 \cdot f' + p_2 \cdot f = 0$ R E. As we have observed, this differential equation is also called a *homogeneous* equation; hence the title of this section. Our purpose here is to tackle the problem of determining a particular solution of a homogeneous equation; we shall consider only the case in which the functions p_0, p_1, and p_2 are constant. Thus we shall restrict ourselves to a differential equation of the form $af^{(2)} + bf' + cf = 0$ R E, where $a \in R$, $b \in R$, and $c \in R$; moreover, since we want our differential equation to be of the second order, we shall assume that $a \neq 0$. Therefore, we can divide through by a. Essentially, this means that we can assume that $a = 1$. Thus we consider

(I) $$f^{(2)} + bf' + cf = 0 \text{ R } E,$$

where $b \in R$ and $c \in R$.

We intend to find a particular solution of (I). We now make an observation that is worth remembering. There is a complex number, say r, such that the function $\exp(rx)$ is a solution of (I). (Notice that we are extending our function concept from real numbers to complex numbers; however, this is easily carried out.) Let r be any complex number; then $[\exp(rx)]' = r \exp(rx)$, and $[\exp(rx)]^{(2)} = r^2 \exp(rx)$. So

$$[\exp(rx)]^{(2)} + b[\exp(rx)]' + c[\exp(rx)] = r^2 \exp(rx) + br \exp(rx) + c \exp(rx)$$

$$= [r^2 + br + c] \exp(rx).$$

We conclude that $\exp(rx)$ is a solution of (I) iff $r^2 + br + c = 0$. The equation $r^2 + br + c = 0$ is said to be the *auxiliary* equation of (I). Since this is a quadratic equation in the unknown r, it is a simple matter to determine r; indeed, $r = -b/2 + \sqrt{b^2/4 - c}$ or $r = -b/2 - \sqrt{b^2/4 - c}$. We must pay attention to the discriminant of the auxiliary equation, namely $b^2/4 - c$. In view of the Trichotomy Law, exactly one of the following holds true:

$$b^2/4 - c > 0, \quad b^2/4 - c = 0, \quad b^2/4 - c < 0.$$

In the first case the auxiliary equation has two real roots; in the second case there is just one real root; in the final case there are two complex roots.

If there are two real roots. let them be r_1 and r_2; then $\exp(r_1 x)$ and $\exp(r_2 x)$ are linearly independent solutions of (I) [note that $W(\exp(r_1 x), \exp(r_2 x)) = (r_2 - r_1)\exp([r_1 + r_2]x) \neq 0]$. Thus $f = k_1 \exp(r_1 x) + k_2 \exp(r_2 x)$ is a complete solution of (I).

If there is just one real root, say r, then $\exp(rx)$ is a particular solution of (I), where $r = -b/2$ and $c = b^2/4$. To obtain a complete solution of (I). we need a solution of (I) which is not a scalar multiple of $\exp(rx)$. Applying the method of Section 9.4 (i.e., the method of variation of parameter), we find that $x \exp(-bx/2)$ is a solution of (I). Let us show, directly, that $x \exp(-bx/2)$ is a particular solution of (I). Let $g = x \exp(-bx/2)$; then $g' = g/x - bg/2$ and $g^{(2)} = g'/x - g/x^2 - bg'/2 = g/x^2 - bg/2x - g/x^2 - bg'/2 = -bg/2x - bg'/2$.

So
$$g^{(2)} + bg' + cg = g^{(2)} + bg' + b^2 g/4$$
$$= -bg/2x - bg'/2 + bg' + b^2 g/4$$
$$= -bg/2x + bg'/2 + b^2 g/4$$
$$= -bg/2x + (bg/2x - b^2 g/4) + b^2 g/4$$
$$= 0 \text{ R } E.$$

We conclude that $x \exp(rx)$ is a particular solution of (I) in case r is the only real root of the auxiliary equation. Moreover, $W(\exp(rx), x \exp(rx)) = \exp(2rx) \neq 0$; so these particular solutions of (I) are linearly independent. Hence, in this case, $f = k_1 \exp(rx) + k_2 x \exp(rx)$ is a complete solution of (I).

Finally, we consider the case in which the auxiliary equation has complex roots. Since the auxiliary equation has real coefficients, its roots are conjugates. Let $\alpha + i\beta$ and $\alpha - i\beta$ be the roots, where $\alpha \in R$ and $\beta \in R$. Then

$$f = c_1 \exp(\alpha x + i\beta x) + c_2 \exp(\alpha x - i\beta x)$$

is a complete solution of (I). This complete solution can be simplified, for

$$c_1 \exp(\alpha x + i\beta x) + c_2 \exp(\alpha x - i\beta x) = e^{\alpha x} \cdot [c_1 \exp(i\beta x) + c_2 \exp(-i\beta x)]$$
$$= e^{\alpha x} \cdot [c_1 (\cos \beta x + i \sin \beta x) + c_2 (\cos \beta x - i \sin \beta x)]$$
$$= e^{\alpha x} \cdot [(c_1 + c_2) \cos \beta x + i(c_1 - c_2) \sin \beta x]$$
$$= e^{\alpha x} \cdot [k_1 \cos \beta x + k_2 \sin \beta x].$$

It is easy to show directly that $e^{\alpha x} \cdot \cos \beta x$ is a solution of (I) in case $\alpha + i\beta$ and $\alpha - i\beta$ are the complex roots of the auxiliary equation, where $\alpha \in R$ and $\beta \in R$. This means that $\alpha = -b/2$ and that $\beta = \sqrt{c - b^2/4}$. Let $g = e^{\alpha x} \cdot \cos \beta x$; then $g' = \alpha g - \beta e^{\alpha x} \cdot \sin \beta x$ and $g^{(2)} = \alpha g' - \beta \alpha e^{\alpha x} \cdot \sin \beta x - \beta^2 g = (\alpha^2 - \beta^2)g - 2\alpha\beta e^{\alpha x} \cdot \sin \beta x$. Thus

$$g^{(2)} + bg' + cg = (\alpha^2 - \beta^2)g - 2\alpha\beta e^{\alpha x} \cdot \sin \beta x + b\alpha g - b\beta e^{\alpha x} \cdot \sin \beta x$$
$$= e^{\alpha x} \cdot [(\alpha^2 - \beta^2 + b\alpha + c) \cos \beta x - (2\alpha + b) \sin \beta x]$$
$$= 0$$

since $\alpha^2 - \beta^2 + b\alpha + c = b^2/4 - c + b^2/4 - b^2/2 + c = 0$ and $2\alpha + b = -b + b = 0$.

Similarly, it is easy to see directly that $e^{\alpha x} \cdot \sin \beta x$ is a particular solution of (I). Since $e^{\alpha x} \cdot \cos \beta x$ and $e^{\alpha x} \cdot \sin \beta x$ are linearly independent, we conclude once again that

$$f = k_1 e^{\alpha x} \cdot \cos \beta x + k_2 e^{\alpha x} \cdot \sin \beta x$$

is a complete solution of (I).

E X E R C I S E S

1. Verify that $\exp(-bx/2)$ is a particular solution of $f^{(2)} + bf' + b^2f/4 = 0$. Apply the method of variation of parameter to derive another particular solution of this differential equation.

2. Verify that $\exp(sx) \cdot \sin(tx)$ is a particular solution of $f^{(2)} - 2sf' + (s^2 + t^2)f = 0$, where $s \in R$ and $t \in R$. Apply the method of variation of parameter to derive another particular solution of this differential equation.

Find a complete solution of each of the following.

3. $f^{(2)} - 5f' + 4f = 0.$

4. $f^{(2)} + f' - 6f = 0.$

5. $f^{(2)} - f = 0.$

6. $f^{(2)} - 5f' + 6f = 0.$

7. $f^{(2)} + f' - 6f = 0.$

8. $f^{(2)} - 4f' + 4f = 0.$

9. $f^{(2)} + 6f' + 9f = 0.$

10. $f^{(2)} - 2f' + 5f = 0.$

11. $f^{(2)} + 2f' + 10f = 0.$

12. $f^{(2)} - 4f' + 5f = 0.$

13. $f^{(2)} - 4f' + 8f = 0.$

14. $f^{(2)} - f = x^2.$

15. $f^{(2)} - f = 2x\exp.$

9.6   The Method of Undetermined Coefficients

There is a simple method for obtaining a particular solution of the linear differential equation

(1) $$f^{(2)} + bf' + cf = p,$$

where b and c are real numbers and p is a nonzero function which is continuous on an interval. The idea is to guess at the *form* of a solution by considering the functions whose first and second derivatives appear on the right-hand side of (1). The following examples bring out the technique.

EXAMPLE 1.   Find a particular solution of $f^{(2)} - 3f' + 2f = 5\sin 3x$.

Solution: Now, $(\cos 3x)' = -3\sin 3x$ and $(\sin 3x)^{(2)} = -9\sin 3x$; accordingly, we guess that a linear combination of $\cos 3x$ and $\sin 3x$ is a particular solution of the given differential equation. Therefore we want to find real numbers A and B such that $A\cos 3x + B\sin 3x$ is a solution. Now,

$$[A\cos 3x + B\sin 3x]^{(2)} - 3[A\cos 3x + B\sin 3x]' + 2[A\cos 3x + B\sin 3x]$$

$$= -9A\cos 3x - 9B\sin 3x + 9A\sin 3x - 9B\cos 3x + 2A\cos 3x + 2B\sin 3x$$

$$= (-7A - 9B)\cos 3x + (9A - 7B)\sin 3x.$$

Hence we want to choose A and B so that $-7A - 9B = 0$ and $9A - 7B = 5$; this means that $A = 9/26$ and $B = -7/26$. Thus $(9/26)\cos 3x - (7/26)\sin 3x$ is a particular solution of the given differential equation.

EXAMPLE 2. Find a particular solution of $f^{(2)} + f' - 2f = 2x^2$.

Solution: Here we try a polynomial of degree two: there is no use considering x^n, where $n > 2$, since f appears on the left-hand side of the given differential equation, whereas x^n does not appear on the right-hand side. Thus we consider the function $A + Bx + Cx^2$. Let $g = A + Bx + Cx^2$; then

$$g^{(2)} + g' - 2g = (-2A - 2Bx - 2Cx^2) + (B + 2Cx) + 2C$$
$$= (-2A + B + 2C) + (2C - 2B)x - 2Cx^2.$$

Hence g is a particular solution of the given differential equation iff $-2A + B + 2C = 0$, $2C - 2B = 0$, and $-2C = 2$. Solving this linear system, we find that $C = -1$, $B = -1$, and $A = -3/2$. So $-3/2 - x - x^2$ is a particular solution of the given differential equation.

EXAMPLE 3. Find a particular solution of $f^{(2)} + f' - 2f = \exp(3x)$.

Solution: Here, we try the function $\exp(3x)$. Let $g = A \exp(3x)$; then $g^{(2)} + g' - 2g = 9A \exp(3x) + 3A \exp(3x) - 2A \exp(3x) = 10A \exp(3x)$. Thus g is a solution of the given differential equation iff $A = 1/10$. We conclude that $.1 \exp(3x)$ is a particular solution of the given differential equation.

Our method is known as the *method of undetermined coefficients* for obvious reasons. In the preceding examples the method of undertermined coefficients led us to a particular solution without much trouble. There can be complications, however; consider the following two examples.

EXAMPLE 4. Find a particular solution of $f^{(2)} - f' - 2f = \exp(2x)$.

Solution: This differential equation is very much like the differential equation of Example 3; however, there is a crucial difference. Again, we try the function which appears on the right-hand side, namely $\exp(2x)$. Let $g = A \exp(2x)$; then $g^{(2)} - g' - 2g = 4A \exp(2x) - 2A \exp(2x) - 2A \exp(2x) = 0$ whenever $A \in R$. The trouble is that 2 is a root of the auxiliary equation of the reduced differential equation, namely the equation $r^2 - r - 2 = 0$; thus, of necessity, the function $\exp(2x)$ is a particular solution of the reduced differential equation; hence $A \exp(2x)$ is a particular solution of the reduced differential equation whenever $A \in R$. To solve our problem, we try the function $x \exp(2x)$. Let $h = Ax \exp(2x)$; then

$$h^{(2)} - h' - 2h = [3A \exp(2x) + 4Ax \exp(2x)] - [A \exp(2x) + 2Ax \exp(2x)] - 2Ax \exp(2x)$$
$$= 2A \exp(2x).$$

Thus h is a solution of the given differential equation iff $A = 1/2$; so $(x/2) \exp(2x)$ is a particular solution of the given differential equation.

EXAMPLE 5. Find a particular solution of $f^{(2)} - 6f' + 9f = 4\exp(3x)$.

Solution: This time we begin by examining the auxiliary equation $r^2 - 6r + 9 = 0$; here, 3 is the only root. Therefore $\exp(3x)$ is a particular solution of the reduced differential equation; also, $x \exp(3x)$ is a particular solution of the reduced differential equation. Hence each linear combination of $\exp(3x)$ and $x \exp(3x)$ is a solution of the reduced differential equation. It is clear that these functions will not help us. Let us try the function $x^2 \exp(3x)$; thus let $g = Ax^2 \exp(3x)$; then

$$g^{(2)} - 6g' + 9g = [2A\exp(3x) + 12Ax\exp(3x) + 9Ax^2\exp)3x)]$$

$$- 6[2Ax\exp(3x) + 3Ax^2\exp(3x)] + 9Ax^2\exp(3x)$$

$$= 2A\exp(3x).$$

Therefore g is a particular solution of the given differential equation iff $A = 2$. Thus $2x^2 \exp(3x)$ is the required function.

Perhaps it looks as if the functions used to work out the two preceding examples were pulled out of a hat. Let us demonstrate that if A is suitably chosen, then one of

$$A \exp(kx), \quad Ax \exp(kx), \quad Ax^2 \exp(kx)$$

is a particular solution of $f^{(2)} + bf' + cf = \exp(kx)$ under any circumstances. As we have observed, the auxilliary equation is the key to the situation. If k is not a root of $r^2 + br + c = 0$, then we can find a real number A such that $A \exp(kx)$ is a solution. Next, suppose that k is a simple root of the auxiliary equation; then the given differential equation is $f^{(2)} - (k + k_1)f' + kk_1 f = \exp(kx)$, where $k_1 \neq k$. It is easy to see that the function $Ax \exp(kx)$ is a solution of this differential equation, where $A = 1/(k - k_1)$. Finally, we consider the case in which k is a double root of the auxiliary equation; then the given differential equation is $f^{(2)} - 2kf' + k^2 f = \exp(kx)$. Again, it is easy to see that $Ax^2 \exp(kx)$ is a solution of the differential equation, where $A = 1/2$.

It may appear that the method of this section is *trial and error*. This is largely, but not entirely, true. There is also an element of *intuition* in the process; i.e., the guessing involved is not entirely random. The whole point of this section is to develop some insight into the nature of a differential equation and to bring out the problem associated with a differential equation, i.e., the problem of finding a function which satisfies the differential equation. It is rather surprising that the idea of this section can be put on a sound basis. In Section 10.5 we shall develop the mathematical theory which underlies the technique of this section.

E X E R C I S E S

Find a particular solution of each of the following.

1. $f^{(2)} - 4f' + 4f = \sin$.

2. $f^{(2)} - 5f' + 6f = \exp$.

3. $f^{(2)} - 4f' + 3f = \cos 2x$.

4. $f^{(2)} + f' - 2f = 3x$.

5. $f^{(2)} + 2f' - 3f = 2x^2 - x + 3$.

6. $f^{(2)} + f' - 6f = 2\sin - \cos$.

7. $f^{(2)} + 3f' - 4f = \sin 2x + 3\cos 2x$.

8. $f^{(2)} - f' - 2f = 3\sin 2x$.

9. $f^{(2)} - 2f' - 3f = \exp$.

10. $f^{(2)} + 3f' - 4f = 2\sin$.

11. $f^{(2)} - 2f' + f = 3\cos$.

12. $f^{(2)} - 2f' + f = 2x - 5$.

13. $f^{(2)} - 2f' + f = 3\exp$.

14. $f^{(2)} - 6f' + 9f = \exp(3x)$.

15. $f^{(2)} - 6f' + 9f = x\exp(3x)$.

Chapter 10 Linear Differential Equations

10.1 A Unique-Existence Theorem; the Wronskian

Let n be any natural number; by a *linear differential equation of order n* we mean

$$(1) \qquad f^{(n)} + p_1 \cdot f^{(n-1)} + \cdots + p_{n-1} \cdot f' + p_n \cdot f = p_{n+1},$$

where each p_i, $1 \le i \le n+1$, is a function with one argument. Moreover, the differential equation

$$(2) \qquad f^{(n)} + p_1 \cdot f^{(n-1)} + \cdots + p_{n-1} \cdot f' + p_n \cdot f = 0 \text{ R } E$$

is said to be the *reduced* equation of (1), or a *homogeneous* linear differential equation of order n.

We now state, without proof, the fundamental *unique-existence* theorem of this chapter.

> **THEOREM 10.1.1.** Let $\mathscr{I}$ be any interval and let $p_1, p_2, \cdots, p_{n+1}$ be continuous on $\mathscr{I}$; let $a \in \mathscr{I}$ and let $a_0, a_1, \cdots, a_{n-1}$ be any real numbers. Then there is a unique function g such that $\mathscr{D}_g = \mathscr{I}$, $g^{(n)} + p_1 \cdot g^{(n-1)} + \cdots + p_{n-1} \cdot g' + p_n \cdot g = p_{n+1}$ R $\mathscr{I}$, and $g(a) = a_0$, $g'(a) = a_1$, $\cdots$, $g^{(n-1)}(a) = a_{n-1}$.

The following theorem is easy to prove.

> **THEOREM 10.1.2.** Let $g_1, g_2, \cdots, g_m$ be any solutions of (2); then each linear combination of $g_1, g_2, \cdots, g_m$ is a solution of (2).
>
> *Proof:* The details are left as an exercise.

Finding a complete solution of a homogeneous linear differential equation of order n requires the notion of the *Wronskian* of n functions.

DEFINITION 10.1.1.   Let $g_1, g_2, \cdots, g_n$ be any functions; by the Wronskian of $g_1, g_2, \cdots, g_n$ we mean the function

$$\begin{vmatrix} g_1 & g_2 & \cdots & g_n \\ g_1' & g_2' & \cdots & g_n' \\ & & \vdots & \\ g_1^{(n-1)} & g_2^{(n-1)} & \cdots & g_n^{(n-1)} \end{vmatrix}.$$

This function is denoted by "$W(g_1, g_2, \cdots, g_n)$".

The following theorems show the importance of our concept.

THEOREM 10.1.3.   Let $g_1, g_2, \cdots, g_n$ be linearly dependent on $\mathscr{I}$, where $\mathscr{D}_{g_i^{(n-1)}} = \mathscr{D}_{g_i} = \mathscr{I}$ whenever $1 \le i \le n$; then $W(g_1, g_2, \cdots, g_n) = 0$ R $\mathscr{I}$.

Proof: Since the given functions have the same domain, namely $\mathscr{I}$, and are linearly dependent on $\mathscr{I}$, it follows that one of these functions is a linear combination of the others. Suppose that $g_1 = c_2 g_2 + c_3 g_3 + \cdots + c_n g_n$; then $g_1' = c_2 g_2' + c_3 g_3' + \cdots + c_n g_n'$ indeed, $g_1^{(k)} = c_2 g_2^{(k)} + c_3 g_3^{(k)} + \cdots + c_n g_n^{(k)}$ whenever $1 \le k \le n - 1$. Let $t \in \mathscr{I}$ and consider $[W(g_1, g_2, \cdots, g_n)](t)$, namely

$$\begin{vmatrix} g_1(t) & g_2(t) & \cdots & g_n(t) \\ g_1'(t) & g_2'(t) & \cdots & g_n'(t) \\ & & \vdots & \\ g_1^{(n-1)}(t) & g_2^{(n-1)}(t) & \cdots & g_n^{(n-1)}(t) \end{vmatrix}.$$

The first column of this matrix is a linear combination of the remaining columns; therefore the determinant vanishes. This establishes our result.

THEOREM 10.1.4.   Let $g_1, g_2, \cdots, g_n$ be solutions of (2) such that $\mathscr{D}_{g_i^{(n-1)}} = \mathscr{D}_{g_i} = \mathscr{I}$ whenever $1 \le i \le n$, where $\mathscr{I}$ is an interval; and suppose that there is a member of $\mathscr{I}$, say t, such that $[W(g_1, g_2, \cdots, g_n)](t) = 0$. Then $g_1, g_2, \cdots, g_n$ are linearly dependent on $\mathscr{I}$.

Proof: Consider the following system of n equations in the n unknowns c_1, $c_2, \cdots, c_n$:

$$\begin{cases} g_1(t)c_1 + g_2(t)c_2 + \cdots + g_n(t)c_n = 0 \\ g_1'(t)c_1 + g_2'(t)c_2 + \cdots + g_n'(t)c_n = 0 \\ \qquad\qquad \vdots \\ g_1^{(n-1)}(t)c_1 + g_2^{(n-1)}(t)c_2 + \cdots + g_n^{(n-1)}(t)c_n = 0. \end{cases}$$

By assumption, the determinant of the coefficient matrix is zero; therefore this system possesses a nontrivial solution. Thus there are real numbers $k_1, k_2, \cdots, k_n$, not all zero, which satisfy the above system. Let g be the corresponding linear combination of $g_1, g_2, \cdots, g_n$; i.e.,

$$g = k_1 g_1 + k_2 g_2 + \cdots + k_n g_n.$$

Then, by Theorem 10.1.2, g is a particular solution of (2); moreover, it follows from the construction of g that $g(t) = 0$, $g'(t) = 0$, $\cdots$, $g^{(n-1)}(t) = 0$. By Theorem 10.1.1, there is a unique solution of (2) which satisfies these boundary conditions. However, the function $0 \text{ R } \mathscr{I}$ is a solution of (2) which satisfies the boundary conditions $f^{(k)}(t) = 0$ whenever $0 \le k \le n - 1$. We conclude that $g = 0 \text{ R } \mathscr{I}$. This means that $k_1 g_1 + k_2 g_2 + \cdots + k_n g_n = 0 \text{ R } \mathscr{I}$, where the k's are not all zero. Thus $g_1, g_2, \cdots, g_n$ are linearly dependent on $\mathscr{I}$. This establishes Theorem 10.1.4.

THEOREM 10.1.5. Let $g_1, g_2, \cdots, g_n$ be solutions of (2) and let $\mathscr{I}$ be an interval; then $g_1, g_2, \cdots, g_n$ are linearly dependent on $\mathscr{I}$ iff $W(g_1, g_2, \cdots, g_n) = 0 \text{ R } \mathscr{I}$.

Proof: If $g_1, g_2, \cdots, g_n$ are linearly dependent on $\mathscr{I}$, then $W(g_1, g_2, \cdots, g_n) = 0 \text{ R } \mathscr{I}$, by Theorem 10.1.3. On the other hand, if $W(g_1, g_2, \cdots, g_n) = 0 \text{ R } \mathscr{I}$, then there certainly is a member of $\mathscr{I}$, say t, such that $[W(g_1, g_2, \cdots, g_n)](t) = 0$; so, by Theorem 10.1.4, $g_1, g_2, \cdots, g_n$ are linearly dependent on $\mathscr{I}$.

One may well ask if there are solutions of (2) with domain $\mathscr{I}$, say $g_1, g_2, \cdots, g_n$, such that $W(g_1, g_2, \cdots, g_n) \ne 0 \text{ R } \mathscr{I}$, and if there is a member of $\mathscr{I}$, say s, such that $[W(g_1, g_2, \cdots, g_n)](s) = 0$. Applying Theorem 10.1.5, we can readily demonstrate that this is impossible. Assume that $[W(g_1, g_2, \cdots, g_n)](s) = 0$; then, by Theorem 10.1.4, $g_1, g_2, \cdots, g_n$ are linearly dependent on $\mathscr{I}$; therefore, by Theorem 10.1.5, $W(g_1, g_2, \cdots, g_n) = 0 \text{ R } \mathscr{I}$. It is interesting to obtain this result by establishing certain properties of the Wronskian.

THEOREM 10.1.6. Let $g_1, g_2, \cdots, g_n$ be any functions; then

$$[W(g_1, g_2, \cdots, g_n)]' = \begin{vmatrix} g_1 & g_2 & \cdots & g_n \\ g_1' & g_2' & \cdots & g_n' \\ & & \vdots & \\ g_1^{(n-2)} & g_2^{(n-2)} & \cdots & g_n^{(n-2)} \\ g_1^{(n)} & g_2^{(n)} & \cdots & g_n^{(n)} \end{vmatrix}.$$

Proof: We shall establish this result for $n = 3$, the following scheme applies to any natural number. Now, let g, h, and k be any functions; then

$$W(g, h, k) = \begin{vmatrix} g & h & k \\ g' & h' & k' \\ g^{(2)} & h^{(2)} & k^{(2)} \end{vmatrix}$$

$$= g \cdot \begin{vmatrix} h' & k' \\ h^{(2)} & k^{(2)} \end{vmatrix} - h \cdot \begin{vmatrix} g' & k' \\ g^{(2)} & k^{(2)} \end{vmatrix} + k \cdot \begin{vmatrix} g' & h' \\ g^{(2)} & h^{(2)} \end{vmatrix}.$$

Therefore

$$[W(g, h, k)]' = g' \cdot \begin{vmatrix} h' & k' \\ h^{(2)} & k^{(2)} \end{vmatrix} - h' \cdot \begin{vmatrix} g' & k' \\ g^{(2)} & k^{(2)} \end{vmatrix} + k' \cdot \begin{vmatrix} g' & h' \\ g^{(2)} & h^{(2)} \end{vmatrix}$$

$$+ g \cdot \begin{vmatrix} h' & k' \\ h^{(2)} & k^{(2)} \end{vmatrix}' - h \cdot \begin{vmatrix} g' & k' \\ g^{(2)} & k^{(2)} \end{vmatrix}' + k \cdot \begin{vmatrix} g' & h' \\ g^{(2)} & h^{(2)} \end{vmatrix}'$$

$$= \begin{vmatrix} g' & h' & k' \\ g' & h' & k' \\ g^{(2)} & h^{(2)} & k^{(2)} \end{vmatrix} + \begin{vmatrix} g & h & k \\ g' & h' & k' \\ g^{(3)} & h^{(3)} & k^{(3)} \end{vmatrix}$$

$$= \begin{vmatrix} g & h & k \\ g' & h' & k' \\ g^{(3)} & h^{(3)} & k^{(3)} \end{vmatrix}.$$

This establishes our result for $n = 3$; as we have observed, the same procedure works for any natural number. We point out that this theorem can be established by mathematical induction.

THEOREM 10.1.7. Let $g_1, g_2, \cdots, g_n$ be any solutions of (2) with domain $\mathscr{I}$; then $W(g_1, g_2, \cdots, g_n) = B \exp\left(-\int_b^x p_1\right)$, where $B = [W(g_1, g_2, \cdots, g_n)](b)$ and $b \in \mathscr{D}_{p_1}$.

Proof: Since $g_1, g_2, \cdots, g_n$ are solutions of (2), it follows that

$$g_i^{(n)} + p_1 \cdot g_i^{(n-1)} + \cdots + p_{n-1} \cdot g_i' + p_n \cdot g_i = 0 \text{ R } \mathscr{I}$$

whenever $1 \le i \le n$. Now,

$$[W(g_1, g_2, \cdots, g_n)]' = \begin{vmatrix} g_1 & g_2 & \cdots & g_n \\ g_1' & g_2' & \cdots & g_n' \\ & & \vdots & \\ g_1^{(n-2)} & g_2^{(n-2)} & \cdots & g_n^{(n-2)} \\ g_1^{(n)} & g_2^{(n)} & \cdots & g_n^{(n)} \end{vmatrix}$$

$$= - \begin{vmatrix} g_1 & g_2 & \cdots & g_n \\ g_1' & g_2' & \cdots & g_n' \\ & & \vdots & \\ g_1^{(n-2)} & g_2^{(n-2)} & \cdots & g_n^{(n-2)} \\ \sum_{j=1}^{n} p_j \cdot g_1^{(n-j)} & \sum_{j=1}^{n} p_j \cdot g_2^{(n-j)} & \cdots & \sum_{j=1}^{n} p_j \cdot g_n^{(n-j)} \end{vmatrix}$$

$$= - \begin{vmatrix} g_1 & g_2 & \cdots & g_n \\ g_1' & g_2' & & g_n' \\ & & \vdots & \\ g_1^{(n-2)} & g_2^{(n-2)} & \cdots & g_n^{(n-2)} \\ p_1 \cdot g_1^{(n-1)} & p_1 \cdot g_2^{(n-1)} & \cdots & p_1 \cdot g_n^{(n-1)} \end{vmatrix}$$

$$= -p_1 \cdot W(g_1, g_2, \cdots, g_n).$$

Thus $\log | W(g_1, g_2, \cdots, g_n)| \equiv \displaystyle\int - p_1$; so $W(g_1, g_2, \cdots, g_n) = k \, \exp \left(\int_b^x -p_1 \right)$, where $k = [W(g_1, g_2, \cdots, g_n)](b)$. This establishes Theorem 10.1.7.

We now have an alternate proof of the comment following Theorem 10.1.5.

COROLLARY 10.1.1. Let $g_1, g_2, \cdots, g_n$ be any solutions of (2) with domain $\mathscr{I}$; then the members of the range of $W(g_1, g_2, \cdots, g_n)$ have the same algebraic sign. *Proof:* Consider Theorem 10.1.7 and recall that $\mathscr{R}_{\exp} = \{t \, | \, t > 0\}$.

Now that we are well acquainted with the Wronskian, let us prove that we can obtain a complete solution of (1) if we have n linearly independent solutions of (2) and a particular solution of (1). The first step is to show that we have a complete solution of the reduced equation.

THEOREM 10.1.8. Let $\mathscr{I}$ be an interval, let $p_1, p_2, \cdots, p_n$ be continuous on $\mathscr{I}$, and let $g_1, g_2, \cdots, g_n$ be particular solutions of (2) which are linearly independent on $\mathscr{I}$. Then $f = k_1 g_1 + k_2 g_2 + \cdots + k_n g_n$ is a complete solution of (2).

Proof: By Theorem 10.1.2, each member of the given family is a particular solution of (2). We must show that each solution of (2) can be obtained from $f = k_1 g_1 + k_2 g_2 + \cdots + k_n g_n$ by choosing $k_1, k_2, \cdots, k_n$ suitably. Let h be any solution of (2), let $a \in \mathscr{I}$, and $h(a) = a_0$, $h'(a) = a_1$, $\cdots$, $h^{(n-1)}(a) = a_{n-1}$. We want to find real numbers $c_1, c_2, \cdots, c_n$ so that the function $c_1 g_1 + c_2 g_2 + \cdots + c_n g_n$ satisfies these same boundary conditions. Consider the following linear system in the unknowns $c_1, c_2, \cdots, c_n$:

$$\begin{cases} g_1(a)c_1 + g_2(a)c_2 + \cdots + g_n(a)c_n = a_0 \\ g_1'(a)c_1 + g_2'(a)c_2 + \cdots + g_n'(a)c_n = a_1 \\ \qquad\qquad \vdots \\ g_1^{(n-1)}(a)c_1 + g_2^{(n-1)}(a)c_2 + \cdots + g_n^{(n-1)}(a)c_n = a_{n-1}. \end{cases}$$

Since $g_1, g_2, \cdots, g_n$ are linearly independent on $\mathscr{I}$, it follows from Theorem 10.1.5 that $[W(g_1, g_2, \cdots, g_n)](a) \neq 0$. Therefore the above linear system possesses a solution (since the determinant of the coefficient matrix is not zero). Thus the function $c_1 g_1 +$

$c_2 g_2 + \cdots + c_n g_n$ is a particular solution of (2) which satisfies the same boundary conditions as h; hence, by Theorem 10.1.1, $h = c_1 g_1 + c_2 g_2 + \cdots + c_n g_n$. This completes our proof.

COROLLARY 10.1.2.   Let $\mathscr{I}$ be an interval and let $p_1, p_2, \cdots, p_n$ be continuous on $\mathscr{I}$; then $f^{(n)} + p_1 \cdot f^{(n-1)} + \cdots + p_{n-1} \cdot f' + p_n \cdot f = 0$ R $\mathscr{I}$ does not possess $n + 1$ particular solutions which are linearly independent on $\mathscr{I}$.

Let us show that (2) actually has n particular solutions which are linearly independent on $\mathscr{I}$.

THEOREM 10.1.9.   Let $\mathscr{I}$ be an interval and let $p_1, p_2, \cdots, p_n$ be continuous on $\mathscr{I}$; then there are n particular solutions of (2), each with domain $\mathscr{I}$, which are linearly independent on $\mathscr{I}$.

Proof: We appeal to Theorem 10.1.1, our unique-existence theorem. Let $a \in \mathscr{I}$; then there are unique solutions of (2), say $g_1, g_2, \cdots, g_n$, each with domain $\mathscr{I}$, which satisfy the following boundary conditions:

$$g_1^{(k)}(a) = \begin{cases} 1 & \text{if } k = 0 \\ 0 & \text{if } k \neq 0, 0 \leq k \leq n - 1; \end{cases}$$

$$g_2^{(k)}(a) = \begin{cases} 1 & \text{if } k = 1 \\ 0 & \text{if } k \neq 1, 0 \leq k \leq n - 1; \end{cases}$$

$$\vdots$$

$$g_n^{(k)}(a) = \begin{cases} 1 & \text{if } k = n - 1 \\ 0 & \text{if } k \neq n - 1, 0 \leq k \leq n - 1. \end{cases}$$

To determine whether the functions $g_1, g_2, \cdots, g_n$ are linearly independent, we apply our acid test contained in Theorem 10.1.5. Now,

$$[W(g_1, g_2, \cdots, g_n)](a) = \begin{vmatrix} 1 & 0 & 0 & \cdots & 0 \\ 0 & 1 & 0 & \cdots & 0 \\ 0 & 0 & 1 & \cdots & 0 \\ & & \vdots & & \\ & & \vdots & & \\ 0 & 0 & 0 & \cdots & 1 \end{vmatrix} = 1.$$

Therefore $g_1, g_2, \cdots, g_n$ are linearly independent on $\mathscr{I}$. This establishes our result.

Finally, we show that we can construct a complete solution of (1) from a particular solution of (1) and a complete solution of (2).

THEOREM 10.1.10.   Let $\mathscr{I}$ be an interval and let $p_1, p_2, \cdots, p_n$ be continuous on $\mathscr{I}$; let $g_1, g_2, \cdots, g_n$ be linearly independent solutions of (2) and let u be a particular solution of (1). Then $f = k_1 g_1 + k_2 g_2 + \cdots + k_n g_n + u$ is a complete solution of (1).

Proof: Clearly, for each choice of $k_1, k_2, \cdots, k_n$ the function $k_1 g_1 + k_2 g_2 + \cdots + k_n g_n + u$ is a particular solution of (1). We must show that we have each solution of (1). Let h be a particular solution of (1); let $h(a) = a_0$, $h'(a) = a_1, \cdots, h^{(n-1)}(a) = a_{n-1}$, where $a \in \mathscr{I}$. By Theorem 10.1.1, there is a unique solution of (1) which satisfies these boundary conditions. Let us show that we can choose real numbers $c_1, c_2, \cdots, c_n$ so that the function $c_1 g_1 + c_2 g_2 + \cdots + c_n g_n + u$ satisfies these same boundary conditions. Consider the following linear system in the unknowns $c_1, c_2, \cdots, c_n$:

$$
\begin{cases}
c_1 g_1(a) + c_2 g_2(a) + \cdots + c_n g_n(a) = a_0 - u(a) \\
c_1 g_1'(a) + c_2 g_2'(a) + \cdots + c_n g_n'(a) = a_1 - u'(a) \\
\quad\quad \vdots \\
c_1 g_1^{(n-1)}(a) + c_2 g_2^{(n-1)}(a) + \cdots + c_n g_n^{(n-1)}(a) = a_{n-1} - u^{(n-1)}(a).
\end{cases}
$$

Since the functions $g_1, g_2, \cdots, g_n$ are linearly independent, the determinant of the coefficient matrix is not zero. Therefore this system of equations possesses a unique solution, say $c_1, c_2, \cdots, c_n$. In view of Theorem 10.1.1, we conclude that $h = c_1 g_1 + c_2 g_2 + \cdots + c_n g_n + u$. This establishes Theorem 10.1.10.

We now show how to obtain a particular solution of (1) provided that we have n particular solutions of (2) which are linearly independent on $\mathscr{I}$. The idea is to vary the parameters; moreover, we shall use the efficient form of this method which is discussed in Section 9.4. Let $g_1, g_2, \cdots, g_n$ be particular solutions of (2) which are linearly independent on $\mathscr{I}$; thus $f = k_1 g_1 + k_2 g_2 + \cdots + k_n g_n$ is a complete solution of (2). We want to find functions $v_1, v_2, \cdots, v_n$ such that $v_1 \cdot g_1 + v_2 \cdot g_2 + \cdots + v_n \cdot g_n$ is a particular solution of (1). Let us assume that

$$v_1' \cdot g_1 + v_2' \cdot g_2 + \cdots + v_n' \cdot g_n = 0 \text{ R } \mathscr{I}$$
$$v_1^{(2)} \cdot g_1 + v_2^{(2)} \cdot g_2 + \cdots + v_n^{(2)} \cdot g_n = 0 \text{ R } \mathscr{I}$$
$$\vdots$$
$$v_1^{(n-1)} \cdot g_1 + v_2^{(n-1)} \cdot g_2 + \cdots + v_n^{(n-1)} \cdot g_n = 0 \text{ R } \mathscr{I}.$$

Let $h = v_1 \cdot g_1 + v_2 \cdot g_2 + \cdots + v_n \cdot g_n$; then

$$h' = v_1 \cdot g_1' + v_2 \cdot g_2' + \cdots + v_n \cdot g_n'$$
$$h^{(2)} = v_1 \cdot g_1^{(2)} + v_2 \cdot g_2^{(2)} + \cdots + v_n \cdot g_n^{(2)}$$
$$\vdots$$
$$h^{(n)} = [v_1 \cdot g_1^{(n)} + v_2 \cdot g_2^{(n)} + \cdots + v_n \cdot g_n^{(n)}]$$
$$\quad\quad\quad\quad + [v_1' \cdot g_1^{(n-1)} + v_2' \cdot g_2^{(n-1)} + \cdots + v_n' \cdot g_n^{(n-1)}].$$

Therefore

$$h^{(n)} + p_1 \cdot h^{(n-1)} + \cdots + p_{n-1} \cdot h' + p_n \cdot h$$

$$= v_1 \cdot [g_1^{(n)} + p_1 \cdot g_1^{(n-1)} + \cdots + p_{n-1} \cdot g_1' + p_n \cdot g_1]$$

$$+ v_2 \cdot [g_2^{(n)} + p_1 \cdot g_2^{(n-1)} + \cdots + p_{n-1} \cdot g_2' + p_n \cdot g_2]$$

$$+ \cdots + v_n \cdot [g_n^{(n)} + p_1 \cdot g_n^{(n-1)} + \cdots + p_{n-1} \cdot g_n' + p_n \cdot g_n]$$

$$+ [v_1' \cdot g_1^{(n-1)} + v_2' \cdot g_2^{(n-1)} + \cdots + v_n' \cdot g_n^{(n-1)}]$$

$$= v_1' \cdot g_1^{(n-1)} + v_2' \cdot g_2^{(n-1)} + \cdots + v_n' \cdot g_n^{(n-1)}.$$

Moreover, by assumption,

$$0 \text{ R } \mathscr{I} = [v_1' \cdot g_1 + v_2' \cdot g_2 + \cdots + v_n' \cdot g_n]'$$

$$= [v_1^{(2)} \cdot g_1 + v_2^{(2)} \cdot g_2 + \cdots + v_n^{(2)} \cdot g_n] + [v_1' \cdot g_1' + v_2' \cdot g_2' + \cdots + v_n' \cdot g_n']$$

$$= v_1' \cdot g_1' + v_2' \cdot g_2' + \cdots + v_n' \cdot g_n'.$$

Similarly, it is easy to see that

(A) $$v_1^{(k)} \cdot g_1' + v_2^{(k)} \cdot g_2' + \cdots + v_n^{(k)} \cdot g_n' = 0 \text{ R } \mathscr{I}$$

whenever $1 \le k \le n - 2$. Considering $[v_1' \cdot g_1 + v_2' \cdot g_2 + \cdots + v_n' \cdot g_n]^{(k)}$ and (A), we see that $v_1' \cdot g_1^{(k)} + v_2' \cdot g_2^{(k)} + \cdots + v_n' \cdot g_n^{(k)} = 0 \text{ R } \mathscr{I}$ whenever $1 \le k \le n - 2$. Thus we want to find functions $v_1', v_2', \cdots, v_n'$ such that

$$\begin{cases} g_1 \cdot v_1' + g_2 \cdot v_2' + \cdots + g_n \cdot v_n' = 0 \text{ R } \mathscr{I} \\ g_1' \cdot v_1' + g_2' \cdot v_2' + \cdots + g_n' \cdot v_n' = 0 \text{ R } \mathscr{I} \\ \qquad \vdots \\ g_1^{(n-2)} \cdot v_1' + g_2^{(n-2)} \cdot v_2' + \cdots + g_n^{(n-2)} \cdot v_n' = 0 \text{ R } \mathscr{I} \\ g_1^{(n-1)} \cdot v_1' + g_2^{(n-1)} \cdot v_2' + \cdots + g_n^{(n-1)} \cdot v_n' = p_{n+1} \text{ R } \mathscr{I}. \end{cases}$$

We are faced with a linear system in the unknowns $v_1', v_2', \cdots, v_n'$. The determinant of the coefficient matrix is $W(g_1, g_2, \cdots, g_n)$; since $[W(g_1, g_2, \cdots, g_n)](t) \ne 0$ whenever $t \in \mathscr{I}$, we conclude that our linear system possesses a unique solution. Of course, once we have determined the functions $v_1', v_2', \cdots, v_n'$, it is easy to obtain the desired functions $v_1, v_2, \cdots, v_n$. So we have our particular solution of (1), namely $v_1 \cdot g_1 + v_2 \cdot g_2 + \cdots + v_n \cdot g_n$. This establishes the following theorem.

THEOREM 10.1.11. Let $\mathscr{I}$ be an interval, let $p_1, p_2, \cdots, p_{n+1}$ be continuous on $\mathscr{I}$, and let $g_1, g_2, \cdots, g_n$ be particular solutions of (2) which are linearly independent on $\mathscr{I}$. Then $v_1 \cdot g_1 + v_2 \cdot g_2 + \cdots + v_n \cdot g_n$ is a particular solution of (1) provided that

$$g_1 \cdot v_1' + g_2 \cdot v_2' + \cdots + g_n \cdot v_n' = 0 \text{ R } \mathscr{I}$$

$$g_1' \cdot v_1' + g_2' \cdot v_2' + \cdots + g_n' \cdot v_n' = 0 \text{ R } \mathscr{I}$$

$$\vdots$$

$$g_1^{(n-2)} \cdot v_1' + g_2^{(n-2)} \cdot v_2' + \cdots + g_n^{(n-2)} \cdot v_n' = 0 \text{ R } \mathscr{I}$$

$$g_1^{(n-1)} \cdot v_1' + g_2^{(n-1)} \cdot v_2' + \cdots + g_n^{(n-1)} \cdot v_n' = p_{n+1} \text{ R } \mathscr{I}.$$

Notice that the method of variation of parameter provides us with a sure-fire technique for finding a particular solution of (1) in case we have a complete solution of (2). Unfortunately, if n is greater than 2, the details become quite messy. We postpone an example of this method to Section 10.3.

E X E R C I S E S

1. Find a complete solution of each of the following.
   a. $f^{(3)} = 6$.   (Answer: $f = k_1 + k_2 x + k_3 x^2 + x^3$)
   b. $f^{(3)} = x^2$.   (Answer: $f = k_1 + k_2 x + k_3 x^2 + x^5/60$)
   c. $f^{(4)} = \exp$.   (Answer: $f = k_1 + k_2 x + k_3 x^2 + k_4 x^3 + \exp$)
   d. $f^{(4)} = \sin 2x$.   (Answer: $f = k_1 + k_2 x + k_3 x^2 + k_4 x^3 + (1/16) \sin 2x$)

2. Find a function, say f, such that $f^{(3)} = x \exp$, $f(1) = 0$, $f'(1) = 5$, $f^{(2)}(1) = -2$.
   (Answer: $f = (x - 3) \exp - 2x^2 + (e + 7)x + e - 5$)

3. Prove Theorem 10.1.2.

4. Simplify the following.
   a. $W(1, x, x^2)$.   (Answer: 2)
   b. $W(x, x^2, x^3)$.   (Answer: $2x^3$)
   c. $W(x, x, x^2, x^2)$.   (Answer: 0)
   d. $W(\sin, \cos, x)$.   (Answer: $-x$)
   e. $[W(\sin, \cos, x)]'$ (in two ways).
   f. $[W(x, x^2, x^3)]'$ (in two ways).

5. Prove that $W(f, g, h) = f \cdot W(g', h') - g \cdot W(f', h') + h \cdot W(f', g')$ whenever f, g, and h are functions.

6. Prove that $W(f, g, h) = -f' \cdot [W(g, h)]' + g' \cdot [W(f, h)]' - h' \cdot [W(f, g)]'$ whenever f, g, and h are functions.

7. Prove that

$$[W(g_1, g_2, \cdots, g_n)]^{(2)} = \begin{vmatrix} g_1 & g_2 & \cdots & g_n \\ g_1' & g_2' & \cdots & g_n' \\ & & \vdots & \\ g_1^{n(-2)} & g_2^{(n-2)} & \cdots & g_n^{(n-2)} \\ g_1^{(n+1)} & g_2^{(n+1)} & \cdots & g_n^{(n+1)} \end{vmatrix}$$

whenever $g_1, g_2, \cdots, g_n$ are functions.

10.2 Homogeneous Linear Differential Equations with Constant Coefficients

In general, it is a difficult matter to determine a complete solution of a homogeneous linear differential equation whose coefficients are not constant functions; indeed, it is hard to find a particular solution of such an equation. On the other hand, it is a simple matter to find a complete solution of a homogeneous linear differential equation whose coefficients are constant functions. We have only to apply the method of Section 9.5.

Let $a_1, a_2, \cdots, a_n$ be real numbers; consider the differential equation

(1)
$$f^{(n)} + a_1 f^{(n-1)} + \cdots + a_{n-1} f' + a_n f = 0.$$

Following the method of Section 9.5, we shall find n linearly independent functions, each with domain R, which satisfy (1). The idea is to consider the function $\exp(rx)$, where r is a complex number. We readily find that this function is a particular solution of (1) iff

(2)
$$r^n + a_1 r^{n-1} + \cdots + a_{n-1} r + a_n = 0.$$

Equation (2) is said to be the *auxiliary* equation of (1), or the *characteristic* equation of (1). The point is that the roots of the characteristic equation lead us to n linearly independent solutions of (1). In particular,

a. If s is a real root of (2), then $\exp(sx)$ is a particular solution of (1).
b. If $\alpha + i\beta$ is a complex root of (2), then so is $\alpha - i\beta$; it follows that $(\cos \beta x) \cdot \exp(\alpha x)$ and $(\sin \beta x) \cdot \exp(\alpha x)$ are linearly independent solutions of (1).
c. If s is a real root of the characteristic equation of multiplicity m, then each of $\exp(sx)$, $x \exp(sx), \cdots, x^{m-1} \exp(sx)$ is a solution of (1). Moreover, these functions are linearly independent.
d. If $\alpha + \beta i$ is a complex root of the characteristic equation of multiplicity m, then so is $\alpha - \beta i$; it follows that

$$(\cos \beta x) \cdot \exp(\alpha x), \quad x(\cos \beta x) \cdot \exp(\alpha x), \quad \cdots, \quad x^{m-1}(\cos \beta x) \cdot \exp(\alpha x),$$
$$(\sin \beta x) \cdot \exp(\alpha x), \quad x(\sin \beta x) \cdot \exp(\alpha x), \quad \cdots, \quad x^{m-1}(\sin \beta x) \cdot \exp(\alpha x)$$

are solutions of (1). Moreover, these functions are linearly independent.

EXAMPLE 1. Find a complete solution of $f^{(4)} - 3f^{(3)} - 3f^{(2)} + 7f' + 6f = 0$.

Solution: The characteristic equation is $r^4 - 3r^3 - 3r^2 + 7r + 6 = 0$, i.e., $(r+1)^2(r-2)(r-3) = 0$. Thus 2 and 3 are simple roots, whereas -1 is a root of multiplicity 2. Accordingly, $\exp(2x)$, $\exp(3x)$, $\exp(-x)$, and $x \exp(-x)$ are linearly independent solutions of the given differential equation. It can be shown directly that these functions are particular solutions of the given differential equation. To see that these functions are linearly independent on R, we have only to examine their Wronskian; indeed,

$$W(\exp(2x), \exp(3x), \exp(-x), x\exp(-x)) = \exp(3x) \cdot \begin{vmatrix} 1 & 1 & 1 & x \\ 2 & 3 & -1 & 1-x \\ 4 & 9 & 1 & x-2 \\ 8 & 27 & -1 & 3-x \end{vmatrix}$$

$$= \exp(3x) \cdot \begin{vmatrix} 1 & 1 & 1 & x \\ 3 & 4 & 0 & 1 \\ 3 & 8 & 0 & -2 \\ 9 & 28 & 0 & 3 \end{vmatrix}$$

$$= -\exp(3x) \cdot \begin{vmatrix} 3 & 4 & 1 \\ 3 & 8 & -2 \\ 9 & 28 & 3 \end{vmatrix}$$

$$= -144 \exp(3x).$$

We conclude that $f = k_1 \exp(2x) + k_2 \exp(3x) + (k_3 + k_4 x) \exp(-x)$ is a complete solution.

EXAMPLE 2.   Find a complete solution of $f^{(4)} + 2f^{(2)} + f = 0$.

Solution: The characteristic equation is $r^4 + 2r^2 + 1 = 0$, i.e., $(r^2 + 1)^2 = 0$. Thus i is a root of multiplicity 2. Accordingly, cos, x cos, sin, and x sin are linearly independent solutions of the given differential equation. It can be shown directly that these functions are particular solutions; moreover, their Wronskian is not zero. We leave it as an exercise to check that $W(\cos, x \cos, \sin, x \sin) = -4$. We conclude that $f = (k_1 + k_2 x) \cos + (k_3 + k_4 x) \sin$ is a complete solution of the given differential equation.

We have pointed out that any homogeneous linear differential equation with constant coefficients can be solved completely provided that the associated characteristic equation can be solved completely. Thus the *theory of equations* has a direct application to *differential equations*. Although the differential equations of the examples of this section possess characteristic equations that are easy to solve, one should not think that this is always the case. Indeed, it can be quite troublesome to solve the associated characteristic equation. However, the theory of equations provides us with several methods of approximating the zeros of a given polynomial.

E X E R C I S E S

Find a complete solution of each of the following.

1. $f^{(3)} - 6f^{(2)} + 11f' - 6f = 0$.   (*Answer:* $f = k_1 \exp + k_2 \exp(2x) + k_3 \exp(3x)$)

2. $f^{(3)} - 2f^{(2)} - f' + 2f = 0$.

3. $f^{(3)} - 3f' + 2f = 0$.   (*Answer:* $f = k_1 \exp(-2x) + (k_2 + k_3 x) \exp$)

4. $f^{(3)} - 2f^{(2)} + f' - 2f = 0$.

5. $f^{(5)} - 2f^{(4)} + 2f^{(3)} - 4f^{(2)} + f' - 2f = 0.$

(*Answer:* $f = k_1 \exp(2x) + (k_2 + k_3 x) \sin + (k_4 + k_5 x) \cos$)

6. $f^{(4)} - 4f^{(3)} + 6f^{(2)} - 4f' + f = 0.$

7. $f^{(4)} - 2f^{(3)} + f^{(2)} + 2f' + f = 0.$

(*Answer:* $f = (k_1 + k_2 x) \exp(-x) + k_3 \sin + k_4 \cos$)

8. $f^{(4)} - 8f^{(3)} + 33f^{(2)} - 68f' + 52f = 0.$

(*Answer:* $f = (k_1 + k_2 x) \exp(2x) + \exp(2x) \cdot [k_3 \sin 3x + k_4 \cos 3x]$)

9. $f^{(4)} - 2f^{(3)} + 30f^{(2)} - 8f' + 104f = 0.$

(*Answer:* $f = k_1 \sin 2x + k_2 \cos 2x + (k_3 \sin 5x + k_4 \cos 5x) \cdot \exp$)

10 $f^{(6)} - 12f^{(5)} + 63f^{(4)} - 184f^{(3)} + 315f^{(2)} - 300f' + 125f = 0.$

(*Answer:* $f = (k_1 + k_2 x + k_3 x^2) \sin \cdot \exp(2x) + (k_4 + k_5 x + k_6 x^2) \cos \cdot \exp(2x)$)

11. Show that $W(\cos, x \cos, \sin, x \sin) = -4.$

10.3   Variation of Parameter

Here, we shall consider the problem of finding a complete solution of a nonhomogeneous linear differential equation with constant coefficients, say

(1) $$f^{(n)} + a_1 f^{(n-1)} + \cdots + a_{n-1} f' + a_n f = p,$$

where p is a nonzero function which is continuous on an interval.

In view of Theorem 10.1.10, we have only to obtain a particular solution of (1) and a complete solution of the reduced equation

(2) $$f^{(n)} + a_1 f^{(n-1)} + \cdots + a_{n-1} f' + a_n f = 0.$$

In Section 10.2 we have seen how to find a complete solution of (2); thus we are free to concentrate on the job of finding a particular solution of (1). There are four well-known methods that can be used: variation of parameter, undetermined coefficients, the **D** operator, and the Laplace transform. We shall postpone a discussion of the Laplace transform to Chapter 13, and we shall discuss the methods of undetermined coefficients and the **D** operator in Sections 10.4 and 10.5. The theory behind the method of variation of parameters has been thoroughly presented in Section 10.1 (and in a more general setting in that the coefficients need not be constant functions); therefore we have only to apply Theorem 10.1.11. We now illustrate the method of variation of parameter.

EXAMPLE 1.   Find a particular solution of $f^{(4)} - 3f^{(3)} - 3f^{(2)} + 7f' + 6f = 2x^2$, given that $f = k_1 \exp(2x) + k_2 \exp(3x) + (k_3 + k_4 x) \exp(-x)$ is a complete solution of the reduced equation.

Solution: Since $f = k_1 \exp(2x) + k_2 \exp(3x) + (k_3 + k_4 x) \exp(-x)$ is a complete solution of the reduced equation, it follows that the functions $\exp(2x)$, $\exp(3x)$, $\exp(-x)$, and $x \exp(-x)$ are linearly independent on R. This is easy to verify by examining the Wronskian; indeed, $W(\exp(2x), \exp(3x), \exp(-x), x \exp(-x)) = 144 \exp(3x)$. Now we apply Theorem 10.1.11; by this theorem, $v_1 \cdot \exp(2x) + v_2 \cdot \exp(3x) + v_3 \cdot \exp(-x) + v_4 \cdot x \cdot \exp(-x)$ is a particular solution of the given differential equation, provided that

$$v_1' \cdot \exp(2x) + v_2' \cdot \exp(3x) + v_3' \cdot \exp(-x) + v_4' \cdot x \cdot \exp(-x) = 0,$$

$$2v_1' \cdot \exp(2x) + 3v_2' \cdot \exp(3x) - v_3' \cdot \exp(-x) + v_4' \cdot (1 - x) \cdot \exp(-x) = 0,$$

$$4v_1' \cdot \exp(2x) + 9v_2' \cdot \exp(3x) + v_3' \cdot \exp(-x) + v_4' \cdot (x - 2) \cdot \exp(-x) = 0,$$

$$8v_1' \cdot \exp(2x) + 27v_2' \cdot \exp(3x) - v_3' \cdot \exp(-x) + v_4' \cdot (3 - x) \cdot \exp(-x) = 2x^2.$$

Here, the calculations are simplified by incorporating the exponential functions into the unknowns. Let us find functions u_1, u_2, u_3, and u_4 such that

$$u_1 + u_2 + u_3 + xu_4 = 0,$$

$$2u_1 + 3u_2 - u_3 + (1 - x)u_4 = 0,$$

$$4u_1 + 9u_2 + u_3 + (x - 2)u_4 = 0,$$

$$8u_1 + 27u_2 - u_3 + (3 - x)u_4 = 2x^2.$$

The determinant of the coefficient matrix is the function

$$
\begin{vmatrix} 1 & 1 & 1 & x \\ 2 & 3 & -1 & 1-x \\ 4 & 9 & 1 & x-2 \\ 8 & 27 & -1 & 3-x \end{vmatrix} = \begin{vmatrix} 1 & 1 & 1 & x \\ 3 & 4 & 0 & 1 \\ 3 & 8 & 0 & -2 \\ 9 & 28 & 0 & 3 \end{vmatrix} = 12 \begin{vmatrix} 1 & 1 & 1 \\ 1 & 2 & -2 \\ 3 & 7 & 3 \end{vmatrix} = 144.
$$

Thus

$$u_1 = \frac{-2x^2}{144} \cdot \begin{vmatrix} 1 & 1 & x \\ 3 & -1 & 1-x \\ 9 & 1 & x-2 \end{vmatrix} = \frac{-2x^2}{9},$$

$$u_2 = \frac{2x^2}{144} \cdot \begin{vmatrix} 1 & 1 & x \\ 2 & -1 & 1-x \\ 4 & 1 & x-2 \end{vmatrix} = \frac{x^2}{8},$$

$$u_3 = \frac{-2x^2}{144} \cdot \begin{vmatrix} 1 & 1 & x \\ 2 & 3 & 1-x \\ 4 & 9 & x-2 \end{vmatrix} = \frac{7x^2}{72} - \frac{x^3}{6},$$

$$u_4 = \frac{2x^2}{144} \cdot \begin{vmatrix} 1 & 1 & 1 \\ 2 & 3 & -1 \\ 4 & 9 & 1 \end{vmatrix} = \frac{x^2}{6}.$$

Hence $v_1' = (-2/9)x^2 \exp(-2x)$, $v_2' = (x^2/8) \exp(-3x)$, $v_3' = (7x^2/72 - x^3/6) \exp$, and $v_4' = (x^2/6) \exp$. Antidifferentiating, we find that

$$v_1 = (x^2/9 + x/9 + 1/18) \exp(-2x), \quad v_2 = -(x^2/24 + x/36 + 1/108) \exp(-3x),$$
$$v_3 = (1/72)(-12x^3 + 43x^2 - 86x + 86) \exp, \quad \text{and} \quad v_4 = (x^2/6 - x/3 + 1/3) \exp.$$

We conclude that

$$(x^2/9 + x/9 + 1/18) - (x^2/24 + x/36 + 1/108)$$

$$+ (-12x^3 + 43x^2 - 86x + 86)/72 + (x^3/6 - x^2/3 + x/3)$$

is a particular solution of the given differential equation; i.e., $x^2/3 - 7x/9 + 67/54$ is a particular solution. Checking, we see that this is correct.

Just what does Example 1 illustrate? Of course, it shows how the method of variation of parameter works in detail. From the length of the solution, one might deduce that Example 1 illustrates how *not* to solve a problem. The point is that this method is so complicated and involved that one will likely make a slip before completing the work. In short, this method is generally not practical (except when $n = 2$). For this reason, in the following sections we shall develop superior methods of finding a particular solution of a differential equation of the type (1).

E X E R C I S E

Find a complete solution of $f^{(3)} - f^{(2)} - 4f' + 4f = x^2$, using the method of this section.
(*Answer:* $f = k_1 \exp + k_2 \exp(2x) + k_3 \exp(-2x) + x^2/4 + x/2 + 5/8$)

10.4   Operators

Elementary calculus is concerned largely with functions with one argument. Recall that a nonvacuous *function* is a special kind of *mapping*; indeed, any mapping of a non-empty subset of R into R is called a function. In elementary calculus we learn how to *differentiate* functions, i.e.; we associate with a given function f a certain function which is called the *derivative of f* and is denoted by "f'". We can regard this as a mapping of $\mathscr{F}$, the set of all functions, into $\mathscr{F}$. Let us agree to call any such mapping an *operator*.

DEFINITION 10.4.1.   Let $\mathscr{F}$ be the set of all functions with one argument; then any mapping of $\mathscr{F}$ into $\mathscr{F}$ is said to be an *operator*.

Essentially, an operator is a rule which associates a function with a given function. For example, the square of a function is again a function; i.e., we can associate f^2 with f. We can associate with f the function $\int_0^x f$; we can associate with f the function $f^{(2)}$.

Since we want to solve differential equations, let us concentrate on the operator which associates f' with f. It is helpful to give this operator a name, say "**D**". Thus $\mathbf{D}f = f'$ whenever f is a function. Clearly, $\mathbf{D}(\mathbf{D}f) = \mathbf{D}f' = f^{(2)}$, and $\mathbf{D}(\mathbf{D}(\mathbf{D}f))) = \mathbf{D}f^{(2)} = f^{(3)}$. Generalizing, if $\mathcal{O}$ is an operator and n is a nonnegative integer, then the operator $\mathcal{O}^n$ is defined as follows:

(i) $\mathcal{O}^0 f = f$ whenever f is a function,

(ii) $\mathcal{O}^{k+1} f = \mathcal{O}(\mathcal{O}^k f)$ whenever f is a function.

For example, $D^3f = D(D^2f) = Df^{(2)} = f^{(3)}$ since $D^2f = D(Df) = f^{(2)}$. Indeed, it is easy to prove that $D^nf = f^{(n)}$ whenever n is a nonnegative integer.

Let us see how to obtain more operators of this sort. Let $a \in R$; then we define the operator a as follows: $af = a \cdot f$ whenever $f \in \mathcal{F}$. Of course, this is a familiar operator. Moreover, if h is a given function with one argument, then we shall regard h as the operator that associates $h \cdot f$ with f whenever $f \in \mathcal{F}$. Notice the use of boldface type to help distinguish between a function and the corresponding operator.

DEFINITION 10.4.2.   Let $h \in \mathcal{F}$; then $\mathbf{h} = \{(f, g) \mid f \in \mathcal{F} \text{ and } g = h \cdot f\}$.

We now introduce the sum and product of operators; of course, these are binary operations on operators and shall be denoted by " $+$ " and " $\cdot$ ", respectively. By the *product* of two operators we mean the composite mapping; note that Definition 10.4.4 is a generalization of $\mathcal{O}^2$.

DEFINITION 10.4.3.   Let $\mathcal{O}_1$ and $\mathcal{O}_2$ be any operators; then $\mathcal{O}_1 + \mathcal{O}_2 = \{(f, g) \mid f \in \mathcal{F}$ and $g = \mathcal{O}_1 f + \mathcal{O}_2 f\}$.

DEFINITION 10.4.4.   Let $\mathcal{O}_1$ and $\mathcal{O}_2$ be any operators; then $\mathcal{O}_1 \cdot \mathcal{O}_2 = \{(f, g) \mid f \in \mathcal{F}$ and $g = \mathcal{O}_1(\mathcal{O}_2 f)\}$.

It is customary to suppress the dot of multiplication, writing " $\mathcal{O}_1\mathcal{O}_2$ " in place of " $\mathcal{O}_1 \cdot \mathcal{O}_2$ ".

To illustrate these concepts, we point out that the operator $D + D^2$ associates $f' + f^{(2)}$ with f whenever $f \in \mathcal{F}$; moreover, the operator $5D^3 + 2D^6$ associates $5f^{(3)} + 2f^{(6)}$ with f whenever $f \in \mathcal{F}$. Also $D \cdot x^3 = \{(f, g) \mid f \in \mathcal{F}$ and $g = (x^3f)'\} = 3x^2 + x^3D$.

The following theorem follows from Definition 10.4.4.

THEOREM 10.4.1.   Let $a \in R$ and let n be any nonnegative integer; then $\mathbf{a}D^n = \{(f, g) \mid f \in \mathcal{F}$ and $g = af^{(n)}\}$.

It is useful to develop an *algebra* of operators.

THEOREM 10.4.2 (Commutative Law). $\mathcal{O}_1 + \mathcal{O}_2 = \mathcal{O}_2 + \mathcal{O}_1$ whenever $\mathcal{O}_1$ and $\mathcal{O}_2$ are operators.

Proof: By Definition 10.4.1, $[\mathcal{O}_1 + \mathcal{O}_2]f = \mathcal{O}_1 f + \mathcal{O}_2 f = \mathcal{O}_2 f + \mathcal{O}_1 f$ since addition of functions is commutative. Also, $[\mathcal{O}_2 + \mathcal{O}_1]f = \mathcal{O}_2 f + \mathcal{O}_1 f$.

THEOREM 10.4.3 (Associative Law). $\mathcal{O}_1 + (\mathcal{O}_2 + \mathcal{O}_3) = (\mathcal{O}_1 + \mathcal{O}_2) + \mathcal{O}_3$ whenever $\mathcal{O}_1$, $\mathcal{O}_2$, and $\mathcal{O}_3$ are operators.
Proof: Apply Definition 10.4.3.

THEOREM 10.4.4 (Associative Law). $\mathcal{O}_1 \cdot (\mathcal{O}_2 \cdot \mathcal{O}_3) = (\mathcal{O}_1 \cdot \mathcal{O}_2) \cdot \mathcal{O}_3$ whenever $\mathcal{O}_1$, $\mathcal{O}_2$, and $\mathcal{O}_3$ are operators.
Proof: Apply Definition 10.4.4.

THEOREM 10.4.5 (Distributive Law).
$(\mathcal{O}_1 + \mathcal{O}_2) \cdot \mathcal{O}_3 = \mathcal{O}_1 \cdot \mathcal{O}_3 + \mathcal{O}_2 \cdot \mathcal{O}_3$ whenever $\mathcal{O}_1$, $\mathcal{O}_2$, and $\mathcal{O}_3$ are operators.
Proof: Apply Definitions 10.4.3 and 10.4.4.

We point out that multiplication of operators is *not* commutative. For example, $\mathbf{x}^2 \cdot \mathbf{D} \neq \mathbf{D} \cdot \mathbf{x}^2$ since the operator $\mathbf{x}^2 \cdot \mathbf{D}$ associates $x^2 f'$ with f whenever $f \in \mathcal{F}$, whereas the operator $\mathbf{D} \cdot \mathbf{x}^2$ associates $2xf + x^2 f'$ with f whenever $f \in \mathcal{F}$.

Since addition and multiplication are both associative, we shall suppress the parentheses which appear in a chain of additions or multiplications. For example, we shall write "$\mathcal{O}_1 + \mathcal{O}_2 + \mathcal{O}_3$" in place of "$\mathcal{O}_1 + (\mathcal{O}_2 + \mathcal{O}_3)$".

Next, let $a_0, a_1, \cdots, a_n$ be real numbers where $a_n \neq 0$, and consider the operator $\mathbf{a}_n \mathbf{D}^n + \mathbf{a}_{n-1} \mathbf{D}^{n-1} + \cdots + \mathbf{a}_1 \mathbf{D} + \mathbf{a}_0$. We need a name for this operator. Let "P" denote the corresponding polynomial function $a_n x^n + a_{n-1} x^{n-1} + \cdots + a_1 x + a_0$; then we shall take "$P(\mathbf{D})$" to be a name of our operator. Thus $P(\mathbf{D}) = \sum_{i=0}^{n} \mathbf{a}_i \mathbf{D}^i$ whenever $P = \sum_{i=0}^{n} a_i x^i$. We shall call $P(\mathbf{D})$ a *polynomial operator*. Let us establish the basic properties of polynomial operators. Notice that in the following theorems we use "$\mathcal{P}$" as a place-holder, or variable, for polynomial operators.

THEOREM 10.4.6. Let $\mathcal{P}$ be any polynomial operator and let $k \in R$; then $\mathcal{P} \cdot \mathbf{k} = \mathbf{k} \cdot \mathcal{P}$.

Proof: Let $\mathcal{P} = \sum_{i=0}^{n} \mathbf{a}_i \mathbf{D}^i$; we must show that $\mathcal{P}(kf) = [k\mathcal{P}]f$ whenever $f \in \mathcal{F}$. But $(kf)^{(t)} = kf^{(t)}$ whenever $t \in N$; hence

$$\mathcal{P}(kf) = \sum_{i=0}^{n} \mathbf{a}_i \mathbf{D}^i(kf) = a_n(kf)^{(n)} + a_{n-1}(kf)^{(n-1)} + \cdots + a_1(kf)' + a_0$$

$$= a_n kf^{(n)} + a_{n-1} kf^{(n-1)} + \cdots + a_1 kf' + a_0$$

$$= k \sum_{i=0}^{n} a_i f^{(i)}$$

$$= [k\mathcal{P}]f.$$

THEOREM 10.4.7. Let $\mathcal{P}$ be any polynomial operator, let $f \in \mathcal{F}$, and let $g \in \mathcal{F}$; then $\mathcal{P}(f + g) = \mathcal{P}f + \mathcal{P}g$.

Proof: Let $\mathcal{P} = \sum_{i=0}^{n} \mathbf{a}_i \mathbf{D}^i$; now, $(f + g)^{(t)} = f^{(t)} + g^{(t)}$ whenever $t \in N$; thus

$$\mathcal{P}(f + g) = \sum_{i=0}^{n} \mathbf{a}_i \mathbf{D}^i(f + g) = \sum_{i=0}^{n} a_i(f + g)^{(i)} = \sum_{i=0}^{n} a_i[f^{(i)} + g^{(i)}]$$

$$= \sum_{i=0}^{n} a_i f^{(i)} + \sum_{i=0}^{n} a_i g^{(i)} = \mathcal{P}f + \mathcal{P}g.$$

THEOREM 10.4.8.   Let $\mathcal{P}$ be any polynomial operator, let $f_1 \in \mathcal{F}, f_2 \in \mathcal{F}, k_1 \in R$, and $k_2 \in R$; then $\mathcal{P}(k_1 f_1 + k_2 f_2) = [k_1 \mathcal{P}] f_1 + [k_2 \mathcal{P}] f_2$.

Proof: $\mathcal{P}(k_1 f_1 + k_2 f_2) = \mathcal{P}(k_1 f_1) + \mathcal{P}(k_2 f_2)$ by Th. 10.4.7

$$= [k_1 \mathcal{P}] f_1 + [k_2 \mathcal{P}] f_2 \quad \text{by Th. 10.4.6.}$$

THEOREM 10.4.9.   Let $\mathcal{P}$ be any polynomial operator, let $f_i \in \mathcal{F}$, and let $k_i \in R$ whenever $1 \le i \le m$; then $\mathcal{P}\left(\sum_{i=1}^{m} k_i f_i \right) = \sum_{i=1}^{m} [k_i \mathcal{P}] f_i$.

Proof: Use mathematical induction on m. The details are left as an exercise.

THEOREM 10.4.10.   Let $\mathcal{P}$ be any polynomial operator; then $\mathbf{D}\mathcal{P} = \mathcal{P}\mathbf{D}$.

Proof: Let $\mathcal{P} = \sum_{i=0}^{n} \mathbf{a}_i \mathbf{D}^i$ and let $f \in \mathcal{F}$. Then

$$[\mathbf{D}\mathcal{P}](f) = \mathbf{D}(\mathcal{P}(f)) = \left[\sum_{i=0}^{n} a_i f^{(i)} \right]' = \sum_{i=0}^{n} a_i f^{(i+1)}$$

and

$$[\mathcal{P}\mathbf{D}](f) = \mathcal{P}(f') = \sum_{i=0}^{n} a_i f^{(i+1)}.$$

COROLLARY 10.4.1.   Let $\mathcal{P}$ be any polynomial operator and let $n \in N$; then $\mathbf{D}^n \mathcal{P} = \mathcal{P}\mathbf{D}^n$.

Proof: Use mathematical induction on n.

We can now establish a useful property of multiplication.

THEOREM 10.4.11. $\mathcal{P}_1 \mathcal{P}_2 = \mathcal{P}_2 \mathcal{P}_1$ whenever $\mathcal{P}_1$ and $\mathcal{P}_2$ are polynomial operators.

Proof: Let $\mathcal{P}_1 = \sum_{i=0}^{n} \mathbf{a}_i \mathbf{D}^i$, let $\mathcal{P}_2 = \sum_{i=0}^{m} \mathbf{b}_i \mathbf{D}^i$, and let $f \in \mathcal{F}$. Then $\mathcal{P}_2(f) = \sum_{i=0}^{m} b_i f^{(i)}$; therefore

$$[\mathcal{P}_1 \mathcal{P}_2](f) = \mathcal{P}_1(\mathcal{P}_2(f)) = \mathcal{P}_1 \left[\sum_{i=0}^{m} b_i f^{(i)} \right] = \sum_{i=0}^{m} [\mathbf{b}_i \mathcal{P}_1](f^{(i)}) \quad \text{by Th. 10.4.9}$$

$$= \sum_{i=0}^{m} \mathbf{b}_i [\mathcal{P}_1 f]^{(i)} \quad\quad\quad\quad\quad\quad \text{by Cor. 10.4.1}$$

$$= \mathcal{P}_2(\mathcal{P}_1 f)$$

$$= [\mathcal{P}_2 \mathcal{P}_1] f.$$

This establishes our result.

Notice that any linear differential equation with constant coefficients can be represented by means of a polynomial operator. For example, let $\mathscr{P} = \sum_{i=0}^{n} a_i D^i$, where $a_n = 1$; then the differential equation $f^{(n)} + a_{n-1} f^{(n-1)} + \cdots + a_1 f' + a_0 f = q$ is expressed compactly by writing "$\mathscr{P}f = q$".

THEOREM 10.4.12. If $\mathscr{P}f = q$, then $\mathscr{P}(f') = q'$.

Proof: We are given that $\mathscr{P}f = q$; therefore $D(\mathscr{P}f) = Dq$. Hence, by Theorem 10.4.10, $\mathscr{P}(Df) = q'$, i.e., $\mathscr{P}(f') = q'$.

The following two theorems show that a polynomial operator can be factored by factoring the corresponding polynomial function.

THEOREM 10.4.13 Let P_2 and P_3 be polynomial functions such that $P_3 = (x + a)P_2$; then $P_3(D) = (D + a) \cdot P_2(D)$.

Proof: Let $P_3 = (x + a)P_2$ and let $P_2 = \sum_{i=0}^{n} b_i x^i$; then

$$P_3 = (x + a)\sum_{i=0}^{n} b_i x^i = ab_0 + \sum_{i=0}^{n-1}(ab_{i+1} + b_i)x^{i+1} + b_n x^{n+1}.$$

Hence
$$P_3(D) = ab_0 + \sum_{i=0}^{n-1}(ab_{i+1} + b_i)D^{i+1} + b_n D^{n+1}.$$

But

$$(D + a) \cdot P_2(D) = (D + a) \cdot \sum_{i=0}^{n} b_i D^i$$

$$= D \cdot \left[\sum_{i=0}^{n} b_i D^i\right] + a \cdot \sum_{i=0}^{n} b_i D^i \qquad \text{by a Distributive Law}$$

$$= \sum_{i=0}^{n} b_i D^{i+1} + \sum_{i=0}^{n} ab_i D^i$$

$$= ab_0 + \sum_{i=0}^{n}(ab_{i+1} + b_i)D^{i+1} + b_n D^{n+1}$$

$$= P_3(D).$$

This establishes Theorem 10.4.13.

THEOREM 10.4.14. Let P_1, and P_3 be polynomial functions such that $P_3 = P_1 \cdot P_2$; then $P_3(D) = P_1(D) \cdot P_2(D)$.

Proof: Apply mathematical induction to the degree of the polynomial function P_1. The details are left as an exercise.

It is clear from Theorem 10.4.14 that we can factor a polynomial operator by factoring the corresponding polynomial function. For example, to factor $D^3 - 7D - 6$, we consider the corresponding polynomial function $x^3 - 7x - 6$; since $x^3 - 7x - 6 = (x + 1)(x^2 - x - 6)$, we conclude that $\mathbf{D}^3 - 7\mathbf{D} - 6 = (\mathbf{D} + 1)(\mathbf{D}^2 - \mathbf{D} - 6)$. Moreover, $\mathbf{D}^2 - \mathbf{D} - 6 = (\mathbf{D} + 2)(\mathbf{D} - 3)$; thus $\mathbf{D}^3 - 7\mathbf{D} - 6 = (\mathbf{D} + 1)(\mathbf{D} + 2)(\mathbf{D} - 3)$.

The power of Theorem 10.4.14 may not be immediately apparent. This result provides us with an easy method of factoring a given polynomial operator: merely factor the polynomial function involved. Thus our knowledge of polynomial functions can be applied to differential equations. Now, each polynomial function with real coefficients can be factored into first-degree or second-degree polynomial functions; therefore the problem of solving a linear differential equation with constant coefficients (say of order n) is reduced to solving several linear differential equations of order one or two.

EXAMPLE 1.   Find a particular solution of $(\mathbf{D} + 2)(\mathbf{D} - 1)(\mathbf{D}^2 + 9)f = x$.

Solution: Let $g = (\mathbf{D} - 1)(\mathbf{D}^2 + 9)(f)$; then $(\mathbf{D} + 2)(g) = x$, i.e., $g' + 2g = x$. This differential equation is easy to solve: $\exp(2x)$ is an integrating factor; thus $g \cdot \exp(2x) \equiv \int x \exp(2x) \equiv (x/2 - 1/4)\exp(2x)$; so $g = x/2 - 1/4 + k_1$. Next, we find a particular solution of $(\mathbf{D} - 1)(\mathbf{D}^2 + 9)f = x/2 - 1/4$. Let $(\mathbf{D}^2 + 9)f = h$; then $(\mathbf{D} - 1)h = x/2 - 1/4$; hence $h = -x/2 - 1/4$. Therefore $(\mathbf{D}^2 + 9)f = -x/2 - 1/4$. A particular solution is easily obtained by the method of variation of parameter; we see that $-x/18 + (1/36)\cos 6x$ is a particular solution of the given differential equation. Checking, we verify that this is correct.

It is helpful to present a linear differential equation with constant coefficients in a form which displays the roots of the characteristic equation. Consider the following examples.

EXAMPLE 2.   Find a complete solution of $(\mathbf{D} + 1)(\mathbf{D} + 2)(\mathbf{D} - 3)f = 0$.

Solution: Since the roots of the characteristic equation are -1, -2, and 3, we see that $f = k_1 \exp(-x) + k_2 \exp(-2x) + k_3 \exp(3x)$ is a complete solution of the given differential equation.

EXAMPLE 3.   Find a complete solution of $(\mathbf{D} + 1)(\mathbf{D} + 2)(\mathbf{D} - 3)f = \exp(5x)$.

Solution: Since we already have a complete solution of the reduced equation, we need only a particular solution of the given equation. Examining the function on the right-hand side, namely $\exp(5x)$, we observe that this function is a particular solution of the homogeneous linear differential equation $(\mathbf{D} - 5)f = 0$, since $(\mathbf{D} - 5)\exp(5x) = 0$. We now apply the operator $\mathbf{D} - 5$ to both sides of the given differential equation; we obtain

$$(\mathbf{D} - 5)(\mathbf{D} + 1)(\mathbf{D} + 2)(\mathbf{D} - 3)f = 0.$$

We are faced with a homogeneous linear differential equation with constant coefficients. A complete solution of this equation is

$$f = k_1 \exp(-x) + k_2 \exp(-2x) + k_3 \exp(3x) + k_4 \exp(5x).$$

Let $f_c = k_1 \exp(-x) + k_2 \exp(-2x) + k_3 \exp(3x)$; by Therem 10.4.7,

$$(\mathbf{D} + 1)(\mathbf{D} + 2)(\mathbf{D} - 3)(f_c + k_4 \exp(5x)) = (\mathbf{D} + 1)(\mathbf{D} + 2)(\mathbf{D} - 3)f_c$$
$$+ (\mathbf{D} + 1)(\mathbf{D} + 2)(\mathbf{D} - 3)(k_4 \exp(5x))$$
$$= (\mathbf{D} + 1)(\mathbf{D} + 2)(\mathbf{D} - 3)(k_4 \exp(5x)).$$

We conclude that there is a real number A such that $A \exp(5x)$ is a particular solution of the given differential equation. But $(\mathbf{D} + 1)(\mathbf{D} + 2)(\mathbf{D} - 3)(A \exp(5x)) = 84A \exp(5x)$; thus $A = 1/84$. This means that $(1/84) \exp(5x)$ is a particular solution; so $f = k_1 \exp(-x) + k_2 \exp(-2x) + k_3 \exp(3x) + (1/84) \exp(5x)$ is a complete solution.

EXAMPLE 4.   Find a particular solution of $(\mathbf{D} + 1)(\mathbf{D} + 2)(\mathbf{D} - 3)f = x^2$.

Solution: Now, x^2 is a solution of the linear homogeneous differential equation $\mathbf{D}^3 f = 0$. Accordingly, we shall apply the operator $\mathbf{D}^3$ to both sides of the given equation: we obtain

$$\mathbf{D}^3(\mathbf{D} + 1)(\mathbf{D} + 2)(\mathbf{D} - 3)f = 0.$$

We have reduced the given nonhomogeneous equation to a homogeneous equation which we can solve completely. A complete solution is

$$f = [k_1 \exp(-x) + k_2 \exp(-2x) + k_3 \exp(3x)] + [k_4 + k_5 x + k_6 x^2].$$

Since $k_1 \exp(-x) + k_2 \exp(-2x) + k_3 \exp(3x)$ is a solution of the reduced equation, i.e., $(\mathbf{D} + 1)(\mathbf{D} + 2)(\mathbf{D} - 3)f = 0$, we conclude that there are real numbers A, B, and C such that $A + Bx + Cx^2$ is a particular solution of the given differential equation, Now, $(\mathbf{D} + 1)(\mathbf{D} + 2)$ $(\mathbf{D} - 3)(A + Bx + Cx^2) = -6A - 7B + x(-6B - 14C) - 6Cx^2$; so we require that $-6A - 7B = 0$, $-6B - 14C = 0$, and $-6C = 1$. Thus $A = -49/108$, $B = 7/18$, and $C = -1/6$. Therefore $-49/108 + 7x/18 - x^2/6$ is a particular solution of the given equation.

E X E R C I S E S

1.   Verify the following statements.
   a. $(\mathbf{D}^2 + 5)f = 5f + f^{(2)}$ whenever $f \in \mathcal{F}$.
   b. $(\mathbf{D}^2 + 5)x^3 = 6x + 5x^3$.
   c. $(\mathbf{D}^2 + 5)x = 5x$.
   d. $(\mathbf{D}^2 + 5)x = 2\mathbf{D} + x\mathbf{D}^2 + 5x$.
   e. $\mathbf{D} \cdot \sin = \{(f, g) \mid f \in \mathcal{F} \text{ and } g = f \cdot \cos + f' \cdot \sin\}$.
   f. $\mathbf{D}^2 = \mathbf{D} \cdot \mathbf{D}$.
   g. $\mathbf{D}^3 = \mathbf{D} \cdot \mathbf{D}^2$.
   h. $\mathbf{D}^3 = \mathbf{D}^2 \cdot \mathbf{D}$.
   i. $\mathbf{D} \cdot \cos \neq \cos \cdot \mathbf{D}$.
   j. $\mathbf{D} \cdot \mathbf{x} \neq \mathbf{x} \cdot \mathbf{D}$.
   k. $\mathbf{D} \cdot (1 + \mathbf{D}^2) = (1 + \mathbf{D}^2) \cdot \mathbf{D}$.

2.   Prove Theorem 10.4.1.

3.   Let $h \in \mathcal{F}$ and let $\mathcal{O}$ be any operator. Prove that $\mathbf{h} \cdot \mathcal{O} = \{(f, g) \mid f \in \mathcal{F} \text{ and } g = h \cdot (\mathcal{O}f)\}$.

4.   Prove Theorem 10.4.3.

5.   Prove Theorem 10.4.4.

6.   Prove Theorem 10.4.5.

7.   Let $P = 3 + 2x - x^3$.
   a. Write down $P(\mathbf{D})$.
   b. Compute $[P(\mathbf{D})]\sin$.   (*Answer:* $3(\sin + \cos)$)
   c. Simplify $\mathbf{D} \cdot P(\mathbf{D})$.   (*Answer:* $3\mathbf{D} + 2\mathbf{D}^2 - \mathbf{D}^4$)
   d. Compute $[\mathbf{D} \cdot P(\mathbf{D})]\sin$ in two ways.   (*Answer:* $3(\cos - \sin)$)

8.   Prove Theorem 10.4.9.

9. a. Let $k \in R$ and let $\mathscr{P}$ be any polynomial operator. Prove that $[k\mathscr{P}]f = k[\mathscr{P}f]$ whenever $f \in \mathscr{F}$.

b. Let $g \in \mathscr{F}$ and let $\mathscr{P}$ be any polynomial operator. Prove that $[g\mathscr{P}]f = g \cdot [\mathscr{P}f]$ whenever $f \in \mathscr{F}$.

10. a. Let $k \in R$ and let $\mathscr{P}$ be any polynomial operator. Prove that $\mathscr{P}(kf) = k[\mathscr{P}f]$ whenever $f \in \mathscr{F}$.

b. Let $\mathscr{P}$ be any polynomial operator, let $f_i \in \mathscr{F}$, and let $k_i \in R$ whenever $i \leq i \leq m$. Prove that $\mathscr{P} \sum_{i=1}^{m} k_i f_i = \sum_{i=1}^{m} k_i [\mathscr{P} f_i]$.

11. Prove Corollary 10.4.1.

12. Factor each of the following polynomial operators.

a. $D^3 + 3D^2 + 3D + 1$.

b. $D^3 + 2D^2 + D$.

c. $D^4 - 5D^3 + 6D^2$.

d. $D^4 + D^3 + 2D^2 + 4D - 8$.

e. $D^4 + D^3 - 5D^2 + D - 6$.

13. Prove Theorem 10.4.14.

14. Find a particular solution of each of the following.

a. $(D^2 - 3D + 2)f = x$.

b. $(D^2 - 3D + 2)f = 3x - x^2$.

c. $(D^2 - 3D + 2)f = \exp(2x)$.

d. $(D^2 - 2D + 1)f = 5x$.

e. $(D^2 - 2D + 1)f = \exp(3x)$.

f. $(D^2 - 2D + 1)f = \exp$.

g. $(D^3 + 3D^2 + 3D + 1)f = x^2$.

h. $(D^4 + D^3 - 5D^2 + D - 6)f = 2 \sin - 3 \cos$.

15. Show that $\mathcal{O} + \mathbf{0} = \mathcal{O}$ whenever $\mathcal{O}$ is an operator.

16. a. Show that $\mathbf{0}(f) = \{(a, 0) \mid a \in \mathscr{D}_f\}$ whenever $f \in \mathscr{F}$.

b. Prove that $\mathcal{O} + -1 \cdot \mathcal{O} = \mathbf{0}$ whenever $\mathcal{O}$ is an operator.

17. Prove that $(Op, +, \mathbf{0})$ is an abelian group, where " Op " denotes the set of all operators.

18. a. Show that $\mathbf{1}(f) = f$ whenever $f \in \mathscr{F}$.

b. Show that $\mathbf{1} \cdot \mathbf{f} = \mathbf{f}$ whenever $f \in \mathscr{F}$.

c. Show that $\mathbf{1} \cdot \mathcal{O} = \mathcal{O}$ whenever $\mathcal{O}$ is an operator.

19. Is $(Op, +, \cdot, \mathbf{0})$ a ring?   (*Answer:* No.)

20. Let $f \in \mathscr{F}$. Is it necessarily true that $\mathbf{0} \cdot \mathbf{f} = \mathbf{0}$?

10.5   Undetermined Coefficients

In Section 9.6 we considered a most effective method of finding a particular solution of a nonhomogeneous linear differential equation with constant coefficients; there we saw that the idea is to guess at the *form* of a solution and then to work out the precise solution by using the differential equation itself. This method depends upon an inspired guess; in other words, we need good insight into the nature of a differential equation. Luckily. by using operators we can clarify the situation; with a little knowledge of operators we can state precise conditions under which the method of undetermined coefficients will work, and we can state in advance the precise form of a particular solution. The idea is based on the fact that we can write down a complete solution of any homogeneous linear differential equation with constant coefficients; indeed, a complete solution can be obtained mechanically by expressing such a differential equation as a product of polynomial operators of first or second degree. Now, this process is reversible; i.e., if g is a particular solution of a homogeneous linear differential equation with constant co-efficients, then we can construct a polynomial operator which associates the function zero with the given function g. Let us clarify this point.

EXAMPLE 1.   Find a polynomial operator $\mathscr{P}$ such that $\mathscr{P} \exp(2x) = 0$.

Solution: We know that $\exp(2x)$ is a particular solution of the differential equation $(\mathbf{D} - 2)f = 0$. Therefore $(\mathbf{D} - 2) \exp(2x) = 0$.

EXAMPLE 2.   Find a polynomial operator $\mathscr{P}$ such that $\mathscr{P}[x^3 \exp(-5x)] = 0$.

Solution: We know that $x^3 \exp(-5x)$ is a particular solution of the differential equation $(\mathbf{D} + 5)^4 f = 0$. Thus $(\mathbf{D} + 5)^4[x^3 \exp(-5x)] = 0$.

EXAMPLE 3.   Find a polynomial operator $\mathscr{P}$ such that $\mathscr{P}[x^2 \cos 3x] = 0$.

Solution: We know that $x^2 \cos 3x$ is a particular solution of the differential equation $(\mathbf{D}^2 + 9)^3 f = 0$. Thus $(\mathbf{D}^2 + 9)^3[x^2 \cos 3x] = 0$.

EXAMPLE 4.   Find a polynomial operator $\mathscr{P}$ such that $\mathscr{P}(x \exp(-2x) \cdot \sin 4x) = 0$.

Solution: We know that $x \exp(-2x) \cdot \sin 4x$ is a particular solution of the differential equation $[(\mathbf{D} + 2)^2 + 16]^2 f = 0$. Thus $[\mathbf{D}^2 + 4\mathbf{D} + 20)^2(x \exp(-2x) \cdot \sin 4x) = 0$.

Now we are in a position to see the connection between polynomial operators and the method of undetermined coefficients. Before discussing the idea, we present two examples.

EXAMPLE 5.   Find a particular solution of $(\mathbf{D} + 1)(\mathbf{D} + 2)f = x^2 \exp(4x)$.

Solution: Let g be a particular solution of the given differential equation; then $(\mathbf{D} + 1)(\mathbf{D} - 2)g = x^2 \exp(4x)$. We concentrate on the function which makes up the right-hand side of this equation, namely $x^2 \exp(4x)$. It is easy to see that $(\mathbf{D} - 4)^3[x^2 \exp(4x)] = 0$; therefore $(\mathbf{D} - 4)^3(\mathbf{D} + 1)(\mathbf{D} - 2)g = 0$. This means that g is a particular solution of the homogeneous linear differential equation

$$(\mathbf{D} - 4)^3(\mathbf{D} + 1)(\mathbf{D} - 2)f = 0.$$

It is easy to find a complete solution of this differential equation:

$$f = (k_1 + k_2 x + k_3 x^2) \exp(4x) + k_4 \exp(-x) + k_5 \exp(2x).$$

Thus there are real numbers A, B, C, D, and E such that $g = (A + Bx + Cx^2) \exp(4x) + D \exp(-x) + E \exp(2x)$. Now that we have the *form* of our solution, we can apply the method of undetermined coefficients. We readily determine that $A = .078$, $B = -.14$, $C = .1$ and that we are free to choose D and E as we wish. Taking $D = E = 0$, we see that $(.078 - .14x + .1x^2) \exp(4x)$ is a particular solution of the given differential equation. Checking, we verify that this is correct.

EXAMPLE 6.   Find a particular solution of $(\mathbf{D} - 2)(\mathbf{D} - 3)f = x \cos$.

Solution: Recall that $x \cos$ is a particular solution of the differential equation $(\mathbf{D}^2 + 1)^2 f = 0$; therefore we introduce the polynomial operator $(\mathbf{D}^2 + 1)^2$. Let g be a particular solution of the given differential equation; then $(\mathbf{D}-2)(\mathbf{D}-3)g = x\cos$, and so $(\mathbf{D}^2+1)^2(\mathbf{D}-2)(\mathbf{D}-3)g = (\mathbf{D}^2+1)^2[x\cos] = 0$. Thus g is a particular solution of the differential equation

$$(\mathbf{D}^2+1)^2(\mathbf{D}-2)(\mathbf{D}-3)f = 0.$$

But $f = (k_1 + k_2 x)\cos + (k_3 + k_4 x)\sin + k_5\exp(2x) + k_6\exp(3x)$ is a complete solution of this differential equation. Therefore there exist real numbers A, B, C, D, E, and F such that $g = (A+Bx)\cos + (C+Dx)\sin + E\exp(2x) + F\exp(3x)$. Now, $(\mathbf{D}-2)(\mathbf{D}-3)[A\cos + Bx\cos + C\sin + Dx\sin + E\exp(2x) + F\exp(3x)]$

$$= (\mathbf{D}-2)[(D-3C-A)\sin + (B+C-3A)\cos - (B+3D)x\sin$$

$$+ (D-3B)x\cos - E\exp(2x)]$$

$$= (5A-2B+5C-5D)\sin + (5A-5B-5C+2D)\cos + (5B-5D)x\cos$$

$$+ (5B+5D)x\sin.$$

Hence we require that $5A-2B+5C-5D = 0$, $5A-5B-5C+2D = 0$, $5B-5D = 1$, and $5B+5D = 0$. Solving this linear system, we find that $A = .04$, $B = .1$, $C = -.1$, and $D = -.1$. Notice that we are free to choose E and F as we wish; let us take $E = F = 0$. Then $(.04 + .1x)\cos - (.1+.1x)\sin$ is a particular solution of the given differential equation. Checking, we verify that this is correct.

In both examples a particular solution of $\mathscr{P}f = g$ is found by considering the differential equation $[\mathscr{Q}\mathscr{P}]f = 0$, where $\mathscr{Q}g = 0$; we argued that one of the solutions of $[\mathscr{Q}\mathscr{P}]f = 0$ is a particular solution of the given differential equation, and so we considered a complete solution of $[\mathscr{Q}\mathscr{P}]f = 0$. We point out now that the computations can be simplified. In Examples 5 and 6 we found that we did not need a complete solution of $[\mathscr{Q}\mathscr{P}]f = 0$; indeed, we found that we could safely ignore each term of our complete solution which was also a particular solution of $\mathscr{P}f = 0$. A simplification of this sort can always be made. The point is that the sum of a particular solution of $\mathscr{P}f = g$ and a particular solution of the reduced equation is again a particular solution of $\mathscr{P}f = g$. Therefore, when we construct a particular solution of $\mathscr{P}f = g$, we are free to ignore any particular solution of $\mathscr{P}f = 0$. Do not think that we have only to consider a complete solution of $\mathscr{Q}f = 0$; rather, we consider a complete solution of $[\mathscr{Q}\mathscr{P}]f = 0$ and eliminate each term which is also a particular solution of the reduced equation $\mathscr{P}f = 0$. The following example brings out this point.

EXAMPLE 7.   Find a particular solution of $\mathbf{D}(\mathbf{D}+1)f = 2x$.

Solution: Now, $2x$ is a particular solution of $\mathbf{D}^2 f = 0$; therefore there is a solution of $\mathbf{D}^3(\mathbf{D}+1)f = 0$ which is also a particular solution of the given differential equation. But

$$f = k_1 + k_2 x + k_3 x^2 + k_4\exp(-x)$$

is a complete solution of $\mathbf{D}^3(\mathbf{D}+1)f = 0$. Ignoring each function which is also a particular solution of $\mathbf{D}(\mathbf{D}+1)f = 0$, we conclude that there are real numbers A and B such that $Ax + Bx^2$

is a particular solution of the given differential equation. But $\mathbf{D}(\mathbf{D} + 1)[Ax + Bx^2] = A + 2B + 2Bx$; so $A + 2B = 0$ and $2B = 2$, i.e., $A = -2$ and $B = 1$. Thus $-2x + x^2$ is a particular solution of the given differential equation.

Let us consider the method illustrated in the preceding examples. The main idea is to transform the function on the right-hand side of a given differential equation into the function 0 by applying a suitable polynomial operator. Given the differential equation $\mathscr{P}f = g$, where $\mathscr{P}$ is a polynomial operator, we look for a polynomial operator, say $\mathscr{Q}$, such that $\mathscr{Q}g = 0$; then $[\mathscr{Q}\mathscr{P}]f = \mathscr{Q}g = 0$. Thus, if h is a particular solution of the given differential equation, then $[\mathscr{Q}\mathscr{P}]h = 0$; i.e.. h is a particular solution of the differential equation $[\mathscr{Q}\mathscr{P}]f = 0$. To predict the form of a particular solution of the given differential equation $\mathscr{P}f = g$, we have only to write down a complete solution of $[\mathscr{Q}\mathscr{P}]f = 0$. Therefore the method of undetermined coefficients will work provided that we can find $\mathscr{Q}$. Now, there is a polynomial operator $\mathscr{Q}$ such that $\mathscr{Q}g = 0$ iff the function g is a particular solution of the differential equation $\mathscr{Q}f = 0$, which is a linear homogeneous differential equation with constant coefficients. We have established the following theorem.

> **THEOREM 10.5.1.** The method of undetermined coefficients applies to a linear nonhomogeneous differential equation with constant coefficients, say $\mathscr{P}f = g$, iff g is a particular solution of a linear homogeneous differential equation with constant coefficients, say $\mathscr{Q}f = 0$. Moreover, there is a particular solution of the differential equation $[\mathscr{Q}\mathscr{P}]f = 0$ which is also a particular solution of the given differential equation $\mathscr{P}f = g$.

Using this method, let us rework Example 1 of Section 10.3.

EXAMPLE 8. Find a particular solution of the differential equation

$$(\mathbf{D}^4 - 3\mathbf{D}^3 - 3\mathbf{D}^2 + 7\mathbf{D} + 6)f = 2x^2.$$

Solution: We shall apply Theorem 10.5.1. Now, $2x^2$ is a particular solution of $\mathbf{D}^3 f = 0$; therefore there is a solution of $\mathbf{D}^3(\mathbf{D}^4 - 3\mathbf{D}^3 - 3\mathbf{D}^2 + 7\mathbf{D} + 6)f = 0$ which is also a particular solution of the given differential equation. But we can ignore each particular solution of the reduced equation $(\mathbf{D}^4 - 3\mathbf{D}^3 - 3\mathbf{D}^2 + 7\mathbf{D} + 6)f = 0$; we conclude that there is a solution of $\mathbf{D}^3 f = 0$ which is also a particular solution of the given differential equation. Hence there are real numbers A, B, and C such that $A + Bx + Cx^2$ is a particular solution of the given differential equation. But

$$(\mathbf{D}^4 - 3\mathbf{D}^3 - 3\mathbf{D}^2 + 7\mathbf{D} + 6)[A + Bx + Cx^2] = 6(A + Bx + Cx^2) + 7(B + 2Cx) - 6C$$

$$= (6A + 7B - 6C) + (6B + 14C)x + 6Cx^2.$$

Thus $6A + 7B - 6C = 0$, $6B + 14C = 0$, and $6C = 2$; hence $A = 67/54$, $B = -7/9$, $C = 1/3$. We conclude that $67/54 - 7x/9 + x^2/3$ is a particular solution of the given differential equation. Notice how easily we have obtained our solution compared to the method of variation of parameter.

EXERCISES

Find a polynomial operator $\mathscr{P}$ such that:

1. $\mathscr{P}(\exp(3x)) = 0.$ (*Answer:* $\mathbf{D} - 3$)

2. $\mathscr{P}(x \exp) = 0.$ (*Answer:* $(\mathbf{D} - 1)^2$)

3. $\mathscr{P}(\sin 2x) = 0.$ (*Answer:* $\mathbf{D}^2 + 4$)

4. $\mathscr{P}(x \sin 2x) = 0.$ (*Answer:* $(\mathbf{D}^2 + 4)^2$)

5. $\mathscr{P}[\sin 2x \cdot \exp(3x)] = 0.$ (*Answer:* $(\mathbf{D} - 3)^2 + 4$)

6. $\mathscr{P}[x^2 \sin 2x \cdot \exp(3x)] = 0.$ (*Answer:* $[(\mathbf{D} - 3)^2 + 4]^3$)

7. $\mathscr{P}[\exp + \sin] = 0.$ (*Answer:* $(\mathbf{D}^2 + 1)(\mathbf{D} - 1)$)

8. $\mathscr{P}[\sin 2x + \sin 3x] = 0.$ (*Answer:* $(\mathbf{D}^2 + 4)(\mathbf{D}^2 + 9)$)

9. $\mathscr{P}[2x^2 \cos + 2x] = 0.$ (*Answer:* $\mathbf{D}^3(\mathbf{D}^2 + 4)$)

Find a particular solution of each of the following.

10. $\mathbf{D}(\mathbf{D} + 4)f = \cos.$ (*Answer:* $(4/17) \sin - (1/17) \cos$)

11. $\mathbf{D}(\mathbf{D} + 4)f = \cos + 4 \sin.$ (*Answer:* $-\cos$)

12. $\mathbf{D}(\mathbf{D} + 4)f = 17 \cos + 8 \sin 2x.$ (*Answer:* $4 \sin - \cos - \frac{2}{5} \sin 2x - \frac{4}{5} \cos 2x$)

13. $(\mathbf{D}^2 - 9)f = x + \exp(4x).$

14. $\mathbf{D}(\mathbf{D} - 2)(\mathbf{D} - 3) = 2x - \exp(2x) + 4 \exp(3x).$

15. $(\mathbf{D}^3 - \mathbf{D}^2 + 1)f = x \cos.$ (*Answer:* $-.72 \sin + .04 \cos - .2x \sin + .4x \cos$)

16. $\mathbf{D}(\mathbf{D} + 2)(\mathbf{D} + 3)f = 20 + 24x.$ (*Answer:* $2x^2$)

17. $\mathbf{D}(\mathbf{D} + 2)(\mathbf{D} + 3)f = 6 \exp(-2x).$ (*Answer:* $-3x \exp(-2x)$)

18. $(\mathbf{D} + 1)(\mathbf{D}^2 + 1)f = 4 \sin.$ (*Answer:* $-x(\sin + \cos)$)

10.6   More About Operators

In connection with the method of undetermined coefficients, we have seen that operators help us to find a particular solution of a nonhomogeneous linear differential equation with constant coefficients, i.e., a differential equation of the form $\mathscr{P}f = q$, where $\mathscr{P}$ is a polynomial operator and q is a function with one argument. In this section we shall make a more direct use of operators to find a particular solution of the differential equation $\mathscr{P}f = q$

We shall need the following theorems.

THEOREM 10.6.1.   Let $a \in R$; then $\mathbf{D} + a = \exp(-\mathbf{a}x) \cdot \mathbf{D} \cdot \exp(\mathbf{a}x).$
Proof: Let $f \in \mathscr{F}$; then

$$[\exp(-\mathbf{a}x) \cdot \mathbf{D} \cdot \exp(\mathbf{a}x)]f = \exp(-\mathbf{a}x)(f \cdot \exp(ax))'$$
$$= \exp(-ax) \cdot [f' \cdot \exp(ax) + af \cdot \exp(ax)]$$
$$= f' + af$$
$$= (\mathbf{D} + a)f.$$

Therefore $\mathbf{D} + a = \exp(-\mathbf{a}x) \cdot \mathbf{D} \cdot \exp(\mathbf{a}x).$

This result is most significant. Let $\mathscr{P}$ be a polynomial operator which can be factored into linear operators; then the differential equation $\mathscr{P}f = q$ can be solved by a series of transformations which involve multiplying the function on the right-hand side of the equation by a function of the form $\exp(bx)$ and antidifferentiating. We illustrate the procedure.

EXAMPLE 1.   Find a complete solution of $(\mathbf{D}+2)(\mathbf{D}-1)f = \sin 2x$.

Solution: We shall use Theorem 10.6.1.   Now, $\mathbf{D}+2 = \exp(-2x) \cdot \mathbf{D} \cdot \exp(2x)$ and $\mathbf{D} - 1 = \exp \cdot \mathbf{D} \cdot \exp(-x)$; thus the given differential equation is

$$[\exp(-2x) \cdot \mathbf{D} \cdot \exp(3x) \cdot \mathbf{D} \cdot \exp(-x)]f = \sin 2x.$$

Let g be any particular solution of this differential equation; then

$$[\exp(-2x) \cdot \mathbf{D} \cdot \exp(3x) \cdot \mathbf{D} \cdot \exp(-x)]g = \sin 2x;$$

so

$$[\mathbf{D} \cdot \exp(3x) \cdot \mathbf{D} \cdot \exp(-x)]g = \exp(2x) \cdot \sin 2x;$$

thus

$$[\exp(3x) \cdot \mathbf{D} \cdot \exp(-x)]g \equiv \mathbf{A}\left[\exp(2x) \cdot \sin 2x\right] = \frac{1}{4}\exp(2x) \cdot [\sin 2x - \cos 2x].$$

Hence there is a real number, say c_1, such that

$$[\exp(3x) \cdot \mathbf{D} \cdot \exp(-x)]g = c_1 + \frac{1}{4}\exp(2x) \cdot [\sin 2x - \cos 2x];$$

so

$$[\mathbf{D} \cdot \exp(-x)]g = c_1 \exp(-3x) + \frac{1}{4}\exp(-x) \cdot [\sin 2x - \cos 2x];$$

thus

$$[\exp(-x)]g \equiv \mathbf{A}\left[c_1 \exp(-3x) + \frac{1}{4}\exp(-x) \cdot [\sin 2x - \cos 2x]\right]$$

$$\equiv -\frac{c_1}{3}\exp(-3x) - \frac{1}{20}\exp(-x) \cdot [3 \sin 2x + \cos 2x].$$

Therefore there is a real number, say c_2, such that

$$\exp(-x) \cdot g = c_2 - \frac{c_1}{3}\exp(-3x) - \frac{1}{20}\exp(-x) \cdot (3 \sin 2x + \cos 2x);$$

hence

$$g = c_2 \exp - \frac{c_1}{3}\exp(-2x) - \frac{1}{20}(3 \sin 2x + \cos 2x).$$

We conclude that

$$f = k_1 \exp + k_2 \exp(-2x) - \frac{1}{20}(3 \sin 2x + \cos 2x)$$

is a complete solution of the given differential equation.

The following two thereoms generalize the result contained in Theorem 10.6.1.

THEOREM 10.6.2.   Let $a \in R$; then $(\mathbf{D} + \mathbf{a})^n = \exp(-\mathbf{ax}) \cdot \mathbf{D}^n \cdot \exp(\mathbf{ax})$ whenever $n \in N$.

Proof: Apply mathematical induction and use Theorem 10.6.1. The details are left as an exercise.

THEOREM 10.6.3.   Let $a \in R$ and let P be any polynomial function; then $P(\mathbf{D} + \mathbf{a}) = \exp(-\mathbf{ax}) \cdot P(\mathbf{D}) \cdot \exp(\mathbf{ax})$.

Proof: Let $P = \sum_{i=0}^{n} a_i x^i$; then

$$P(\mathbf{D} + \mathbf{a}) = \sum_{i=0}^{n} a_i (\mathbf{D} + \mathbf{a})^i$$

$$= \sum_{i=0}^{n} [a_i \cdot \exp(-\mathbf{ax}) \cdot \mathbf{D}^i \cdot \exp(\mathbf{ax})] \qquad \text{by Th. 10.6.2}$$

$$= \exp(-\mathbf{ax}) \cdot \left[\sum_{i=0}^{n} a_i \cdot \mathbf{D}^i \right] \cdot \exp(\mathbf{ax})$$

$$= \exp(-\mathbf{ax}) \cdot P(\mathbf{D}) \cdot \exp(\mathbf{ax}).$$

This establishes our result.

We now illustrate these theorems.

EXAMPLE 2.   Find a particular solution of $(\mathbf{D} - 1)^3 f = \exp(4x)$.

Solution: By Theorem 10.6.2, $(\mathbf{D} - 1)^3 = \exp \cdot \mathbf{D}^3 \cdot \exp(-x)$; thus the given differential equation is $[\exp \cdot \mathbf{D}^3 \cdot \exp(-x)]f = \exp(4x)$, i.e., $[\mathbf{D}^3 \cdot \exp(-x)]f = \exp(3x)$. Here is a useful idea: we can write this differential equation as $\mathbf{D}^3(\exp(-x) \cdot f) = \exp(3x)$, where $\exp(-x) \cdot f$ is the unknown function. We now look for a particular solution of this differential equation. Clearly, $[\frac{1}{27} \exp(3x)]^{(3)} = \exp(3x)$; so $\frac{1}{27} \exp(3x)$ is a particular solution of $\mathbf{D}^3[\exp(-x) \cdot f] = \exp(3x)$. We conclude that $\frac{1}{27} \exp(4x)$ is a particular solution of the given differential equation.

EXAMPLE 3.   Find a particular solution of $(\mathbf{D} - 3)^4 f = 12 \exp(3x)$.

Solution: By Theorem 10.6.2, $(\mathbf{D} - 3)^4 = \exp(3x) \cdot \mathbf{D}^4 \cdot \exp(-3x)$; thus the given differential equation is $[\exp(3x) \cdot \mathbf{D}^4 \cdot \exp(-3x)]f = 12 \exp(3x)$, i.e., $[\mathbf{D}^4 \cdot \exp(-3x)]f = 12$. We now consider $\mathbf{D}^4[\exp(-3x) \cdot f] = 12$, a differential equation in the unknown function $\exp(-3x) \cdot f$. Clearly, $x^4/2$ is a particular solution of this differential equation; we conclude that $.5x^4 \exp(3x)$ is a particular solution of the given differential equation.

EXAMPLE 4.   Find a particular solution of $(\mathbf{D}^3 + \mathbf{D} - 4)f = x \exp(2x)$.

Solution: The given differential equation can be written as

$[\exp(-2x) \cdot (\mathbf{D}^3 + \mathbf{D} - 4)]f = x$. By Theorem 10.6.3,

$$\exp(-2x) \cdot (\mathbf{D}^3 + \mathbf{D} - 4) = [(\mathbf{D} + 2)^3 + (\mathbf{D} + 2) - 4] \cdot \exp(-2x)$$

$$= [\mathbf{D}^3 + 6\mathbf{D}^2 + 13\mathbf{D} + 6] \cdot \exp(-2x).$$

So the given differential equation is $[(D^3 + 6D^2 + 13D + 6) \cdot \exp(-2x)]f = x$. Now consider $[D^3 + 6D^2 + 13D + 6](\exp(-2x) \cdot f) = x$, a differential equation in the unknown $\exp(-2x) \cdot f$. We shall use the method of undetermined coefficients to find a particular solution of this differential equation. Let $A + Bx$ be a particular solution; then $6(A + Bx) + 13B = x$; so $B = 1/6$ and $A = -13/36$. Therefore $-13/36 + x/6$ is a particular solution of $[D^3 + 6D^2 + 13D + 6]f = x$. We conclude that $(-13/36 + x/6)\exp(2x)$ is a particular solution of the given differential equation. Checking, we see that this is correct.

EXERCISES

Find a complete solution of each of the following.

1. $(D - 2)(D + 3)f = 5 \exp(2x)$.

                (*Answer:* $f = k_1 \exp(2x) + k_2 \exp(-3x) + (x - 1/5) \exp(2x)$)

2. $(D - 2)(D + 3)f = x \exp(2x)$.

3. $(D - 2)(D + 3)f = 2x$.

                (*Answer:* $f = k_1 \exp(2x) + k_2 \exp(-3x) - x/3 - 1/18$)

4. $(D^3 - 3D^2 + 3D - 1)f = 4 \sin$.

Find a particular solution of each of the following.

5. $(D - 1)^4 f = \exp(4x)$.

6. $(D + 1)^3 f = \exp(2x)$.

7. $(D + 3)^3 f = \exp(3x)$.

8. $(D^3 - 3D + 5)f = x \exp$.

9. $(D^3 + 2D^2 - 3D)f = \sin$.

10. $(D^3 + 2D^2 - 3D)f = \sin$.

11. $(D^3 - 3D + 2)(D + 2)^2 f = x \exp(2x)$.

12. $(D^2 + 4)(D + 4)(D - 3)f = x^2 \exp(-x)$.

13. Prove Theorem 10.6.2.

10.7   Exploiting the Algebra of Operators

In this section we shall use the algebraic properties of operators to assist us in solving differential equations. For example, consider the differential equation $\mathscr{P}f = q$, where $\mathscr{P}$ is a polynomial operator and $q \in \mathscr{F}$. Now suppose that $\mathcal{O}$ is an operator such that $[\mathscr{P} \cdot \mathcal{O}]q = q$ (e.g., let $\mathcal{O}$ be an *inverse* of $\mathscr{P}$); then $\mathscr{P}(\mathcal{O}q) = q$. So $\mathcal{O}q$ is a particular solution of the differential equation $\mathscr{P}f = q$.

It is essential that we build up a good working knowledge of the effect of polynomial operators on certain basic functions, in particular, functions of the form $\exp(ax)$. Let $\mathscr{P}$ be any polynomial operator, say $\mathscr{P} = P(D)$; then $\mathscr{P}[\exp(ax)] = P(a) \cdot \exp(ax)$ (this is easy to see). Thus $\mathscr{P}[(1/P(a)) \exp(ax)] = \exp(ax)$ provided $P(a) \neq 0$. In view of this, it is a simple matter to find a particular solution of the differential equation $\mathscr{P}f = \exp(ax)$ provided that $P(a) \neq 0$.

THEOREM 10.7.1. $P(\mathbf{D})[\exp(ax)/P(a)] = \exp(ax)$ provided $P(a) \neq 0$.

We now illustrate this idea.

EXAMPLE 1.   Find a particular solution of $(\mathbf{D}^4 + 2\mathbf{D}^3 - \mathbf{D}^2 + 3\mathbf{D} - 5)f = \exp(-2x)$.
   Solution: Here, $P = x^4 + 2x^3 - x^2 + 3x - 5$; so $P(-2) = -15$. Thus $P(\mathbf{D})[-\exp(-2x)/15]$
$= \exp(-2x)$; so $(-1/15)\exp(-2x)$ is a particular solution of the given differential equation.

To treat the case in which $P(a) = 0$, we need the following fact.

THEOREM 10.7.2.   Let $n \in N$ and let $a \in R$; then

$$(\mathbf{D} - \mathbf{a})^n[x^n \exp(ax)] = n!\, \exp(ax).$$

   Proof: By Theorem 10.6.2, $(\mathbf{D} - \mathbf{a})^n = \exp(\mathbf{ax}) \cdot \mathbf{D}^n \cdot \exp(-\mathbf{ax})$; therefore

$$(\mathbf{D} - \mathbf{a})^n[x^n \exp(ax)] = (\exp(\mathbf{ax}) \cdot \mathbf{D}^n \cdot \exp(-\mathbf{ax}))[x^n \exp(ax)]$$
$$= [\exp(\mathbf{ax}) \cdot \mathbf{D}^n]x^n$$
$$= n!\, \exp(ax).$$

This establishes our result.

THEOREM 10.7.3.   Let P be any polynomial function, let $n \in N$, and let $a \in R$;
then $[P(\mathbf{D}) \cdot (\mathbf{D} - \mathbf{a})^n](x^n \exp(ax)) = n!\, P(a) \exp(ax)$ provided $P(a) \neq 0$.
   Proof: $[P(\mathbf{D}) \cdot (\mathbf{D} - \mathbf{a})^n](x^n \exp(ax)) = P(\mathbf{D})[n!\, \exp(ax)]$ by Th. 10.7.2
$$= n!\, P(a) \exp(ax)   \text{by Th. 10.7.1.}$$

The point is this: if Q is a polynomial function such that $Q(a) = 0$, then there is a
natural number n and a polynomial function P such that $P(a) \neq 0$ and $Q = (x - a)^n P$.
Thus $Q(\mathbf{D}) = P(\mathbf{D}) \cdot (\mathbf{D} - \mathbf{a})^n$. Applying Theorem 10.7.3, we can easily find a particular
solution of the differential equation $[P(\mathbf{D}) \cdot (\mathbf{D} - \mathbf{a})^n]f = \exp(ax)$, for

$$[P(\mathbf{D}) \cdot (\mathbf{D} - \mathbf{a})^n]\, \frac{x^n \exp(ax)}{n!\, P(a)} = \exp(ax).$$

EXAMPLE 2.   Find a particular solution of $(\mathbf{D} + 1)(\mathbf{D} - 3)(\mathbf{D} + 2)^3 f = \exp(-2x)$.
   Solution: By Theorem 10.7.3,

$$[(\mathbf{D} + 1)(\mathbf{D} - 3)(\mathbf{D} + 2)^3](x^3 \exp(-2x)) = 30 \exp(-2x);$$

therefore $\frac{1}{30}x^3 \exp(-2x)$ is a particular solution of the given differential equation.

We now show that our results can be used in a more subtle fashion. Consider the
following example.

EXAMPLE 3. Find a particular solution of $(\mathbf{D}-2)(\mathbf{D}+1)^2 f = 4x^2 \exp(3x)$.

Solution: By   Theorem   10.7.2, $(\mathbf{D}-3)^2(x^2 \exp(3x)) = 2 \exp(3x)$;

therefore $(\mathbf{D}-3)^2[4x^2\exp(3x)] = 8 \exp(3x)$;

so we consider

(1) $(\mathbf{D}-3)^2(\mathbf{D}-2)(\mathbf{D}+1)^2 f = 8 \exp(3x)$.

Clearly, $\frac{1}{4}x^2 \exp(3x)$ is a particular solution of this differential equation. Therefore a complete solution of (1) is

$$f = (k_1 + k_2 x) \exp(3x) + k_3 \exp(2x) + (k_4 + k_5 x) \exp(-x) + \tfrac{1}{4}x^2 \exp(3x).$$

Now, there is a solution of (1) which is also a solution of the given differential equation; moreover, $(\mathbf{D}-2)(\mathbf{D}+1)^2[k_3 \exp(2x) + (k_4 + k_5 x) \exp(-x)] = 0$. Thus there exist real numbers A and B such that $(A + Bx) \exp(3x) + \tfrac{1}{4}x^2 \exp(3x)$ is a particular solution. By the method of undetermined coefficients, we find that $A = 27/32$ and $B = -3/4$. Hence $(27/32 - 3x/4 + x^2/4) \exp(3x)$ is a particular solution of the given differential equation.

We now consider a theorem that displays the power of our approach.

THEOREM 10.7.4. Let $\mathscr{P}$, $\mathscr{Q}$, and $\mathscr{R}$ be polynomial operators such that $\mathscr{P}\mathscr{Q} + \mathscr{R} = 1$, and let g be a function such that $\mathscr{R}g = 0$; then $\mathscr{Q}g$ is a particular solution of the differential equation $\mathscr{P}f = g$.
    Proof: $[\mathscr{P}\mathscr{Q} + \mathscr{R}]g = 1(g) = g$; therefore $\mathscr{P}(\mathscr{Q}g) + \mathscr{R}g = g$. But $\mathscr{R}g = 0$; thus $\mathscr{P}(\mathscr{Q}g) = g$. This means that $\mathscr{Q}g$ is a particular solution of the differential equation $\mathscr{P}f = g$.

THEOREM 10.7.5. Let $\mathscr{P}$, $\mathscr{Q}$, and $\mathscr{R}$ be polynomial operators such that $\mathscr{P}\mathscr{Q} + \mathscr{R} = 1$, and let g be a function such that $\mathscr{R}g = kg$, where $k \in R$ and $k \neq 1$. Then $\dfrac{1}{(1-k)}\mathscr{Q}g$ is a particular solution of the differential equation $\mathscr{P}f = g$.
    Proof: By   assumption, $g = [\mathscr{P}\mathscr{Q} + \mathscr{R}]g = \mathscr{P}(\mathscr{Q}g) + kg$;   therefore $\mathscr{P}(\mathscr{Q}g) = (1-k)g$; hence

$$\mathscr{P}\left(\frac{1}{1-k}\mathscr{Q}g\right) = g.$$

Thus $\dfrac{1}{1-k}\mathscr{Q}g$ is a particular solution of $\mathscr{P}f = g$.

We now illustrate these results.

EXAMPLE 4. Find a particular solution of $(\mathbf{D}^3 + 1)f = x^4$.
    Solution: Now, $1 = (\mathbf{D}^3 + 1)(1 - \mathbf{D}^3) + \mathbf{D}^6$ and $\mathbf{D}^6(x^4) = 0$. Therefore, by Theorem 10.7.4, $(1 - \mathbf{D}^3)x^4$ is a particular solution of the given differential equation; i.e., $x^4 - 24x$ is a particular solution.

EXAMPLE 5.   Find a particular solution of $(\mathbf{D}^4 + 3\mathbf{D} - 1)f = 3x^2$.

Solution: Now, $1 = (\mathbf{D}^4 + 3\mathbf{D} - 1)(-1 - 3\mathbf{D} - 9\mathbf{D}^2) + \mathscr{R}$ and $\mathscr{R}(3x^2) = 0$. Therefore, by Theorem 10.7.4, $(-1 - 3\mathbf{D} - 9\mathbf{D}^2)3x^2$ is a particular solution of the given differential equation; i.e., $-3x^2 - 18x - 54$ is a particular solution.

EXAMPLE 6.   Find a particular solution of $(\mathbf{D}^3 - 3\mathbf{D} - 1)f = x^2 \exp(2x)$.

Solution: The given differential equation can be written as $[\exp(-2x) \cdot (\mathbf{D}^3 - 3\mathbf{D} - 1)]f = x^2$. Let $P = x^3 - 3x - 1$; by Theorem 10.6.3, $\exp(-ax) \cdot P(\mathbf{D}) = P(\mathbf{D} + a) \cdot \exp(-ax)$; thus

$$\exp(-2x) \cdot (\mathbf{D}^3 - 3\mathbf{D} - 1) = [(\mathbf{D} + 2)^3 - 3(\mathbf{D} + 2) - 1] \cdot \exp(-2x)$$
$$= (\mathbf{D}^3 + 6\mathbf{D}^2 + 9\mathbf{D} + 1) \cdot \exp(-2x).$$

Therefore the given differential equation is

$$[(\mathbf{D}^3 + 6\mathbf{D}^2 + 9\mathbf{D} + 1) \cdot \exp(-2x)]f = x^2.$$

We shall solve for $\exp(-2x) \cdot f$, i.e., we shall consider the differential equation

(2) $$[\mathbf{D}^3 + 6\mathbf{D}^2 + 9\mathbf{D} + 1]g = x^2.$$

But $1 = (\mathbf{D}^3 + 6\mathbf{D}^2 + 9\mathbf{D} + 1)(1 - 9\mathbf{D} + 75\mathbf{D}^2) + \mathscr{R}$, where $\mathscr{R}(x^2) = 0$. So, by Theorem 10.7.4, $(1 - 9\mathbf{D} + 75\mathbf{D}^2)x^2$ is a particular solution of (2); i.e., $x^2 - 18x + 150$ is a particular solution of (2). Thus $(x^2 - 18x + 150) \exp(2x)$ is a particular solution of the given differential equation.

THEOREM 10.7.6.   Let $\mathscr{P}, \mathscr{P}_1, \mathscr{Q}$, and $\mathscr{R}$ be polynomial operators such that $\mathscr{P} = \mathscr{Q}\mathscr{P}_1 + \mathscr{R}$ and suppose that $\mathscr{P}_1h = 0$ and that $\mathscr{R}h = g$; then h is a particular solution of $\mathscr{P}f = g$.

Proof: By assumption, $\mathscr{P}h = [\mathscr{Q}\mathscr{P}_1]h + \mathscr{R}h = \mathscr{R}h = g$.

EXAMPLE 7.   Find a particular solution of $(\mathbf{D}^3 - 2\mathbf{D}^2 + 1)f = \sin$.

Solution: We shall apply Theorem 10.7.6. The main point here is that $(\mathbf{D}^2 + 1) \sin = 0$ and $(\mathbf{D}^2 + 1) \cos = 0$; thus we shall divide $\mathbf{D}^3 - 2\mathbf{D}^2 + 1$ by $\mathbf{D}^2 + 1$. Now, $\mathbf{D}^3 - 2\mathbf{D}^2 + 1 = (\mathbf{D}^2 + 1)(\mathbf{D} - 2) + (3 - \mathbf{D})$. Therefore, by Theorem 10.7.6, $A \sin + B \cos$ is a particular solution of the given differential equation provided that $(3 - \mathbf{D})(A \sin + B \cos) = \sin$. But $(3 - \mathbf{D}) (A \sin + B \cos) = (3A + B) \sin + (3B - A) \cos$; therefore we require that $3A + B = 1$ and that $3B - A = 0$, i.e., $A = .3$ and $B = .1$. Thus $.1(3 \sin + \cos)$ is a particular solution of the given differential equation.

Of course, rather than quote Theorem 10.7.6, it is much better to apply the algebraic process behind the theorem.

EXAMPLE 8.   Find a particular solution of $(\mathbf{D}^7 - 3\mathbf{D}^6 + 2\mathbf{D} - 2)f = 2 \sin - 3 \cos$.

Solution: Now, $\mathbf{D}^7 - 3\mathbf{D}^6 + 2\mathbf{D} - 2 = (\mathbf{D}^2 + 1)(\mathbf{D}^5 - 3\mathbf{D}^4 - \mathbf{D}^3 + 3\mathbf{D}^2 + \mathbf{D} - 3) + (\mathbf{D} + 1)$ therefore

$$(\mathbf{D}^7 - 3\mathbf{D}^6 + 2\mathbf{D} - 2)(A \sin + B \cos) = (\mathbf{D} + 1)(A \sin + B \cos)$$
$$= (A - B) \sin + (A + B) \cos.$$

Hence $A \sin + B \cos$ is a particular solution of the given differential equation provided that $A - B = 2$ and that $A + B = -3$, i.e., $A = -.5$ and $B = -2.5$. We conclude that $-.5(\sin + 5\cos)$ is a particular solution.

THEOREM 10.7.7. Let $\mathscr{P} = \sum\limits_{i=0}^{n} a_i D^i$, let $\mathscr{Q} = \sum\limits_{i=0}^{n} a_i b^i D^i$, where $b \in R$, and suppose that h is a particular solution of $\mathscr{Q}f = g$. Then $h(bx)$ is a particular solution of $\mathscr{P}f = g(bx)$.

Proof: Consider $\mathscr{P}[h(bx)]$, and observe that $[h(bx)]^{(i)} = b^i h^{(i)}(bx)$ whenever i is a nonnegative integer. The details are left as an exercise

E X E R C I S E S

Find a particular solution of each of the following.

1. $(D^3 + 4D^2 - 2D + 7)f = \exp.$ *(Answer: .1 exp)*
2. $(D^3 + 4D^2 - 2D + 7)f = 10 \exp.$ *(Answer: exp)*
3. $(D^4 - 2D^3 + 3D^2 + D - 1)f = 28 \exp(3x).$ *(Answer: .5 exp(3x))*
4. $(D^5 + 2D^4 - 3D^3 + 2D^2 + D + 3)f = 16 \exp(-x).$ *(Answer: 2 exp(-x))*
5. $(D + 2)^5 f = \exp(-3x).$ *(Answer: -exp(-3x))*
6. $(D + 5)^7 f = 32 \exp(-3x).$ *(Answer: .25 exp(-3x))*
7. $(D - 2)^3 f = \exp(2x).$ *(Answer: $\frac{1}{6}x^3$ exp(2x))*
8. $(D - 3)^5 f = 120 \exp(3x).$ *(Answer: x^5 exp(3x))*
9. $(D + 3)^2 f = 6 \exp(-3x).$ *(Answer: $3x^2$ exp(-3x))*
10. $(D - 2)(D + 3)^2 f = 2 \exp(-3x).$ *(Answer: $-.2x^2$ exp(-3x))*
11. $(D + 5)^2(D + 3)^2 f = 16 \exp(-3x).$ *(Answer: $2x^2$ exp(-3x))*
12. $(D^2 - D - 1)(D + 3)^2 f = 2 \exp(-3x).$ *(Answer: $\frac{1}{11}x^2$ exp(-3x))*
13. $(D^3 + 2D^2 - 2D + 5)(D + 3)^2 f = 8 \exp(-3x).$ *(Answer: $2x^2$ exp(-3x))*
14. $(D + 3)(D - 1)f = x \exp(2x).$
15. $(D + 3)(D - 1)f = x^2 \exp(2x).$
16. $(D + 3)(D + 2)(D - 1)f = x \exp(-x).$
17. $(D + 3)(D + 2)(D - 1)f = x^2 \exp(-x).$
18. $(D + 3)^2(D - 1)^2 f = x^3 \exp(-x).$
19. $(D + 1)^2(D - 2)^3 f = .5x^3 \exp(-2x).$
20. $(D + 1)^2(D + 2)f = x^2 \exp(-2x).$
21. $(D^3 + 1)f = 3 + 2x - x^2 + 2x^3.$
22. $(D^4 - 2D + 1)f = 2 - 3x + x^2.$
23. $(D^3 + 3D - 1)f = 7 + 2x - 3x^2.$
24. $(D^3 + 2D + 1)f = 2x \exp(3x).$
25. $(D^4 - D + 1)f = x \exp(-x).$
26. $(D^4 - D + 1)f = (5 - x + 2x^2) \exp(-x).$

27. $(D^3 - D - 1)f = \sin.$

28. $(D^4 + 2D^3 - 3D^2 + 2D + 1)f = 2 \sin + 5 \cos.$

29. $(D^5 - 2D^2 + 1)f = \sin 2x.$

30. $(D^5 - 2D^3 + 1)f = 3 \sin 2x - \cos 2x.$

31. $(D^7 - D^5 - D^2 + 1)f = x \sin.$

32. Prove Theorem 10.7.7.

Chapter 11

Power Series Methods

11.1 Introduction

The purpose of this chapter is to demonstrate the role of power series in solving differential equations. We shall see that a wide class of differential equations can be solved easily and effectively by power series methods. Let us recall certain significant facts about power series.

> **THEOREM 11.1.1.** Let $\mathcal{N}$ be a neighborhood of a, let f be a function whose domain contains $\mathcal{N}$, and let $\Sigma\, a_{n-1}(x-a)^{n-1}$ be a power series such that $f\,\mathrm{R}\,\mathcal{N} = \Sigma\, a_{n-1}(x-a)^{n-1}\mathrm{R}\,\mathcal{N}$; then $a_{n-1} = f^{(n-1)}(a)/(n-1)!$ whenever $n \in N$.
>
> *Note:* Recall that $0! = 1$ and $f^{(0)} = f$.

> **THEOREM 11.1.2.** Let $\mathcal{N}$ be a neighborhood of a which is contained in the domain of $\Sigma\, a_{n-1}(x-a)^{n-1}$; then $[\Sigma\, a_{n-1}(x-a)^{n-1}]'\mathrm{R}\,\mathcal{N} = \Sigma\, na_n(x-a)^{n-1}\mathrm{R}\,\mathcal{N}$.

> **THEOREM 11.1.3.** Suppose that the domain of $\Sigma\, a_{n-1}(x-a)^{n-1}$ contains a neighborhood of a; then $\Sigma\, a_{n-1}(x-a)^{n-1} = \Sigma\, b_{n-1}(x-a)^{n-1}$ iff $a_{n-1} = b_{n-1}$ whenever $n \in N$.

Do not think that each function can be represented by a power series! Since power series are *continuous* functions, it follows that no discontinuous function can be represented by a power series. For example, there is no power series $\Sigma\, a_{n-1}(x-a)^{n-1}$ such that $\{(t, t)\,|\,t \neq 3\} \cup \{(3, 4)\} = \Sigma\, a_{n-1}(x-a)^{n-1}$. Indeed, there are continuous and differentiable functions which possess no power series representation. As an example, consider the function $\exp(-1/x^2) \cup \{(0, 0)\}$. Let us denote this function by "f"; then

$$f(t) = \begin{cases} \exp(-1/t^2) & \text{if } t \neq 0 \\ 0 & \text{if } t = 0. \end{cases}$$

Now, $f'(0) = \lim_{0} \dfrac{\exp(-1/x^2)}{x} = \lim_{\infty} \dfrac{x}{\exp(x^2)}$

$$= \lim_{\infty} \dfrac{1}{2x \exp(x^2)} \quad \text{by l'Hospital's Rule}$$

$$= 0.$$

Thus $f' = \dfrac{-\exp(-1/x^2)}{x^3} \cup \{(0,0)\}$. Continuing, we see that $f^{(2)}(0) = 0$, and so $f^{(2)} = [x^{-6} + 3x^{-4}] \cdot \exp(-1/x^2) \cup \{(0,0)\}$. Since $\lim_{\infty} \dfrac{x^t}{\exp(x^2)} = 0$ whenever $t \in N$, it follows that $\mathscr{D}_{f^{(n)}} = R$ whenever $n \in N$, and that $f^{(n)}(0) = 0$ whenever $n \in N$. Thus, if there is a power series for f, it can only be $\sum a_{n-1} x^{n-1}$, where $a_{n-1} = 0$ for each n; this conclusion follows from Theorem 11.1.1. Of course, this means that $f = 0$, contrary to the definition of f; we conclude that f does not possess a power series representation about 0. We point out that if $\mathscr{I}$ is an interval such that $0 \bar{\in} \mathscr{I}$, then $f R \mathscr{I}$ possesses a power series representation.

The important point is this: we cannot assume that a given function possesses a power series representation. Let f be any function; we cannot assume that $\sum \dfrac{f^{(n-1)}(a)}{(n-1)!} (x-a)^{n-1}$ is a power series representation of f. Of course, $\sum \dfrac{f^{(n-1)}(a)}{(n-1)!} (x-a)^{n-1}$ is a function, but it might not be f. Our example illustrates this observation.

To find out whether $\sum \dfrac{f^{(n-1)}(a)}{(n-1)!} (x-a)^{n-1}$ is f, we apply the Fundamental Theorem of the Taylor's Series, which we now recall. Let $\mathscr{I}$ be any interval such that $\mathscr{I} \subset \mathscr{D}_{f^{(n)}}$ whenever $n \in N$, and let $a \in \mathscr{I}$ and let $b \in \mathscr{I}$; then

$$f(b) = \sum \dfrac{(b-a)^{n-1}}{(n-1)!} f^{(n-1)}(a) \quad \text{iff} \quad \lim\left(\dfrac{(b-a)^n}{n!} f^{(n)}(c_n)\right) = 0,$$

where each c_n is between a and b and is given by Taylor's Theorem.

Thus suppose that $\lim\left(\dfrac{(b-a)^n}{n!} \max_{t \in \mathscr{I}} |f^{(n)}(t)|\right) = 0$ iff $b \in \mathscr{I}$; then

$$f(b) = \sum \dfrac{(b-a)^{n-1}}{(n-1)!} f^{(n-1)}(a)$$

whenever $b \in \mathscr{I}$, and so

$$f R \mathscr{I} = \sum \dfrac{f^{(n-1)}(a)}{(n-1)!} (x-a)^{n-1}.$$

In particular, let $\mathcal{D}_f = \mathcal{I}$, and suppose that $\lim\left(\dfrac{(b-a)^n}{n!}\max_{t\in\mathcal{I}}|f^{(n)}(t)|\right) = 0$ iff $b \in \mathcal{I}$; then

$$f = \Sigma\,\frac{f^{(n-1)}(a)}{(n-1)!}(x-a)^{n-1}.$$

We shall need the following concepts (see Definition 9.3.1).

DEFINITION 11.1.1.   Let f be a function and let $a \in R$; then f is said to be *analytic at* a iff there is a neighborhood of a, say $\mathcal{I}$, and a power series in $x - a$, ·say $\Sigma\,a_{n-1}(x-a)^{n-1}$, such that $f\,R\,\mathcal{I} = \Sigma\,a_{n-1}(x-a)^{n-1}\,R\,\mathcal{I}$.

For example, log is analytic at 1 since $\log R\,(0,2) = \Sigma\,(-1)^{n+1}(x-1)^n/n\,R\,(0,2)$. Moreover, log is analytic at a whenever $a \in \mathcal{D}_{\log}$; to see this, let $a > 0$ and let $\mathcal{I} = (a-1,\ a+1) \cap \mathcal{D}_{\log}$; then

$$\log R\,\mathcal{I} = \log a + \Sigma\,\frac{(-1)^{n+1}(x-a)^n}{na^2}\,R\,\mathcal{I}.$$

DEFINITION 11.1.2.   Let f be a function and let $S \subset R$; then f is said to be *analytic on* S iff f is analytic at a whenever $a \in S$.

For example, x^2 is analytic on R, sin is analytic on R, log is analytic on $\{t\,|\,t > 0\}$, and $\Sigma\,x^{n-1}/(n-1)!$ is analytic on R.

DEFINITION 11.1.3.   We shall say that f is *analytic* iff f is analytic on $\mathcal{D}_f$.

Clearly, each power series is analytic.

To see the connection with differential equations, consider the following unique-existence theorem, which we state without proof.

THEOREM 11.1.4.   Let $a, b_0, b_1, \cdots, b_{n-1}$ be real numbers, and let $p_1, p_2, \cdots, p_{n+1}$ be functions which are analytic at a; then there is a unique function f such that $f^{(n)} + p_1 \cdot f^{(n-1)} + \cdots + p_{n-1} \cdot f' + p_n \cdot f = p_{n+1}\,R\,E$ and $f(a) = b_0,\ f'(a) = b_1,$ $\cdots, f^{(n-1)}(a) = b_{n-1}$. Moreover, f is analytic at a and has a power series representation in $x - a$ whose radius of convergence is at least as great as the smallest radius of convergence of $p_1, p_2, \cdots, p_{n+1}$.

We shall now illustrate two methods of determining the coefficients of the power series solution of a given differential equation which satisfies the conditions of Theorem 11.1.4.

EXAMPLE 1.   Find a function f such that $f^{(2)} - xf' - f = 0\,R\,E$, $f(0) = 1$, and $f'(0) = 2$.

First Solution: Here, the coefficient functions are $-x$, -1, and 0. These are analytic functions; indeed, each is a power series with domain R. Therefore there is a unique power series solution of the given differential equation which has domain R and satisfies the boundary conditions. Let this solution be $\sum a_{n-1}x^{n-1}$; our job is to determine the coefficients. From the given boundary conditions we see that $a_0 = 1$ and that $a_1 = 2$. Let $f = \sum a_{n-1}x^{n-1}$; then, by Theorem 11.1.2, $f' = \sum na_n x^{n-1}$ and $f^{(2)} = \sum n(n+1)a_{n+1}x^{n-1}$. Therefore

$$\sum n(n+1)a_{n+1}x^{n-1} - x\sum na_n x^{n-1} - \sum a_{n-1}x^{n-1} = 0 \text{ R } E;$$

i.e.,

$$\sum [n(n+1)a_{n+1} - a_{n-1}]x^{n-1} = \sum na_n x^n = \sum (n-1)a_{n-1}x^{n-1}.$$

Hence, by the uniqueness theorem for power series (Th. 11.1.3), we see that

$$n(n+1)a_{n+1} - a_{n-1} = (n-1)a_{n-1}$$

whenever $n \in N$; thus $a_{n+1} = a_{n-1}/(n+1)$ whenever $n \in N$. This is a recursion relation which expresses a_{n+1} in terms of a_{n-1} whenever $n \in N$. Therefore, if $n \in N$, we can express a_{2n} in terms of a_0, which we know, and we can express a_{2n+1} in terms of a_1, which we know. Indeed,

$$a_{2n} = \frac{a_0}{2^n n!} = \frac{1}{2^n n!} \quad \text{and} \quad a_{2n+1} = \frac{a_1}{(2n+1)(2n-1)\cdots(3)} = \frac{2}{(2n+1)(2n-1)\cdots(3)}$$

whenever $n \in N$. Thus

$$f = \sum \frac{x^{2n-2}}{2^{n-1}(n-1)!} + \sum \frac{2x^{2n-1}}{(2n-1)(2n-3)\cdots(1)}.$$

Furthermore, as we have already indicated, we can deduce from Theorem 11.1.4 that R is the domain of this power series. We write out the first few terms of our power series:

$$f = 1 + 2x + x^2/2 + 2x^3/3 + x^4/8 + 2x^5/15 + x^6/48 + \cdots.$$

Second Solution: Our second method of finding a power series solution of the given differential equation is based on Theorem 11.1.1. Let $f = \sum a_{n-1}x^{n-1}$; then $a_{n-1} = \frac{f^{(n-1)}(0)}{(n-1)!}$ whenever $n \in N$. We are given $f(0)$ and $f'(0)$; so $a_0 = \frac{f(0)}{0!} = \frac{1}{1} = 1$, and $a_1 = \frac{f'(0)}{1!} = \frac{2}{1} = 2$. The given differential equation itself helps us to compute the remaining terms of the power series. Clearly,

$$f^{(2)} = f + xf',$$
$$f^{(3)} = 2f' + xf^{(2)},$$
$$f^{(4)} = 3f^{(2)} + xf^{(3)},$$

and, in general, $f^{(n+1)} = nf^{(n-1)} + xf^{(n)}$ whenever $n \in N$. Thus $f^{(n+1)}(0) = nf^{(n-1)}(0)$ whenever $n \in N$; so $(n+1)! \, a_{n+1} = n! \, a_{n-1}$, i.e., $a_{n+1} = \frac{a_{n-1}}{n+1}$ whenever $n \in N$. This is the recursion relation that we obtained in the first solution. As before, it follows that

$$f = \sum \frac{x^{2n-2}}{2^{n-1}(n-1)!} + \sum \frac{2x^{2n-1}}{(2n-1)(2n-3)\cdots(1)}.$$

The second solution presented above provides us with a *direct* method of computing as many terms of a power series as we require.

EXAMPLE 2. Find f such that $f^{(3)} + 2xf^{(2)} - x^2f' - 3x^2f = 0$, $f(0) = 3$, $f'(0) = -1$, and $f^{(2)}(0) = 4$.

Solution: Let $f = \Sigma a_{n-1}x^{n-1}$; then $a_{n-1} = f^{(n-1)}(0)/(n-1)!$ whenever $n \in N$, and, by assumption, $a_0 = 3$, $a_1 = -1$, and $a_2 = 2$. We shall compute three more terms of the power series. Now,

$$f^{(3)} = -2xf^{(2)} + x^2f' + 3x^2f;$$
$$f^{(4)} = -2xf^{(3)} - 2f^{(2)} + x^2f^{(2)} + 2xf' + 3x^2f' + 6xf,$$
$$f^{(5)} = -2xf^{(4)} - 4f^{(3)} + x^2f^{(3)} + 4xf^{(2)} + 2f' + 3x^2f^{(2)} + 12xf' + 6f,$$
$$f^{(6)} = -2xf^{(5)} - 6f^{(4)} + x^2f^{(4)} + 6xf^{(3)} + 6f^{(2)} + 3x^2f^{(3)} + 18xf^{(2)} + 18f'.$$

Therefore

$$a_3 = f^{(3)}(0)/3! = 0,$$
$$a_4 = f^{(4)}(0)/4! = -8/24 = -1/3,$$
$$a_5 = f^{(5)}(0)/5! = 16/120 = 2/15,$$
$$a_6 = f^{(6)}(0)/6! = 54/720 = 3/40.$$

Hence $f = 3 - x + 2x^2 - x^4/3 + 2x^5/15 + 3x^6/40 + \cdots$.

EXAMPLE 3. Find f such that $f^{(3)} - 2f^{(2)} + 3xf' + 2x^2f = 0$, $f(1) = 2$, $f'(1) = -1$, and $f^{(2)}(1) = 3$.

Solution: Let $f = \Sigma a_{n-1}(x-1)^{n-1}$; then $a_{n-1} = f^{(n-1)}(1)/(n-1)!$ whenever $n \in N$. Thus $a_0 = 2$, $a_1 = -1$, and $a_2 = 3/2$, by assumption. We shall compute the next four terms of our power series. Now, by assumption,

$$f^{(3)} = 2f^{(2)} - 3xf' - 2x^2f;$$

so

$$f^{(4)} = 2f^{(3)} - 3xf^{(2)} - 3f' - 2x^2f' - 4xf,$$
$$f^{(5)} = 2f^{(4)} - 3xf^{(3)} - 6f^{(2)} - 2x^2f^{(2)} - 8xf' - 4f,$$
$$f^{(6)} = 2f^{(5)} - 3xf^{(4)} - 9f^{(3)} - 2x^2f^{(3)} - 12xf^{(2)} - 12f'.$$

Therefore

$$a_3 = f^{(3)}(1)/3! = 5/6,$$
$$a_4 = f^{(4)}(1)/4! = -2/4! = -1/12,$$
$$a_5 = f^{(5)}(1)/5! = -43/120,$$
$$a_6 = f^{(6)}(1)/6! = -159/6! = -53/240.$$

Hence $f = 2 - (x-1) + 3(x-1)^2/2 + 5(x-1)^3/6 - (x-1)^4/12 - 43(x-1)^5/120$
$$-53(x-1)^6/240 + \cdots.$$

EXERCISES

1. Find f such that $f^{(2)} - xf' - 2f = 0$, $f(0) = 0$, and $f'(0) = 1$. (*Answer:* $\Sigma x^{2n-1}/2^{n-1}(n-1)!$)

2. Find f such that $f^{(2)} - xf' - 2f = 0$, $f(0) = 1$, and $f'(0) = 0$.
$$(Answer: 1 + \Sigma x^{2n}/(2n-1)(2n-3) \cdots (1))$$

3. Find f such that $f^{(2)} - 2xf' + 6f = 0$, $f(0) = 1$, and $f'(0) = 2$.

(*Answer:* $1 + 2x - 3x^2 - 4x^3/3 + x^4/2 + x^6/30 + x^8/280 + x^{10}/2520 + \cdots$)

4. Find f such that $f^{(3)} - x^2 f^{(2)} - xf' - f = 0$, $f(0) = 1$, $f'(0) = 1$, and $f^{(2)}(0) = 1$.

(*Answer:* $1 + x + x^2/2 + x^3/6 + x^4/12 + x^5/24 + x^6/72 + 34x^7/7! + \cdots$)

5. Find f such that $f^{(4)} - 2xf^{(3)} + x^2 f^{(2)} - 3f' + 2f = 0$, $f(0) = -1$, $f'(0) = 0$, $f^{(2)}(0) = 2$, and $f^{(3)}(0) = 1$.

6. Find f such that $f^{(4)} - 3x^2 f^{(2)} + 2f' - xf = 0$, $f(0) = 2$, $f'(0) = 1$, $f^{(2)}(0) = 0$, and $f^{(3)}(0) = 3$.

7. Find f such that $f^{(2)} - 3f' + 2xf = 0$, $f(2) = 1$, and $f'(2) = 0$.

8. Find f such that $f^{(2)} - xf' + 3f = 0$, $f(-1) = 2$, and $f'(-1) = 1$.

(*Answer:* $2 + (x + 1) - 7(x + 1)^2/2 + 5(x + 1)^3/6 + (x - 1)^4/12$
$+ (x + 1)^5/60 + (x + 1)^6/180 - (x - 1)^7/630 + \cdots$)

11.2   Legendre Differential Equations; Legendre Polynomials

Since Theorem 11.1.4 is a *unique-existence* theorem, it is clear that we can *define* a function by presenting a differential equation with boundary conditions, provided the conditions of the theorem are met. This can be a convenient way of approaching a particular function, particularly if the fundamental properties of the function are disclosed by the differential equation involved. For example, the function exp can be defined by the differential equation $f' - f = 0$ and the boundary condition $f(0) = 1$. Since the coefficient functions -1 and 0 are analytic at 0 and have domain R, it follows from Theorem 11.1.4 that f has a power series representation with domain R. Moreover, $f^{(n)} = f$ whenever $n \in N$; therefore $f^{(n)}(0) = 1$ whenever $n \in N$; so our unique power series solution is $\Sigma x^{n-1}/(n-1)!$. Thus $\exp = \Sigma x^{n-1}/(n-1)!$.

Let us prove that $\exp(2x) = \exp^2$. Now, $[\exp(2x)]' = 2 \exp'(2x) = 2 \exp(2x)$, and $[\exp^2]' = 2 \exp \cdot \exp' = 2 \exp^2$. Therefore both functions satisfy the differential equation with boundary condition

$$f' = 2f \qquad \text{and} \qquad f(0) = 1.$$

But, by Theorem 11.1.4 there is a unique function with these properties; we conclude that $\exp(2x) = \exp^2$.

Let us prove that $\exp \cdot \exp(-x) = 1$. Now,

$$[\exp \cdot \exp(-x)]' = \exp' \cdot \exp(-x) - \exp \cdot \exp'(-x)$$

$$= \exp \cdot \exp(-x) - \exp \cdot \exp(-x)$$

$$= 0,$$

and $\exp(0) \cdot \exp(-0) = 1$. Thus the functions $\exp \cdot \exp(-x)$ and 1 both satisfy the differential equation with boundary condition

$$f' = 0 \qquad \text{and} \qquad f(0) = 1.$$

Hence, by Theorem 11.1.4, $\exp \cdot \exp(-x) = 1$.

We can now derive the fundamental property of exp, namely $\exp(a + b) = \exp(a) \cdot \exp(b)$ whenever $a \in R$ and $b \in R$. Consider the functions $\exp(a + x)$ and $\exp(a) \cdot \exp$, where $a \in R$. Since the derivatives of these functions are $\exp(a + x)$ and $\exp(a) \cdot \exp$, respectively, we conclude that both functions satisfy the differential equation $f' = f$. Moreover, $\exp(a + -a) = 1$ and $\exp(a) \cdot \exp(-a) = 1$. But there is just one function f such that $f' = f$ and $f(-a) = 1$; hence $\exp(a + x) = \exp(a) \cdot \exp$ whenever $a \in R$. This establishes the fundamental property of exp.

We turn now to Legendre differential equations. By a *Legendre differential equation* we mean any differential equation of the form

(1) $$(1 - x^2)f^{(2)} - 2xf' + c(c + 1)f = 0 \ R \ E,$$

where $c \in R$. Thus each of the following is a Legendre differential equation:

$$(1 - x^2)f^{(2)} - 2xf' + 6f = 0 \ R \ E,$$
$$(1 - x^2)f^{(2)} - 2xf' = 0 \ R \ E,$$
$$(1 - x^2)f^{(2)} - 2xf' + 2.64f = 0 \ R \ E,$$
$$(1 - x^2)f^{(2)} - 2xf' - .21f = 0 \ R \ E.$$

If we specify c and introduce boundary conditions, we can use (1) to define a function; certain of these functions are said to be *Legendre functions*.

If the domain of f does not include either zero of the function $1 - x^2$, we can divide (1) throughout by $1 - x^2$; thus we obtain

(2) $$f^{(2)} - \frac{2x}{1 - x^2}f' + \frac{c(c + 1)}{1 - x^2}f = 0 \ R \ E.$$

In (2) the coefficient functions are analytic at zero. Indeed, $1/(1 - x^2) \ R \ (-1, 1) = \Sigma x^{2n-2}$; so $-2x/(1 - x^2) \ R \ (-1, 1) = \Sigma - 2x^{2n-1}$ and $c(c + 1)/(1 - x^2) \ R \ (-1, 1) = \Sigma c(c + 1)x^{2n-2}$. Thus there is a unique Maclaurin series which exists on $(-1, 1)$ and satisfies (2) together with boundary conditions, say $f(0) = a_0$ and $f'(0) = a_1$. This means that we can determine the coefficients of $\Sigma a_{n-1}x^{n-1}$ in terms of a_0 and a_1. We now proceed to do just that. Let $f = \Sigma a_{n-1}x^{n-1}$; then $f' = \Sigma na_n x^{n-1}$ and $f^{(2)} = \Sigma n(n + 1)a_{n+1}x^{n-1}$. Thus

$$(1 - x^2) \Sigma n(n + 1)a_{n+1}x^{n-1} - 2x \Sigma na_n x^{n-1} + c(c + 1) \Sigma a_{n-1}x^{n-1} = 0 \ R \ E$$

whenever $n \in N$. Hence

$$n(n + 1)a_{n+1} = a_{n-1}[n(n - 1) - c(c + 1)]$$
$$= a_{n-1}(n^2 - c^2 - n - c)$$
$$= a_{n-1}(n + c)(n - c - 1).$$

Therefore $a_{n+1} = -\dfrac{(c + 1 - n)(c + n)}{n(n + 1)} a_{n-1}$ whenever $n \in N$.

In particular,

$$a_2 = -\frac{c(c+1)}{1\cdot 2}\,a_0,$$

$$a_3 = -\frac{(c-1)(c+2)}{2\cdot 3}\,a_1,$$

$$a_4 = -\frac{(c-2)(c+3)}{3\cdot 4}\,a_2 = \frac{c(c+1)(c-2)(c+3)}{1\cdot 2\cdot 3\cdot 4}\,a_0,$$

$$a_5 = -\frac{(c-3)(c+4)}{4\cdot 5}\,a_3 = \frac{(c-1)(c+2)(c-3)(c+4)}{2\cdot 3\cdot 4\cdot 5}\,a_1.$$

In general,

$$(3)\quad a_{2n} = (-1)^n\,\frac{c(c+1)(c-2)(c+3)\cdots(c-2n+2)(c+2n-1)}{(2n)!}\,a_0 \quad\text{whenever } n\in N,$$

$$(4)\quad a_{2n+1} = (-1)^n\,\frac{(c-1)(c+2)(c-3)\cdots(c-2n+1)(c+2n)}{(2n+1)!}\,a_1 \quad\text{whenever } n\in N.$$

Of course, we can characterize the unique solution of (1) which satisfies the boundary conditions $f(0) = b_0$ and $f'(0) = b_1$, where b_0 and b_1 are given real numbers, in terms of two linearly independent solutions of (1). We now present two linearly independent solutions of (1), u_0 and u_1. Let u_0 be the unique solution of (1) which satisfies the boundary conditions $f(0) = 1$ and $f'(0) = 0$; then $u_0 = 1 + \Sigma\, a_{2n}x^{2n}$, where each a_{2n} is given by (3) with $a_0 = 1$. And let u_1 be the unique solution of (1) which satisfies the boundary conditions $f(0) = 0$ and $f'(0) = 1$; then $u_1 = x + \Sigma\, a_{2n+1}x^{2n+1}$, where each a_{2n+1} is given by (4) with $a_1 = 1$. Finally, we observe that the unique solution of (1) which satisfies the boundary conditions $f(0) = b_0$ and $f'(0) = b_1$ is the corresponding linear combination of u_0 and u_1, namely $b_0 u_0 + b_1 u_1$.

Now that we have completely solved (1), let us concentrate on the parameter c. In view of (3), u_0 reduces to a polynomial function in case c is zero, a positive even integer, or a negative odd integer; e.g., $u_0 = 1 - 3x^2$ if $c = 2$, and $u_0 = 1 - 10x^2 + 35x^4/3$ if $c = 4$. In view of (4), u_1 reduces to a polynomial function in case c is a positive odd integer or a negative even integer; e.g., $u_1 = x$ if $c = 1$, and $u_1 = x - 5x^3/3$ if $c = 3$. If c is not an integer, then neither u_0 nor u_1 is a polynomial function; however, in this case both u_0 and u_1 are functions with domain $(-1, 1)$. These functions are said to be the *Legendre functions*. Thus the Legendre functions are

$$1 + \Sigma\,\frac{(-1)^n}{(2n)!}\,c(c+1)(c-2)(c+3)\cdots(c-2n+2)(c+2n-1)x^{2n}$$

and

$$x + \Sigma\,\frac{(-1)^n}{(2n+1)!}\,(c-1)(c+2)(c-3)\cdots(c-2n+1)(c+2n)x^{2n+1}$$

provided c is not an integer.

We now fix our attention on the solutions of (1) which are *not* Legendre functions; in particular, we shall concentrate on the case in which c is a nonnegative integer. In this connection the following theorem is particularly relevant.

THEOREM 11.2.1. $\mathbf{D}^n(x^2 - 1)^n$ is a particular solution of the differential equation $(1 - x^2)f^{(2)} - 2xf' + n(n + 1)f = 0$ whenever n is a nonnegative integer.

To prove this theorem, we need the $n + 2$nd derivative of $(x^2 - 1)^n$. This operation is facilitated by the following lemma, which we shall find useful throughout this section.

LEMMA 11.2.1. $[f \cdot g]^{(n)} = \sum_{k=0}^{n} \binom{n}{k} f^{(k)} \cdot g^{(n-k)}$ whenever n is a nonnegative integer.

Proof: Apply mathematical induction.

Now we are in a position to prove Theorem 11.2.1.

Proof of Theorem 11.2.1: Let $g = (x^2 - 1)^n$; then $g' = 2nx(x^2 - 1)^{n-1}$; so $(x^2 - 1)g' = 2nxg$. Hence $\mathbf{D}^{n+1}[(x^2 - 1)g'] = \mathbf{D}^{n+1}[2nxg]$; this is easily computed by using Lemma 11.2.1. So

$$(x^2 - 1)g^{(n+2)} + 2x(n + 1)g^{(n+1)} + n(n + 1)g^{(n)} = 2nxg^{(n+1)} + 2n(n + 1)g^{(n)};$$

hence $(x^2 - 1)g^{(n+2)} + 2xg^{(n+1)} - n(n + 1)g^{(n)} = 0$,   i.e., $(1 - x^2)g^{(n+2)} - 2xg^{(n+1)} + n(n + 1)g^{(n)} = 0$. This establishes Theorem 11.2.1.

Notice that $\mathbf{D}^n(x^2 - 1)^n$ is a polynomial function of degree n whenever n is a non-negative integer. Accordingly, we introduce the *Legendre polynomials*.

DEFINITION 11.2.1. $\dfrac{1}{2^n n!} \mathbf{D}^n(x^2 - 1)^n$ is said to be the *Legendre polynomial of degree* n whenever n is a nonnegative integer; the Legendre polynomial of degree n is denoted by "P_n".

For example, $P_0 = 1$, $P_1 = x$, and $P_2 = 3x^2/2 - 1/2$. Legendre polynomials possess many interesting properties. These functions have been intensively studied because of their importance in both pure and applied mathematics. We shall now develop some properties of Legendre polynomials; in particular, we shall work out a recursion relation on Legendre polynomials which will enable us to compute more of the Legendre polynomials quite efficiently.

THEOREM 11.2.2. $P_n' = xP_{n-1}' + nP_{n-1}$ whenever $n \in N$.

Proof: Let $n \in N$; then

$$[(x^2 - 1)]^{(n+1)} = [(x^2 - 1)(x^2 - 1)^{n-1}]^{(n+1)}$$

$$= (x^2 - 1)[(x^2 - 1)^{n-1}]^{(n+1)} + 2(n + 1)x[(x^2 - 1)^{n-1}]^{(n)}$$

$$+ n(n + 1)[(x^2 - 1)^{n-1}]^{(n-1)} \qquad \text{by Lemma 11.2.1.}$$

Thus

$$\frac{1}{2^n n!} [(x^2 - 1)^n]^{(n+1)} = \frac{x^2 - 1}{2^n n!} [(x^2 - 1)^{n-1}]^{(n+1)} + \frac{(n+1)x}{2^{n-1} n!} [(x^2 - 1)^{n-1}]^{(n)}$$

$$+ \frac{n+1}{2^n (n-1)!} [(x^2 - 1)^{n-1}]^{(n-1)}.$$

Therefore, by Definition 11.2.1,

$$P_n' = \frac{x^2 - 1}{2n} P_{n-1}^{(2)} + \frac{n+1}{n} x P_{n-1}' + \frac{n+1}{2} P_{n-1};$$

so

$$2n P_n' = -2x P_{n-1}' + n(n-1)P_{n-1} + 2(n+1)x P_{n-1}' + n(n+1)P_{n-1} \qquad \text{by (1)}$$

$$= 2nx P_{n-1}' + 2n^2 P_{n-1};$$

thus $P_n' = x P_{n-1}' + n P_{n-1}$ since $n \neq 0$.

THEOREM 11.2.3. $(1 - x^2)P_{n-1}' = nx P_{n-1} - n P_n$ whenever $n \in N$.

Proof: Let $n \in N$; then $P_n' = x P_{n-1}' + n P_{n-1}$, by Theorem 11.2.2. Thus $P_n^{(2)} = x P_{n-1}^{(2)} + (1+n)P_{n-1}'$; therefore

$$(x^2 - 1)P_n^{(2)} = x(x^2 - 1)P_{n-1}^{(2)} + (x^2 - 1)(1+n)P_{n-1}'.$$

Hence, by (1),

$$-2x P_n' + n(n+1)P_n = x[-2x P_{n-1}' + n(n-1)P_{n-1}] + (x^2 - 1)(1+n)P_{n-1}'$$

$$= x[-2P_n' + 2n P_{n-1} + n(n-1)P_{n-1}] + (x^2 - 1)(1+n)P_{n-1}'$$

$$\text{by Th. 11.2.2;}$$

thus $n(n+1)P_n = n(n+1)x P_{n-1} + (x^2 - 1)(n+1)P_{n-1}'$; so $n P_n = nx P_{n-1} + (x^2 - 1)P_{n-1}'$ since $n + 1 \neq 0$.

THEOREM 11.2.4. $P_{n-1}' = x P_n' - n P_n$ whenever $n \in N$.

Proof: Let $n \in N$; then $(1 - x^2)P_{n-1}' = nx P_{n-1} - n P_n$, by Theorem 11.2.3. But $x^2 P_{n-1}' = x[P_n' - n P_{n-1}]$, by Theorem 11.2.2; hence

$$P_{n-1}' = x[P_n' - n P_{n-1}] + nx P_{n-1} - n P_n = x P_n' - n P_n.$$

THEOREM 11.2.5. $(1 - x^2)P_n' = n P_{n-1} - nx P_n$ whenever $n \in N$.

Proof: Let $n \in N$; then, by Theorem 11.2.4, $P_{n-1}' = x P_n' - n P_n$; thus $x P_{n-1}' = x^2 P_n' - nx P_n$. Hence $P_n' - n P_{n-1} = x^2 P_n' - nx P_n$, by Theorem 11.2.2, i.e., $(1 - x^2)P_n' = n P_{n-1} - nx P_n$.

We are now in a position to develop a useful recursion relation.

THEOREM 11.2.6. $(n + 1)P_{n+1} = (2n + 1)xP_n - nP_{n-1}$ whenever $n \in N$.

Proof: Let $n \in N$; then

$$(1 - x^2)P'_n = (n + 1)xP_n - (n + 1)P_{n+1} \qquad \text{by Th. 11.2.3}$$

$$(1 - x^2)P'_n = nP_{n-1} - nxP_n \qquad \text{by Th. 11.2.5.}$$

Therefore $(n + 1)xP_n - (n + 1)P_{n+1} = nP_{n-1} - nxP_n$, i.e., $(n + 1)P_{n+1} = (2n + 1)xP_n - nP_{n-1}$.

We know that $P_0 = 1$ and that $P_1 = x$; so we can use our recursion relation to work out P_2, P_3, P_4, etc. For example,

$$P_2 = (1/2)(3x^2 - 1),$$

$$P_3 = (1/3)(5xP_2 - 2P_1) = 5x^3/2 - 3x/2,$$

$$P_4 = (1/4)(7xP_3 - 3P_2) = 35x^4/8 - 15x^2/4 + 3/8,$$

$$P_5 = (1/5)(9xP_4 - 4P_3) = 63x^5/8 - 35x^3/4 + 15x/8.$$

Our recursion relation is very valuable.

THEOREM 11.2.7. $P_n(1) = 1$ whenever n is a nonnegative integer.

Proof: We apply mathematical induction. Since $P_0 = 1$ and $P_1 = x$, it is clear that $P_0(1) = 1$ and $P_1(1) = 1$. Suppose that $P_t(1) = 1$ and that $P_{t+1}(1) = 1$; we shall prove that $P_{t+2}(1) = 1$. Now, by Theorem 11.2.6, $(t + 2)P_{t+2} = (2t + 3)xP_{t+1} - (t + 1)P_t$. Thus

$$(t + 2)P_{t+2}(1) = (2t + 3)P_{t+1}(1) - (t + 1)P_t(1)$$

$$= 2t + 3 - (t + 1)$$

$$= t + 2.$$

Therefore $P_{t+2}(1) = 1$. By mathematical induction, our theorem is established.

THEOREM 11.2.8. $P_n(-1) = (-1)^n$ whenever n is a nonnegative integer.

Proof: Apply mathematical induction and use Theorem 11.2.6. The details are left as an exercise.

THEOREM 11.2.9. $n \bigwedge P_n \equiv P_{n+1} - xP_n$ whenever n is a nonnegative integer.

Proof: Let n be a nonnegative integer; then

$$(P_{n+1} - xP_n)' = P'_{n+1} - P_n - xP'_n$$

$$= P'_{n+1} - P_n - [P'_{n+1} - (n + 1)P_n] \qquad \text{by Th. 11.2.2}$$

$$= nP_n.$$

THEOREM 11.2.10. $\int_{-1}^{1} P_n = 0$ whenever $n \in N$.

Proof: Let $n \in N$; then

$$\int_{-1}^{1} P_n = \frac{1}{n}\left[P_{n+1} - xP_n \right]_{-1}^{1} = \frac{1}{n}[P_{n+1}(1) - P_n(1)] - \frac{1}{n}[P_{n+1}(-1) + P_n(-1)]$$

$$= 0 \qquad \text{by Th. 11.2.7 and Th. 11.2.8.}$$

THEOREM 11.2.11. $\int_{-1}^{1} P_n^2 = 2/(2n + 1)$ whenever n is a nonnegative integer.

Proof: Clearly, $\int_{-1}^{1} P_0^2 = \int_{-1}^{1} 1 = 2$. Next, let $n \in N$; then

$$\int_{-1}^{1} P_n^2 = \left[\frac{P_n}{n} \cdot (P_{n+1} - xP_n) \right]_{-1}^{1} - \frac{1}{n}\int_{-1}^{1} P_n' \cdot (P_{n+1} - xP_n).$$

Hence $n \int_{-1}^{1} P_n^2 = \int_{-1}^{1} (xP_n - P_{n+1}) \cdot P_n'$. Now,

$$\int_{-1}^{1} (xP_n \cdot P_n') = \left[xP_n \cdot P_n \right]_{-1}^{1} - \int_{-1}^{1} P_n \cdot (P_n + xP_n')$$

$$= 2 - \int_{-1}^{1} (P_n \cdot P_n) - \int_{-1}^{1} (xP_n \cdot P_n')$$

$$= 1 - \frac{1}{2}\int_{-1}^{1} P_n^2.$$

Also,

$$\int_{-1}^{1} (P_{n+1} \cdot P_n') = \int_{-1}^{1} P_{n+1} \cdot [xP_{n+1}' - (n + 1)P_{n+1}]$$

$$= 1 - \frac{1}{2}\int_{-1}^{1} P_{n+1}^2 - (n + 1)\int_{-1}^{1} P_{n+1}^2.$$

Thus

$$n \int_{-1}^{1} P_n^2 = 1 - \frac{1}{2}\int_{-1}^{1} P_n^2 - 1 + \frac{2n + 3}{2}\int_{-1}^{1} P_{n+1}^2$$

$$= \frac{2n + 3}{2}\int_{-1}^{1} P_{n+1}^2 - \frac{1}{2}\int_{-1}^{1} P_n^2.$$

Therefore $\dfrac{2n+1}{2}\displaystyle\int_{-1}^{1}P_n^2 = \dfrac{2n+3}{2}\displaystyle\int_{-1}^{1}P_{n+1}^2;\ \text{ so }\ \displaystyle\int_{-1}^{1}P_n^2 = \dfrac{2n-1}{2n+1}\displaystyle\int_{-1}^{1}P_{n-1}^2.$

Thus $\displaystyle\int_{-1}^{1}P_n^2 = \dfrac{2n-1}{2n+1}\dfrac{2n-3}{2n-1}\cdots\dfrac{2n-1-2(n-1)}{2n+1-2(n-1)}\displaystyle\int_{-1}^{1}P_0^2 = \dfrac{1}{2n+1}\displaystyle\int_{-1}^{1}1 = \dfrac{2}{2n+1}.$

This establishes our result.

THEOREM 11.2.12. $\displaystyle\int_{-1}^{1}(P_s\cdot P_t)=0$ whenever $s\neq t$.

Proof: Suppose that $s\neq t$. Now,

$$P_t \equiv \dfrac{1}{t}(P_{t+1}-xP_t) = \dfrac{1}{t(t+1)}(x^2-1)P_t' \qquad \text{by Th. 11.2.3;}$$

thus $t(t+1)\displaystyle\int_{-1}^{1}(P_s\cdot P_t) = \left[P_s\cdot(x^2-1)\cdot P_t'\right]_{-1}^{1} - \displaystyle\int_{-1}^{1}(x_2-1)P_s'\cdot P_t';$

i.e., $t(t+1)\displaystyle\int_{-1}^{1}(P_s\cdot P_t) = \displaystyle\int_{-1}^{1}(x^2-1)P_s'\cdot P_t'.$

Similarly, $s(s+1)\displaystyle\int_{-1}^{1}(P_s\cdot P_t) = \displaystyle\int_{-1}^{1}(x^2-1)P_s'\cdot P_t'.$

Therefore $t(t+1)\displaystyle\int_{-1}^{1}(P_s\cdot P_t) = s(s+1)\displaystyle\int_{-1}^{1}P_s\cdot P_t;$

i.e., $(t-s)(t+s+1)\displaystyle\int_{-1}^{1}(P_s\cdot P_t) = 0.$

Since $(t-s)(t+s+1)\neq0$, we conclude that $\displaystyle\int_{-1}^{1}(P_s\cdot P_t)=0.$

Here is a fascinating property of Legendre polynomials: let n be any nonnegative integer; then each zero of P_n is a member of $(-1,1)$; moreover, P_n has exactly n distinct zeros. We shall derive this result in a moment (see Theorem 11.2.18). For the moment, let us use this property to make a rough sketch of P_n. Since the graph of P_n intersects H exactly n times over the interval $(-1,1)$, there are $n-1$ wiggles between -1 and 1. Recall that $P_n(1)=1$, and that $P_n(-1)=1$ if n is even, and that $P_n(-1)=-1$ if n is odd; moreover, the graph of P_n increases, numerically, without bound outside of the interval $(-1,1)$. Thus we obtain the graphs displayed in Figures 11.2.1 and 11.2.2.

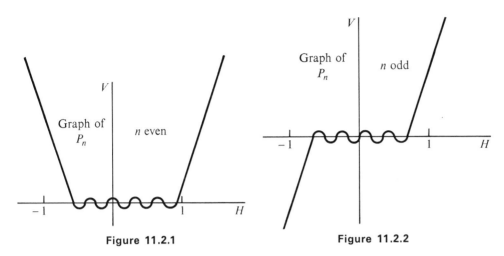

Figure 11.2.1   Figure 11.2.2

Now to work. The following two theorems are aimed at proving that each zero of P_n is simple.

THEOREM 11.2.13.   If there is a nonnegative integer n such that P_n and P_{n+1} have a common zero, say r, then r is a zero of each Legendre polynomial.
Proof: Apply Theorem 11.2.6.

COROLLARY 11.2.1.   There is no nonnegative integer n such that P_n and P_{n+1} have a common zero.
Proof: P_0 has no zeros.

THEOREM 11.2.14.   Let $n \in N$; then each zero of P_n is simple.
Proof: Suppose that there is a natural number n such that P_n has a multiple zero, say r; then r is a zero of P_n'. Applying Theorem 11.2.5, we see that r is a zero of P_{n-1}. This contradicts Corollary 11.2.1. We conclude that P_n has only simple zeros.
Next we shall prove that P_n has exactly n zeros, and that each zero of P_n is a member of $(-1, 1)$.

THEOREM 11.2.15.   Let $n \in N$; then P_n has at least one zero, say r, such that $r \in (-1, 1)$.
Proof: Let $n \in N$; then, by Theorem 11.2.10, $\int_{-1}^{1} P_n = 0$. Now, there is a member of $(-1, 1)$, say r, such that $\int_{-1}^{1} P_n = 2P_n(r)$. Thus $P_n(r) = 0$.

THEOREM 11.2.16.   Let $t \in N$ and let Q be any polynomial function of degree t. Then there are real numbers $k_0, k_1, \cdots, k_t$ such that $Q = k_0 P_0 + k_1 P_1 + \cdots + k_t P_t$; moreover, the real numbers $k_0, k_1, \cdots, k_t$ are unique and not all zero.
Proof: Apply mathematical induction.

THEOREM 11.2.17.   Let Q be any polynomial function and let n be any natural number greater than the degree of Q; then $\int_{-1}^{1}(Q \cdot P_n) = 0$.

Proof: Apply Theorems 11.2.16 and 11.2.12.

We come now to our main theorem.

THEOREM 11.2.18   Let n be any nonnegative integer; then P_n has exactly n zeros; moreover, each zero of P_n is a member of $(-1, 1)$.

Proof: Clearly, P_0 has no zeros. Let $n \in N$, and consider P_n. In view of Theorem 11.2.15, there is a natural number t such that P_n has exactly t zeros on $(-1, 1)$, say $r_1, r_2, \cdots, r_t$. Now, P_n is a polynomial function of degree n; therefore $t \le n$. We shall assume that $t < n$ and shall try to obtain a contradiction. Let $Q = (x - r_1)(x - r_2) \cdots (x - r_t)$; then $P_n = Q \cdot S$, where S is a polynomial function which has no zeros on $[-1, 1]$. Since $P_n(1) = 1$ and $Q(1) > 0$, we see that $S(1) > 0$; it follows that $S(u) > 0$ whenever $u \in [-1, 1]$. Thus $P_n(a)$ and $Q(a)$ have the same algebraic sign whenever $a \in [-1, 1]$. But Q is a polynomial function whose degree is less than n; therefore, by Theorem 11.2.17, $\int_{-1}^{1}(Q \cdot P_n) = 0$. Since $Q \cdot P_n$ has only t zeros on $[-1, 1]$ and is positive everywhere else on $[-1, 1]$, it follows that $\int_{-1}^{1}(Q \cdot P_n) > 0$. This contradiction demonstrates that P_n has exactly n zeros which are members of $(-1, 1)$.

For later use we display the first ten Legendre polynomials:

$$P_0 = 1,$$
$$P_1 = x,$$
$$P_2 = \tfrac{1}{2}(3x^2 - 1),$$
$$P_3 = \tfrac{1}{2}(5x^3 - 3x),$$
$$P_4 = \tfrac{1}{8}(35x^4 - 30x^2 + 3),$$
$$P_5 = \tfrac{1}{8}(63x^5 - 70x^3 + 15x),$$
$$P_6 = \tfrac{1}{16}(231x^6 - 315x^4 + 105x^2 - 5),$$
$$P_7 = \tfrac{1}{16}(429x^7 - 693x^5 + 315x^3 - 35x),$$
$$P_8 = \tfrac{1}{128}(6435x^8 - 12012x^6 + 6930x^4 - 1260x^2 + 35),$$
$$P_9 = \tfrac{1}{128}(12155x^9 - 25740x^7 + 18018x^5 - 4620x^3 + 315x),$$
$$P_{10} = \tfrac{1}{256}(46189x^{10} - 109395x^8 + 90090x^6 - 30030x^4 + 3465x^2 - 63).$$

E X E R C I S E S

1. Prove that $P_n(-x) = (-1)^n P_n$ whenever $n \in N$.

2. a. Prove that $P_{2n}(0) = (-1)^n \dfrac{(2n)!}{(2^n n!)^2}$ whenever $n \in N$.

   b. Prove that $P_{2n-1}(0) = 0$ whenever $n \in N$.

3. Show directly that $[(x^2 - 1)^n]^{(n)}$ is a particular solution of $(1 - x^2)f^{(2)} - 2xf' + n(n + 1)f = 0$ whenever $n \in N$. (*Hint:* Let $g = (x^2 - 1)^n$ and show that $(x^2 - 1)g' = 2nxg$; then expand $[(x^2 - 1)g']^{(n+1)}$, i.e., expand $[2nxg]^{(n+1)}$.)

4. Find f such that:
   a. $(1 - x^2)f^{(2)} - 2xf' + 6f = 0$ R E, $f(0) = 1$, and $f'(0) = 2$.
   b. $(1 - x^2)f^{(2)} - 2xf' = 0$ R E, $f(0) = -1$, and $f'(0) = 1$.
   c. $(1 - x^2)f^{(2)} - 2xf' + 3/4 = 0$ R E, $f(0) = 1$, and $f'(0) = 0$.

5. Prove Lemma 11.2.1.

6. Use Definition 11.2.1 to compute P_3 and P_4.

7. Prove Theorem 11.2.8.

8. Prove Theorem 11.2.13.

9. **a.** Prove Theorem 11.2.16.

   b. Let f be a polynomial of degree less than m; prove that $\int_{-1}^{1} (f \cdot P_m) = 0$.

10. Prove Theorem 11.2.17.

11. Let f be a function with domain $[-1, 1]$, and assume that there is a sequence (a_{n-1}) such that $f = \Sigma a_{n-1} P_{n-1}$ R $[-1,1]$. Prove that $a_{n-1} = \dfrac{2n - 1}{2} \int_{-1}^{1} (f \cdot P_{n-1})$ whenever $n \in N$.

11.3   Approximation by Polynomial Functions

Let f be a function which is continuous on $[-1, 1]$ and let n be a nonnegative integer; consider the problem of finding a polynomial function p_n with degree at most n such that $\int_{-1}^{1} (f - p_n)^2$ is minimum; i.e., we want a polynomial function p_n such that

$$\int_{-1}^{1} (f - p_n)^2 \leq \int_{-1}^{1} (f - p)^2$$

whenever p is a polynomial function with degree at most n. If we can find a polynomial function p_n with this property, then it will possess the following outstanding characteristic: of all the polynomial functions with degree at most n, it is p_n that approximates f most closely over the interval $[-1, 1]$.

The Legendre polynomials are closely associated with this problem; indeed, the Legendre polynomials are the key to solving our problem. Recall that

$$\int_{-1}^{1} (P_s \cdot P_t) = \begin{cases} 0 & \text{if } s \neq t \\ \dfrac{2}{2s + 1} & \text{if } s = t. \end{cases}$$

Subsequent calculations are simplified by *normalizing* the Legendre polynomials. Let $\varphi_n = \left(\dfrac{2n + 1}{2}\right)^{1/2} P_n$ whenever n is a nonnegative integer; then

(1)
$$\int_{-1}^{1} (\varphi_s \cdot \varphi_t) = \begin{cases} 0 & \text{if } s \neq t \\ 1 & \text{if } s = t. \end{cases}$$

Clearly, each polynomial function whose degree does not exceed n is a linear combination of $\varphi_0, \varphi_1, \cdots, \varphi_n$. Thus if p is a polynomial function whose degree does not exceed n, then there are real numbers $c_0, c_1, \cdots, c_n$ such that $p = \sum\limits_{k=0}^{n} c_k \varphi_k$. Let $b_k = \int_{-1}^{1} (f \cdot \varphi_k)$ whenever $0 \le k \le n$; then

$$\int_{-1}^{1} (f - p)^2 = \int_{-1}^{1} \left(f - \sum_{k=0}^{n} c_k \varphi_k \right)^2$$

$$= \int_{-1}^{1} f^2 - 2 \int_{-1}^{1} \left(f \cdot \sum_{k=0}^{n} c_k \varphi_k \right) + \int_{-1}^{1} \left(\sum_{k=0}^{n} c_k \varphi_k \right)^2$$

$$= \int_{-1}^{1} f^2 - 2 \sum_{k=0}^{n} b_k c_k + \sum_{k=0}^{n} c_k^2 \qquad \text{by (1)}$$

$$= \int_{-1}^{1} f^2 + \sum_{k=0}^{n} (c_k - b_k)^2 - \sum_{k=0}^{n} b_k^2.$$

In particular, $\quad \int_{-1}^{1} \left(f - \sum\limits_{k=0}^{n} b_k \varphi_k \right)^2 = \int_{-1}^{1} f^2 + \sum\limits_{k=0}^{n} (b_k - b_k)^2 - \sum\limits_{k=0}^{n} b_k^2$

$$= \int_{-1}^{1} f^2 - \sum_{k=0}^{n} b_k^2.$$

Thus $\int_{-1}^{1} \left(f - \sum\limits_{k=0}^{n} b_k \varphi_k \right)^2 \le \int_{-1}^{1} (f - p)^2$ whenever p is a polynomial function whose degree does not exceed n. This establishes the following theorem.

THEOREM 11.3.1. Let f be continuous on $[-1, 1]$, let n be any nonnegative integer, and let $b_k = \int_{-1}^{1} (f \cdot \varphi_k)$ whenever $0 \le k \le n$. Then $\int_{-1}^{1} \left(f - \sum\limits_{k=0}^{n} b_k \varphi_k \right)^2 \le \int_{-1}^{1} (f - p)^2$ whenever p is a polynomial function whose degree does not exceed n. Moreover,

$$\int_{-1}^{1} \left(f - \sum_{k=0}^{n} b_k \varphi_k \right)^2 = \int_{-1}^{1} f^2 - \sum_{k=0}^{n} b_k^2.$$

Things are even better than they appear to be. Consider the following theorem, which we state without proof.

THEOREM 11.3.2. Let f be continuous on $[-1, 1]$ and let ε be any positive real number. Then there is a nonnegative integer n such that $\int_{-1}^{1} \left(f - \sum\limits_{k=0}^{n} b_k \varphi_k \right)^2 < \varepsilon$, where $b_k = \int_{-1}^{1} (f \cdot \varphi_k)$ whenever $0 \le k \le n$.

Thus not only is $\sum\limits_{k=0}^{n} b_k \varphi_k$ the best polynomial function approximation to f over $[-1, 1]$ of degree n or less, but given $\varepsilon > 0$ we can choose n so that the error in the approximation, as measured by the integral of the square of the difference, is less than ε.

Note that $b_n \varphi_n = \dfrac{2n+1}{2} P_n \int_{-1}^{1} (f \cdot P_n)$ whenever n is a nonnegative integer. For reference we list the first eight of the functions $b_n \varphi_n$:

$$b_0 \varphi_0 = \frac{1}{2} \int_{-1}^{1} f,$$

$$b_1 \varphi_1 = \frac{3}{2} x \int_{-1}^{1} xf,$$

$$b_2 \varphi_2 = \frac{5}{8} (3x^2 - 1) \int_{-1}^{1} (3x^2 - 1)f,$$

$$b_3 \varphi_3 = \frac{7}{8} (5x^3 - 3x) \int_{-1}^{1} (5x^3 - 3x)f,$$

$$b_4 \varphi_4 = \frac{9}{128} (35x^4 - 30x^2 + 3) \int_{-1}^{1} (35x^4 - 30x^2 + 3)f,$$

$$b_5 \varphi_5 = \frac{11}{128} (63x^5 - 70x^3 + 15x) \int_{-1}^{1} (63x^5 - 70x^3 + 15x)f,$$

$$b_6 \varphi_6 = \frac{13}{512} (231x^6 - 315x^4 + 105x^2 - 5) \int_{-1}^{1} (231x^6 - 315x^4 + 105x^2 - 5)f,$$

$$b_7 \varphi_7 = \frac{15}{512} (429x^7 - 693x^5 + 315x^3 - 35x) \int_{-1}^{1} (429x^7 - 693x^5 + 315x^3 - 35x)f.$$

We now present some examples.

EXAMPLE 1.   Of the polynomial functions with degree 4 or less, find the best approximation to x^6 over $[-1, 1]$.

Solution: By Theorem 11.3.1, the required polynomial function is $\sum\limits_{k=0}^{4} b_k \varphi_k$, where $f = x^6$, namely

$$\frac{1}{2} \int_{-1}^{1} x^6 + \frac{3}{2} x \int_{-1}^{1} x^7 + \frac{5}{8} (3x^2 - 1) \int_{-1}^{1} (3x^2 - 1)x^6 + \frac{7}{8} (5x^3 - 3x) \int_{-1}^{1} (5x^3 - 3x)x^6$$

$$+ \frac{9}{128} (35x^4 - 30x^2 + 3) \int_{-1}^{1} (35x^4 - 30x^2 + 3)x^6.$$

Notice that $\int_{-1}^{1} x^n = 0$ whenever n is odd. Now, $\int_{-1}^{1} x^6 = 2/7$, $\int_{-1}^{1} x^8 = 2/9$, and $\int_{-1}^{1} x^{10} = 2/11$; thus

$$\sum_{k=0}^{4} b_k \varphi_k = \frac{1}{7} + \frac{5}{8}\left(\frac{2}{3} - \frac{2}{7}\right)(3x^2 - 1) + \frac{9}{128}\left(\frac{70}{11} - \frac{20}{3} + \frac{6}{7}\right)(35x^4 - 30x^2 + 3)$$

$$= \frac{1}{7} + \frac{5}{21}(3x^2 - 1) + \frac{3}{77}(35x^4 - 30x^2 + 3)$$

$$= \frac{5}{11}\left(\frac{1}{21} - x^2 + 3x^4\right).$$

We conclude that $\frac{5}{11}(\frac{1}{21} - x^2 + 3x^4)$ is the required polynomial function. Note that $\int_{-1}^{1} \frac{5}{11}(\frac{1}{21} - x^2 + 3x^4) = \frac{2}{7}$ and that $\int_{-1}^{1} x^6 = \frac{2}{7}$; thus the functions $\frac{5}{11}(\frac{1}{21} - x^2 + 3x^4)$ and x^6 have the same average value over $[-1, 1]$.

To compute the best polynomial function approximation of degree at most n, to a given function f over $[-1, 1]$, we need the numbers $\int_{-1}^{1} f, \int_{-1}^{1} xf, \cdots, \int_{-1}^{1} x^n f$. Indeed, the required polynomial function can be expressed in terms of these numbers. Accordingly, we shall denote $\int_{-1}^{1} x^t f$ by "c_t" whenever $0 \le t \le n$.

EXAMPLE 2. Find the best polynomial function approximation to $\sin$ over $[-1, 1]$ of degree at most 5.

Solution: By Theorem 11.3.1, the required polynomial function is $\sum_{k=0}^{5} b_k \varphi_k$, where $f = \sin$, namely

$$\frac{1}{2}\int_{-1}^{1} \sin + \frac{3}{2}x\int_{-1}^{1} x \sin + \frac{5}{8}(3x^2 - 1)\int_{-1}^{1} (3x^2 - 1) \sin$$

$$+ \frac{7}{8}(5x^3 - 3x)\int_{-1}^{1} (5x^3 - 3x) \sin + \frac{9}{128}(35x^4 - 30x^2 + 3)\int_{-1}^{1} (35x^4 - 30x^2 + 3) \sin$$

$$+ \frac{11}{128}(63x^5 - 70x^3 + 15x)\int_{-1}^{1} (63x^5 - 70x^3 + 15x) \sin.$$

Clearly, $\int_{-1}^{1} x^n \sin = 0$ if n is even; so $c_0 = c_2 = c_4 = 0$. Now,

$$c_1 = \int_{-1}^{1} x \sin = 2 \sin 1 - 2 \cos 1,$$

$$c_3 = \int_{-1}^{1} x^3 \sin = 10 \cos 1 - 6 \sin 1,$$

$$c_5 = \int_{-1}^{1} x^5 \sin = 130 \sin 1 - 202 \cos 1.$$

Thus

$$\sum_{k=0}^{5} b_k \varphi_k = \frac{3}{2} c_1 x + \frac{7}{8} (5c_3 - 3c_1)(5x^3 - 3x) + \frac{11}{128} (63c_5 - 70c_3 + 15c_1)(63x^5 - 70x^3 + 15x).$$

We have presented the required function in a form which is suitable for computation by an automatic digital computer. To display our function, we shall compute 25 of its values over the interval [0, 1]. Also, we shall compare this polynomial function to the polynomial function of degree 5 obtained from the Maclaurin series for sin, namely $x - x^3/3! + x^5/5!$. Notice that our function is about 14 times as accurate as the Maclaurin polynomial function of the same degree.

```
                        PROGRAM FOR THE
               BEST APPROXIMATION TO SIN OVER (-1,1)
                 BY POLYNOMIAL OF DEGREE AT MOST 5

*FANDK1504
        L = 0
        AVL = 0.0
        AVM = 0.0
      1 FORMAT(1H ,4X,1HT,6X,8HLEGENDRE,3X,9HMACLAURIN,7X,3HSIN,6X,
       19H/SIN - L/,2X,11H/SIN - MAC/)
        PRINT 1
      2 FORMAT(1H )
        PRINT 2
      3 FORMAT(1H ,F6.2,1X,3F12.7,2F13.8)
        C1 = 2.*SINF(1.) - 2.*COSF(1.)
        C3 = 10.*COSF(1.) - 6.*SINF(1.)
        C5 = 130.*SINF(1.) - 202.*COSF(1.)
        DO 30 K = 1,25
        C = K - 1
        T = C*.04
        X = T
        PL = 1.5*C1*T + .875*(5.*C3-3.*C1)*(5.*T*T-3.)*T + 11.*(63.*C5
       1-70.*C3 + 15.*C1)*(63.*T**4 - 70.*T*T + 15.)*T/128.
        PMAC = X - X*X*X/6. + X**5/120.
        EL = ABSF(SINF(X) - PL)
        EMAC = ABSF(SINF(X) - PMAC)
        RPL = PL + .00000005
        RPM = PMAC + .00000005
        RSIN = SINF(X) + .00000005
        REL = EL + .000000005
        REM = EMAC + .000000005
        PRINT 3,X,RPL,RPM,RSIN,REL,REM
        AVL = AVL + EL
        AVM = AVM + EMAC
        L = L + 1
        IF(L-5)30,40,30
     40 PRINT 2
        L = L-5
     30 CONTINUE
        AL = AVL*.04
        AM = AVM*.04
        PRINT 4,AL,AM
      4 FORMAT(1H0,8X,27HAVERAGE ERROR IN LEGENDRE =F11.8/
       18X,28HAVERAGE ERROR IN MACLAURIN = F11.8)
        CALL EXIT
        END
```

Table 11.3.1

T	LEGENDRE	MACLAURIN	SIN	/SIN - L/	/SIN - MAC/
0.00	0.0000000	0.0000000	0.0000000	0.00000000	0.00000000
.04	.0399887	.0399893	.0399893	.00000062	0.00000000
.08	.0799135	.0799147	.0799147	.00000119	0.00000000
.12	.1197106	.1197122	.1197122	.00000166	0.00000000
.16	.1593162	.1593182	.1593182	.00000197	0.00000000
.20	.1986672	.1986693	.1986693	.00000212	0.00000000
.24	.2377006	.2377026	.2377026	.00000206	.00000001
.28	.2763538	.2763557	.2763556	.00000181	.00000003
.32	.3145652	.3145666	.3145666	.00000137	.00000007
.36	.3522734	.3522744	.3522742	.00000079	.00000016
.40	.3894182	.3894187	.3894183	.00000010	.00000032
.44	.4259401	.4259401	.4259395	.00000062	.00000063
.48	.4617805	.4617803	.4617792	.00000131	.00000116
.52	.4968820	.4968822	.4968801	.00000187	.00000203
.56	.5311884	.5311896	.5311862	.00000223	.00000341
.60	.5646448	.5646480	.5646425	.00000232	.00000553
.64	.5971975	.5972041	.5971954	.00000208	.00000868
.68	.6287945	.6288063	.6287930	.00000149	.00001325
.72	.6593853	.6594044	.6593847	.00000058	.00001976
.76	.6889209	.6889503	.6889214	.00000055	.00002883
.80	.7173544	.7173973	.7173561	.00000173	.00004124
.84	.7446405	.7447011	.7446431	.00000266	.00005798
.88	.7707360	.7708191	.7707389	.00000293	.00008022
.92	.7955997	.7957110	.7956016	.00000194	.00010939
.96	.8191927	.8193388	.8191916	.00000109	.00014720

```
AVERAGE ERROR IN LEGENDRE =   .00000148
AVERAGE ERROR IN MACLAURIN =   .00002079
```

It may appear that we are tied to the interval $[-1, 1]$. This is not an accurate impression. Let $a > 0$ and let $n \in N$; we shall determine the best polynomial function approximation to f over $[-a, a]$ of degree at most n. To this purpose consider the function $f(ax)$, and let p_n be the best polynomial function approximation to $f(ax)$ over $[-1, 1]$ of degree at most n. Then $\int_{-1}^{1}[f(ax) - p_n]^2 \leq \int_{-1}^{1}[f(ax) - p]^2$ whenever p is a polynomial function of degree at most n. But

and

$$\int_{-1}^{1}[f(ax) - p_n]^2 = \frac{1}{a}\int_{-a}^{a}[f - p_n(x/a)]^2$$

$$\int_{-1}^{1}[f(ax) - p]^2 = \frac{1}{a}\int_{-a}^{a}[f - p(x/a)]^2.$$

Therefore $\int_{-a}^{a}[f - p_n(x/a)]^2 \leq \int_{-a}^{a}(f - p)^2$ whenever p is a polynomial function of degree at most n. Thus $p_n(x/a)$ is the best polynomial function approximation to f over $[-a, a]$ of degree at most n. We now formalize this result.

THEOREM 11.3.3. Let $a > 0$, let n be any nonnegative integer, let f be continuous on $[-a, a]$, and let p_n be the best polynomial function approximation to $f(ax)$ over

[−1, 1] of degree at most n; then $p_n(x/a)$ is the best polynomial function approximation to f over $[−a, a]$ of degree at most n.

We now illustrate this theorem.

EXAMPLE 3.   Find the best polynomial function approximation to x^6 over $[−.1, .1]$ of degree at most 4.

Solution: First, we observe that if p_n is the best polynomial function approximation to f over $[−1, 1]$ of degree at most n, then kp_n is the best polynomial function approximation to kf over $[−1, 1]$ of degree at most n. Now, from Example 1 we see that $\frac{5}{11} 10^{-6}(\frac{1}{21} − x^2 + 3x^4)$ is the best polynomial function approximation to $(x/10)^6$ over $[−1, 1]$. Therefore, by Theorem 11.3.3, $\frac{5}{11} 10^{-6}(\frac{1}{21} − 100x^2 + 30000x^4)$ is the best polynomial function approximation to x^6 over $[−.1, .1]$ of degree at most 4.

Next, let us find the best polynomial function approximation to f over $[0, a]$ of degree at most n, where $a > 0$. The idea is to construct a function, say g, such that $g(t) = f\left(\dfrac{a + t}{2}\right)$ whenever $t \in [−a, a]$. This is easy: $g = f\left(\dfrac{a + x}{2}\right)$. Let p_n be the best polynomial function approximation to g over $[−a, a]$ of degree at most n. But $\displaystyle\int_{−a}^{a} (g − p_n)^2 =$
$2\displaystyle\int_{0}^{a} (g − p_n)^2 \circ (2x − a) = 2\displaystyle\int_{0}^{a} [f − p_n(2x − a)]^2$. We conclude that $p_n(2x − a)$ is the best polynomial function approximation to f over $[0, a]$ of degree at most n. We now state our result.

THEOREM 11.3.4.   Let $a > 0$, let n be any nonnegative integer, let f be continuous on $[0, a]$, and let p_n be the best polynomial function approximation to $f((a + x)/2)$ over $[−a, a]$ of degree at most n; then $p_n \circ (2x − a)$ is the best polynomial function approximation to f over $[0, a]$ of degree at most n.

It is convenient to incorporate the two preceding theorems into one result; i.e., we want to express the best polynomial function approximation to f over $[0, a]$ of degree at most n in terms of the best polynomial function approximation to a related function over $[−1, 1]$. Clearly, $p_n \circ x/a \circ (2x − a) = p_n \circ (2x/a − 1)$, and $f \circ (a + x)/2 \circ ax = f((a + ax)/2)$. Thus we have the following theorem.

THEOREM 11.3.5.   Let $a > 0$, let n be any nonnegative integer, let f be continuous on $[0, a]$, and let p_n be the best polynomial function approximation to $f((a + ax)/2)$ over $[−1, 1]$ of degree at most n; then $p_n \circ (2x/a − 1)$ is the best polynomial function approximation to f over $[0, a]$ of degree at most n.

In Example 2 we considered the best polynomial function approximation to sin over $[-1, 1]$ of degree at most 5. There we saw that our method produced an approximation to sin which is much superior to the polynomial function of degree 5 obtained by the Maclaurin series method. However, the Maclaurin polynomial function gives good results over a short interval about 0; examining Table 11.3.1, we see that the Maclaurin polynomial function is an excellent approximation to sin over $[0, .2]$. Let us demonstrate that our method produces an even better approximation to sin over this interval. Consider the following example.

EXAMPLE 4.   Find the best polynomial function approximation to sin over $[0, .2]$ of degree at most 5.

Solution: By Theorem 11.3.5, the required function is $\left(\sum\limits_{k=0}^{5} b_k \varphi_k \right) \circ (10x - 1)$, where $\sum\limits_{k=0}^{5} b_k \varphi_k$ is the best polynomial function approximation to $\sin(.1 + .1x)$ over $[-1, 1]$; thus

$$\sum_{k=0}^{5} b_k \varphi_k = \frac{1}{2} \int_{-1}^{1} \sin(.1 + .1x) + \frac{3}{2} x \int_{-1}^{1} x \sin(.1 + .1x)$$

$$+ \frac{5}{8}(3x^2 - 1) \int_{-1}^{1} (3x^2 - 1) \sin(.1 + .1x) + \frac{7}{8}(5x^3 - 3x) \int_{-1}^{1} (5x^3 - 3x) \sin(.1 + .1x)$$

$$+ \frac{9}{128}(35x^4 - 30x^2 + 3) \int_{-1}^{1} (35x^4 - 30x^2 + 3) \sin(.1 + .1x)$$

$$+ \frac{11}{128}(63x^5 - 70x^3 + 15x) \int_{-1}^{1} (63x^5 - 70x^3 + 15x) \sin(.1 + .1x).$$

It is easy to verify that

$$c_0 = \int_{-1}^{1} \sin(.1 + .1x) = 10 - 10 \cos .2,$$

$$c_1 = \int_{-1}^{1} x \sin(.1 + .1x) = -10 - 10 \cos .2 + 100 \sin .2,$$

$$c_2 = \int_{-1}^{1} x^2 \sin(.1 + .1x) = 10 - 10 \cos .2 + 200 \sin .2 - 200c_0,$$

$$c_3 = \int_{-1}^{1} x^3 \sin(.1 + .1x) = -10 - 10 \cos .2 + 300 \sin .2 - 600c_1,$$

$$c_4 = \int_{-1}^{1} x^4 \sin(.1 + .1x) = 10 - 10 \cos .2 + 400 \sin .2 - 1200c_2,$$

$$c_5 = \int_{-1}^{1} x^5 \sin(.1 + .1x) = -10 - 10 \cos .2 + 500 \sin .2 - 2000c_3.$$

Thus

$$\sum_{k=0}^{5} b_k \varphi_k = \frac{1}{2}c_0 + \frac{3}{2}c_1 x + \frac{5}{8}(3c_2 - c_0)(3x^2 - 1) + \frac{7}{8}(5c_3 - 3c_1)(5x^3 - 3x)$$

$$+ \frac{9}{128}(35c_4 - 30c_2 + 3c_0)(35x^4 - 30x^2 + 3) + \frac{11}{128}(63c_5 - 70c_3 + 15c_1)(63x^5 - 70x^3 + 15x).$$

We point out that the required function is $\left(\sum_{k=0}^{5} b_k \varphi_k \right) \circ (10x - 1)$. We shall now program an automatic digital computer to compute 25 values of our function over [0, .2]. Also, we shall compare our polynomial function to the Maclaurin polynomial function of the same degree.

```
                        PROGRAM FOR THE
              BEST APPROXIMATION TO SIN OVER (0,.2)
                BY POLYNOMIAL OF DEGREE AT MOST 5

   *FANDK2004
           L = 0
           AVL = 0.0
           AVM = 0.0
         1 FORMAT(1H ,4X,1HT,5X,8HLEGENDRE,5X,9HMACLAURIN,8X,3HSIN,7X,
           19H/SIN - L/,4X,11H/SIN - MAC/,/)
           PRINT 1
         2 FORMAT(1H )
         3 FORMAT(1H ,F6.3,1X,3F13.9,2F14.10)
           C = COSF(.2)
           S = SINF(.2)
           C0 = 10. - 10.*C
           C1 = -10. - 10.*C + 100.*S
           C2 = 10. - 10.*C + 200.*S - 200.*C0
           C3 = -10. - 10.*C + 300.*S - 600.*C1
           C4 = 10. - 10.*C + 400.*S - 1200.*C2
           C5 = -10. - 10.*C + 500.*S - 2000.*C3
           DO 30 K = 1,25
           B = K - 1
           T = B*.008
           X = 10.*T - 1.
           PL = .5*C0 + 1.5*C1*X + .625*(3.*C2 - C0)*(3.*X*X - 1.) + .875*
           1(5.*C3 - 3.*C1)*(5.*X*X - 3.)*X + 9.*(35.*C4 - 30.*C2 + 3.*C0)*
           2(35.*X**4 - 30.*X*X + 3.)/128. + 11.*(63.*C5 - 70.*C3 + 15.*C1)*
           3(63.*X**4 - 70.*X*X + 15.)*X/128.
           PMAC = T - T*T*T/6. + T**5/120.
           EL = ABSF(SINF(T) - PL)
           EMAC = ABSF(SINF(T) - PMAC)
           RPL = PL + .0000000005
           RPM = PMAC + .0000000005
           RSIN = SINF(T) + .0000000005
           REL = EL + .00000000005
           REM = EMAC + .00000000005
           PRINT 3,T,RPL,RPM,RSIN,REL,REM
           AVL = AVL + EL
           AVM = AVM + EMAC
           L = L + 1
           IF(L-5)30,40,30
        40 PRINT 2
           L = L-5
        30 CONTINUE
           AL = AVL*.04
           AM = AVM*.04
           PRINT 4,AL,AM
         4 FORMAT(1H0,8X,27HAVERAGE ERROR IN LEGENDRE =F13.10/
           18X,28HAVERAGE ERROR IN MACLAURIN =F13.10)
           CALL EXIT
           END
```

Table 11.3.2

T	LEGENDRE	MACLAURIN	SIN	/SIN - L/	/SIN - MAC/
0.000	0.000000000	0.000000000	0.000000000	0.0000000000	0.0000000000
.008	.007999915	.007999915	.007999915	0.0000000000	0.0000000000
.016	.015999317	.015999317	.015999317	0.0000000000	0.0000000000
.024	.023997696	.023997696	.023997696	0.0000000000	0.0000000000
.032	.031994539	.031994539	.031994539	0.0000000000	0.0000000000
.040	.039989334	.039989334	.039989334	0.0000000000	0.0000000000
.048	.047981570	.047981570	.047981570	0.0000000000	0.0000000000
.056	.055970735	.055970735	.055970735	0.0000000000	0.0000000000
.064	.063956318	.063956318	.063956318	0.0000000000	0.0000000000
.072	.071937808	.071937808	.071937808	0.0000000000	0.0000000000
.080	.079914694	.079914694	.079914694	0.0000000000	0.0000000000
.088	.087886465	.087886465	.087886465	0.0000000000	0.0000000000
.096	.095852612	.095852612	.095852612	0.0000000000	0.0000000000
.104	.103812624	.103812624	.103812624	0.0000000000	0.0000000000
.112	.111765992	.111765992	.111765992	0.0000000000	0.0000000000
.120	.119712207	.119712207	.119712207	0.0000000000	.0000000001
.128	.127650761	.127650761	.127650761	0.0000000000	.0000000001
.136	.135581145	.135581145	.135581145	0.0000000000	.0000000002
.144	.143502852	.143502852	.143502852	0.0000000000	.0000000003
.152	.151415374	.151415375	.151415374	0.0000000000	.0000000004
.160	.159318207	.159318207	.159318207	0.0000000000	.0000000005
.168	.167210842	.167210843	.167210842	0.0000000000	.0000000007
.176	.175092777	.175092778	.175092777	0.0000000000	.0000000010
.184	.182963505	.182963507	.182963505	0.0000000000	.0000000014
.192	.190822524	.190822526	.190822524	0.0000000000	.0000000019

```
AVERAGE ERROR IN LEGENDRE = 0.0000000000
AVERAGE ERROR IN MACLAURIN =   .0000000002
```

Examining Table 11.3.2, it is clear that our polynomial function is a better approximation to sin over [0, .2] than is the corresponding Maclaurin polynomial function. However, Table 11.3.2 does not provide us with enough information to assess the situation. The trouble is that we have rounded off the errors involved to ten decimal places. Let us repeat our analysis, this time rounding off the errors to twelve decimal places. Notice that this is achieved by a slight alteration to six lines of the program. Now look at Table 11.3.3; it is evident that our function is considerably more accurate than the corresponding Maclaurin function. Of course, we knew in advance that the Maclaurin function of degree 5 cannot be a better approximation than the best possible approximating polynomial function of degree at most 5. Our point here is to demonstrate precisely how much better the best approximating polynomial function is.

```
                          PROGRAM FOR THE
                  BEST APPROXIMATION TO SIN OVER (0,.2)
                    BY POLYNOMIAL OF DEGREE AT MOST 5

*FANDK2004
      L = 0
      AVL = 0.0
      AVM = 0.0
    1 FORMAT(1H ,4X,1HT,5X,8HLEGENDRE,5X,9HMACLAURIN,8X,3HSIN,7X,
     19H/SIN - L/,4X,11H/SIN - MAC/,/)
      PRINT 1
    2 FORMAT(1H )
    3 FORMAT(1H ,F6.3,3F13.9,2F16.12)
      C = COSF(.2)
      S = SINF(.2)
      CO = 10. - 10.*C
      C1 = -10. - 10.*C + 100.*S
      C2 = 10. - 10.*C + 200.*S - 200.*CO
      C3 = -10. - 10.*C + 300.*S - 600.*C1
      C4 = 10. - 10.*C + 400.*S - 1200.*C2
      C5 = -10. - 10.*C + 500.*S - 2000.*C3
      DO 30 K = 1,25
      B = K - 1
      T = B*.008
      X = 10.*T - 1.
      PL = .5*CO + 1.5*C1*X + .625*(3.*C2 - CO)*(3.*X*X - 1.) + .875*
     1(5.*C3 - 3.*C1)*(5.*X*X - 3.)*X + 9.*(35.*C4 - 30.*C2 + 3.*CO)*
     2(35.*X**4 - 30.*X*X + 3.)/128. + 11.*(63.*C5 - 70.*C3 + 15.*C1)*
     3(63.*X**4 - 70.*X*X + 15.)*X/128.
      PMAC = T - T*T*T/6. + T**5/120.
      EL = ABSF(SINF(T) - PL)
      EMAC = ABSF(SINF(T) - PMAC)
      RPL = PL + .0000000005
      RPM = PMAC + .0000000005
      RSIN = SINF(T) + .0000000005
      REL = EL + .0000000000005
      REM = EMAC + .0000000000005
      PRINT 3,T,RPL,RPM,RSIN,REL,REM
      AVL = AVL + EL
      AVM = AVM + EMAC
      L = L + 1
      IF(L-5)30,40,30
   40 PRINT 2
      L = L-5
   30 CONTINUE
      AL = AVL*.04
      AM = AVM*.04
      PRINT 4,AL,AM
    4 FORMAT(1H0,8X,27HAVERAGE ERROR IN LEGENDRE =F15.12/
     18X,28HAVERAGE ERROR IN MACLAURIN =F15.12)
      CALL EXIT
      END
```

Table 11.3.3

T	LEGENDRE	MACLAURIN	SIN	/SIN − L/	/SIN − MAC/
0.000	0.000000000	0.000000000	0.000000000	.000000000006	0.000000000000
.008	.007999915	.007999915	.007999915	.000000000002	0.000000000000
.016	.015999317	.015999317	.015999317	.000000000001	0.000000000000
.024	.023997696	.023997696	.023997696	.000000000003	0.000000000000
.032	.031994539	.031994539	.031994539	.000000000004	0.000000000000
.040	.039989334	.039989334	.039989334	.000000000003	0.000000000000
.048	.047981570	.047981570	.047981570	.000000000002	0.000000000000
.056	.055970735	.055970735	.055970735	0.000000000000	0.000000000000
.064	.063956318	.063956318	.063956318	.000000000003	.000000000001
.072	.071937808	.071937808	.071937808	.000000000004	.000000000002
.080	.079914694	.079914694	.079914694	.000000000005	.000000000004
.088	.087886465	.087886465	.087886465	.000000000005	.000000000008
.096	.095852612	.095852612	.095852612	.000000000004	.000000000015
.104	.103812624	.103812624	.103812624	.000000000001	.000000000026
.112	.111765992	.111765992	.111765992	.000000000001	.000000000044
.120	.119712207	.119712207	.119712207	.000000000004	.000000000071
.128	.127650761	.127650761	.127650761	.000000000006	.000000000112
.136	.135581145	.135581145	.135581145	.000000000007	.000000000171
.144	.143502852	.143502852	.143502852	.000000000006	.000000000255
.152	.151415374	.151415375	.151415374	.000000000003	.000000000372
.160	.159318207	.159318207	.159318207	.000000000001	.000000000532
.168	.167210842	.167210843	.167210842	.000000000006	.000000000749
.176	.175092777	.175092778	.175092777	.000000000010	.000000001037
.184	.182963505	.182963507	.182963505	.000000000009	.000000001416
.192	.190822524	.190822526	.190822524	.000000000001	.000000001907

AVERAGE ERROR IN LEGENDRE = .000000000003
AVERAGE ERROR IN MACLAURIN = .000000000268

Finally, we state the most general result in this direction.

THEOREM 11.3.6. Let $a < b$, let n be any nonnegative integer, let f be continuous on $[a, b]$, and let p_n be the best polynomial function approximation to $f \circ (a + b + (b - a)x)/2$ over $[-1, 1]$. Then $p_n \circ (2x - a - b)/(b - a)$ is the best polynomial function approximation to f over $[a, b]$ of degree at most n.

Proof: Follow the pattern of the proof of Theorem 11.3.5; the details are left as an exercise.

E X E R C I S E S

1. Find the best polynomial function approximation to $x^5 + 3x^2$ over $[-1, 1]$ of degree at most 3.

2. Find the best polynomial function approximation to cos over $[-1, 1]$ of degree at most 4.

3. Find the best polynomial function approximation to exp over $[-1, 1]$ of degree at most 5.

4. Find the best polynomial function approximation to x sin over $[-1, 1]$ of degree at most 5.

5. Find the best polynomial function approximation to arcsin over $[-1, 1]$ of degree at most 3.

6. Find the best polynomial function approximation to $x^5 + 3x^2$ over $[-.1, .1]$ of degree at most 3.

7. Find the best polynomial function approximation to exp over $[-.1, .1]$ of degree at most 5.

8. Find the best polynomial function to arcsin over $[-.2, .2]$ of degree at most 3.

9. Find the best polynomial function approximation to cos over $[0, .2]$ of degree at most 4; compare the corresponding Maclaurin polynomial function.

10. Find the best polynomial function approximation to exp over $[0, .2]$ of degree at most 5; compare the corresponding Maclaurin polynomial function.

11. Find the best polynomial function approximation to exp over $[1, 2]$ which has degree at most 5; compare the corresponding Taylor polynomial function about the midpoint of the interval.

12. Find the best polynomial function approximation to sin over $[1, 2]$ of degree at most 5.

13. Find the best polynomial function approximation to log over $[1, 2]$ of degree at most 5.

14. Find the best polynomial function approximation to $\log/x$ over $[1, 2]$ of degree at most 5.

15. Find the best polynomial function approximation to $\sin/x$ over $[1, 2]$ of degree at most 3. Express your answer in terms of $\int_1^2 \sin/x$.

16. Find the best polynomial function approximation to $\sin/x^2$ over $[1, 2]$ of degree at most 5.

17. a. Let $a < b$, let n be any nonnegative integer, let f be continuous on $[a, b]$, and let p_n be the best polynomial function approximation to $f(a + x)$ over $[0, b - a]$ of degree at most n. Prove that $p_n \circ (x - a)$ is the best polynomial function approximation to f over $[a, b]$ of degree at most n.

   b. Prove Theorem 11.3.6.

11.4   The Method of Frobenius

In Section 11.1 we found that a linear differential equation, say $f^{(n)} + p_1 \cdot f^{(n-1)} + \cdots + p_{n-1} \cdot f' + p_n \cdot f = p_{n+1} \mathrm{RE}$, is satisfied by a power series in $x - a$ provided that the coefficient functions $p_1, p_2, \cdots, p_{n+1}$ are analytic at a. This result emphasizes the value and importance of power series. In this section we shall relax the requirement that the coefficient functions be analytic at a; it turns out that the method Section 11.1 can handle a more extensive set of linear differential equations. To this purpose we need to generalize the notion of a power series. We introduce the concept of a *Frobenius series*.

> DEFINITION 11.4.1.   Let $m \in R$ and let $\sum a_{n-1}(x - a)^{n-1}$ be any power series in $x - a$ such that $a_0 \neq 0$; then $(x - a)^m \cdot \sum a_{n-1}(x - a)^{n-1}$ is said to be a Frobenius series.

For example, $x^{-3} \cdot \sum x^{n-4}/(n - 1)!$ and $\sum (x + 2)^{n+3}$ are Frobenius series. Notice that each power series in $x - a$ is also a Frobenius series.

Now that we have a useful tool, let us use it to solve linear differential equations. As we have said, Frobenius series can handle a more extensive class of differential equations than can power series (see Section 11.1). We need the following concepts.

> DEFINITION 11.4.2.   We shall say that the differential equation $f^{(n)} + p_1 \cdot f^{(n-1)} + \cdots + p_{n-1} \cdot f' + p_n \cdot f = p_{n+1} \mathrm{RE}$ is *ordinary at* a iff each of the coefficient functions is analytic at a.

DEFINITION 11.4.3. We shall say that the differential equation $f^{(n)} + p_1 \cdot f^{(n-1)} + \cdots + p_{n-1} \cdot f' + p_n \cdot f = p_{n+1}$ RE is *singular at a* iff this differential equation is not ordinary at a.

Linear differential equations of the second order are particularly important; hence we present the following concept.

DEFINITION 11.4.4. We shall say that the differential equation

$$f^{(2)} + \frac{p_1}{x - a} \cdot f' + \frac{p_2}{(x - a)^2} \cdot f = 0 \text{ R } E$$

is *regular singular at a* iff p_1 and p_2 are analytic at a.

For example $f^{(3)} + x^2 f^{(2)} + (1 - x)f' - 2f = x^3$ RE is regular at 5; $f^{(3)} + x^2 f^{(2)}/(x - 5) + (1 - x)f' - 2f = x^3$ RE is singular at 5; $f^{(2)} + x^2 f'/(x - 5) + (1 - x)f = 0$ R E is regular singular at 5 [note that $(1 - x)(x - 5)^2$ is analytic at 5].

We state without proof the following *existence* theorem.

THEOREM 11.4.1. Suppose that $f^{(2)} + p_1 \cdot f'/(x - a) + p_2 \cdot f/(x - a)^2 = 0$ R E is regular singular at a; then there is at least one Frobenius series $\sum a_{n-1}(x - a)^{m+n-1}$ which satisfies this differential equation and exists on $\mathscr{D}_{p_1} \cap \mathscr{D}_{p_2} - \{a\}$.

We now illustrate the method of Frobenius.

EXAMPLE 1. Find a Frobenius series which satisfies $f^{(2)} + 2f'/x + f = 0$ R E on $R - \{0\}$.

Solution: The given differential equation is regular singular at 0. Let $\sum a_{n-1} x^{m+n-1}$ be a Frobenius series which satisfies this equation. Now,

$$[\sum a_{n-1} x^{m+n-1}]' = \sum(m + n - 1)a_{n-1} x^{m+n-2}$$

and
$$[\sum(m + n - 1)a_{n-1} x^{m+n-2}]' = \sum(m + n - 2)(m + n - 1)a_{n-1} x^{m+n-3}.$$

Thus
$$\sum(m + n - 2)(m + n - 1)a_{n-1} x^{m+n-3} + 2\sum(m + n - 1)a_{n-1} x^{m+n-3} + \sum a_{n-1} x^{m+n-1} = 0 \text{ R } E.$$

Therefore

(1) $\qquad (m - 1)ma_0 + 2ma_0 = 0,$

(2) $\qquad m(m + 1)a_1 + 2(m + 1)a_1 = 0,$

(3) $\qquad (m + 1)(m + 2)a_2 + 2(m + 2)a_2 + a_0 = 0.$

Moreover, if $n > 2$, then

(4) $\qquad (m + n - 2)(m + n - 1)a_{n-1} + 2(m + n - 1)a_{n-1} + a_{n-3} = 0.$

From (1), since $a_0 \neq 0$, $m^2 + m = 0$; thus $m = 0$ or $m = -1$. From (2), $a_1 = 0$ or $m = -1$ or $m = -2$. Let us choose $m = -1$ and consider our recursion relation (4), which becomes

$$[(n - 3)(n - 2) + 2(n - 2)]a_{n-1} + a_{n-3} = 0,$$

i.e., $a_{n-1} = \dfrac{-a_{n-3}}{(n-2)(n-1)}$. Notice that

$$a_2 = \frac{-a_0}{1 \times 2}, \quad a_4 = \frac{-a_2}{3 \times 4}, \quad a_6 = \frac{-a_4}{5 \times 6}, \quad \cdots, \quad a_{2n} = \frac{-a_{2n-2}}{(2n-1)2n}.$$

Thus

(5) $$a_{2n} = (-1)^n a_0/(2n)! \quad \text{whenever} \quad n \in N.$$

Similarly, we see that $a_{2n+1} = (-1)^n a_1/(2n+1)!$ whenever $n \in N$. We conclude that the Frobenius series

$$(1/x)(a_0 + a_1 x - a_0 x^2/2! - a_1 x^3/3! + a_0 x^4/4! + a_1 x^5/5! - a_0 x^6/6! - a_1 x^7/7! + \ldots)$$

satisfies the given differential equation. Since we have two parameters a_0 and a_1, we have a complete solution of the given differential equation. In particular, let $a_0 = 1$ and let $a_1 = 0$; then our solution is $(1/x) \cdot \Sigma(-1)^{n-1} x^{2n-2}/(2n-2)!$, namely $\cos/x$. It is easy to verify that $\cos/x$ is a particular solution of the given equation.

There is one more point in connection with this example. Equation (1) is satisfied if $m = 0$; using this value for m, it follows from (2) that $a_1 = 0$, and it follows from (4) that $a_{n-1} = -a_{n-3}/(n-1)n$ whenever $n > 2$. Thus, if $m = 0$, then $a_{2n-1} = 0$ whenever $n \in N$, and $a_{2n} = (-1)^n a_0/(2n+1)!$ whenever $n \in N$. Therefore $a_0 \Sigma(-1)^{n-1} x^{2n-2}/(2n-1)!$ is a particular solution of the given differential equation. Notice that this function has domain R.

EXERCISES

1. Find a particular solution of $xf^{(2)} + f' + xf = 0$ R E. $\left(\text{Answer: } \Sigma \dfrac{(-1)^{n-1}\, x^{2n-2}}{[2^{n-1}(n-1)]^2} \right)$

2. Find a particular solution of $x^2 f^{(2)} + xf' + (x^2 - 1)f = 0$ R E.

$$\left(\text{Answer: } x\Sigma \frac{(-1)^{n-1}(x/2)^{2n-2}}{(n-1)!n!} \right)$$

3. Find a complete solution of $2xf^{(2)} + (1 + 2x)f' - 5f = 0$ R E.

$$\left(\text{Answer: } f = k_1(15x^{.5} + 20x^{1.5} + 4x^{2.5}) + k_2\Sigma \frac{15(-1)^{n+1}x^n}{n!\,(2n-1)(2n-3)(2n-5)} \right)$$

11.5   The Gamma Function

It is useful to generalize the *factorial n* concept by permitting n to be any real number other than a negative integer; i.e., we wish to define $k!$, where k may be any real number except a negative integer. To this purpose we introduce the *gamma* function, which is denoted by "Γ" and is defined as follows.

DEFINITION 11.5.1. $\Gamma(k) = \int_0^\infty x^{k-1} \cdot \exp(-x)$ whenever $k > 0$, and $\Gamma(k) = (1/k)\Gamma(k+1)$ whenever $k < 0$ and k is not a negative integer.

We point out that our definition involves an improper integral; the "$\mathcal{I}$", which usually precedes an improper integral, has been suppressed. We shall suppress this sign of an improper integral from now on.

Notice that $\mathscr{D}_\Gamma = R - \{k \mid k$ is a negative integer or zero$\}$. We now establish some properties of the gamma function.

THEOREM 11.5.1 $\Gamma(1) = 1$.

Proof: Apply Definition 11.5.1.

THEOREM 11.5.2. $\Gamma(k + 1) = k\Gamma(k)$ whenever $k \in \mathscr{D}_\Gamma$.

Proof: There are two cases: (1) $k < 0$: apply the second part of Definition 11.5.1; (2) $k > 0$: apply the first part of Definition 11.5.1 and integrate by parts.

THEOREM 11.5.3.   Let $k \in \mathscr{D}_\Gamma$ and let $n \in N$; then

$$\Gamma(k + n) = k(k + 1)(k + 2) \cdots (k + n - 1)\Gamma(k).$$

Proof: We shall apply mathematical induction. By Theorem 11.5.2, 1 has the property. Suppose that t is a natural number with the property, i.e., $\Gamma(k + t) = k(k + 1) \cdots (k + t - 1)\Gamma(k)$. Then

$$\Gamma(k + t + 1) = (k + t)\Gamma(k + t) \qquad \text{by Th. 11.5.2}$$

$$= k(k + 1) \cdots (k + t - 1)(k + t)\Gamma(k) \qquad \text{by assumption.}$$

This proves that $t + 1$ has the property whenever t has the property. Thus, by mathematical induction, each natural number has the property.

COROLLARY 11.5.1 $\Gamma(n + 1) = n!$ whenever $n \in N$.

THEOREM 11.5.4. $\Gamma(k) = 2 \int_0^\infty x^{2k-1} \cdot \exp(-x^2)$ whenever $k > 0$.

Proof: Let $k > 0$; then, by Definition 11.5.1,

$$\Gamma(k) = \int_0^\infty x^{k-1} \cdot \exp(-x) = \int_0^\infty ([x^{k-1} \cdot \exp(-x)] \circ x^2) \cdot 2x$$

$$= 2 \int_0^\infty x^{2k-1} \cdot \exp(-x^2).$$

COROLLARY 11.5.2. $\Gamma(.5) = \sqrt{\pi}$.

Proof: By Theorem 11.5.4, $\Gamma(\cdot 5) = 2 \int_0^\infty \exp(-x^2) = \sqrt{\pi}$ by Example 9, Section 7.6.

To compute values of the gamma function, we need the following result, derived from *Stirling's formula*, which we state without proof.

THEOREM 11.5.5. If $t > 20$, then $\Gamma(t) \approx h \times e^{-t} \times t^{t-.5}\sqrt{2\pi}$, where

$$h = 1 + \frac{1}{12t} + \frac{1}{t^2}\left(\frac{1}{288} - \frac{139}{51840t} - \frac{571}{2488320t^2}\right);$$

the error in the approximation is less than 10^{-10}.

With the aid of an automatic digital computer, we easily obtain the table of values of the gamma function given in Table 1, pages 469–472. Here we present a short table of values of Γ (Table 11.5.1). This table is obtained by the program shown on this page.

```
                 PROGRAM FOR THE GAMMA FUNCTION

*FANDK 1504

        DIMENSION A(14,10)
        DO 50 I = 1,14
        DO 50 J = 1,10
   50 A(I,J) = 0.0
    1 FORMAT(1H1,50X,18HTHE GAMMA FUNCTION)
        PRINT 1
    2 FORMAT(1H0,3X,1HT,8X,2H.0,8X,2H.1,8X,2H.2,8X,2H.3,8X,2H.4,
       18X,2H.5,8X,2H.6,8X,2H.7,8X,2H.8,8X,2H.9/)
        PRINT 2
    4 FORMAT(1H ,I4,F12.5,9F10.5)
    5 FORMAT(1H ,I4,12X,9F10.5)
        S = 40.
        DO 9 K = 1, 10
        C = K - 1
        X = S + C*.1
        H=1.+1./(12.*X)+1./(X*X)*(1./288.-139./(51840.*X)-571./(2488320.
       1*X*X))
        G1 = EXPF(-X)*X**(X-.5)*2.506628274631*H
    8 X = X - 1.
        G1 = G1/X
        IF (X - 7.)9,8,8
    9 A(14,K) = G1
        U = 0.0
        DO 20 I = 1,13
        DO 20 J = 1,10
        X = 6 - I
        Y = J - 1
        N = 14 - I
        D = X + .1*Y
        IF (D-U)15,14,15
   14 U = U-1.
        GO TO 20
   15 A(N,J) = A(N+1,J)/D
   20 CONTINUE
        DO 80 I = 1,14
        DO 80 J = 1,10
        IF (A(I,J))60,70,70
   60 A(I,J) = A(I,J) - .000005
        GO TO 80
   70 A(I,J) = A(I,J) + .000005
   80 CONTINUE
        DO 11 I = 1,14
        L = I - 8
        IF (L)7,7,6
    7 PRINT 5, L, (A(I,K),K=2,10)
        GO TO 11
    6 PRINT 4, L, (A(I,K),K=1,10)
   11 CONTINUE
        CALL EXIT
        END
```

Table 11.5.1

THE GAMMA FUNCTION

T	.0	.1	.2	.3	.4	.5	.6	.7	.8	.9
-7		-.00247	-.00158	-.00140	-.00145	-.00168	-.00214	-.00305	-.00509	-.0117
-6		.01702	.01076	.00939	.00958	.01091	.01372	.01924	.03155	.0713
-5		-.10039	-.06242	-.05354	-.05366	-.06002	-.07407	-.10198	-.16406	-.3639
-4		.49191	.29963	.25164	.24686	.27009	.32589	.43852	.68906	1.4922
-3		-1.91843	-1.13860	-.93108	-.88869	-.94531	-1.10803	-1.44711	-2.20498	-4.6261
-2		5.56345	3.18809	2.51392	2.31058	2.36327	2.65927	3.32835	4.85096	9.7148
-1		-10.57056	-5.73855	-4.27367	-3.69693	-3.54491	-3.72298	-4.32685	-5.82115	-10.6862
0		9.51351	4.59084	2.99157	2.21816	1.77245	1.48919	1.29806	1.16423	1.0686
1	1.00000	.95135	.91817	.89747	.88726	.88623	.89352	.90864	.93138	.9617
2	1.00000	1.04649	1.10180	1.16671	1.24217	1.32934	1.42962	1.54469	1.67649	1.8273
3	2.00000	2.19762	2.42397	2.68344	2.98121	3.32335	3.71702	4.17065	4.69417	5.2993
4	6.00000	6.81262	7.75669	8.85534	10.13610	11.63173	13.38129	15.43141	17.83786	20.6673
5	24.00000	27.93175	32.57810	38.07798	44.59885	52.34278	61.55392	72.52763	85.62174	101.2701
6	120.00000	142.45194	169.40610	201.81328	240.83378	287.88528	344.70192	413.40752	496.60608	597.4941

We display in Figure 11.5.1 a portion of the graph of Γ; recall that $\mathcal{D}_\Gamma = R - \{t \mid t$ is a negative integer or $t = 0\}$.

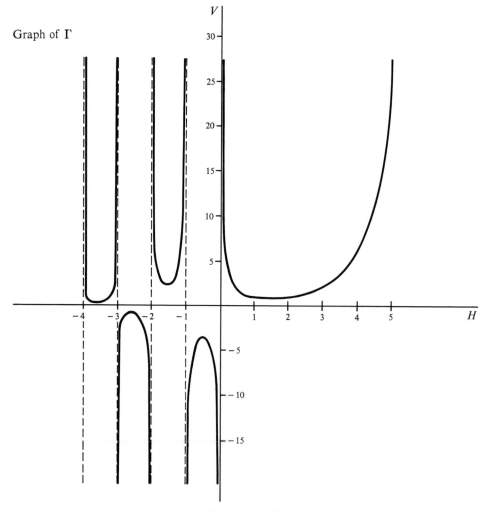

Graph of Γ

Figure 11.5.1

In view of Corollary 11.5.1, we now extend our factorial notation as follows.

DEFINITION 11.5.2.   Let k be any real number other than a negative integer; then "$k!$" denotes $\Gamma(k + 1)$.

E X E R C I S E S

1. Prove Theorem 11.5.1.

2. Prove Theorem 11.5.2.

3. Use Definition 11.5.1 to prove that $\Gamma(k) > 0$ whenever $k > 0$.

4. Prove that Γ is continuous at k whenever $k > 0$.

5. a. Prove that $\lim_{0+} \Gamma = \infty$.

   b. Prove that $\lim_{0-} \Gamma = -\infty$.

6. Prove that $\displaystyle\int_0^\infty x^{k-1} \cdot \exp(-ax) = \frac{\Gamma(k)}{a^k}$ whenever $a > 0$.

7. Prove that $\displaystyle\int_0^1 x^{p-1} \cdot (1 - x^{q-1})$ exists whenever $p > 0$ and $q > 0$.

8. Let $B(p, q) = \displaystyle\int_0^1 x^{p-1} \cdot (1 - x^{q-1})$ whenever $p > 0$ and $q > 0$; this defines a function B known as the *beta* function. Prove the following.

   a. $B(p, q) = B(q, p)$ whenever $p > 0$ and $q > 0$.

   b. $B(p, q) = a^{1-p-q} \displaystyle\int_0^a x^{p-1} \cdot (a - x)^{q-1}$ whenever $p > 0$, $q > 0$, and $a > 0$.

   c. $B(p, q) = 2\displaystyle\int_0^{\pi/2} \sin^{2p-1} \cdot \cos^{2q-1}$ whenever $p > 0$ and $q > 0$.

   d. $B(p, q) = \displaystyle\int_0^\infty x^{p-1}/(1 + x)^{p+q}$ whenever $p > 0$ and $q > 0$.

   (*Hint:* Consider $\displaystyle\int_{g*(0)}^{g*(1)} ([x^{p-1} \cdot (1 - x^{q-1})] \circ g) \cdot g'$, where $g = x/(1 + x)$ and $g* = x/(1 - x)$.)

9. Use Theorem 11.5.4 to prove that $\Gamma(p)\Gamma(q) = \displaystyle\int_D 4X^{2p-1} \cdot Y^{2q-1} \cdot \exp(-X^2 - Y^2)$, where $D = \{(a, b) \mid a \geq 0 \text{ and } b \geq 0\}$.

   b. Use the technique based on Theorem 7.6.5 to evaluate the double integral which appears in part **a**, and prove that $\Gamma(p)\Gamma(q) = B(p, q)\Gamma(p + q)$ whenever $p > 0$ and $q > 0$.

   c. Use part **b** to prove that $\displaystyle\int_0^1 (1 - x^{1/2})^{-1/2} = 8/3$.

11.6   Bessel's Differential Equations

Any differential equation of the form

(1) $$x^2 f^{(2)} + xf' + (x^2 - k^2)f = 0 \text{ R } E,$$

where $k \in R$, is said to be *Bessel's differential equation of order* k. Bessel's differential equation of order zero, namely $x^2 f^{(2)} + xf' + x^2 f = 0$ R E, is especially important.

Notice that (1) is regular singular at 0; thus there is at least one Frobenius series which satisfies (1). Let $x^m \cdot \sum a_{n-1} x^{n-1}$ be a particular solution of (1); then

$$\sum (m + n - 2)(m + n - 1)a_{n-1} x^{m+n-1} + \sum (m + n - 1)a_{n-1} x^{m+n-1}$$

$$- k^2 \sum a_{n-1} x^{m+n-1} + \sum a_{n-1} x^{m+n-1} = 0 \text{ R } E.$$

Thus

(2) $\qquad (m^2 - k^2)a_0 = 0,$
(3) $\qquad [(m + 1)^2 - k^2]a_1 = 0,$
(4) $\qquad [(m + n - 1)^2 - k^2]a_{n-1} + a_{n-3} = 0 \qquad$ whenever $n > 2.$

Since $a_0 \neq 0$, it follows from (2) that $m = k$ or $m = -k$. We can solve (4) for a_{n-1} in terms of a_{n-3} provided that $(m + n - 1)^2 - k^2 \neq 0$. But $m = k$ or $m = -k$; so, if m is not a negative integer, then $(m + n - 1)^2 - k^2 \neq 0$ whenever $n > 2$. Now, if one of k or $-k$ is a negative integer, the other is not a negative integer. Thus we let $m = k$ provided that k is not a negative integer. We now proceed to our solution of (1). From (3), $a_1 = 0$, and from (4),

$$a_{2n} = \frac{-a_{2n-2}}{(k + 2n)^2 - k^2} = \frac{-a_{2n-2}}{4n(n + k)}.$$

Thus $\quad a_2 = \dfrac{-a_0}{(1 + k)2^2}, \quad a_4 = \dfrac{-a_2}{8(2 + k)} = \dfrac{a_0}{2! \, (1 + k)(2 + k)2^4},$

$$a_6 = \frac{-a_4}{12(3 + k)} = \frac{-a_0}{3! \, (1 + k)(2 + k)(3 + k)2^6};$$

moreover,

$$a_{2n} = \frac{(-1)^n a_0}{n! \, (1 + k)(2 + k) \cdots (n + k)2^{2n}} \text{ whenever } n \in N.$$

We now utilize the gamma function. By Theorem 11.5.3, $\Gamma(k + n + 1) = (k + 1)(k + 2) \cdots (k + n)\Gamma(k + 1)$ whenever $n \in N$; hence

$$a_{2n} = \frac{(-1)^n a_0 \Gamma(k + 1)}{n! \, \Gamma(k + n + 1)2^{2n}} \text{ whenever } n \in N.$$

Thus the following Frobenius series is a particular solution of Bessel's differential equation of order k provided that k is not a negative integer:

(5) $\qquad a_0 \Gamma(k + 1)x^k \sum \dfrac{(-1)^{n-1}(x/2)^{2n-2}}{(n - 1)! \, \Gamma(k + n)}.$

We are now in a position to introduce the *Bessel functions of the first kind of index k*
In (5) let $a_0 = 2^{-k}/\Gamma(k + 1)$, where k is not a negative integer. In this way each real
number k which is not a negative integer gives rise to a function, namely

$$(x/2)^k \sum \frac{(-1)^{n-1}(x/2)^{2n-2}}{(n-1)! \, \Gamma(k+n)},$$

which is said to be Bessel's function of the first kind of index k; this function is denoted
by "J_k". Hence we have the following definition.

DEFINITION 11.6.1.   Let k be any real number other than a negative integer; then

$$J_k = (x/2)^k \sum \frac{(-1)^{n-1}(x/2)^{2n-2}}{(n-1)! \, \Gamma(k+n)}.$$

We want to determine the domain of J_k. Now, the function

$$\sum \frac{(-1)^{n-1}(x/2)^{2n-2}}{(n-1)! \, \Gamma(k+n)}$$

has domain R. However, the domain of $(x/2)^k$ depends upon k; e.g., the domain of
$(x/2)^5$ is R; the domain of $(x/2)^{1/2}$ is $\{t \mid t > 0\}$; the domain of $(x/2)^{1/3}$ is R. We conclude
that $\mathcal{D}_{J_k} = \mathcal{D}_{x^k}$ whenever k is not a negative integer. Notice that we have not yet defined
J_k if k is a negative integer; we shall do this presently.
     The Bessel functions J_0 and J_1 have particular importance.

Now,
$$J_0 = \sum \frac{(-1)^{n-1}(x/2)^{2n-2}}{(n-1)! \, \Gamma(n)} = \sum \frac{(-1)^{n-1}x^{2n-2}}{[2^{n-1}(n-1)]^2}$$

$$= \sum \frac{(-1)^{n-1}x^{2n-2}}{2^2 \cdot 4^2 \cdots [2(n-1)]^2}$$

$$= 1 - \frac{x^2}{2^2} + \frac{x^4}{2^2 \cdot 4^2} - \frac{x^6}{2^2 \cdot 4^2 \cdot 6^2} + \cdots,$$

and
$$J_1 = \frac{x}{2} \sum \frac{(-1)^{n-1}(x/2)^{2n-2}}{(n-1)! \, \Gamma(1+n)}$$

$$= \frac{x}{2}\left(\frac{1}{2^0 \cdot 0! \cdot 1!} - \frac{x^2}{2^2 \cdot 1! \cdot 2!} + \frac{x^4}{2^4 \cdot 2! \cdot 3!} - \frac{x^6}{2^6 \cdot 3! \cdot 4!} + \cdots\right).$$

     By using an automatic digital computer, it is easy to develop a table of values for each
of the functions J_0 and J_1 (see Tables 2 and 3, pages 473–490). Here we present short tables
for these functions (Tables 11.6.1 and 11.6.2); also, we present the programs that produced
the tables.

PROGRAM FOR J_0

*FANDK1504

```
      DIMENSION A(10)
    1 FORMAT(46X,2HJ0)
      PRINT 1
    2 FORMAT(1H0,3X,1HT,6X,2H.0,6X,2H.1,6X,2H.2,6X,2H.3,6X,2H.4,6X,2H.5,
     16X,2H.6,6X,2H.7,6X,2H.8,6X,2H.9/)
      PRINT 2
    3 FORMAT(1H ,I4,F10.5,9F8.5)
    4 FORMAT(1H0,I4,F10.5,9F8.5)
      L = 0
      M = 0
      T = -1.
    6 T = T + 1.
      I = T
      DO 9 K = 1,10
      S = 1.
      D = 2.
      C = K - 1
      X = T + C*.1
      BJO = 1.
    7 S = -S*(X/D)**2
      IF (ABSF(S) - .0000001)20,20,8
    8 BJO = BJO + S
      D = D + 2.
      GO TO 7
   20 IF (BJO)10,11,11
   10 A(K) = BJO - .000005
      GO TO 9
   11 A(K) = BJO + .000005
    9 CONTINUE
      IF (L-5)12,13,13
   12 PRINT 3, I, A
      L = L + 1
      GO TO 6
   13 PRINT 4, I, A
      L = 1
      M = M+1
      IF (M-5)6,14,14
   14 CALL EXIT
      END
```

Table 11.6.1

T	.0	.1	.2	.3	.4	.5	.6	.7	.8	.9
0	1.00000	.99750	.99003	.97763	.96040	.93847	.91200	.88120	.84629	.80752
1	.76520	.71962	.67113	.62009	.56686	.51183	.45540	.39798	.33999	.28182
2	.22389	.16661	.11036	.05554	.00251	-.04838	-.09680	-.14245	-.18504	-.22431
3	-.26005	-.29206	-.32019	-.34430	-.36430	-.38013	-.39177	-.39923	-.40256	-.40183
4	-.39715	-.38867	-.37656	-.36101	-.34226	-.32054	-.29614	-.26933	-.24043	-.20974
5	-.17760	-.14433	-.11029	-.07580	-.04121	-.00684	.02697	.05992	.09170	.12203
6	.15065	.17729	.20175	.22381	.24331	.26009	.27404	.28506	.29310	.29810
7	.30008	.29905	.29507	.28822	.27860	.26634	.25160	.23456	.21541	.19436
8	.17165	.14752	.12222	.09601	.06916	.04194	.01462	-.01252	-.03923	-.06525
9	-.09033	-.11424	-.13675	-.15766	-.17677	-.19393	-.20898	-.22180	-.23228	-.24034
10	-.24594	-.24903	-.24962	-.24772	-.24337	-.23665	-.22764	-.21644	-.20320	-.18806
11	-.17119	-.15277	-.13299	-.11207	-.09021	-.06765	-.04462	-.02133	.00197	.02505
12	.04596	.06967	.09077	.11080	.12956	.14688	.16261	.17659	.18870	.19884
13	.20693	.21289	.21669	.21830	.21773	.21499	.21013	.20322	.19434	.18358
14	.17107	.15695	.14137	.12449	.10648	.08754	.06786	.04764	.02708	.00639
15	-.01422	-.03456	-.05442	-.07361	-.09194	-.10923	-.12533	-.14007	-.15333	-.16497
16	-.17490	-.18302	-.18927	-.19360	-.19597	-.19638	-.19483	-.19134	-.18597	-.17878
17	-.16985	-.15929	-.14719	-.13370	-.11896	-.10311	-.08633	-.06878	-.05065	-.03211
18	-.01336	.00543	.02405	.04234	.06010	.07716	.09337	.10856	.12259	.13532
19	.14663	.15642	.16461	.17111	.17587	.17885	.18004	.17943	.17703	.17288
20	.16702	.15954	.15049	.14000	.12816	.11510	.10095	.08587	.07001	.05352
21	.03658	.01935	.00202	-.01526	-.03230	-.04894	-.06502	-.08037	-.09485	-.10832
22	-.12065	-.13172	-.14143	-.14968	-.15640	-.16154	-.16504	-.16688	-.16705	-.16555
23	-.16241	-.15767	-.15137	-.14358	-.13441	-.12393	-.11226	-.09951	-.08584	-.07135
24	-.05623	-.04060	-.02464	-.00849	.00768	.02370	.03943	.05468	.06935	.08325
25	.09627	.10828	.11916	.12879	.13713	.14408	.14953	.15350	.15590	.15674

PROGRAM FOR J_1

*FANDK1504

```
      DIMENSION A(10)
    1 FORMAT(46X,2HJ1)
      PRINT 1
    2 FORMAT(1H0,3X,1HT,6X,2H.0,6X,2H.1,6X,2H.2,6X,2H.3,6X,2H.4,6X,2H.5,
     16X,2H.6,6X,2H.7,6X,2H.8,6X,2H.9/)
      PRINT 2
    3 FORMAT(1H ,I4,F10.5,9F8.5)
    4 FORMAT(1H0,I4,F10.5,9F8.5)
      L = 0
      M = 0
      T = -1.
    6 T = T + 1.
      I = T
      DO 9 K = 1,10
      D = 1.
      C = K - 1
      X = T + C*.1
      BJ1 = .5*X
      S = BJ1
    7 S = -S*(.5*X)**2/(D*(D+1.))
      IF (ABSF(S) - .0000001)20,20,8
    8 BJ1 = BJ1 + S
      D = D + 1.
      GO TO 7
   20 IF (BJ1)10,11,11
   10 A(K) = BJ1 - .000005
      GO TO 9
   11 A(K) = BJ1 + .000005
    9 CONTINUE
      IF (L-5)12,13,13
   12 PRINT 3, I, A
      L = L + 1
      GO TO 6
   13 PRINT 4, I, A
      L = 1
      M = M+1
      IF (M-5)6,14,14
   14 CALL EXIT
      END
```

Table 11.6.2

$$J_1$$

T	.0	.1	.2	.3	.4	.5	.6	.7	.8	.9
0	0.00000	.04994	.09950	.14832	.19603	.24227	.28670	.32900	.36884	.40595
1	.44005	.47090	.49829	.52202	.54195	.55794	.56990	.57777	.58152	.58116
2	.57672	.56829	.55596	.53987	.52019	.49709	.47082	.44160	.40971	.37543
3	.33906	.30092	.26134	.22066	.17923	.13738	.09547	.05383	.01282	-.02724
4	-.06604	-.10327	-.13865	-.17190	-.20278	-.23106	-.25655	-.27908	-.29850	-.31469
5	-.32758	-.33710	-.34322	-.34596	-.34534	-.34144	-.33433	-.32415	-.31103	-.29514
6	-.27668	-.25586	-.23292	-.20809	-.18164	-.15384	-.12498	-.09534	-.06522	-.03490
7	-.00468	.02515	.05433	.08257	.10963	.13525	.15921	.18131	.20136	.21918
8	.23464	.24761	.25800	.26574	.27079	.27312	.27275	.26972	.26407	.25590
9	.24531	.23243	.21741	.20041	.18163	.16126	.13952	.11664	.09284	.06837
10	.04347	.01840	-.00662	-.03132	-.05547	-.07885	-.10123	-.12240	-.14217	-.16035
11	-.17679	-.19133	-.20385	-.21426	-.22245	-.22838	-.23200	-.23330	-.23228	-.22898
12	-.22345	-.21575	-.20598	-.19426	-.18071	-.16548	-.14874	-.13066	-.11143	-.09125
13	-.07032	-.04885	-.02707	-.00518	.01660	.03805	.05896	.07914	.09839	.11652
14	.13338	.14878	.16261	.17473	.18503	.19343	.19985	.20425	.20660	.20688
15	.20510	.20131	.19555	.18788	.17840	.16721	.15444	.14022	.12469	.10803
16	.09040	.07198	.05296	.03354	.01389	-.00576	-.02525	-.04436	-.06292	-.08075
17	-.09767	-.11352	-.12815	-.14142	-.15322	-.16342	-.17194	-.17871	-.18366	-.18677
18	-.18799	-.18735	-.18485	-.18052	-.17443	-.16663	-.15723	-.14631	-.13399	-.12041
19	-.10570	-.09002	-.07353	-.05639	-.03878	-.02088	-.00286	.01510	.03282	.05012
20	.06683	.08280	.09787	.11188	.12472	.13625	.14638	.15500	.16203	.16742
21	.17112	.17310	.17335	.17187	.16869	.16385	.15740	.14942	.13998	.12920
22	.11718	.10405	.08994	.07500	.05938	.04324	.02674	.01005	-.00667	-.02324
23	-.03952	-.05533	-.07052	-.08495	-.09847	-.11095	-.12227	-.13233	-.14103	-.14829
24	-.15404	-.15823	-.16084	-.16183	-.16120	-.15898	-.15518	-.14985	-.14305	-.13486
25	-.12535	-.11463	-.10282	-.09004	-.07639	-.06205	-.04714	-.03182	-.01625	-.00058

Using our short tables for J_0 and J_1, we readily construct a portion of the graphs of these functions (see Figures 11.6.1 and 11.6.2).

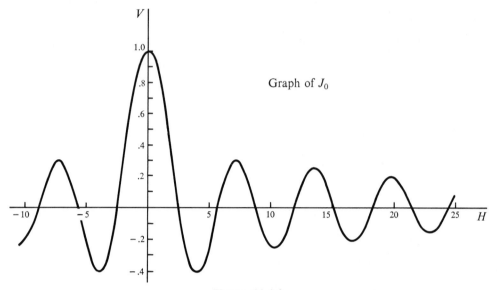

Figure 11.6.1

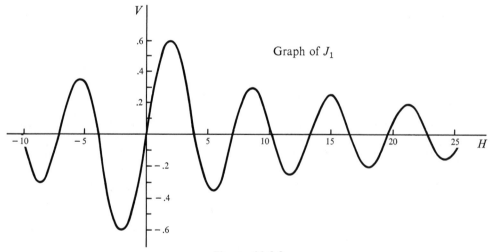

Figure 11.6.2

Next, we want to introduce Bessel functions of the first kind of index k, where k is a negative integer; i.e., we want to extend Definition 11.6.1 to cover negative integers. To do this, we consider the formal expression that occurs in Definition 11.6.1. There, J_k is defined to be

$$(x/2)^k \sum \frac{(-1)^{n-1}(x/2)^{2n-2}}{(n-1)!\,\Gamma(k+n)}$$

provided that k is not a negative integer. Now, $\Gamma(t)$ is *not* defined if t is a negative integer or zero. Thus the expression

$$(x/2)^k \sum \frac{(-1)^{n-1}(x/2)^{2n-2}}{(n-1)!\,\Gamma(k+n)}$$

has no meaning if k is a negative integer. To give meaning to this expression, let us delete each term which is not meaningful; this means that if k is a negative integer, we shall delete the first $|k|$ terms of the series. But, if k is a negative integer, then

$$\sum_{n>|k|} \frac{(-1)^{n-1}(x/2)^{2n-2}}{(n-1)!\,\Gamma(k+n)} = \sum \frac{(-1)^{n-k-1}(x/2)^{2n-2k-2}}{(n-k-1)!\,(n-1)!}.$$

Thus we obtain the following definition.

DEFINITION 11.6.2.   Let k be any negative integer; then

$$J_k = (x/2)^k \sum \frac{(-1)^{n-k-1}(x/2)^{2n-2k-2}}{(n-k-1)!\,(n-1)!}.$$

For example,

$$J_{-3} = (x/2)^{-3} \sum \frac{(-1)^{n+2}(x/2)^{2n+4}}{(n+2)!\,(n-1)!}$$

$$= -\frac{(x/2)^3}{3!\,0!} + \frac{(x/2)^5}{4!\,1!} - \frac{(x/2)^7}{5!\,2!} + \frac{(x/2)^9}{6!\,3!} - \cdots.$$

Thus $J_{-3} = -J_3$. In this connection the following theorem is relevant.

THEOREM 11.6.1.   Let k be any positive integer; then $J_{-k} = (-1)^k J_k$.

Proof: If k is a positive integer, then

$$J_{-k} = (x/2)^{-k} \sum \frac{(-1)^{n+k-1}(x/2)^{2n+2k-2}}{(n+k-1)!\,(n-1)!} \qquad \text{by Def. 11.6.2}$$

$$= (-1)^k(x/2)^k \sum \frac{(-1)^{n-1}(x/2)^{2n-2}}{(n-1)!\,\Gamma(k+n)} \qquad \text{by Cor. 11.5.1}$$

$$= (-1)^k J_k.$$

COROLLARY 11.6.1.   Let k be any positive integer; then J_{-k} is a particular solution of Bessel's differential equation of order k.

Proof: J_k is a particular solution of Bessel's differential equation of order k; therefore $(-1)^k J_k$ is a particular solution of this differential equation.

We saw earlier that if k is not an integer, then each of J_k and J_{-k} is a particular solution of $x^2 f^{(2)} + xf' + (x^2 - k^2)f = 0$ R E.

Since
$$J_k = (x/2)^k \sum \frac{(-1)^{n-1}(x/2)^{2n-2}}{(n-1)! \ \Gamma(n+k)}$$

and
$$J_{-k} = (x/2)^{-k} \sum \frac{(-1)^{n-1}(x/2)^{2n-2}}{(n-1)! \ \Gamma(n-k)},$$

it is clear that J_k and J_{-k} are linearly independent. Thus $f = c_1 J_k + c_2 J_{-k}$ is a complete solution of (1); i.e., g is a particular solution of (1) with domain $\mathscr{D}_{x^k}$ iff there exist real numbers c_1 and c_2 such that $g = c_1 J_k + c_2 J_{-k}$.

If k is an integer, then J_k and J_{-k} are linearly dependent; indeed, $J_{-k} = (-1)^k J_k$. This means that there is essentially just one Bessel function of the first kind which satisfies a Bessel's differential equation of integral order. However, we can determine a particular solution of (1) which is linearly independent of J_k by applying the method of variation of parameter (see Section 9.4). This leads us to the function

$$J_k \int_c^x \frac{1}{xJ_k^2},$$

where $c > 0$, which is said to be a *Bessel function of the second kind*. Hence, if k is a positive integer, then

$$f = c_1 J_k + c_2 J_k \int_c^x \frac{1}{xJ_k^2}$$

is a complete solution of Bessel's differential equation of order k.

E X E R C I S E S

1. a. Prove that $J_0(-x) = J_0$.
   b. Prove that $J_1(-x) = -J_1$.
2. Prove the following.
   a. $\lim_\infty J_0 = 0$.
   b. $\lim_0 J_0 = 1$.
   c. $\lim_0 J_k = 0$ whenever $k > 0$.
   d. $\lim_0 |J_k| = \infty$ whenever $k < 0$ and k is not an integer.
3. Given that k is not a negative integer, show the following.
   a. $J_k = \sum \dfrac{(-1)^{n-1}(x/2)^{2n-2+k}}{(n-1)! \ \Gamma(k+n)}$.

   b. $xJ_k' = \sum \dfrac{(-1)^{n-1}(2n-2+k)(x/2)^{2n-2+k}}{(n-1)! \ \Gamma(k+n)}$.

4. Show that $J_0' = -J_1$.

5. Given that $k - 1$ is not a negative integer, prove the following.

    a. $2J_k' = J_{k-1} - J_{k+1}$.

    b. $J_{k+1} = 2kJ_k/x - J_{k-1}$.

6. Show that $2J_0^{(2)} = J_2 - J_0$.

7. a. Prove that $2J_0' = -x(J_0 + J_2)$. (*Hint:* Use Bessel's differential equation of order zero.)

    b. Prove that $2J_1 = x(J_0 + J_2)$.

Chapter 12

Numerical Approximations

12.1   Introduction

We now take a second look at the problem of finding a particular solution of a given differential equation which satisfies specified boundary conditions. Although we have already worked out a variety of methods for solving this problem, to be honest we must point out that our analytic procedures are limited in their applicability. As we have seen, a differential equation with boundary conditions is sometimes used to *define* a function; moreover, we cannot rely on power series methods since some functions do not have a power series representation. For example, the function $\exp(-1/x^2) \cup \{(0, 0)\}$ does not have a power series representation; yet this function satisfies the differential equation with boundary condition $x^3 f' = 2f, f(0) = 0$.

It is clear that we need a different approach to our problem. Let us concentrate on the idea that a differential equation with boundary conditions *defines* a function; the main task, then, is to exhibit the function which is so defined. In particular, we want to produce a table which lists members of the function. In other words, we want to *compute*, to some desired accuracy, various values of the function spread over a subset of the domain of the function.

In this chapter we shall consider only differential equations of the first order; the technique for handling these differential equations can be extended to a wider class of differential equations. The simplest sort of first-order differential equation with boundary condition is

$$f' = g \qquad f(a) = b,$$

where g is a given function. There is no difficulty in computing values of f: clearly, $f = b + \int_a^x g$; therefore $f(t) = b + \int_a^t g$ whenever $t \in \mathcal{D}_f$. Thus the problem of computing $f(t)$ is reduced to that of computing $\int_a^t g$, where g is a given function. This computation is easily carried out by means of a quadrature formula, say Simpson's Rule. Thus $\int_a^t g \approx \dfrac{t-a}{6}\left[g(a) + 4g\left(\dfrac{a+t}{2}\right) + g(t) \right]$; moreover, we have an upper bound on the error in the approximation since there is a real number c between a and t such that

$$\int_a^t g = \frac{t-a}{6}\left[g(a) + 4g\left(\frac{a+t}{2}\right) + g(t) \right] - \frac{1}{90}\left(\frac{t-a}{2}\right)^5 g^{(4)}(c).$$

Thus

$$\left| \int_a^t g - \frac{t-a}{6}\left[g(a) + 4g\left(\frac{a+t}{2}\right) + g(t) \right] \right| \leq \frac{|t-a|^5}{2880} M,$$

where $M = \max\{|g^{(4)}(s)| \ |s \in [a, t] \text{ or } s \in [t, a]\}$.

It is clear that quadrature formulas are our basic tools. In this chapter we shall see how to refine these tools so that they can be applied to a wider class of first-order differential equations.

12.2 Some Quadrature Formulas

In this section we shall develop the quadrature formulas that we shall use throughout this chapter. In Volume I of *Concepts of Calculus* we have had a taste of this topic (see Sections 11.8 and 11.9). There we used geometric arguments to develop several quadrature rules, namely the Rectangle Rule, Trapezoid Rule, and Simpson's Rule; we then found expressions for the remainder terms by analytic methods. It is possible to develop more quadrature formulas from these quadrature formulas by algebraic methods. The idea is to form a linear combination of two quadrature rules; the multipliers are chosen by considering the remainder terms of the quadrature formulas involved.

We begin by demonstrating how the fundamental quadrature formulas can be obtained algebraically. First, we need the following analytic result, which was established in Volume I.

THEOREM 12.2.1. Suppose that $(a - h, a + h) \subset \mathcal{D}_{f^{(2)}}$ and that f is continuous on $[a - h, a + h]$; then there is a real number c such that $c \in (a - h, a + h)$ and $f(a + h) + f(a - h) - 2f(a) = h^2 f^{(2)}(c)$.

Proof: Let B be a real number such that $f(a + h) + f(a - h) - 2f(a) = Bh^2$; we consider the function $f(a + x) + f(a - x) - 2f(a) - Bx^2$. Applying Rolle's Theorem and the Mean Value Theorem, it follows that there is a member of $(a - h, a + h)$, say c, such that $B = f^{(2)}(c)$.

Let us consider the Rectangle Rule with Remainder.

RECTANGLE RULE WITH REMAINDER. There is a real number c such that $c \in (a - h, a + h)$ and $\int_{a-h}^{a+h} f = 2hf(a) + (h^3/3)f^{(2)}(c)$ provided that $(a - h, a + h) \subset \mathcal{D}_{f^{(2)}}$ and that f is continuous on $[a - h, a + h]$.

Development: We now proceed to develop this result. Recall that a definite integral is the limit of a sequence; thus $2hf(a)$ is the first term of a sequence whose limit is $\int_{a-h}^{a+h} f$. This suggests that $2hf(a)$ is an approximation to the limit of the sequence. Thus we obtain the Rectangle Rule: $\int_{a-h}^{a+h} f \approx 2hf(a)$. Our goal is to determine a bound on the error in this approximation. We make use of the following analytic technique. Let t be any natural number; then there is a real number, say B, such that $\int_{a-h}^{a+h} f = 2hf(a) + h^t B/t!$. Consider the function F, where $F = \int_{a-x}^{a+x} f - 2xf(a) - Bx^t/t!$. Now, $F(h) = F(0) = 0$ and F meets the remaining conditions of Rolle's Theorem; thus there is a real number d such that $d \in (0, h)$ and $F'(d) = 0$. But $F' = f(a + x) + f(a - x) - 2f(a) - Bx^{t-1}/(t-1)!$; therefore

$$
\begin{aligned}
0 = F'(d) &= f(a + d) + f(a - d) - 2f(a) - Bd^{t-1}/(t-1)! \\
&= d^2 f^{(2)}(c) - Bd^{t-1}/(t-1)! \quad \text{by Th. 12.2.1, where } c \in (a - d, a + d) \\
&= d^2[f^{(2)}(c) - Bd^{t-3}/(t-1)!]
\end{aligned}
$$

Since $d \neq 0$, it follows that $f^{(2)}(c) = Bd^{t-3}/(t-1)!$. We can simplify this result by setting $t = 3$; thus $f^{(2)}(c) = B/2$, i.e., $B = 2f^{(2)}(c)$. Hence there is a real number c such that $c \in (a - h, a + h)$ and $\int_{a-h}^{a+h} f = 2hf(a) + (h^3/3)f^{(2)}(c)$. We have developed the Rectangle Rule with Remainder.

Now we are in a position to obtain the Trapezoid Rule with Remainder algebraically; we shall use only the Rectangle Rule with Remainder and Theorem 12.2.1.

TRAPEZOID RULE WITH REMAINDER.   There is a real number c such that $c \in (a - h, a + h)$ and $\int_{a-h}^{a+h} f = h[f(a - h) + f(a + h)] - \frac{2}{3}h^3 f^{(2)}(c)$ provided that $(a - h, a + h) \subset \mathcal{D}_{f^{(2)}}$ and that f is continuous on $[a - h, a + h]$.

Development: In view of the Rectangle Rule with Remainder and Theorem 12.2.1, there are members of $(a - h, a + h)$, say c_1 and c_2, such that $\int_{a-h}^{a+h} f = 2hf(a) + (h^3/3)f^{(2)}(c_2)$ and $2hf(a) = h[f(a - h) + f(a + h)] - h^3 f^{(2)}(c_1)$. Therefore $\int_{a-h}^{a+h} f = h[f(a - h) + f(a + h)] - (h^3/3)[3f^{(2)}(c_1) - f^{(2)}(c_2)]$. This suggests that $h[f(a - h) + f(a + h)]$ is an approximation to $\int_{a-h}^{a+h} f$ and that the error in the approximation is $-\frac{2}{3}h^3 f^{(2)}(c)$, where $c \in (a - h, a + h)$. By applying the analytic technique based on Rolle's Theorem, it is easy to verify this conjecture. We have developed and established the Trapezoid Rule with Remainder.

Next, we consider Simpson's Rule with Remainder.

SIMPSON'S RULE WITH REMAINDER.   There is a real number c such that $c \in (a - h, a + h)$ and $\int_{a-h}^{a+h} f = (h/3)[f(a - h) + 4f(a) + f(a + h)] - (h^5/90)f^{(4)}(c)$ provided that $(a - h, a + h) \subset \mathcal{D}_{f^{(4)}}$ and that f is continuous on $[a - h, a + h]$.

Development: We base our development primarily on the Trapezoid Rule with Remainder. There is a member of $(a - h, a)$, say c_1, such that $\int_{a-h}^{a} f = (h/2)[f(a - h) + f(a)] - (h^3/12)f^{(2)}(c_1)$; and there is a member of $(a, a + h)$, say c_2, such that $\int_{a}^{a+h} f = (h/2)[f(a) + f(a + h)] - (h^3/12)f^{(2)}(c_2)$. Thus, by a consequence of the Intermediate Value Theorem, there is a real number c_3 between c_1 and c_2 such that

(1)
$$
\int_{a-h}^{a+h} f = \frac{h}{2}[f(a - h) + 2f(a) + f(a + h)] - \frac{h^3}{6}f^{(2)}(c_3).
$$

Again, by the Trapezoid Rule with Remainder, there is a member of $(a - h, a + h)$, say c_4, such that

(2)
$$\int_{a-h}^{a+h} f = h[f(a - h) + f(a + h)] - \frac{2}{3} h^3 f^{(2)}(c_4).$$

In view of the remainder terms of (1) and (2), we consider $4 \times (1) - (2)$; thus we obtain

$$3 \int_{a-h}^{a+h} f = h[f(a - h) + 4f(a) + f(a + h)] - \frac{2}{3} h^3 [f^{(2)}(c_3) - f^{(2)}(c_4)];$$

so
$$\int_{a-h}^{a+h} f = \frac{h}{3} [f(a - h) + 4f(a) + f(a + h)] - \frac{2}{9} h^3 [f^{(2)}(c_3) - f^{(2)}(c_4)].$$

This suggests Simpson's Rule:

$$\int_{a-h}^{a+h} f \approx \frac{h}{3} [f(a - h) + 4f(a) + f(a + h)];$$

it also suggests that the error in the approximation is $-\frac{2}{9}h^3[f^{(2)}(c_3) - f^{(2)}(c_4)]$. By applying our analytic technique, it is easy to demonstrate that there is a member of $(a - h, a + h)$, say c, such that the error in the approximation is $-(h^5/90)f^{(4)}(c)$. This completes our development of Simpson's Rule with Remainder.

A quadrature formula which involves values of the given function at the endpoints of the given interval is said to be a *closed* quadrature formula. A quadrature formula which uses only values of the function over the corresponding open interval is said to be an *open* quadrature formula. For example, Simpson's Rule and the Trapezoid Rule are closed quadrature formulas, whereas the Rectangle Rule is an open quadrature formula.

We shall now develop another open quadrature formula. We shall follow the pattern which led us to the closed formula, Simpson's Rule; however, we shall use the Rectangle Rule, an open formula, in place of the Trapezoid Rule, a closed formula.

THEOREM 12.2.2.   There is a real number c such that $c \in (a - 2h, a + 2h)$ and $\int_{a-2h}^{a+2h} f = (4h/3)[2f(a - h) - f(a) + 2f(a + h)] + \frac{14}{45}h^5 f^{(4)}(c)$ provided that $(a - 2h, a + 2h) \subset \mathscr{D}_{f^{(4)}}$ and that f is continuous on $[a - 2h, a + 2h]$.

Development: By the Rectangle Rule with Remainder, there is a member of $(a - 2h, a)$, say c_1, and a member of $(a, a + 2h)$, say c_2, such that

$$\int_{a-2h}^{a} f = 2hf(a - h) + \frac{h^3}{3} f^{(2)}(c_1) \qquad \text{and} \qquad \int_{a}^{a+2h} f = 2hf(a + h) + \frac{h^3}{3} f^{(2)}(c_2).$$

Thus

(3) $$\int_{a-2h}^{a+2h} f = 2h[f(a-h) + f(a+h)] + \frac{h^3}{3}[f^{(2)}(c_1) + f^{(2)}(c_2)]$$

$$= 2h[f(a-h) + f(a+h)] + \frac{2}{3}h^3 f^{(2)}(c_3),$$

where c_3 is between c_1 and c_2 (this follows from a consequence of the Intermediate Value Theorem). Again, by the Rectangle Rule with Remainder, there is a member of $(a - 2h, a + 2h)$, say c_4, such that

(4) $$\int_{a-2h}^{a+2h} f = 4hf(a) + \frac{8}{3}h^3 f^{(2)}(c_4).$$

Examining the remainder terms in (3) and (4), we are led to consider $4 \times (3) - (4)$; thus we obtain

$$3\int_{a-2h}^{a+2h} f = 4h[2f(a-h) - f(a) + 2f(a+h)] + \frac{8}{3}h^3[f^{(2)}(c_3) - f^{(2)}(c_4)].$$

This suggests that $\int_{a-2h}^{a+2h} f \approx (4h/3)[2f(a-h) - f(a) + 2f(a+h)]$ and that the error in the approximation is given by $\frac{8}{9}h^3[f^{(2)}(c_3) - f^{(2)}(c_4)]$. Applying our analytic technique, we find that we can do a bit better: there is a member of $(a - 2h, a + 2h)$, say c, such that the error in the approximation is $\frac{14}{45}h^5 f^{(4)}(c)$. This completes our development of Theorem 12.2.2.

Later we shall require a quadrature formula which, like the Rectangle Rule, approximates a definite integral in terms of the value of the given function at the midpoint of the interval involved, but which provides greater accuracy than does the Rectangle Rule. Actually, we shall permit our approximating formula to involve values of certain derivatives of the given function at the midpoint of the given interval. Consider the following quadrature formula.

THEOREM 12.2.3.   There is a real number c such that $c \in (a - h, a + h)$ and $\int_{a-h}^{a+h} f = 2hf(a) + (h^3/3)f^{(2)}(a) + (h^5/60)f^{(4)}(c)$ provided that $(a - h, a + h) \subset \mathscr{D}_{f^{(4)}}$ and that f is continuous on $[a - h, a + h]$.

Development: This result is based on the Rectangle Rule with Remainder. Clearly, there is a member of $(a - h, a + h)$, say c, such that $\int_{a-h}^{a+h} f = 2hf(a) + (h^3/3)f^{(2)}(c)$. Let us express $f^{(2)}(c)$ in terms of $f^{(2)}(a)$: $f^{(2)}(c) = f^{(2)}(a) + (c - a)f^{(3)}(c_1)$, where c_1 is between a and c. Thus

$$\int_{a-h}^{a+h} f = 2hf(a) + \frac{h^3}{3}f^{(2)}(a) + \frac{h^3}{3}(c - a)f^{(3)}(c_1).$$

This suggests that $\int_{a-h}^{a+h} f \approx 2hf(a) + (h^3/3)f^{(2)}(a)$; hence we have our quadrature rule. To find an expression for the remainder, we apply our analytic technique. Let t be a natural number and let B be a real number such that $\int_{a-h}^{a+h} f = 2hf(a) + (h^3/3)f^{(2)}(a) + Bh^t$. Keeping one eye on this equation, we introduce F;

$$F = -\int_{a-x}^{a+x} f + 2xf(a) + \frac{x^3}{3}f^{(2)}(a) + Bx^t.$$

Now, by Rolle's Theorem, there is a member of $(0, h)$, say c_2, such that $F'(c_2) = 0$. But

$$F' = -f(a + x) - f(a - x) + 2f(a) + x^2 f^{(2)}(a) + tBx^{t-1}.$$

Note that $F'(0) = F'(c_2) = 0$. Again, by Rolle's Theorem, there is a member of $(0, c_2)$, say c_3, such that $F^{(2)}(c_3) = 0$. But

$$F^{(2)} = -f'(a + x) + f'(a - x) + 2xf^{(2)}(a) + t(t - 1)Bx^{t-2}.$$

Again, it follows from Rolle's Theorem that there is a member of $(0, c_3)$, say c_4, such that $F^{(3)}(c_4) = 0$. But

$$F^{(3)} = -f^{(2)}(a + x) - f^{(2)}(a - x) + 2f^{(2)}(a) + t(t - 1)(t - 2)Bx^{t-3}.$$

Thus $0 = F^{(3)}(c_4) = -f^{(2)}(a + c_4) - f^{(2)}(a - c_4) + 2f^{(2)}(a) + t(t - 1)(t - 2)Bc_4^{t-3}$. But, by Theorem 12.2.1, there is a member of $(a - c_4, a + c_4)$, say c, such that $f^{(2)}(a + c_4) + f^{(2)}(a - c_4) - 2f^{(2)}(a) = c_4^2 f^{(4)}(c)$. Hence $t(t - 1)(t - 2)Bc_4^{t-3} = c_4^2 f^{(4)}(c)$. We want to choose t so that we can solve for B. Let $t = 5$; then $60Bc_4^2 = c_4^2 f^{(4)}(c)$; so $B = f^{(4)}(c)/60$. We have developed our quadrature formula.

We emphasize that the value of Theorem 12.2.3 lies in the fact that the approximation to the definite integral requires only the values of the function and its second derivative at the midpoint of the interval involved; we do not require the values of the function at the endpoints of the interval. Moreover, this quadrature formula has roughly the same accuracy as Simpson's Rule.

Next, we shall use Simpson's Rule and the quadrature formula of Theorem 12.2.3 to develop another useful quadrature formula. Again, the idea is to form the linear combination of these quadrature rules which is dictated by the remainder terms.

THEOREM 12.2.4.   There is a real number c such that $c \in (a - h, a + h)$ and $\int_{a-h}^{a+h} f = (h/5)[f(a - h) + 8f(a) + f(a + h)] + \frac{2}{15}h^3 f^{(2)}(a) - (h^7/6300)f^{(6)}(c)$ provided that $(a - h, a + h) \subset \mathscr{D}_{f^{(6)}}$ and that f is continuous on $[a - h, a + h]$.

Development: In view of Simpson's Rule and Theorem 12.2.3, there are members of $(a - h, a + h)$, say c_1 and c_2, such that

(5) $$\int_{a-h}^{a+h} f = \frac{h}{3}[f(a - h) + 4f(a) + f(a + h)] - \frac{h^5}{90}f^{(4)}(c_1),$$

(6) $$\int_{a-h}^{a+h} f = 2hf(a) + \frac{h^3}{3}f^{(2)}(a) + \frac{h^5}{60}f^{(4)}(c_2).$$

Considering the remainder terms leads us to form $9 \times (5) + 6 \times (6)$; so

$$15 \int_{a-h}^{a+h} f = 3h[f(a-h) + 8f(a) + f(a+h)] + 2h^3 f^{(2)}(a) - \frac{h^5}{10}[f^{(4)}(c_1) - f^{(4)}(c_2)];$$

thus

$$\int_{a-h}^{a+h} f = \frac{h}{5}[f(a-h) + 8f(a) + f(a+h)] + \frac{2}{15}h^3 f^{(2)}(a) - \frac{h^5}{150}[f^{(4)}(c_1) - f^{(4)}(c_2)].$$

This suggests that

$$\int_{a-h}^{a+h} f \approx \frac{h}{5}[f(a-h) + 8f(a) + f(a+h)] + \frac{2}{15}h^3 f^{(2)}(a);$$

thus we have our quadrature rule. An exact expression for the remainder term can be obtained by the usual analytic technique; it turns out that there is a member of $(a-h, a+h)$, say c, such that the remainder is $-(h^7/6300)f^{(6)}(c)$.

Geometric Development: The quadrature rule contained in Theorem 12.2.4 can be obtained geometrically. The idea is to approximate the graph of f by that of a polynomial function, say g, which has the same values as f at $a-h$, a, $a+h$, and which has the same curvature at a as does f. The latter requirement means that $g'(a) = f'(a)$ and $g^{(2)}(a) = f^{(2)}(a)$. For g we take the polynomial function

$$f(a) + A(x-a) + B(x-a)^2 + C(x-a)^3 + D(x-a)^4.$$

Then $g'(a) = A$ and $g^{(2)}(a) = 2B$; therefore $A = f'(a)$ and $B = f^{(2)}(a)/2$. Now,

$$\int_{a-h}^{a+h} g = \left[f(a)(x-a) + f'(a)(x-a)^2/2 + f^{(2)}(a)(x-a)^3/6 \right.$$
$$\left. + C(x-a)^4/4 + D(x-a)^5/5 \right]_{a-h}^{a+h}$$
$$= 2hf(a) + f^{(2)}(a)h^2/3 + 2Dh^5/5.$$

We have only to determine D. But $g(a-h) = f(a-h)$ and $g(a+h) = f(a+h)$, by construction; therefore

$$f(a) + f'(a)h + f^{(2)}h^2/2 + h^3 C + h^4 D = f(a+h),$$
$$f(a) - hf'(a) + h^2 f^{(2)}/2 - h^3 C + h^4 D = f(a-h),$$

and it follows that $2h^4 D = f(a+h) + f(a-h) - 2f(a) - h^2 f^{(2)}(a)$. Thus

$$\int_{a-h}^{a+h} g = 2hf(a) + \frac{h^3}{3}f^{(2)}(a) + \frac{h}{5}[f(a+h) + f(a-h) - 2f(a) - h^2 f^{(2)}(a)]$$
$$= \frac{h}{5}[f(a-h) + 8f(a) + f(a+h)] + \frac{2}{15}h^3 f^{(2)}(a).$$

This completes our development.

We return now to Theorem 12.2.3; this result can be generalized as follows.

THEOREM 12.2.5.   There is a real number c such that $c \in (a - h, a + h)$ and

$$\int_{a-h}^{a+h} f = 2[hf(a) + h^3 f^{(2)}(a)/3! + \cdots + h^{2n-1} f^{(2n-2)}(a)/(2n-1)!]$$
$$+ 2h^{2n+1} f^{(2n)}(c)/(2n+1)!$$

provided that $n \in N$, $(a - h, a + h) \subset \mathcal{D}_{f^{(2n)}}$, and that f is continuous on $[a - h, a + h]$.

Proof: Apply Taylor's Theorem to the function $\int_{a-x}^{a+x} f$. The details are left as an exercise.

COROLLARY 12.2.1.   Let $(a - h, a + h) \subset \mathcal{D}_{f^{(n)}}$ whenever $n \in N$, let f be continuous on $[a - h, a + h]$, and let $\lim \left(\dfrac{2h^{2n+1}}{(2n+1)!} \max_{(a-h, a+h)} |f^{(2n)}| \right) = 0$; then

$$\int_{a-h}^{a+h} f = 2 \sum h^{2n-1} f^{(2n-2)}(a)/(2n-1)!.$$

We now illustrate Simpson's Rule and the quadrature rules contained in Theorems 12.2.3 and 12.2.4.

EXAMPLE 1.   Approximate $\int_0^1 1/(1 + x^2)$, using Simpson's Rule.

Solution: $\displaystyle\int_0^1 \frac{1}{1 + x^2} \approx \frac{1}{6}\left[1 + 4\left(\frac{1}{1 + \frac{1}{4}}\right) + \frac{1}{2}\right] = \frac{4.7}{6} \approx .783$.   Note that

$$\int_0^1 \frac{1}{1 + x^2} = \arctan 1 = \frac{\pi}{4} \approx .7854.$$

EXAMPLE 2.   Use Theorem 12.2.3 to approximate $\int_0^1 1/(1 + x^2)$.

Solution: Now, $[1/(1 + x^2)]^{(2)} = (6x^2 - 2)/(1 + x^2)^3$; thus

$$\int_0^1 \frac{1}{1 + x^2} \approx \frac{4}{5} + \frac{1}{24}(1.5 - 2)\left(\frac{4}{5}\right)^3 = .8 - \frac{.8^3}{48} \approx .789.$$

EXAMPLE 3.   Use Theorem 12.2.4 to approximate $\int_0^1 1/(1 + x^2)$.

Solution: $$\int_0^1 \frac{1}{1+x^2} \approx .1\left[1 + 8\left(\frac{4}{5}\right) + \frac{1}{2}\right] + \frac{1}{60}(-.5)\left(\frac{4}{5}\right)^3$$

$$\approx .79 - .0043 = .7857.$$

The accuracy of the quadrature rule used in Example 3 is quite impressive. Let us try out this method by using an automatic digital computer. In fact, let us determine the first fifteen digits of π by evaluating $\int_0^1 1/(1+x^2)$. (See the following programs and Tables 12.2.1 and 12.2.2.)

```
              PROGRAM TO COMPUTE PI
                      USING
                 THEOREM 12.2.4

*FANDK2804

      F(T) = 1./(1. + T*T)
      D2F(T) = (6.*T*T - 2.)/(1. + T*T)**3
    1 FORMAT (I5)
    2 FORMAT (1H0, I12, F10.4, F25.20)
    4 FORMAT (1H1, 10X, 1HN, 8X, 1HH, 17X, 2HPI)
      PRINT 4
    3 READ 1, N
      TOTMID = 0.0
      TOTEND = 0.0
      TOTD2 = 0.0
      Y = N
      H = .5/Y
      DO 10 J = 1,N
      T = 2*J
      X = (T - 1.)*H
      TOTMID = TOTMID + F(X)
      TOTD2 = TOTD2 + D2F(X)
   10 TOTEND = TOTEND + F(X+H)
      SUM = .2*H*(F(.0)+8.*TOTMID+2.*TOTEND-F(1.)+H*H*TOTD2/1.5)
      PI = 4.*SUM
      PRINT 2, N,H,PI
      IF (SENSE SWITCH 1)3,11
   11 CALL EXIT
      END
```

Table 12.2.1

N.	H	PI
1	.5000	3.14293333333333333333
2	.2500	3.14159631084876857317
5	.1000	3.14159265834626919053
10	.0500	3.14159265366419266037
20	.0250	3.14159265359095580765
50	.0100	3.14159265358979800036
100	.0050	3.14159265358979331286
200	.0025	3.14159265358979323962
500	.0010	3.14159265358979323846

```
                    PROGRAM TO COMPUTE PI
                             USING
                       SIMPSON'S RULE

*FANDK2804

        F(T) = 1./(1. + T*T)
      1 FORMAT (I5)
      2 FORMAT (1H0, I12, F10.4, F25.20)
      4 FORMAT (1H1, 10X, 1HN, 8X, 1HH, 17X, 2HPI)
        PRINT 4
      3 READ 1, N
        TOTMID = 0.0
        TOTEND = 0.0
        Y = N
        H = .5/Y
        DO 10 J = 1,N
        T = 2*J
        X = (T - 1.)*H
        TOTMID = TOTMID + F(X)
     10 TOTEND = TOTEND + F(X+H)
        SUM = H*(F(.0) + 4.*TOTMID + 2.*TOTEND - F(1.))/3.
        PI = 4.*SUM
        PRINT 2, N,H,PI
        IF (SENSE SWITCH 1)3,11
     11 CALL EXIT
        END
```

Table 12.2.2

N	H	PI
1	.5000	3.13333333333333333333
2	.2500	3.14156862745098039215
5	.1000	3.14159261393921521967
10	.0500	3.14159265296978498960
20	.0250	3.14159265358010514912
50	.0100	3.14159265358975355592
100	.0050	3.14159265358979261842
200	.0025	3.14159265358979322877
500	.0010	3.14159265358979323842
1000	.0005	3.14159265358979323846

We now develop another quadrature formula which is based on Simpson's Rule.

THEOREM 12.2.6. Let $(a - 2h, a + 2h) \subset \mathscr{D}_{f^{(8)}}$ and let f be continuous on $[a - 2h, a + 2h]$; then there are members of $(a - 2h, a + 2h)$, say c_1 and c_2, and there is a member of $(0, h)$, say t, such that

$$\int_{a-2h}^{a+2h} f = \frac{2h}{45} \left[7f(a - 2h) + 32f(a - h) + 12f(a) + 32f(a + h) + 7f(a + 2h) \right]$$

$$- \frac{4h^7}{14175} \left[30f^{(6)}(c_1) + 153t^2 f^{(8)}(c_2) \right].$$

Development: By Simpson's Rule and a consequence of the intermediate value theorem, there are members of $(a - 2h, a + 2h)$, say t_1 and t_2, such that

(7) $\int_{a-2h}^{a+2h} f = \frac{h}{3} [f(a - 2h) + 4f(a - h) + 2f(a) + 4f(a + h) + f(a + 2h)] - \frac{h^5}{45} f^{(4)}(t_1),$

(8) $\int_{a-2h}^{a+2h} f = \frac{2h}{3} [f(a - 2h) + 4(a) + f(a + 2h)] - \frac{16}{45} h^5 f^{(4)}(t_2),$

In view of the remainder terms of (7) and (8), we consider $16 \times (7) - (8)$; thus we obtain

$$15 \int_{a-2h}^{a+2h} f = \frac{2h}{3} [7f(a - 2h) + 32f(a - h) + 12f(a) + 32f(a + h) + 7f(a + 2h)]$$

$$- \frac{16}{45} h^5 [f^{(4)}(t_1) - f^{(4)}(t_2)].$$

This suggests the following quadrature rule:

$$\int_{a-2h}^{a+2h} f \approx \frac{2h}{45} [7f(a - 2h) + 32f(a - h) + 12f(a) + 32f(a + h) + 7f(a + 2h)].$$

Applying our analytic technique, we find that the error in this approximation is $-(4h^7/14175)[30f^{(6)}(c_1) + 153t^2 f^{(8)}(c_2)]$, where c_1 and c_2 are members of $(a - 2h, a + 2h)$ and $t \in (0, h)$. This completes the development of Theorem 12.2.6.

Here is another quadrature formula which we shall find useful later (see Section 12.6).

THEOREM 12.2.7. Let $(a - h, a + h) \subset \mathscr{D}_{f^{(8)}}$ and let f be continuous on $[a - h, a + h]$; then there are members of $(a - h, a + h)$, say c_1 and c_2, and there is a member of $(0, h)$, say t, such that

$$\int_{a-h}^{a+h} f = 2hf(a) + \frac{h^3}{60} [f^{(2)}(a - h) + 18f^{(2)}(a) + f^{(2)}(a + h)]$$

$$- \frac{h^7}{1008} \left[f^{(6)}(c_1) + \frac{t^2}{75} f^{(8)}(c_2) \right].$$

Development: By Theorem 12.2.3, there is a member of $(a - h, a + h)$, say c, such that

$$\int_{a-h}^{a+h} f = 2hf(a) + \frac{h^3}{3} f^{(2)}(a) + \frac{h^5}{60} f^{(4)}(c)$$

$$\approx 2hf(a) + \frac{h^3}{3} f^{(2)}(a) + \frac{h^3}{60} [f^{(2)}(a+h) + f^{(2)}(a-h) - 2f^{(2)}(a)] \qquad \text{by Th. 12.2.1}$$

$$= 2hf(a) + \frac{h^3}{60} [f^{(2)}(a - h) + 18f^{(2)}(a) + f^{(2)}(a + h)].$$

Thus we have our quadrature rule. Applying our analytic technique, we find that there are members of $(a - h, a + h)$, say c_1 and c_2, and there is a member of $(0, h)$, say t, such that the error in this approximation is $-(h^7/1008)[f^{(6)}(c_1) + (t^2/75)f^{(8)}(c_2)]$. This completes the development of Theorem 12.2.7.

E X E R C I S E S

1. Prove Theorem 12.2.1.

2. Find a real number c such that $c \in (3, 5)$ and $f(3) + f(5) - 2f(4) = f^{(2)}(c)$, given that:
   a. $f = x^2$.
   b. $f = x^3$.
   c. $f = \sin$.

3. Complete the development of the Trapezoid Rule with Remainder.

4. Use the Rectangle Rule with Remainder to compute $\int_0^1 1/(1 + x^2)$ and determine an upper bound on the error:
   a. with 1 interval;
   b. with 2 intervals.

5. Complete the development of Simpson's Rule with Remainder.

6. Complete the development of Theorem 12.2.2.

7. Use Theorem 12.2.2 to compute $\int_0^1 1/(1 + x^2)$ and determine an upper bound on the error:
   a. with 1 interval;
   b. with 2 intervals.

8. Complete the development of Theorem 12.2.4.

9. Compute an upper bound on the error in the following.
   a. Example 1.
   b. Example 2.
   c. Example 3.

10. Prove Theorem 12.2.5.

11. Complete the development of Theorem 12.2.6.

12. Use Theorem 12.2.6 to compute $\int_0^1 1/(1 + x^2)$ and determine an upper bound on the error:
   a. with 1 interval;
   b. with 2 intervals.

13. Complete the development of Theorem 12.2.7.

14. Use Theorem 12.2.7 to approximate the definite integral of Exercise 12.

12.3 Starting Methods

We shall now consider how to obtain, by numerical methods, a particular solution of a first-order differential equation which satisfies a given boundary condition. Ultimately, what we want is a table of values for the function specified by the differential equation with boundary condition. Let f be a function such that $f' = F(x, f)$ and $f(a) = b$. Our immediate goal is to compute $f(a + h)$, where $h > 0$. Any method which will produce $f(a + h)$ in terms of $f(a)$ is said to be a *starting method*. It turns out that there are efficient methods for continuing a table of values for the function f, once we have the first few entries. Such methods are called *continuing methods*. Of course, any starting method is also a continuing method. We now present a useful starting method.

THEOREM 12.3.1.   There is a real number c such that $c \in (a, a + h)$ and $f(a + h) = f(a) + (2h/3)f'(a) + (h^2/6)f^{(2)}(a) + (h/3)f'(a + h) - (h^4/72)f^{(4)}(c)$ provided   that $(a, a + h) \subset \mathcal{D}_{f^{(4)}}$ and that f is continuous on $[a, a + h]$.

Development: We shall base our development on Taylor's Theorem and the Rectangle Rule with Remainder. In view of these results, there are members of $(a, a + h)$, say t_1 and t_2, such that

(1) $$f(a + h) = f(a) + hf'(a) + \frac{h^2}{2} f^{(2)}(a) + \frac{h^3}{6} f^{(3)}(t_1),$$

(2) $$f(a + h) = f(a) + \int_a^{a+h} f' = f(a) + \frac{h}{2}[f'(a) + f'(a + h)] - \frac{h^3}{12} f^{(3)}(t_2).$$

We shall now form the linear combination of (1) and (2) which is dictated by the remainder terms; thus we consider $(1) + 2 \times (2)$. Hence

$$3f(a + h) = 3f(a) + 2hf'(a) + \frac{h^2}{2} f^{(2)}(a) + hf'(a + h) + \frac{h^3}{6} [f^{(3)}(t_1) - f^{(3)}(t_2)].$$

This suggests that

$$f(a + h) \approx f(a) + \frac{2h}{3} f'(a) + \frac{h^2}{6} f^{(2)}(a) + \frac{h}{3} f'(a + h)$$

and that the error in the approximation has the form $(h^4/18)f^{(4)}(c)$, where $c \in (a, a + h)$. Applying our usual analysis, we find that there is a real number c such that $c \in (a, a + h)$ and the error in our approximation is $-(h^4/72)f^{(4)}(c)$. The details are routine and are left as an exercise. This completes our development of Theorem 12.3.1.

We now present an example.

EXAMPLE 1.   Approximate $f(.1)$ given that $f' = x + f$ and that $f(0) = 1$.
Solution: Here, $f^{(2)} = 1 + f' = 1 + x + f$; thus, by Theorem 12.3.1,

$$f(.1) \approx 1 + \frac{2}{3}(.1)[0 + 1] + \frac{.01}{6}[1 + 1] + \frac{.1}{3}[1 + f(.1)]$$

$$= 1.07333 + f(.1)/30;$$

thus $$f(.1) = \frac{30}{29}(1.07\dot{3}3\dot{3}) = \frac{32.2}{29} \approx 1.110345.$$

Note: Here, $f = 2 \exp - x - 1$; thus $f(.1) = 1.110341836\cdots$.

The error in our starting formula has the form $(h^4/72)f^{(4)}(c)$, and so the error varies as the fourth power of h. This suggests strongly that we can improve our accuracy by reducing h; e.g., take $h/2$ and run through the procedure twice, or use a continuing method once $f(a + h/2)$ has been computed. Before carrying out this idea, let us demonstrate that Theorem 12.2.3 provides us with a continuing method. Consider the following illustration.

EXAMPLE 2.   Use Theorem 12.2.3 to compute $f(2.2)$ and $f(2.3)$ to five significant figures, given that $f' = f^2$, $f(2) = 1$, and $f(2.1) = 1.11111$.

Solution: Now, $[f^2]' = 2f^3$; so $[f^2]^{(2)} = 6f^2 \cdot f' = 6f^4$. Thus, by Theorem 12.2.3,

$$f(2.2) = f(2.0) + \int_{2.0}^{2.2} f^2$$

$$\approx 1 + .2f^2(2.1) + .002f^4(2.1)$$

$$= 1 + .2(1.11111^2) + .002(1.11111^4)$$

$$\approx 1.24996.$$

We now compute $f(2.3)$ by this method:

$$f(2.3) = f(2.1) + \int_{2.1}^{2.3} f^2$$

$$\approx 1.11111 + .2f^2(2.2) + .002f^4(2.2)$$

$$= 1.11111 + .2(1.24996^2) + .002(1.24996^4)$$

$$\approx 1.42847.$$

We conclude that $f(2.3) \approx 1.4285$. Notice that the final digit is incorrect since $f(2.3) \approx 1.4286$ to five significant digits. In view of the error term in Theorem 12.2.3, it is clear that we can expect an error of this magnitude since $[f^2]^{(4)} = 120f^6$; also, $f(2.3) \approx 1.4$, and so

$$\frac{.1^5}{60} [f^2]^{(4)}(c) \approx \frac{.1^5}{60} 120(1.4^6) \approx 2(.1^5)7.5 = .00015.$$

In Example 2 the factor "$f^{(2)}(c)$" of the remainder term is quite large and affects the accuracy of the approximation adversely. In the following example, this factor turns out to be small; consequently, we obtain excellent accuracy.

EXAMPLE 3.   Use Theorem 12.2.3 to compute $f(2.2)$ and $f(2.3)$ to six significant digits, given that $f' = 1/f$, $f(2.0) = 4$, and $f(2.1) = 4.02492236$.

Solution: Here, $f^{(2)} = (1/f)' = -f^{-2} \cdot f' = -f^{-3}$; so $f^{(3)} = 3f^{-4} \cdot f' = 3f^{-5}$. Thus, by Theorem 12.2.3,

$$f(2.2) = f(2.0) + \int_{2.0}^{2.2} 1/f \approx 4 + .2/f(2.1) + .001f^{-5}(2.1)$$

$$= 4 + .2/4.02492 + .001/4.02492^5$$

$$\approx 4.04969.$$

So
$$f(2.3) \approx f(2.1) + \int_{2.1}^{2.3} 1/f$$

$$\approx 4.024922 + .2/4.04969 + .001/4.04969^5$$

$$\approx 4.07431.$$

Note: We point out that here $f = \sqrt{2x + 12}$; thus $f(2.2) = \sqrt{16.4} \approx 4.0496914$ and $f(2.3) = \sqrt{16.6} \approx 4.0743098$.

Now we are in a position to use a continuing method to improve our solution of Example 1. We rework that problem as follows.

EXAMPLE 4.   Approximate $f(.1)$, given that $f' = x + f$ and $f(0) = 1$.
Solution: First, we approximate $f(.05)$. Now, by Theorem 12.3.1,

$$f(.05) \approx 1 + \frac{2}{3}(.05) + \frac{.05^2}{3} + \frac{.05}{3}[.05 + f(.05)] = 1.035 + f(.05)/60.$$

Thus $f(.05) = \frac{60}{59}(1.035) \approx 1.05254237$. We now use Theorem 12.2.3 to compute $f(.1)$. By this quadrature formula,

$$f(.1) = f(0) + \int_0^{.1} f'$$

$$\approx 1 + .1f'(.05) + \frac{.05^3}{3} f^{(3)}(.05)$$

$$= 1 + .1[x + f](.05) + \frac{.05^3}{3} [1 + x + f](.05)$$

$$\approx 1 + .1[.05 + 1.05254237] + \frac{.000125}{3}[1 + .05 + 1.05254237]$$

$$\approx 1.110341843.$$

We hasten to point out that the problem of Examples 1 and 4 was specially chosen so that the details offer no particular difficulty; i.e., it is easy to apply Theorem 12.3.1. In general, we shall require a little more mathematics to compute $f(a + h)$ in this way. To see the point, suppose that $f' = F(x, f)$ and that $f(a) = b$; then, by Theorem 12.3.1,

$$f(a + h) \approx f(a) + \frac{2h}{3} f'(a) + \frac{h^2}{6} f^{(2)}(a) + \frac{h}{3} f'(a + h)$$

$$= b + \frac{2h}{3} F(a, b) + \frac{h^2}{6} [F_1(x, f) + F_2(x, f) \cdot f'](a) + \frac{h}{3} F(a + h, f(a + h))$$

$$= b + \frac{2h}{3} F(a, b) + \frac{h^2}{6} [F_1(a, b) + F_2(a, b) \cdot f'(a)] + \frac{h}{3} F(a + h, f(a + h))$$

$$= b + \frac{2h}{3} F(a, b) + \frac{h^2}{6} [F_1(a, b) + F_2(a, b)F(a, b)] + \frac{h}{3} F(a + h, f(a + h)).$$

We cannot compute $f(a + h)$ directly; nonetheless, there is a mathematical technique which gives us $f(a + h)$. Let us consider the abstract situation. Let g be a given function; our purpose is to find a real number t such that $t = g(t)$. Consider the sequence (u_n), where $u_{n+1} = g(u_n)$ whenever $n \in N$, and $u_1 = g(a)$. We point out that $\lim(u_n)$ is the required number t, i.e., $\lim(u_n) = g(\lim(u_n))$. This is easy to see: assume that (u_n) converges; then so does (u_{n+1}). Indeed, $\lim(u_n) = \lim(u_{n+1}) = \lim(g(u_n)) = g(\lim(u_n))$ provided g is continuous. Thus $\lim(u_n)$ is the required number. It remains to establish the conditions under which (u_n) converges. Consider the following theorem.

THEOREM 12.3.2.   Let (u_n) be a sequence such that $u_{n+1} = g(u_n)$ whenever $n \in N$, where g is a function which meets the requirements of the Mean Value Theorem; and suppose that there is a real number K such that $|g'(s_n)| \le K < 1$ whenever s_n is between u_n and u_{n+1}. Then (u_n) converges.

Proof: Let $n \in N$; then $u_{n+1} - u_n = g(u_n) - g(u_{n-1}) = g'(s_n)[u_n - u_{n-1}]$, by the Mean Value Theorem, where s_n is between u_{n-1} and u_n. By assumption, $|g'(s_n)| \le K$; thus $|u_{n+1} - u_n| \le K|u_n - u_{n-1}|$. So

(3) $$|u_{n+1} - u_n| \le K^{n-1}|u_2 - u_1|$$

whenever $n \in N$. Now, let $a_{n+1} = u_{n+1} - u_n$ whenever $n \in N$, and let $a_1 = u_1$. From (3) and the First Comparison Test, it follows that $\Sigma\, a_n$ exists. Let $n \in N$; then

$$u_n = u_1 + (u_2 - u_1) + (u_3 - u_2) + \cdots + (u_n - u_{n-1})$$
$$= a_1 + a_2 + a_3 + \cdots + a_n.$$

But the series $\Sigma\, a_n$ exists iff the sequence $(a_1 + a_2 + \cdots + a_n)$ converges. Since $\Sigma\, a_n$ exists, we conclude that the sequence (u_n) converges. This establishes Theorem 12.3.2.

COROLLARY 12.3.1.   Suppose that g is a function which meets the requirements of the Mean Value Theorem, that $u_{n+1} = g(u_n)$ whenever $n \in N$, and that there is a real number K such that $|g'(s_n)| \le K < 1$ whenever s_n is between u_n and u_{n+1}. Then $\lim(u_n)$ is a zero of $x - g$.

We now illustrate this mathematical technique.

EXAMPLE 5.   Approximate $f(2.1)$, given that $f' = f^2$ and $f(2) = 1$.
Solution: Here, $f^{(2)} = 2f \cdot f' = 2f^3$; thus, by Theorem 12.3.1,

$$f(2.1) \approx f(2) + \frac{2}{3}(.1)f^2(2) + \frac{.1^2}{3}f^3(2) + \frac{.1}{3}f^2(2.1)$$

$$= 1.07 + \frac{.1}{3}f^2(2.1).$$

We want to find t such that $t = 1.07 + (.1/3)t^2$. Referring to Corollary 12.3.1, we see that $g = 1.07 + x^2/30$. Since $g' = x/15$, it follows that (u_n) converges if $0 < u_n < 15$ whenever $n \in N$. Let $u_1 = 1$; then $u_2 = g(u_1) = 1.103$, $u_3 = g(u_2) \approx 1.11057$, $u_4 = g(u_3) \approx 1.111113$, $u_5 = g(u_4) \approx 1.1111524$, $u_6 = g(u_5) \approx 1.11115532$, $u_7 = g(u_6) \approx 1.11115554$. It is evident that $t \approx 1.11116$; so $f(2.1) \approx 1.111$ (we use only four significant figures in view of the remainder term in Theorem 12.3.1).

Note 1:   It is easy to solve the differential equation of this example; indeed, $f = 1/(3 - x)$. Thus $f(2.1) = 1/.9 = 1.\dot{1}$.

Note 2:   The accuracy of our computation can be improved by using the method of Example 4; i.e., first approximate $f(2.05)$ by Theorem 12.3.1, and then use Theorem 12.2.3 to compute $f(2.1)$. We find that $f(2.05) \approx 1.05263$ and that

$$f(2.1) = f(2) + \int_2^{2.1} f' \approx 1 + .1 f^2(2.05) + \frac{.1^3}{4} f^4(2.05) \approx 1.11111.$$

It is clear that any *starting* method is also a *continuing* method; i.e., a starting method can be used to compute a table of values for a function which satisfies a given differential equation with boundary condition. Needless to say, it is advisable to use a machine to do the actual computations. Consider the following example.

EXAMPLE 6.   Write a program for the self-starting continuing method based on Theorems 12.3.1 and 12.2.3. Use this program to obtain a table of values for f, given that $f' = 1/f$ and $f(2) = 3$.

Solution: We present a suitable program (see page 397) and the resulting tables (Tables 12.3.1 and 12.3.2) (see page 398).   First we take $h = .2$, and then we take $h = .1$ (see the comment which precedes Example 9). Note that $f = (2x + 5)^{1/2}$.

We have observed that any starting method is also a continuing method. It is not quite so obvious that a starting method plus a continuing method constitutes another starting method. The fact of the matter is that we require greater accuracy from a starting method than from a continuing method (since the error in the starting values will likely be amplified by the continuing method). Therefore it is desirable that we devise a highly accurate starting method. Unfortunately, the standard starting methods are generally less accurate than the standard continuing methods. We can take advantage of this situation to devise an improved starting method. To be specific, let us consider the problem of computing $f(a + h)$, given $f(a)$ and a differential equation satisfied by f. The idea is to use the given starting method to approximate $f(a + h/n)$ and then to use the given continuing method to approximate in turn $f(a + 2h/n)$, $f(a + 3h/n)$, $\cdots$, $f(a + h)$. Here, n is a natural number which we choose so that the error in computing $f(a + h/n)$ is no greater than the error in computing the other values of f. It is clear that this procedure produces $f(a + h)$ to an accuracy which is better than that of the original starting method and the original continuing method. For this purpose it is helpful, perhaps downright necessary, to use an automatic digital computer.

PROGRAM
FOR
SELF-STARTING CONTINUING METHOD

*FANDK1504

```
      1 FORMAT(1H1,3X,31HSELF-STARTING CONTINUING METHOD/4X,28H(THEOREMS 1
       12.3.1 AND 12.2.3)//12X,8HCOMPUTED,8X,6HACTUAL/4X,1HT,8X,5HVALUE,
       210X,5HVALUE,8X,1HN/)
        PRINT 1
      2 FORMAT(1H ,F6.2,16X,F15.10)
      3 FORMAT(1H ,F6.2,1X,2F15.10,I4)
      4 FORMAT(1H0,F6.2,1X,2F15.10,I4)
      5 FORMAT(4F6.3)
     40 READ 5, T, B, H, FINAL
        AF = F(T) + .00000000005
        PRINT 2, T, AF
        L = 2
        N = 0
        QF = B + H*DF(T,B) + H*H*.5*D2F(T,B)
      8 CF = B + 2.*H*DF(T,B)/3. + H*H*D2F(T,B)/6. + H*DF(T,QF)/3.
        IF (ABSF(CF - QF) - .00000000001)10,10,9
      9 QF = CF
        N = N+1
        GO TO 8
     10 AF = F(T)
        T = T+H
        B1 = CF
        AF = F(T)
        PRINT 3, T, B1, AF, N
        GO TO 21
     11 B = B1
        B1 = CF
        T = T+H
        IF (CF)50,60,60
     50 RCF = CF - .00000000005
        GO TO 61
     60 RCF = CF + .00000000005
     61 AF = F(T)
        IF (AF)70,80,80
     70 RAF = AF - .00000000005
        GO TO 63
     80 RAF = AF + .00000000005
     63 IF (L-5)62,64,64
     62 PRINT  3, T, RCF, RAF
        L = L+1
        GO TO 71
     64 PRINT 4, T, RCF, RAF
        L = 1
     71 IF(T - FINAL)21,20,20
     20 PRINT 1
        IF (SENSE SWITCH 1)40,31
     21 CALL FNS(T,B1,A1,A3)
        CF = B + 2.*H*A1 + H**3*A3/3.
        GO TO 11
     31 CALL EXIT
        END

        FUNCTION F(X)
        F = SQRTF(2.*X + 5.)
        RETURN
        END

        FUNCTION DF(X,F)
        DF = 1./F
        RETURN
        END

        FUNCTION D2F(X,Y)
        D2F = -1./Y**3
        RETURN
        END

        SUBROUTINE FNS(X,F,DF,D3F)
        DF = 1./F
        D2F = -DF**3
        D3F = -3.*DF*DF*D2F
        RETURN
        END
```

Table 12.3.1

SELF-STARTING CONTINUING METHOD
(THEOREMS 12.3.1 AND 12.2.3)

T	COMPUTED VALUE	ACTUAL VALUE	N
2.00		3.0000000000	
2.20	3.0659418009	3.0659419433	3
2.40	3.1304951511	3.1304951685	
2.60	3.1937437235	3.1937438845	
2.80	3.2557640920	3.2557641192	
3.00	3.3166246167	3.3166247904	
3.20	3.3763885708	3.3763886032	
3.40	3.4351126251	3.4351128075	
3.60	3.4928498046	3.4928498393	
3.80	3.5496476814	3.5496478099	
4.00	3.6055512405	3.6055512755	

Table 12.3.2

SELF-STARTING CONTINUING METHOD
(THEOREMS 12.3.1 AND 12.2.3)

T	COMPUTED VALUE	ACTUAL VALUE	N
2.00		3.0000000000	
2.10	3.0331501684	3.0331501776	3
2.20	3.0659419427	3.0659419434	
2.30	3.0983866670	3.0983866770	
2.40	3.1304951674	3.1304951685	
2.50	3.1622776497	3.1622776602	
2.60	3.1937438831	3.1937438845	
2.70	3.2249030883	3.2249030993	
2.80	3.2557641176	3.2557641192	
2.90	3.2863353337	3.2863353450	
3.00	3.3166247885	3.3166247904	
3.10	3.3466400944	3.3466401061	
3.20	3.3763886013	3.3763886032	
3.30	3.4058772612	3.4058772732	
3.40	3.4351128054	3.4351128075	
3.50	3.4641016029	3.4641016151	
3.60	3.4928498372	3.4928498393	
3.70	3.5213633599	3.5213633723	
3.80	3.5496478678	3.5496478699	
3.90	3.5777087514	3.5777087640	
4.00	3.6055512734	3.6055512755	
4.10	3.6331804122	3.6331804249	
4.20	3.6606010415	3.6606010435	
4.30	3.6878177701	3.6878177829	
4.40	3.7148351222	3.7148351242	
4.50	3.7416573739	3.7416573868	
4.60	3.7682887344	3.7682887363	
4.70	3.7947331792	3.7947331922	
4.80	3.8209946331	3.8209946349	
4.90	3.8470767993	3.8470768123	
5.00	3.8729833444	3.8729833462	

EXAMPLE 7. Write a program for the improved starting method based on Theorems 12.3.1 and 12.2.3. Use this program to compute $f(2 + h)$, given that $f' = 1/f$ and $f(2) = 3$. Take $h = 1$, .5, .2, .1, .05.

Solution: We present a suitable program and the resulting tables (Tables 12.3.3–12.3.7).

We can now improve on the self-starting continuing method of Example 6. Obviously, the thing to do is to take advantage of the improved starting method of Example 7. We now rework Example 6 (see Example 8, page 400).

```
                    PROGRAM
                      FOR
                   IMPROVED
                STARTING METHOD
          BASED ON THEOREMS 12.3.1 AND 12.2.3

*FANDK1504

    40 READ 5,T, B, H
     1 FORMAT(1H1,7X,24HIMPROVED STARTING METHOD/6X,28H(THEOREMS 12.3.1 A
       1ND 12.2.3)//12X,8HCOMPUTED,8X,6HACTUAL/4X,1HT,8X,5HVALUE,10X,
       25HVALUE,8X,1HN/)
       PRINT 1
     2 FORMAT(1H ,F6.3,16X,F15.10)
     3 FORMAT(1H ,F6.3,1X,2F15.10,I4)
     5 FORMAT(4F6.3)
       N = 0
       AF = F(T)
       IF (AF)100,101,101
   100 AF = AF - .00000000005
       GO TO 102
   101 AF = AF + .00000000005
   102 PRINT 2, T, AF
       H = .1*H
       QF = B + H*DF(T,B) + H*H*.5*D2F(T,B)
     8 CF = B + 2.*H*DF(T,B)/3. + H*H*D2F(T,B)/6. + H*DF(T,QF)/3.
       IF (ABSF(CF - QF) - .00000000001)10,10,9
     9 QF = CF
       N = N+1
       GO TO 8
    10 T = T+H
       B1 = CF
       AF = F(T)
       PRINT 3, T, B1, AF, N
       DO 62 I = 1,9
       CALL FNS(T,B1,A1,A3)
       CF = B + 2.*H*A1 + H**3*A3/3.
       B = B1
       B1 = CF
       T = T+H
       IF (CF)50,60,60
    50 RCF = CF - .00000000005
       GO TO 61
    60 RCF = CF + .00000000005
    61 AF = F(T)
       IF (AF)70,80,80
    70 RAF = AF - .00000000005
       GO TO 62
    80 RAF = AF + .00000000005
    62 PRINT  3, T, RCF, RAF
       IF (SENSE SWITCH 1)40,31
    31 CALL EXIT
       END


       FUNCTION F(X)
       F = SQRTF(2.*X + 5.)
       RETURN
       END

       FUNCTION DF(X,F)
       DF = 1./F
       RETURN
       END

       FUNCTION D2F(X,Y)
       D2F = -1./Y**3
       RETURN
       END

       SUBROUTINE FNS(X,F,DF,D3F)
       DF = 1./F
       D2F = -DF**3
       D3F = -3.*DF*DF*D2F
       RETURN
       END
```

Table 12.3.3

IMPROVED STARTING METHOD
(THEOREMS 12.3.1 AND 12.2.3)

T	COMPUTED VALUE	ACTUAL VALUE	N
2.000		3.0000000000	
2.100	3.0331501684	3.0331501776	3
2.200	3.0659419427	3.0659419434	
2.300	3.0983866670	3.0983866770	
2.400	3.1304951674	3.1304951685	
2.500	3.1622776497	3.1622776602	
2.600	3.1937438831	3.1937438845	
2.700	3.2249030883	3.2249030993	
2.800	3.2557641176	3.2557641192	
2.900	3.2863353337	3.2863353450	
3.000	3.3166247885	3.3166247904	

Table 12.3.4

IMPROVED STARTING METHOD
(THEOREMS 12.3.1 AND 12.2.3)

T	COMPUTED VALUE	ACTUAL VALUE	N
2.000		3.0000000000	
2.050	3.0166206252	3.0166206257	2
2.100	3.0331501776	3.0331501776	
2.150	3.0495901358	3.0495901364	
2.200	3.0659419433	3.0659419434	
2.250	3.0822070009	3.0822070015	
2.300	3.0983866769	3.0983866770	
2.350	3.1144822998	3.1144823005	
2.400	3.1304951684	3.1304951685	
2.450	3.1464265438	3.1464265445	
2.500	3.1622776601	3.1622776602	

Table 12.3.5

IMPROVED STARTING METHOD
(THEOREMS 12.3.1 AND 12.2.3)

T	COMPUTED VALUE	ACTUAL VALUE	N
2.000		3.0000000000	
2.020	3.0066592756	3.0066592756	2
2.040	3.0133038347	3.0133038347	
2.060	3.0199337741	3.0199337741	
2.080	3.0265491901	3.0265491901	
2.100	3.0331501776	3.0331501776	
2.120	3.0397368307	3.0397368307	
2.140	3.0463092423	3.0463092423	
2.160	3.0528675045	3.0528675045	
2.180	3.0594117081	3.0594117082	
2.200	3.0659419434	3.0659419434	

Table 12.3.6

IMPROVED STARTING METHOD
(THEOREMS 12.3.1 AND 12.2.3)

T	COMPUTED VALUE	ACTUAL VALUE	N
2.000		3.0000000000	
2.010	3.0033314835	3.0033314835	1
2.020	3.0066592757	3.0066592757	
2.030	3.0099833887	3.0099833887	
2.040	3.0133038347	3.0133038347	
2.050	3.0166206258	3.0166206258	
2.060	3.0199337741	3.0199337741	
2.070	3.0232432916	3.0232432916	
2.080	3.0265491901	3.0265491901	
2.090	3.0298514815	3.0298514815	
2.100	3.0331501776	3.0331501776	

Table 12.3.7

IMPROVED STARTING METHOD
(THEOREMS 12.3.1 AND 12.2.3)

T	COMPUTED VALUE	ACTUAL VALUE	N
2.000		3.0000000000	
2.005	3.0016662039	3.0016662039	1
2.010	3.0033314835	3.0033314835	
2.015	3.0049958403	3.0049958403	
2.020	3.0066592757	3.0066592757	
2.025	3.0083217913	3.0083217913	
2.030	3.0099833887	3.0099833887	
2.035	3.0116440693	3.0116440693	
2.040	3.0133038347	3.0133038347	
2.045	3.0149626863	3.0149626863	
2.050	3.0166206258	3.0166206258	

EXAMPLE 8.   Program a computer to produce a table of values for f, given that $f' = 1/f$ and $f(2) = 3$.

Solution: We present a program and the resulting table (Table 12.3.8).

In the preceding examples we have tabulated the actual values of the function so that the accuracy of the computed values is evident. In a genuine problem we cannot check on the accuracy of our computations in this easy way. Naturally, we need an estimate of the accuracy of our work. One common method of testing the results of a computation

```
                    PROGRAM
                      FOR
                   IMPROVED
          SELF-STARTING CONTINUING METHOD

*FANDK1504

    40 READ 5, T, B, H, FINAL
     1 FORMAT(1H1,40HIMPROVED SELF-STARTING CONTINUING METHOD/6X,
      128H(THEOREMS I2.3.1 AND I2.2.3)//12X,8HCOMPUTED,8X,6HACTUAL/
      24X,1HT,8X,5HVALUE,10X,5HVALUE/)
       PRINT 1
     2 FORMAT(1H ,F6.2,16X,F15.10)
     3 FORMAT(1H ,F6.2,1X,2F15.10)
     4 FORMAT(1H0,F6.2,1X,2F15.10)
     5 FORMAT(4F6.3)
       AF = F(T) + .00000000005
       PRINT 2, T, AF
       L = 1
       H = .1*H
       QF = B + H*DF(T,B) + H*H*.5*D2F(T,B)
     8 CF = B + 2.*H*DF(T,B)/3. + H*H*D2F(T,B)/6. + H*DF(T,QF)/3.
       IF (ABSF(CF - QF) - .00000000001)10,10,9
     9 QF = CF
       GO TO 8
    10 T = T+H
       B1 = CF
       BB = B
       DO 19 I = 1,9
       CALL FNS(T,B1,A1,A3)
       CF = B + 2.*H*A1 + H**3*A3/3.
       B = B1
       B1 = CF
    19 T = T+H
       B = BB
       H = 10.*H
    90 IF (CF)50,60,60
    50 RCF = CF - .00000000005
       GO TO 61
    60 RCF = CF + .00000000005
    61 AF = F(T)
       IF (AF)70,80,80
    70 RAF = AF - .00000000005
       GO TO 63
    80 RAF = AF + .00000000005
    63 IF (L-5)62,64,64
    62 PRINT   3, T, RCF, RAF
       L = L+1
       GO TO 71
    64 PRINT 4, T, RCF, RAF
       L = 1
    71 IF(T - FINAL)21,20,20
    20 IF (SENSE SWITCH 1)40,31
    21 CALL FNS(T,B1,A1,A3)
       CF = B + 2.*H*A1 + H**3*A3/3.
       T = T+H
       B = B1
       B1 = CF
       GO TO 90
    31 CALL EXIT
       END

       FUNCTION F(X)
       F = SQRTF(2.*X + 5.)
       RETURN
       END

       FUNCTION DF(X,F)
       DF = 1./F
       RETURN
       END

       FUNCTION D2F(X,Y)
       D2F = -1./Y**3
       RETURN
       END

       SUBROUTINE FNS(X,F,DF,D3F)
       DF = 1./F
       D2F = -DF**3
       D3F = -3.*DF*DF*D2F
       RETURN
       END
```

Table 12.3.8

IMPROVED SELF-STARTING CONTINUING METHOD
(THEOREMS 12.3.1 AND 12.2.3)

T	COMPUTED VALUE	ACTUAL VALUE
2.00		3.0000000000
2.10	3.0331501776	3.0331501776
2.20	3.0659419425	3.0659419434
2.30	3.0983866763	3.0983866770
2.40	3.1304951670	3.1304951685
2.50	3.1622776589	3.1622776602
2.60	3.1937438826	3.1937438845
2.70	3.2249030976	3.2249030993
2.80	3.2557641168	3.2557641192
2.90	3.2863353429	3.2863353450
3.00	3.3166247876	3.3166247904
3.10	3.3466401037	3.3466401061
3.20	3.3763886002	3.3763886032
3.30	3.4058772705	3.4058772732
3.40	3.4351128042	3.4351128075
3.50	3.4641016122	3.4641016151
3.60	3.4928498358	3.4928498393
3.70	3.5213633693	3.5213633723
3.80	3.5496478662	3.5496478699
3.90	3.5777087608	3.5777087640
4.00	3.6055512717	3.6055512755
4.10	3.6331804216	3.6331804249
4.20	3.6606010397	3.6606010435
4.30	3.6878177795	3.6878177829
4.40	3.7148351202	3.7148351242
4.50	3.7416573833	3.7416573868
4.60	3.7682887322	3.7682887363
4.70	3.7947331887	3.7947331922
4.80	3.8209946306	3.8209946349
4.90	3.8470768087	3.8470768123
5.00	3.8729833421	3.8729833462

is to repeat the computation using $h/2$ in place of h. If the resulting table agrees with the original table to t decimal places, then we certainly have accuracy to t decimal places in the new table. We now illustrate this idea.

EXAMPLE 9.   Produce a table for f between 2 and 3 which is accurate to five significant figures, given that $f' = x^2 f + xf^2$ and $f(2) = -2$.

Solution: We shall use our improved self-starting continuing method. Here $f^{(2)} = 2xf + f^2 + (x^2 + 2xf) \cdot f'$ and $f^{(3)} = 2f + 2(2x + 2f + xf') \cdot f' + (x^2 + 2xf) \cdot f^{(2)}$. We now display a suitable program and the tables obtained by taking $h = .1, .05, .02, .01$, and $.005$ (Tables 12.3.9–12.3.13). Comparing the entries in Tables 12.3.12 and 12.3.13, we see that these tables are accurate to at least six significant figures.

In Sections 12.5 and 12.6 we shall develop efficient continuing methods which produce an estimate of the error as the computation proceeds. In Section 12.4 we shall present another widely used starting method which is sometimes used as a continuing method (this practice is *not* recommended).

```
   40 READ 5, T, B, H, FINAL
    1 FORMAT(1H1,40HIMPROVED SELF-STARTING CONTINUING METHOD/6X,
      128H(THEOREMS 12.3.1 AND 12.2.3)//12X,8HCOMPUTED/
      24X,1HT,8X,5HVALUE/)
      PRINT 1
    2 FORMAT(1H ,F6.3,F16.10)
      PRINT 2, T, B
      L = 1
    3 FORMAT(1H ,F6.3,F16.10)
    4 FORMAT(1H0,F6.3,F16.10)
    5 FORMAT(4F6.3)
      H = .1*H
      QF = B + H*DF(T,B) + H*H*.5*D2F(T,B)
    8 CF = B + 2.*H*DF(T,B)/3. + H*H*D2F(T,B)/6. + H*DF(T,QF)/3.
      IF (ABSF(CF - QF) - .00000000001)10,10,9
    9 QF = CF
      GO TO 8
   10 T = T+H
      B1 = CF
      BB = B
      DO 19 I = 1,9
      CALL FNS(T,B1,A1,A3)
      CF = B + 2.*H*A1 + H**3*A3/3.
      B = B1
      B1 = CF
   19 T = T+H
      B = BB
      H = 10.*H
   90 IF (CF)50,60,60
   50 RCF = CF - .00000000005
      GO TO 63
   60 RCF = CF + .00000000005
   63 IF (L-5)62,64,64
   62 PRINT 3, T, RCF
      L = L+1
      GO TO 71
   64 PRINT 4, T, RCF
      L = 1
   71 IF(T - FINAL)21,20,20
   20 IF (SENSE SWITCH 1)40,31
   21 CALL FNS(T,B1,A1,A3)
      CF = B + 2.*H*A1 + H**3*A3/3.
      T = T+H
      B = B1
      B1 = CF
      GO TO 90
   31 CALL EXIT
      END

      FUNCTION DF(X,Y)
      DF = X*X*Y + X*Y*Y
      RETURN
      END

      FUNCTION D2F(X,Y)
      D2F = 2.*X*Y + Y*Y + (X*X + 2.*X*Y)*DF(X,Y)
      RETURN
      END

      SUBROUTINE FNS(X,F,DF,D3F)
      DF = X*X*F + X*F*F
      D2F = 2.*X*F + F*F + (X*X + 2.*X*F)*DF
      D3F = 2.*F + 2.*DF*(2.*X + 2.*F + X*DF) + (X*X + 2.*X*F)*D2F
      RETURN
      END
```

Table 12.3.9

Table 12.3.10

IMPROVED SELF-STARTING CONTINUING METHOD
(THEOREMS 12.3.1 AND 12.2.3)

IMPROVED SELF-STARTING CONTINUING METHOD
(THEOREMS 12.3.1 AND 12.2.3)

T	COMPUTED VALUE
2.000	-2.0000000000
2.100	-2.0182297613
2.200	-2.0664697864
2.300	-2.1374107741
2.400	-2.2244750304
2.500	-2.3232868316
2.600	-2.4285162677
2.700	-2.5389391796
2.800	-2.6486949750
2.900	-2.7630759801
3.000	-2.8677523225

T	COMPUTED VALUE	T	COMPUTED VALUE
2.000	-2.0000000000	2.500	-2.3230851412
2.050	-2.0047683688	2.550	-2.3753236261
2.100	-2.0181736724	2.600	-2.4287537794
2.150	-2.0390924515	2.650	-2.4833476054
2.200	-2.0664844789	2.700	-2.5383304185
2.250	-2.0995132606	2.750	-2.5940717515
2.300	-2.1373197534	2.800	-2.6495040828
2.350	-2.1792526654	2.850	-2.7056752657
2.400	-2.2245517251	2.900	-2.7607603071
2.450	-2.2727304135	2.950	-2.8171357615
		3.000	-2.8711566540

Table 12.3.11

IMPROVED SELF-STARTING CONTINUING METHOD
(THEOREMS 12.3.1 AND 12.2.3)

T	COMPUTED VALUE	T	COMPUTED VALUE
2.000	-2.0000000000	2.500	-2.3231140495
2.020	-2.0007847378	2.520	-2.3437928735
2.040	-2.0030767942	2.540	-2.3647344015
2.060	-2.0067923454	2.560	-2.3858928300
2.080	-2.0118494807	2.580	-2.4072631488
2.100	-2.0181756520	2.600	-2.4287979581
2.120	-2.0256981597	2.620	-2.4505006237
2.140	-2.0343532329	2.640	-2.4723207068
2.160	-2.0440751205	2.660	-2.4942715336
2.180	-2.0548070284	2.680	-2.5162976374
2.200	-2.0664884732	2.700	-2.5384244186
2.220	-2.0790683811	2.720	-2.5605886546
2.240	-2.0924902975	2.740	-2.5828306956
2.260	-2.1067080438	2.760	-2.6050758250
2.280	-2.1216682876	2.780	-2.6273833178
2.300	-2.1373292683	2.800	-2.6496618261
2.320	-2.1536401126	2.820	-2.6719951132
2.340	-2.1705632841	2.840	-2.6942680977
2.360	-2.1880498701	2.860	-2.7165968911
2.380	-2.2060665974	2.880	-2.7388327795
2.400	-2.2245661089	2.900	-2.7611354155
2.420	-2.2435196303	2.920	-2.7833085238
2.440	-2.2628809772	2.940	-2.8055713517
2.460	-2.2826262819	2.960	-2.8276602618
2.480	-2.3027101031	2.980	-2.8498772860
		3.000	-2.8718629830

404

Table 12.3.12

IMPROVED SELF-STARTING CONTINUING METHOD
(THEOREMS 12.3.1 AND 12.2.3)

T	COMPUTED VALUE	T	COMPUTED VALUE	T	COMPUTED VALUE
2.000	-2.0000000000	2.340	-2.1705622314	2.670	-2.5052747694
2.010	-2.0001980730	2.350	-2.1792383889	2.680	-2.5163024917
2.020	-2.0007843075	2.360	-2.1880506587	2.690	-2.5273526071
2.030	-2.0017476085	2.370	-2.1969949633	2.700	-2.5384172723
2.040	-2.0030768395	2.380	-2.2060653475	2.710	-2.5495008716
2.050	-2.0047617324	2.390	-2.2152580136	2.720	-2.5605949302
2.060	-2.0067918854	2.400	-2.2245670871	2.730	-2.5717046610
2.070	-2.0091577557	2.410	-2.2339890609	2.740	-2.5828214249
2.080	-2.0118495786	2.420	-2.2435181291	2.750	-2.5939511942
2.090	-2.0148584490	2.430	-2.2531510890	2.760	-2.6050840101
2.100	-2.0181751552	2.440	-2.2628821902	2.770	-2.6162277562
2.110	-2.0217913554	2.450	-2.2727085502	2.780	-2.6273711778
2.120	-2.0256983177	2.460	-2.2826244594	2.790	-2.6385236509
2.130	-2.0298882007	2.470	-2.2926273746	2.800	-2.6496725998
2.140	-2.0343526894	2.480	-2.3027116104	2.810	-2.6608291201
2.150	-2.0390843889	2.490	-2.3128749839	2.820	-2.6719790643
2.160	-2.0440753472	2.500	-2.3231118144	2.830	-2.6831355004
2.170	-2.0493185713	2.510	-2.3334203039	2.840	-2.6942824121
2.180	-2.0548064254	2.520	-2.3437947539	2.850	-2.7054351481
2.190	-2.0605322810	2.530	-2.3542337781	2.860	-2.7165754694
2.200	-2.0664887789	2.540	-2.3647316336	2.870	-2.7277213742
2.210	-2.0726696251	2.550	-2.3752873767	2.880	-2.7388519810
2.220	-2.0790677023	2.560	-2.3858951886	2.890	-2.7499883783
2.230	-2.0856770271	2.570	-2.3965546032	2.900	-2.7611065423
2.240	-2.0924906949	2.580	-2.4072596886	2.910	-2.7722311811
2.250	-2.0995030144	2.590	-2.4180104956	2.920	-2.7833345326
2.260	-2.1067072687	2.600	-2.4288009357	2.930	-2.7944455597
2.270	-2.1140980450	2.610	-2.4396316219	2.940	-2.8055320488
2.280	-2.1216687928	2.620	-2.4504962576	2.950	-2.8166279825
2.290	-2.1294143690	2.630	-2.4613960698	2.960	-2.8276958408
2.300	-2.1373283709	2.640	-2.4723244935	2.970	-2.8387755476
2.310	-2.1454059202	2.650	-2.4832834294	2.980	-2.8498232489
2.320	-2.1536407463	2.660	-2.4942659735	2.990	-2.8608859231
2.330	-2.1620282343			3.000	-2.8719121434

Table 12.3.13

IMPROVED SELF-STARTING CONTINUING METHOD
(THEOREMS 12.3.1 AND 12.2.3)

T	COMPUTED VALUE	T	COMPUTED VALUE	T	COMPUTED VALUE	T	COMPUTED VALUE
2.000	-2.0000000000	2.250	-2.0995029209	2.500	-2.3231120295	2.750	-2.5939499324
2.005	-2.0000497579	2.255	-2.1030814931	2.505	-2.3282574792	2.755	-2.5995169336
2.010	-2.0001980195	2.260	-2.1067073273	2.510	-2.3334200050	2.760	-2.6050850569
2.015	-2.0004433559	2.265	-2.1103797517	2.515	-2.3385994150	2.765	-2.6106553151
2.020	-2.0007843108	2.270	-2.1140979445	2.520	-2.3437949942	2.770	-2.6162263140
2.025	-2.0012195115	2.275	-2.1178612508	2.525	-2.3490065770	2.775	-2.6217991587
2.030	-2.0017475537	2.280	-2.1216688585	2.530	-2.3542334453	2.780	-2.6273723777
2.035	-2.0023671172	2.285	-2.1255201294	2.535	-2.3594754612	2.785	-2.6329471748
2.040	-2.0030768461	2.290	-2.1294142606	2.540	-2.3647319024	2.790	-2.6385219939
2.045	-2.0038754693	2.295	-2.1333506304	2.545	-2.3700026595	2.795	-2.6440981445
2.050	-2.0047616760	2.300	-2.1373284443	2.550	-2.3752870053	2.800	-2.6496739783
2.055	-2.0057342410	2.305	-2.1413470973	2.555	-2.3805848599	2.805	-2.6552509179
2.060	-2.0067918956	2.310	-2.1454058031	2.560	-2.3858954899	2.810	-2.6608272145
2.065	-2.0079334576	2.315	-2.1495039729	2.565	-2.3912188462	2.815	-2.6664044120
2.070	-2.0091576975	2.320	-2.1536408282	2.570	-2.3965541878	2.820	-2.6719806519
2.075	-2.0104634735	2.325	-2.1578157967	2.575	-2.4019014979	2.825	-2.6775576085
2.080	-2.0118495924	2.330	-2.1620281072	2.580	-2.4072600268	2.830	-2.6831333036
2.085	-2.0133149506	2.335	-2.1662772040	2.585	-2.4126297907	2.835	-2.6887095520
2.090	-2.0148583886	2.340	-2.1705623227	2.590	-2.4180100299	2.840	-2.6942842447
2.095	-2.0164788387	2.345	-2.1748829242	2.595	-2.4234007956	2.845	-2.6998593476
2.100	-2.0181751728	2.350	-2.1792382507	2.600	-2.4288013160	2.850	-2.7054326094
2.105	-2.0199463569	2.355	-2.1836277800	2.605	-2.4342116788	2.855	-2.7110061591
2.110	-2.0217912925	2.360	-2.1880507602	2.610	-2.4396310987	2.860	-2.7165775899
2.115	-2.0237089770	2.365	-2.1925066864	2.615	-2.4450597013	2.865	-2.7221492067
2.120	-2.0256983395	2.370	-2.1969948124	2.620	-2.4504966861	2.870	-2.7277184334
2.125	-2.0277584073	2.375	-2.2015146507	2.625	-2.4559422185	2.875	-2.7332877649
2.130	-2.0298881349	2.380	-2.2060654604	2.630	-2.4613954805	2.880	-2.7388554405
2.135	-2.0320865782	2.385	-2.2106467717	2.635	-2.4668566793	2.885	-2.7444211607
2.140	-2.0343527154	2.390	-2.2152578485	2.640	-2.4723249773	2.890	-2.7499849632
2.145	-2.0366856291	2.395	-2.2198982393	2.645	-2.4778006254	2.895	-2.7555487709
2.150	-2.0390843199	2.400	-2.2245672126	2.650	-2.4832827642	2.900	-2.7611094022
2.155	-2.0415478956	2.405	-2.2292643351	2.655	-2.4887716906	2.905	-2.7666700205
2.160	-2.0440753778	2.410	-2.2339888797	2.660	-2.4942665207	2.910	-2.7722272055
2.165	-2.0466658985	2.415	-2.2387404321	2.665	-2.4997675998	2.915	-2.7777843810
2.170	-2.0493184985	2.420	-2.2435182687	2.670	-2.5052740169	2.920	-2.7833378661
2.175	-2.0520323329	2.425	-2.2483219947	2.675	-2.5107861680	2.925	-2.7888913684
2.180	-2.0548064608	2.430	-2.2531508898	2.680	-2.5163031120	2.930	-2.7944409200
2.185	-2.0576400591	2.435	-2.2580045792	2.685	-2.5218252988	2.935	-2.7999905385
2.190	-2.0605322040	2.440	-2.2628823455	2.690	-2.5273517538	2.940	-2.8055359441
2.195	-2.0634820935	2.445	-2.2677838342	2.695	-2.5328829837	2.945	-2.8110814894
2.200	-2.0664888195	2.450	-2.2727083305	2.700	-2.5384179770	2.950	-2.8166225543
2.205	-2.0695516006	2.455	-2.2776555009	2.705	-2.5439573003	2.955	-2.8221638564
2.210	-2.0726695432	2.460	-2.2826246323	2.710	-2.5494999018	2.960	-2.8277004039
2.215	-2.0758418857	2.465	-2.2876154132	2.715	-2.5550464113	2.965	-2.8332373113
2.220	-2.0790677485	2.470	-2.2926271318	2.720	-2.5605957325	2.970	-2.8387691810
2.225	-2.0823463887	2.475	-2.2976594987	2.725	-2.5661485626	2.975	-2.8443015604
2.230	-2.0856769398	2.480	-2.3027118031	2.730	-2.5717037560	2.980	-2.8498286076
2.235	-2.0890586773	2.485	-2.3077837787	2.735	-2.5772620818	2.985	-2.8553563423
2.240	-2.0924907471	2.490	-2.3128747147	2.740	-2.5828223403	2.990	-2.8608784370
2.245	-2.0959724425	2.495	-2.3179843688	2.745	-2.5883853767	2.995	-2.8664014267
						3.000	-2.8719184524

E X E R C I S E S

1. Complete the development of Theorem 12.3.1.

2. Use Theorem 12.3.1 to approximate $f(.01)$, given that $f' = -2xf$ and $f(0) = 1$.

(Answer: .99996)

3. Use the self-starting continuing method of Example 6 to obtain a table of values of f between 0 and .3, given that $f' = -2xf$ and $f(0) = 1$. Take $h = .01$.

(Answer: $f(.3) = .9139251787$)

4. Use the improved starting method of Example 7 to compute $f(.1)$, given that $f = -2xf$ and $f(0) = 1$.   *(Answer: .9900491672)*

5. Use the improved self-starting continuing method of Example 8 to produce a table of values of f between 0 and 1, given that $f' = -2xf$ and $f(0) = 1$. Take $h = .05$.

(Answer: $f(1) = .3678799856$)

6. Use the method of Example 9 to produce a table of values of f between 2 and 3, given that $f' = x^2f - 2f^2$ and $f(2) = 1$.

12.4   Runge-Kutta Method

We now introduce the famous Runge-Kutta method. This is a widely used starting method which is sometimes used as a continuing method. There are a number of variations of this method. Let us begin by presenting the method in its simplest form. Throughout this section we shall consider the differential equation $f' = F(x, f)$ and the boundary condition $f(a) = b$.

RUNGE-KUTTA SECOND-ORDER FORMULA. $f(a + h) \approx f(a) + (u_1 + u_2)/2$,
where $u_1 = hF(a, b)$ and $u_2 = hF(a + h, b + u_1)$.

Development: The idea is to approximate the first three terms of the Taylor series for f without actually computing the derivatives involved. Let α and β be real numbers such that a linear combination of $u_1 = hF(a, b)$ and $u_2 = hF(a + \alpha h, b + \beta u_1)$ agrees with the Taylor series for f up to the first three powers of h. Recall that $f^{(2)} = F_1(x, f) + f' \cdot F_2(x, f)$ since $f' = F(x, f)$. Now,

$$s_1 u_1 + s_2 u_2 = b + s_1 hf'(a) + s_2 hF(a + \alpha h, b + \beta u_1)$$
$$\approx b + s_1 hf'(a) + s_2 h[F + \alpha hF_1 + \beta u_1 F_2](a, b)$$
$$= b + h[s_1 f'(a) + s_2 f'(a)] + s_2 h^2 [\alpha F_1 + \beta F \cdot F_2](a, b).$$

Notice that we shall obtain the first three terms of the Taylor's series for f by setting $s_1 + s_2 = 1$ and $\alpha = \beta = 1$. Thus we have the Runge-Kutta second-order formula. We now state the Runge-Kutta third- and fourth-order formulas.

RUNGE-KUTTA THIRD-ORDER FORMULA. $f(a + h) \approx f(a) + (v_1 + 4v_2 + v_3)/6$, where $v_1 = hF(a, b)$, $v_2 = hF(a + h/2, b + v_1/2)$, $v_3 = hF(a + h, b + 2v_2 - v_1)$.

RUNGE-KUTTA FOURTH-ORDER FORMULA. $f(a + h) \approx f(a) + (w_1 + 2w_2 + 2w_3 + w_4)/6$, where $w_1 = hF(a, b)$, $w_2 = Fh(a + h/2, b + w_1/2)$, $w_3 = hF(a + h/2, b + w_2/2)$, and $w_4 = hF(a + h, b + w_3)$.

A marked disadvantage of this method is the lack of an expression for the error. This means that, in order to estimate our accuracy, we must rely on repeating our computations with half the step size*.

On the basis of its derivation, one would judge that the fourth-order Runge-Kutta formula is the most accurate of the formulas listed here. We now illustrate this formula.

EXAMPLE 1.   Approximate $f(.1)$, given that $f' = x + f$ and $f(0) = 1$.
Solution: Here, $F = X + Y$, $a = 0$, and $b = 1$; thus

$$w_1 = .1(0 + 1) = .1,$$

$$w_2 = .1(.05 + 1.05) = .11,$$

$$w_3 = .1(.05 + 1.055) = .1105,$$

$$w_4 = .1(.1 + 1.1105) = .12105.$$

Thus $f(.1) \approx 1 + (.1 + .22 + .221 + .12105)/6 = 1.1103416$.

EXAMPLE 2.   Approximate $f(2.1)$, given that $f' = f^2$ and $f(2) = 1$.
Solution: Here, $F = Y^2$, $a = 2$, and $b = 1$; thus

$$w_1 = .1(1) = .1,$$

$$w_2 = .1(1.05^2) = .11025,$$

$$w_3 = .1(1.055125^2) \approx .1113289,$$

$$w_4 = .1(1.1113289^2) \approx .1235052.$$

Hence $f(2.1) \approx 1 + (.1 + .2205 + .2226578 + .1235052)/6 = 1.1111105$.

We now illustrate the fact that any *starting* method can be used as a *continuing* method.

EXAMPLE 3.   Use the Runge-Kutta method to compute $f(2.2)$ and $f(2.3)$ to five significant figures, given that $f' = f^2$ and $f(2) = 1$.

---

* The following books contain discussions of this method which may be helpful: Morris Tenenbaum and Harry Pollard, *Ordinary Differential Equations*, New York, Harper & Row, 1963; Garrett Birkhoff and Gian-Carlo Rota, *Ordinary Differential Equations*, Boston, Ginn and Company, 1962; L. Fox, *Numerical Solution of Ordinary and Partial Differential Equations*, Oxford, Pergamon Press, 1962.

Solution: We note that, by Example 5, $f(2.1) = 1.11111$ to six significant digits. Let us compute $f(2.2)$; now,

$$w_1 = .1(1.11111^2) \approx .123457,$$

$$w_2 = .1(1.172838^2) \approx .137555,$$

$$w_3 = .1(1.179889^2) \approx .139214,$$

$$w_4 = .1(1.250324^2) \approx .156331.$$

Thus $f(2.2) \approx 1.11111 + .833325/6 \approx 1.249998$; hence $f(2.2) \approx 1.25$ to five significant digits. Now we can compute $f(2.3)$; this time,

$$w_1 = .1(1.25^2) = .15625,$$

$$w_2 = .1(1.328125^2) \approx .176392,$$

$$w_3 = .1(1.338196^2) \approx .179077,$$

$$w_4 = .1(1.429077^2) \approx .204226.$$

Thus $f(2.3) \approx 1.25 + 1.071414/6 = 1.428569$; hence $f(2.3) \approx 1.4286$ to five significant digits.

Let us compare this method to the continuing method based on Theorem 12.2.3 (see Example 3, Section 12.3).

EXAMPLE 4. Use the Runge-Kutta method to compute $f(2.2)$ and $f(2.3)$ to six significant digits, given that $f' = 1/f$, $f(2.0) = 4$, and $f(2.1) = 4.0249224$.

Solution: We compute $f(2.2)$. Here, $F = 1/Y$, $h = .1$, $a = 2.1$, and $b = 4.0249224$. Thus

$$w_1 = .1/4.0249224 \approx .02484520,$$

$$w_2 = .1/(b + .5w_1) = .1/4.03734524 \approx .02476875,$$

$$w_3 = .1/(b + .5w_2) = .1/4.03730678 \approx .024768987,$$

$$w_4 = .1/(b + w_3) = .1/4.0496914 \approx .02469324.$$

So $f(2.2) \approx 4.0249224 + .1486139/6 \approx 4.0496914$. Next we compute $f(2.3)$; this time $a = 2.2$ and $b = 4.0496914$. Thus

$$w_1 = .1/40496914 \approx .02469324,$$

$$w_2 = .1/(b + .5w_1) = .1/4.06203802 \approx .02461818,$$

$$w_3 = .1/(b + .5w_2) \approx .1/4.06200049 \approx .02461841,$$

$$w_4 = .1/(b + w_3) = .1/4.07430981 \approx .02454403.$$

So $f(2.3) \approx 4.0496914 + .14771045/6 \approx 4.0743098$.

Comment: The accuracy of the Runge-Kutta method, in the case of this example, is highly impressive.

The following example will give us a better idea of the accuracy of this method.

EXAMPLE 5. Use the Runge-Kutta method to compute $f(2.1)$ to six significant digits, given that $f' = 1/f$ and $f(2.0) = 1$.

Solution: We compute $f(2.1)$. Here, $h = .1$, $F = 1/Y$, $a = 2$, and $b = 1$; thus

$$w_1 = .1/1 = .1,$$
$$w_2 = .1/(b + .5w_1) = .1/1.05 = .095238095,$$
$$w_3 = .1/(b + .5w_2) = .1/1.04761905 \approx .095454545,$$
$$w_4 = .1/(b + w_3) \approx .1/1.0954545 \approx .091286307.$$

So $f(2.1) \approx 1 + .57267161/6 \approx 1.09544527$. We note that $f(2.1) = \sqrt{1.2} = 1.09544511 \cdots$.

Let us use an automatic digital computer to explore the potential of the Runge-Kutta method.

EXAMPLE 6.   Program the Runge-Kutta method for a digital computer; compute a table of values for f, given that $f' = 1/f$ and $f(2) = 3$; take $h = .2$ and then take $h = .1$.

Solution: We present a program for the Runge-Kutta method and the tables produced by this program (Tables 12.4.1 and 12.4.2). Note that $f = (2x + 5)^{1/2}$.

```
                    PROGRAM
                       FOR
               RUNGE-KUTTA METHOD

   40 READ 5, T, B, H, FINAL
    1 FORMAT(1H1,9X,18HRUNGE-KUTTA METHOD//4X,1HT,6X,11HRUNGE-KUTTA,6X,
      16HACTUAL/)
      PRINT 1
    2 FORMAT(1H ,F6.2,16X,F15.10)
    3 FORMAT(1H ,F6.2,1X,2F15.10)
    4 FORMAT(1H0,F6.2,1X,2F15.10)
    5 FORMAT(4F6.3)
      AF = F(T) + .0000000005
      PRINT 2, T, AF
      L = 1
   21 W1 = H*DF(T,B)
      W2 = H*DF(T+.5*H,B+.5*W1)
      W3 = H*DF(T+.5*H,B+.5*W2)
      W4 = H*DF(T+H,B+W3)
      CF = B + (W1 + 2.*W2 + 2.*W3 + W4)/6.
      B = CF
      T = T+H
      IF (CF)50,60,60
   50 RCF = CF - .0000000005
      GO TO 61
   60 RCF = CF + .0000000005
   61 AF = F(T)
      IF (AF)70,80,80
   70 RAF = AF - .0000000005
      GO TO 63
   80 RAF = AF + .0000000005
   63 IF (L-5)62,64,64
   62 PRINT   3, T, RCF, RAF
      L = L+1
      GO TO 71
   64 PRINT 4, T, RCF, RAF
      L = 1
   71 IF(T - FINAL)21,20,20
   20 IF (SENSE SWITCH 1)40,31
   31 CALL EXIT
      END

      FUNCTION F(X)
      F = SQRTF(2.*X + 5.)
      RETURN
      END

      FUNCTION DF(X,Y)
      DF = 1./Y
      RETURN
      END
```

Table 12.4.1

RUNGE-KUTTA METHOD

T	RUNGE-KUTTA	ACTUAL
2.00		3.0000000000
2.20	3.0659419437	3.0659419434
2.40	3.1304951691	3.1304951685
2.60	3.1937438853	3.1937438845
2.80	3.2557641202	3.2557641192
3.00	3.3166247914	3.3166247904
3.20	3.3763886044	3.3763886032
3.40	3.4351128087	3.4351128075
3.60	3.4928498407	3.4928498393
3.80	3.5496478713	3.5496478699
4.00	3.6055512769	3.6055512755
4.20	3.6606010450	3.6606010435
4.40	3.7148351257	3.7148351242
4.60	3.7682887378	3.7682887363
4.80	3.8209946365	3.8209946349
5.00	3.8729833478	3.8729833462
5.20	3.9242833757	3.9242833741
5.40	3.9749213845	3.9749213829
5.60	4.0249223611	4.0249223595
5.80	4.0743097591	4.0743097575
6.00	4.1231056272	4.1231056256

Table 12.4.2

RUNGE-KUTTA METHOD

T	RUNGE-KUTTA	ACTUAL
2.00		3.0000000000
2.10	3.0331501776	3.0331501776
2.20	3.0659419434	3.0659419434
2.30	3.0983866770	3.0983866770
2.40	3.1304951685	3.1304951685
2.50	3.1622776602	3.1622776602
2.60	3.1937438846	3.1937438845
2.70	3.2249030994	3.2249030993
2.80	3.2557641193	3.2557641192
2.90	3.2863353451	3.2863353450
3.00	3.3166247904	3.3166247904
3.10	3.3466401062	3.3466401061
3.20	3.3763886033	3.3763886032
3.30	3.4058772733	3.4058772732
3.40	3.4351128075	3.4351128075
3.50	3.4641016152	3.4641016151
3.60	3.4928498394	3.4928498393
3.70	3.5213633724	3.5213633723
3.80	3.5496478699	3.5496478699
3.90	3.5777087641	3.5777087640
4.00	3.6055512756	3.6055512755
4.10	3.6331804250	3.6331804249
4.20	3.6606010436	3.6606010435
4.30	3.6878177830	3.6878177829
4.40	3.7148351243	3.7148351242
4.50	3.7416573869	3.7416573868
4.60	3.7682887364	3.7682887363
4.70	3.7947331923	3.7947331922
4.80	3.8209946350	3.8209946349
4.90	3.8470768124	3.8470768123
5.00	3.8729833463	3.8729833462

E X E R C I S E S

Use the Runge-Kutta fourth-order formula in each of the following.

1. Approximate $f(.1)$, given that $f' = x + f$ and $f(0) = 1$.

2. Approximate $f(2.1)$, given that $f' = f^2$ and $f(2) = 1$.

3. Compute $f(5.1)$, given that $f' = 1/f$ and $f(5) = 3$.

4. Compute a table for f between 2 and 3 which is accurate to six significant figures, given that $f' = x^2 f + x f^2$ and $f(2) = -2$. Use an automatic digital computer.

5. Prepare a table of values for f between 0 and 1, given that $f' = -2xf$ and $f(0) = 1$. Work to ten decimal places.

a. Take $h = .1$.   *(Answer: $f(1) \approx .3678810664$)*
b. Take $h = .05$.   *(Answer: $f(1) \approx .3678795437$)*
c. Take $h = .02$.   *(Answer: $f(1) \approx .3678794438$)*

6. Prepare a table of values for f between 0 and 1, given that $f' = 2x \exp(-f)$ and $f(0) = 0$. Work to ten decimal places.

a. Take $h = .5$.   *(Answer: $f(1) \approx .6937433198$)*
b. Take $h = .2$.   *(Answer: $f(1) \approx .6931570090$)*
c. Take $h = .1$.   *(Answer: $f(1) \approx .6931477078$)*
d. Take $h = .05$.   *(Answer: $f(1) \approx .6931472111$)*

12.5   Milne's Method

The starting methods discussed in Sections 12.3 and 12.4 can be used as continuing methods; it turns out, however, that it is more efficient to continue a numerical solution by applying the quadrature formulas of Section 12.2. For example, suppose that $f(a)$, $f(a + h)$, $f(a + 2h)$, and $f(a + 3h)$ are known; then we can compute $f(a + 4h)$ by applying the quadrature formula contained in Theorem 12.2.2. Indeed,

$$f(a + 4h) = f(a) + \int_a^{a+4h} f'$$

$$= f(a) + \frac{4h}{3} [2f'(a + h) - f'(a + 2h) + 2f'(a + 3h)] + \frac{14}{45} h^5 f^{(5)}(c),$$

where $c \in (a, a + 4h)$. Thus

(P) $$f(a + 4h) \approx f(a) + \frac{4h}{3} [2f'(a + h) - f'(a + 2h) + 2f'(a + 3h)].$$

This approximation can be improved by applying Simpson's Rule:

$$f(a + 4h) = f(a + 2h) + \int_{a+2h}^{a+4h} f'$$

$$= f(a + 2h) + \frac{h}{3} [f'(a + 2h) + 4f'(a + 3h) + f'(a + 4h)] - \frac{h^5}{90} f^{(5)}(t),$$

where $t \in (a + 2h, a + 4h)$. Thus

(C) $f(a + 4h) \approx f(a + 2h) + \dfrac{h}{3} [f'(a + 2h) + 4f'(a + 3h) + f'(a + 4h)]$.

The remainder terms of the two quadrature formulas suggest that Simpson's Rule is about 28 times as accurate as the quadrature formula of Theorem 12.2.2. Notice that the term "$f'(a + 4h)$" which appears in (C) depends upon the number $f(a + 4h)$; this means that to obtain $f(a + 4h)$ we must solve (C) by our recursive procedure based on Corollary 12.3.1. The idea is to get off to a good start by plugging in the approximation to $f(a + 4h)$ given by (P); this makes our recursive procedure more efficient. Notice that in (C) the term $f'(a + 4h)$ is multiplied by $h/3$; thus, if $h/3$ is small (which is usually the case since we choose h), the effect of the error in $f'(a + 4h)$ is reduced.

We now introduce some terminology. Since formula (P) is used to obtain a first estimate of $f(a + 4h)$, this formula is called a *predictor* formula. The resulting estimate is improved by applying formula (C); accordingly, (C) is called a *corrector* formula. Of course, we do not really need a predictor formula, since we can compute $f(a + 4h)$ directly from (C) in view of our recursive technique. Moreover, we can get along without (C) if the accuracy of (P) is sufficient for our purpose. Now, the accuracy of a quadrature formula depends, in part at least, upon the magnitude of h; thus we can get along without (C) by reducing h until we obtain the required accuracy. We pay a severe price for a rather small benefit, since reducing h means that we increase the number of lines in our table; ordinarily, the step size h is kept as large as possible. Summarizing, we shall look upon (C) as our main formula, so that we compute $f(a + 4h)$ by our recursive procedure; we shall use (P) only to help out the recursive computation.

We now illustrate Milne's method.

EXAMPLE 1.   Use Milne's method to compute $f(2.4)$ and $f(2.5)$ to five significant digits, where $f' = f^2$ and $f(2) = 1$.

Solution: We must choose a step size first; let us take $h = .1$. Clearly, we need to compute $f(2.1)$, $f(2.2)$, and $f(2.3)$ by applying a suitable starting method. In Examples 5 and 6 of Section 12.3 we used the Runge-Kutta method to compute these numbers. There, we found that $f(2.1) \approx 1.11111$, $f(2.2) \approx 1.25$, and $f(2.3) \approx 1.42847$. Thus $f'(2.1) \approx 1.23457$, $f'(2.2) \approx 1.5625$, $f'(2.3) \approx 2.04081$. We shall now use (P) to obtain a first approximation to $f(2.4)$:

$$f(2.4) \approx f(2) + \frac{.4}{3} [2f'(2.1) - f'(2.2) + 2f'(2.3)]$$

$$= 1 + \frac{.4}{33} [4.98826] \approx 1.6651.$$

So $f'(2.4) \approx 2.7726$. We shall now improve this result by applying (C):

$$f(2.4) \approx f(2.2) + \frac{.1}{3} [f'(2.2) + 4f'(2.3) + f'(2.4)]$$

$$\approx 1.25 + \frac{.1}{3} [12.4983] = 1.6666.$$

So $f'(2.4) \approx 2.77756$. We apply (C) once more:

$$f(2.4) \approx 1.25 + \frac{.1}{3}(12.5033) \approx 1.66678.$$

We now take 1.6668 as the value of $f(2.4)$; so $f'(2.4) \approx 2.7782$. We are now ready to compute $f(2.5)$. From (P),

$$f(2.5) \approx f(2.1) + \frac{.4}{3}[2f'(2.2) - f'(2.3) + 2f'(2.4)]$$

$$\approx 1.11111 + \frac{.4}{3}[6.6404] \approx 1.9965.$$

So $f'(2.5) \approx 3.9860$. Correcting with (C), we obtain

$$f(2.5) \approx f(2.3) + \frac{.1}{3}[f'(2.3) + 4f'(2.4) + f'(2.5)]$$

$$\approx 1.42857 + \frac{.1}{3}[17.1396) \approx 1.9999.$$

So $f'(2.5) \approx 3.9996$. Applying (C) once again, we find that

$$f(2.5) \approx 1.42857 + \frac{.1}{3}(17.1532) \approx 2.0003.$$

We conclude that $f(2.4) \approx 1.6668$ and that $f(2.5) \approx 2.0003$. Notice that our method has produced four-digit accuracy.

Our goal is to produce a table which lists members of the function characterized by a given differential equation and boundary condition. This means that we must first choose a suitable step size, apply a starting method to compute the first few entries, and then use a continuing method over and over until we have obtained the required table. It must be recognized that the task of computing 10,000 members of a function is quite different from that of computing only one or two members. Indeed, few mortals would care to carry out the former task; luckily, high-speed digital computers are willing and able to do the numerical computations and print the results. This explains our interest in these machines.

Let us consider the source of errors in a machine-produced table. First, there is the error introduced by the approximating formula itself; this is called the *truncation* error. Also, there is the *inherited* error, i.e., the error introduced by using a preceding result. Also, there is the *round-off* error, i.e., the error introduced by rounding off the calculations to a given number of digits. We must maintain some control over these errors. Errors tend to accumulate; moreover, if there are many entries in our table, a small error at each step will result in a large error in the entries near the end of the table. The round-off error is easily handled; merely carry all computations to several more digits than required in the final result. The number of extra digits will depend upon the number of calculations involved.

Now let us see about the truncation error. Let us denote the truncation error of formula (P) by "T_p" and the truncation error of formula (C) by "T_c"; moreover, let "P" denote the value of $f(a + 4h)$ given by (P), and let "C" denote the value of $f(a + 4h)$ obtained by applying our recursive procedure to (C). Then

$$f(a + 4h) = P + T_p;$$
$$f(a + 4h) = C + T_c;$$
thus
$$C - P = T_p - T_c.$$

Now, there are members of $(a, a + 4h)$, say t_1 and t_2, such that

$$T_p = \frac{14}{45} h^5 f^{(5)}(t_1) \quad \text{and} \quad T_c = -\frac{h^5}{90} f^{(5)}(t_2).$$

So

$$C - P = \frac{14}{45} h^5 f^{(5)}(t_1) + \frac{h^5}{90} f^{(5)}(t_2) = \frac{29}{90} h^5 f^{(5)}(t),$$

where t is between t_1 and t_2. Assuming that there is little variation in the values of $f^{(5)}$ over $(a, a + 4h)$, this provides us with an estimate of both truncation errors; $T_p \approx 28(C - P)/29$ and $T_c \approx (P - C)/29$. We shall keep an eye on the truncation error throughout our computations; if this error, in total, is negligible, we keep on; otherwise we reduce the step size h. Moreover, we can improve the accuracy of our procedure by incorporating the truncation error T_c into our corrector formula. Thus we shall add T_c to C, so obtaining a *refined* corrected value for $f(a + 4h)$.
  We now illustrate this refinement.

EXAMPLE 2.   Approximate $f(2.4)$, given that $f' = f^2$, $f(2) = 1$, $f(2.1) = 1.1111111$, $f(2.2) = 1.25$, and $f(2.3) = 1.4285714$.
  Solution: We display the given values of f and the corresponding values of f' in the following table.

t	$f(t)$	$f'(t)$
2.0	1.0	1.0
2.1	1.1111111	1.2345679
2.2	1.25	1.5625
2.3	1.4285714	2.0408163

We shall now compute $f(2.4)$. First, we apply (P):

$$\text{Predictor:} \quad f(2.4) \approx f(2) + \frac{.4}{3} [2f'(2.1) - f'(2.2) + 2f'(2.3)]$$

$$= 1.0 + \frac{.4}{3} [4.9882684) \approx 1.665102;$$

so $f'(2.4) \approx 2.772566$. Next, we use (C):

$$\text{Corrector:} \quad f(2.4) \simeq f(2.2) + \frac{.1}{3}[f'(2.2) + 4f'(2.3) + f'(2.4)]$$

$$= 1.25 + \frac{.1}{3}[12.49833] \approx 1.666611;$$

so $f'(2.4) \approx 2.777592$. Applying (C) again, we find that $f(2.4) \approx 1.666779$; so $f'(2.4) \approx 2.778152$. Applying (C) again, we obtain $f(2.4) \approx 1.666797$. Clearly, another application of (C) will not affect the first seven digits of $f(2.4)$. Here, therefore, $C = 1.666797$ and $P = 1.665102$; so $T_c \approx (P - C)/29 = -.001695/29 \approx -.000058$. Therefore $f(2.4) \approx 1.666797 - .000058 = 1.666739$. Now, the error in a computation of this sort is usually of the order of T_c; therefore we conclude that $f(2.4) \approx 1.6667$.

We now make use of an automatic digital computer to analyse this method.

EXAMPLE 3. Program an automatic digital computer to compute a table of values for f, given that $f' = f^2$, $f(0) = 1/3$, $f(.1) = 1/2.9$, $f(.2) = 1/2.8$, and $f(.3) = 1/2.7$. Take $h = .1$ and continue the table to 2.8. Repeat with $h = .05$.

Solution: We present a program and the resulting tables. In Table 12.5.1 the entries in the column headed "Trunc" provide us with a measure of the error in the corresponding entry under "Modified". It is characteristic of this method that the total error grows as the computation proceeds. This brings out the necessity for keeping in touch with the error at each step. Thus, examining "Trunc", we see that we have five-decimal-place accuracy throughout the first 20 lines of Table 12.5.1; thereafter the accuracy drops off rapidly.

```
                          PROGRAM
                            FUR
                      MILNE'S METHOD

*FANDK1504

      5 FORMAT (2F6.3)
     40 READ 5, H, FINAL
        A1 = F(0.0)
        A2 = F(H)
        A3 = F(2.*H)
        A4 = F(3.*H)
        B1 = DF(0.0,A1)
        B2 = DF(H,A2)
        B3 = DF(2.*H,A3)
        B4 = DF(3.*H,A4)
        T = 0.0
        H1 = H*1.3333333333333
        H2 = H*.3333333333333
      1 FORMAT(1H1,3X,1HT,5X,9HPREDICTED,4X,9HCORRECTED,6X,8HMODIFIED,
       18X,6HACTUAL,6X,7HF PRIME,9X,5HTRUNC,7X,1HN,/)
        PRINT 1
      2 FORMAT (1H0,F5.2,4F14.10,F13.8,F15.10,I5)
      3 FORMAT (1H ,F5.2,42X,F14.10,F13.8)
      4 FORMAT (1H ,F5.2,4F14.10,F13.8,F15.10,I5)
        K = 1
        L = 4
        PRINT 3,T,A1,B1
        T = T + H
        PRINT 3,T,A2,B2
        T = T + H
        PRINT 3,T,A3,B3
        T = T + H
        PRINT 3,T,A4,B4
      6 N = 0
        T = T + H
        IF (T - FINAL)21,20,20
     21 PA = A1 + H1*(2.*B2 - B3 + 2.*B4)
        DA = PA
      7 CA = A3 + H2*(B3 + 4.*B4 + DF(T,DA))
        IF (ABSF(CA-DA) - .0000000005)9,9,8
      8 DA = CA
        N = N+1
        GO TO 7
      9 TRUNC = (PA - CA)/29.
        F4 = CA + TRUNC
        AF = F(T) + .00000000005
        RPA = PA + .00000000005
        RCA = CA + .00000000005
        RTRUNC = TRUNC + .00000000005
        RF = F4 + .00000000005
        RFP = DF(T,F4) + .000000005
        A1 = A2
        A2 = A3
        A3 = A4
        A4 = F4
        B2 = B3
        B3 = B4
        B4 = DF(T,F4)
        IF (L - 5)15,25,25
     25 L = 1
        IF (K - 10)10,70,70
     10 PRINT 2,T,RPA,RCA,RF,AF,RFP,RTRUNC,N
        K = K + 1
        GO TO 6
     70 PRINT 1
        K = 1
        L = 0
     15 PRINT 4,T,RPA,RCA,RF,AF,RFP,RTRUNC,N
        L = L + 1
        GO TO 6
     20 PRINT 50
     50 FORMAT (1H1)
        IF (SENSE SWITCH 1)40,31
     31 CALL EXIT
        END

        FUNCTION F(X)

        F = 1./(3. - X)
        RETURN
        END

        FUNCTION DF(X,Y)

        DF = Y*Y
        RETURN
        END
```

Table 12.5.1

T	PREDICTED	CORRECTED	MODIFIED	ACTUAL	F PRIME	TRUNC	N
0.00				.3333333333	.11111111		
.10				.3448275862	.11890606		
.20				.3571428571	.12755102		
.30				.3703703703	.13717421		
.40	.3846146041	.3846154200	.3846153919	.3846153846	.14792900	-.0000000280	3
.50	.3999990301	.4000000452	.4000000102	.4000000000	.16000001	-.0000000349	3
.60	.4166654490	.4166667318	.4166666876	.4166666667	.17361113	-.0000000441	3
.70	.4347810701	.4347826940	.4347826380	.4347826087	.18903594	-.0000000559	3
.80	.4545434949	.4545455735	.4545455018	.4545454545	.20661161	-.0000000716	3
.90	.4761879491	.4761906352	.4761905426	.4761904762	.22675743	-.0000000925	3
1.00	.4999967059	.5000002206	.5000000994	.5000000000	.25000010	-.0000001211	3
1.10	.5263114370	.5263160912	.5263159307	.5263157895	.27700846	-.0000001604	3
1.20	.5555497263	.5555559788	.5555557632	.5555555556	.30864221	-.0000002155	3
1.30	.5882273629	.5882358888	.5882355948	.5882352941	.34602112	-.0000002939	3
1.40	.6249890250	.6250008543	.6250004464	.6250000000	.39062556	-.0000004078	4
1.50	.6666511858	.6666679098	.6666673331	.6666666667	.44444533	-.0000005766	4
1.60	.7142634082	.7142875670	.7142867339	.7142857143	.51020554	-.0000008330	4
1.70	.7691978428	.7692335933	.7692323605	.7692307692	.59171842	-.0000012327	4
1.80	.8332833766	.8333377697	.8333358941	.8333333333	.69444871	-.0000018755	4
1.90	.9090126767	.9090981158	.9090951696	.9090909091	.82645403	-.0000029461	5
2.00	.9998728928	1.0000122016	1.0000073979	1.0000000000	1.00001480	-.0000048037	5
2.10	1.1108954257	1.1111328143	1.1111246285	1.1111111111	1.23459794	-.0000081857	5
2.20	1.2496144460	1.2500410361	1.2500263261	1.2500000000	1.56256582	-.0000147099	6
2.30	1.4278369408	1.4286551904	1.4286269749	1.4285714286	2.04097503	-.0000282154	7
2.40	1.6651514154	1.6668554246	1.6667966657	1.6666666667	2.77821112	-.0000587588	7
2.50	1.9965351416	2.0004857313	2.0003495041	2.0000000000	4.00139814	-.0001362271	8
2.60	2.4908976887	2.5015082370	2.5011423560	2.5000000000	6.25571308	-.0003658809	10
2.70	3.3041536790	3.3395855819	3.3383637922	3.3333333333	11.14467281	-.0012217897	12
2.80	4.8716538404	5.0435284863	5.0376017744	5.0000000000	25.37743164	-.0059267118	18

Table 12.5.2

T	PREDICTED	CORRECTED	MODIFIED	ACTUAL	F PRIME	TRUNC	N
0.00				.3333333333	.11111111		
.05				.3389830508	.11490950		
.10				.3448275862	.11890606		
.15				.3508771929	.12311480		
.20	.3571428375	.3571428579	.3571428572	.3571428571	.12755102	-.0000000006	1
.25	.3636363418	.3636363645	.3636363637	.3636363636	.13223141	-.0000000007	1
.30	.3703703461	.3703703714	.3703703706	.3703703704	.13717421	-.0000000008	1
.35	.3773584636	.3773584918	.3773584908	.3773584906	.14239943	-.0000000009	1
.40	.3846153545	.3846153860	.3846153849	.3846153846	.14792899	-.0000000010	1
.45	.3921568291	.3921568643	.3921568631	.3921568627	.15378701	-.0000000011	1
.50	.3999999624	.4000000019	.4000000005	.4000000000	.16000000	-.0000000013	2
.55	.4081632231	.4081632675	.4081632659	.4081632653	.16659725	-.0000000014	2
.60	.4166666192	.4166666692	.4166666675	.4166666667	.17361111	-.0000000016	2
.65	.4255318613	.4255319178	.4255319159	.4255319149	.18107741	-.0000000018	2
.70	.4347825482	.4347826121	.4347826099	.4347826087	.18903592	-.0000000021	2
.75	.4444443758	.4444444484	.4444444459	.4444444444	.19753087	-.0000000024	2
.80	.4545453765	.4545454591	.4545454563	.4545454545	.20661157	-.0000000027	2
.85	.4651161901	.4651162844	.4651162811	.4651162791	.21633315	-.0000000032	2
.90	.4761903745	.4761904824	.4761904787	.4761904762	.22675737	-.0000000036	2
.95	.4878047614	.4878048853	.4878048810	.4878048780	.23795360	-.0000000042	2
1.00	.4999998657	.5000000085	.5000000036	.5000000000	.25000000	-.0000000048	2
1.05	.5128203577	.5128205227	.5128205171	.5128205128	.26298488	-.0000000056	2
1.10	.5263156097	.5263158012	.5263157946	.5263157895	.27700832	-.0000000065	2
1.15	.5405403314	.5405405503	.5405405466	.5405405405	.29218408	-.0000000076	2
1.20	.5555553112	.5555555719	.5555555629	.5555555556	.30864198	-.0000000089	2
1.25	.5714282848	.5714285908	.5714285803	.5714285714	.32653062	-.0000000105	2
1.30	.5882349563	.5882353173	.5882353048	.5882352941	.34602077	-.0000000123	2
1.35	.6060602061	.6060606337	.6060606190	.6060606061	.36730947	-.0000000146	2
1.40	.6249995241	.6250000333	.6250000158	.6250000000	.39062502	-.0000000175	2
1.45	.6451607211	.6451613306	.6451613096	.6451612903	.41623312	-.0000000209	2

Table 12.5.2 (*Continued*)

T	PREDICTED	CORRECTED	MODIFIED	ACTUAL	F PRIME	TRUNC	N
1.50	.6666659821	.6666667156	.6666666903	.6666666667	.44444448	-.0000000252	2
1.55	.6896543441	.6896552322	.6896552016	.6896551724	.47562430	-.0000000305	2
1.60	.7142847057	.7142857878	.7142857505	.7142857143	.51020413	-.0000000372	3
1.65	.7407395043	.7407408317	.7407407860	.7407407407	.54869691	-.0000000457	3
1.70	.7692292426	.7692308827	.7692308262	.7692307692	.59171606	-.0000000565	3
1.75	.7999981004	.8000001426	.8000000721	.8000000000	.64000012	-.0000000703	3
1.80	.8333309499	.8333335140	.8333334256	.8333333333	.69444460	-.0000000883	3
1.85	.8695621999	.8695654484	.8695653364	.8695652174	.75614387	-.0000001119	3
1.90	.9090870516	.9090912076	.9090910643	.9090909091	.82644656	-.0000001432	3
1.95	.9523759687	.9523813422	.9523811569	.9523809524	.90702987	-.0000001852	3
2.00	.9999934870	1.0000005154	1.0000002730	1.0000000000	1.00000055	-.0000002423	3
2.05	1.0526229598	1.0526322693	1.0526319483	1.0526315789	1.10803402	-.0000003209	3
2.10	1.1110995461	1.1111120498	1.1111116186	1.1111111111	1.23456903	-.0000004311	4
2.15	1.1764548323	1.1764718855	1.1764712975	1.1764705882	1.38408471	-.0000005879	4
2.20	1.2499781687	1.2500018261	1.2500010104	1.2500000000	1.56250253	-.0000008157	4
2.25	1.3333025081	1.3333359574	1.3333348039	1.3333333333	1.77778170	-.0000011533	4
2.30	1.4285269720	1.4285752883	1.4285736222	1.4285714286	2.04082259	-.0000016660	4
2.35	1.5383958669	1.5384673693	1.5384649037	1.5384615385	2.36687426	-.0000024655	4
2.40	1.6665669653	1.6666757504	1.6666719992	1.6666666667	2.77779555	-.0000037511	5
2.45	1.8180256062	1.8181964859	1.8181905935	1.8181818182	3.30581703	-.0000058923	5
2.50	1.9997460912	2.0000247079	2.0000151004	2.0000000000	4.00006040	-.0000096074	5
2.55	2.2217912287	2.2222660076	2.2222496359	2.2222222222	4.93839344	-.0000163716	6
2.60	2.4992293696	2.5000825492	2.5000531293	2.5000000000	6.25026565	-.0000294199	6
2.65	2.8556745040	2.8573110064	2.8572545753	2.8571428571	8.16390371	-.0000564310	7
2.70	3.3303036774	3.3337116988	3.3335941808	3.3333333333	11.11285016	-.0001175179	8
2.75	3.9930714969	4.0009726888	4.0007002339	4.0000000000	16.00560236	-.0002724548	9
2.80	4.9817972611	5.0030183913	5.0022866282	5.0000000000	25.02287151	-.0007317630	10
2.85	6.6083106409	6.6791745952	6.6767310106	6.6666666667	44.57873699	-.0024435845	13

EXERCISES

Use an automatic digital computer for the following.

1. a. Compute a table of values for f, given that $f' = 2x \exp(-f)$, $f(0) = 0$, $f(.1) = .0099503308$, $f(.2) = .0392207131$, and $f(.3) = .0861776962$. Take $h = .1$ and continue the table to 1.9. Work to ten decimal places.   (*Answer:* $f(1.9) \approx 1.5282269750$)

b. How accurate is this table?   (*Answer:* Six decimal places)

2. a. Compute a table of values for f, given that $f' = -2xf$, $f(0) = 1$, $f(.1) = .9900498337$, $f(.2) = .9607894391$, and $f(.3) = .9139311852$. Take $h = .1$ and continue the table to 2.0. Work to ten decimal places.   (*Answer:* $f(2.0) \approx .0183142316$)

b. How accurate is this table?   (*Answer:* Five decimal places)

3. Prepare a table of values for f, given that $f' = (1 + \tan) \cdot f$, $f(0) = 1$, $f(h) = e^h \cos h$, $f(2h) = e^{2h} \cos 2h$, and $f(3h) = e^{3h} \cos 3h$. Work to ten decimal places.

a. Take $h = .01$; stop at .20.

b. Take $h = .005$; stop at .20.

c. Take $h = .001$; stop at .04.

4. Prepare a table of values for f between 2 and 3 which is accurate to six significant figures, given that $f' = x^2 f + x f^2$ and $f(2) = -2$. Use Milne's method; use any starting method to obtain the required starting values. Comment on the use of the Runge-Kutta method as a continuing method (see Exercise 4, Section 12.4).

12.6   Another Predictor-Corrector Method

If we are willing to use $f^{(3)}$ in our computations, we can improve on Milne's method. The idea is to use the quadrature rule contained in Theorem 12.2.3 for our predictor formula; this means that we shall replace (P) by

$$(P') \qquad f(a+2h) = f(a) + \int_a^{a+2h} f' \approx f(a) + 2hf'(a+h) + \frac{h^3}{3}f^{(3)}(a+h).$$

The error in this approximation is $(h^5/60)f^{(5)}(c)$, where $c \in (a, a+2h)$. Notice that to use (P') we have only to compute one starting value of f; of course, we need two starting values, $f(a)$ and $f(a+h)$, but $f(a)$ is given. So the merit of the predictor formula (P') over (P) is (1) (P') is more accurate than (P) and (2) we must compute just one starting value to use (P'), whereas to use (P) we must compute three starting values.

Let us compare the accuracy of (P') with that of (P) (see Example 2, Section 12.5).

EXAMPLE 1.   Compute $f(2.4)$ to five significant digits, given that $f' = f^2$, $f(2.2) = 1.25$, and $f(2.3) = 1.42857$.

Solution: Here, $f^{(2)} = 2f \cdot f' = 2f^3$ and $f^{(3)} = 6f^2 \cdot f' = 6f^4$; moreover, $f'(2.3) = 2.04081$. Thus, by (P'),

$$f(2.4) = f(2.2) + \int_{2.2}^{2.4} f^2 \approx 1.25 + .2(2.04081) + \frac{.006}{3}(4.16491) \approx 1.66649;$$

thus $f'(2.4) \approx 2.77719$. To improve our accuracy, we apply (C):

$$f(2.4) \approx f(2.2) + \frac{.1}{3}[f'(2.2) + 4f'(2.3) + f'(2.4)]$$

$$= 1.25 + \frac{.1}{3}[12.50293] \approx 1.66676.$$

So $f(2.4) \approx 1.6668$. Notice that applying (C) again will not alter this result (i.e., to five significant digits).

The next step in developing an improved predictor–corrector method is to use the quadrature rule contained in Theorem 12.2.4 in place of Simpson's Rule. Therefore we shall use the formula (C'), which follows, for our corrector formula:

$$(C') \qquad f(a+2h) = f(a) + \int_{a-h}^{a+2h} f' \approx \frac{h}{5}[f'(a) + 8f'(a+h) + f'(a+2h)]$$

$$+ \frac{2}{15}h^3 f^{(3)}(a+h).$$

We point out that the error in (C') is $(-h^7/6300)f^{(7)}(c)$, where $c \in (a, a+2h)$.

EXAMPLE 2.   Use (P') and (C') to compute $f(2.4)$, $f(2.5)$, and $f(2.6)$ to five significant digits, given that $f' = f^2$, $f(2.2) = 1.25$, and $f(2.3) = 1.42857$.

Solution: As in Example 1, $f^{(2)} = 2f^3$ and $f^{(3)} = 6f^4$; also, $f'(2.2) = 1.5625$ and $f'(2.3) =$ 2.04081. First, we compute $f(2.4)$:

$$\text{Predictor:}\quad f(2.4) = f(2.2) + \int_{2.2}^{2.4} f' \approx 1.25 + .2f^2(2.3) + \frac{.006}{3} f^4(2.3)$$

$$\approx 1.25 + .4081624 + .002(4.16491) \approx 1.66649;$$

so $f'(2.4) \approx 2.77719$.

$$\text{Corrector:}\quad f(2.4) = f(2.2) + \int_{2.2}^{2.4} f' \approx 1.25 + \frac{.1}{5} [f'(2.2) + 8f'(2.3) + f'(2.4)]$$

$$+ \frac{2}{15} .001 f^{(3)}(2.3)$$

$$\approx 1.25 + .02[20.66619] + .003332$$

$$= 1.666656;$$

so $f'(2.4) \approx 2.777742$. Applying the corrector formula a second time, we obtain

$$f(2.4) \approx 1.25 + \frac{.1}{5} [20.66674] + .003332 = 1.666667;$$

thus $f'(2.4) \approx 2.777779$. Next, we compute $f(2.5)$:

$$\text{Predictor:}\quad f(2.5) = f(2.3) + \int_{2.3}^{2.5} f' \approx 1.42857 + .2f'(2.4) + \frac{.001}{3} f^{(3)}(2.4)$$

$$\approx 1.42857 + .2(2.777779) + .002(7.7160562)$$

$$\approx 1.999558;$$

so $f'(2.5) \approx 3.998232$.

$$\text{Corrector:}\quad f(2.5) = f(2.3) + \int_{2.3}^{2.5} f'$$

$$\approx 1.42857 + .02[f'(2.3) + 8f'(2.4) + f'(2.5)] + 8(.1^4) f^4(2.4)$$

$$\approx 1.42857 + .02(28.261276) + .0008(7.7160562)$$

$$\approx 1.999968;$$

so $f'(2.5) \approx 3.999872$. Applying the corrector formula again, we obtain $f(2.5) \approx 1.42857 +$ .02(28.262916) + .0008(7.7160562) ≈ 2.000001; so $f'(2.5) \approx 4.000004$. Finally, we compute $f(2.6)$.

$$\text{Predictor:}\quad f(2.6) = f(2.4) + \int_{2.4}^{2.6} f' \approx 1.66667 + .2f^2(2.5) + \frac{.1^3}{3} 6f^4(2.5)$$

$$\approx 2.49867;$$

so $f'(2.6) \approx 6.24335$.

Corrector: $f(2.6) = f(2.4) + \int_{2.4}^{2.6} f'$

$$\approx 1.66667 + .02[f'(2.4) + 8f'(2.5) + f'(2.6)] + \frac{2}{15}(.1)^3 f^{(3)}(2.5)$$

$$\approx 1.66667 + .02(41.02113) + .0128 \approx 2.49989;$$

so $f'(2.6) \approx 6.24945$. Applying the corrector formula once more, we have

$$f(2.6) \approx 1.66667 + .02(41.02723) + .0128 \approx 2.5000.$$

Just as in the case of Milne's method, the next step is to improve the accuracy of our method and at the same time to obtain a measure of the error involved. To this purpose we need a quadrature formula in which the remainder term has the form $Kf^{(7)}(c)$. Luckily, Theorem 12.2.7 fits the bill (indeed, this is why we presented that theorem). Notice that the terms required for the quadrature rule of Theorem 12.2.7 are also needed for (C'); therefore we can easily incorporate this rule into our method. The idea is to obtain two approximations to $f(a + 2h)$, one from (C') and the other from the following quadrature rule:

(D) $f(a + 2h) \approx f(a) + 2hf'(a + h) + \dfrac{h^3}{60}[f^{(3)}(a) + 18f^{(3)}(a + h) + f^{(3)}(a + 2h)].$

The truncation error in (D) is approximately $(-h^7/1008)f^{(7)}(c)$, where $c \in (a, a + 2h)$. Let us denote the truncation error of formula (C') by "T_c", and the truncation error of formula (D) by "T_d"; moreover, let "C" denote the approximation to $f(a + 2h)$ obtained from (C'), and let "D" denote the approximation to $f(a + 2h)$ obtained from (D). Then

$$f(a + 2h) = C + T_c \quad \text{and} \quad f(a + 2h) = D + T_d.$$

Thus $D - C = T_c - T_d = \dfrac{h^7}{1008}f^{(7)}(c_1) - \dfrac{h^7}{6300}f^{(7)}(c_2)$

$\approx h^7 \left[\dfrac{1}{1008} - \dfrac{1}{6300} \right] f^{(7)}(t)$ provided there is little change in the values of $f^{(7)}$ over $(a, a + 2h)$, where $t \in (a, a + 2h)$

$= \dfrac{h^7}{1200}f^{(7)}(t).$

So we have the following approximation to $f^{(7)}(t)$:

$$f^{(7)}(t) \approx 1200h^{-7}[D - C].$$

Thus $T_c = \dfrac{-h^7}{6300} f^{(7)}(c_2) \approx \dfrac{1200}{6300}(C - D) = \dfrac{4}{21}(C - D) \approx .190476(C - D),$

and $T_d = \dfrac{-h^7}{1008} f^{(7)}(c_1) \approx \dfrac{1200}{1008}(C - D) = \dfrac{25}{21}(C - D) \approx 1.190476(C - D).$

We shall keep an eye on the truncation error T_c throughout our computations. If this error, in total, is negligible, we keep on; otherwise we reduce the step size h. Moreover, we can improve the accuracy of our method by incorporating the truncation error T_c into our corrector formula. Thus we shall add T_c to C, thereby obtaining a *refined* corrected value for $f(a + 2h)$. Notice that we do not actually use the truncation error T_d; our only purpose in introducing (D) is to obtain an estimate for $f^{(7)}(t)$ so that we can approximate the truncation error in (C').

We now present a number of examples to illustrate our improved predictor–corrector method. As in the case of Milne's method, we shall take the required starting values as known. In a real situation the one starting value which is not given in the problem is obtained by using a starting method.

EXAMPLE 3.   Write a program for the continuing method of this section. Use an automatic digital computer to compute a table of values for f, given that $f' = f^2$, $f(0) = 1/3$, and $f(h) = 1/(3 - h)$. Take $h = .5, .2, .1,$ and $.05$.

Solution: We present a suitable program and the resulting tables (Tables 12.6.1–12.6.4). Notice that we obtain the same accuracy as Milne's method with three to four times the step size used in Milne's method. Also notice that we have incorporated a round-off subprogram into the main program; this simplifies the task of rounding off our results before printing them.

```
*FANDK1504
      5 FORMAT (2F6.3)
     40 READ 5, H, FINAL
        A1 = F(0.0)
        A2 = F(H)
        CALL FNS(0.0,A1,B1,D1)
        CALL FNS(H,A2,B2,D2)
      1 FORMAT(1H1,29X,35HIMPROVED PREDICTOR-CORRECTOR METHOD//4X,1HT,6X,
       19HPREDICTED,5X,9HCORRECTED,7X,6HACTUAL,10X,2HDF,11X,3HD3F,6X,
       211HTRUNC ERROR,4X,1HN/)
        PRINT 1
      2 FORMAT(1H0,F5.2,F15.10,3F14.10,F12.6,F16.12,I4)
      3 FORMAT(1H ,F5.2,29X,2F14.10,F12.6)
      4 FORMAT(1H ,F5.2,F15.10,3F14.10,F12.6,F16.12,I4)
        K = 1
        L = 2
        T = 0.0
        H3 = H*H*H
        RA1 = RNDOFF(A1,10)
        RB1 = RNDOFF(B1,10)
        RD1 = RNDOFF(D1,6)
        PRINT 3, T, RA1, RB1, RD1
        T = T + H
        RA2 = RNDOFF(A2,10)
        RB2 = RNDOFF(B2,10)
        RD2 = RNDOFF(D2,6)
        PRINT 3, T, RA2, RB2, RD2
      6 N = 0
        T = T + H
        A12HB2 = A1 + 2.*H*B2
        H3D2 = H3*D2
        IF (T - FINAL)21,20,20
     21 PA3 = A12HB2 + H3D2*.3333333333333
        QA = PA3
     17 CALL FNS(T,QA,B3,D3)
        CA3 = A12HB2 + H3*(D1 + 18.*D2 + D3)*.01666666666667
        IF (ABSF(CA3-QA) - .0000000005)19,19,18
     18 QA = CA3
        N = N + 1
        GO TO 17
     19 CALL FNS(T,CA3,B3,D3)
        CF = A1 + .2*H*(B1 + 8.*B2 + B3) + H3D2*.13333333333333
        CALL FNS(T,CF,B3,D3)
        CF = A1 + .2*H*(B1 + 8.*B2 + B3) + H3D2*.13333333333333
        TRUNC1 = (CF - CA3)*.190476
        CF = CF + TRUNC1
        CALL FNS(T,CF,B3,D3)
        A1 = A2
        A2 = CF
        B1 = B2
        B2 = B3
        D1 = D2
        D2 = D3
        AF = F(T)
        RPA3 = RNDOFF(PA3,10)
        RCF = RNDOFF(CF,10)
        RAF = RNDOFF(AF,10)
        RB2 = RNDOFF(B2,10)
        RD2 = RNDOFF(D2,6)
        RTRUNC = RNDOFF(TRUNC1,12)
        IF (L - 5)15,25,25
     25 L = 1
        IF (K - 7)10,70,70
     10 PRINT 2, T, RPA3, RCF, RAF, RB2, RD2, RTRUNC, N
        K = K + 1
        GO TO 6
     70 PRINT 1
        K = 1
        L = 0
     15 PRINT 4, T, RPA3, RCF, RAF, RB2, RD2, RTRUNC, N
        L = L + 1
        GO TO 6
     20 PRINT 50
     50 FORMAT (1H1)
        IF (SENSE SWITCH 1)40,31
     31 CALL EXIT
        END

        FUNCTION F(X)
        F = 1./(3. - X)
        RETURN
        END

        FUNCTION DF(X,Y)
        DF = Y*Y
        RETURN
        END

        SUBROUTINE FNS(X,F,DF,D3F)
        DF = F*F
        D2F = 2.*F**3
        D3F = 6.*F*F*DF
        RETURN
        END

        FUNCTION RNDOFF(T,N)
        IF (T)100,200,300
    100 RNDOFF = T - .5*.1**N
        GO TO 400
    200 RNDOFF = T
        GO TO 400
    300 RNDOFF = T + .5*.1**N
    400 RETURN
        END
```

424

Table 12.6.1

IMPROVED PREDICTOR-CORRECTOR METHOD

T	PREDICTED	CORRECTED	ACTUAL	DF	D3F	TRUNC ERROR	N
0.00			.3333333333	.1111111111	.074074		
.50			.4000000000	.1600000000	.153600		
1.00	.4997333333	.5000006262	.5000000000	.2500006262	.375002	-.000004553588	3
1.50	.6656257044	.6666729553	.6666666667	.4444528293	1.185230	-.000029147225	4
2.00	.9938380348	1.0001247422	1.0000000000	1.0002494999	6.002994	-.000347405476	6
2.50	1.9170472207	2.0212136270	2.0000000000	4.0853045261	100.138278	-.024355359693	29

Table 12.6.2

IMPROVED PREDICTOR-CORRECTOR METHOD

T	PREDICTED	CORRECTED	ACTUAL	DF	D3F	TRUNC ERROR	N
0.00			.3333333333	.1111111111	.074074		
.20			.3571428571	.1275510204	.097616		
.40	.3846140497	.3846153847	.3846153846	.1479289942	.131298	-.000000002736	1
.60	.4166645826	.4166666669	.4166666667	.1736111113	.180845	-.000000004960	1
.80	.4545420823	.4545454551	.4545454545	.2066115708	.256130	-.000000009433	2
1.00	.4999943087	.5000000014	.5000000000	.2500000014	.375000	-.000000018986	2
1.20	.5555454557	.5555555559	.5555555556	.3086419790	.571559	-.000000040878	2
1.40	.6249809509	.6250000088	.6250000000	.3906250109	.915527	-.000000095546	2
1.60	.7142469697	.7142857397	.7142857143	.5102041179	1.561849	-.000000247303	2
1.80	.8332465878	.8333334185	.8333333333	.6944445864	2.893520	-.000000729199	2
2.00	.9997796268	1.0000003497	1.0000000000	1.0000006993	6.000008	-.000002555309	3
2.20	1.2493337206	1.2500019200	1.2500000000	1.5625047999	14.648527	-.000011389266	3
2.40	1.6640650096	1.6666831762	1.6666666667	2.7778328099	46.298131	-.000072863003	4
2.60	2.4845967258	2.5003135039	2.5000000000	6.2515676178	234.492586	-.000868522466	6
2.80	4.7926237862	5.0530414244	5.0000000000	25.5332276371	3911.674281	-.060889057206	30

Table 12.6.3

IMPROVED PREDICTOR-CORRECTOR METHOD

T	PREDICTED	CORRECTED	ACTUAL	DF	D3F	TRUNC ERROR	N
0.00			.3333333333	.1111111111	.074074		
.10			.3448275862	.1189060642	.084832		
.20	.3571428235	.3571428571	.3571428571	.1275510204	.097616	-.000000000016	1
.30	.3703703288	.3703703704	.3703703704	.1371742112	.112901	-.000000000021	1
.40	.3846153329	.3846153846	.3846153846	.1479289941	.131298	-.000000000028	1
.50	.3999999352	.4000000000	.4000000000	.1600000000	.153600	-.000000000038	1
.60	.4166665846	.4166666667	.4166666667	.1736111111	.180845	-.000000000053	1
.70	.4347825039	.4347826087	.4347826087	.1890359168	.214407	-.000000000073	1
.80	.4545453192	.4545454546	.4545454545	.2066115703	.256130	-.000000000102	1
.90	.4761902994	.4761904762	.4761904762	.2267573696	.308513	-.000000000146	1
1.00	.4999997663	.5000000000	.5000000000	.2500000000	.375000	-.000000000212	1
1.10	.5263154762	.5263157895	.5263157895	.2770083103	.460402	-.000000000314	1
1.20	.5555551293	.5555555556	.5555555556	.3086419753	.571559	-.000000000473	1
1.30	.5882347043	.5882352942	.5882352941	.3460207613	.718382	-.000000000729	1
1.40	.6249997686	.6250000001	.6250000000	.3906250001	.915527	-.000000001153	1
1.50	.6666654700	.6666666668	.6666666667	.4444444446	1.185185	-.000000001875	1
1.60	.7142839507	.7142857145	.7142857143	.5102040819	1.561849	-.000000003146	1
1.70	.7692280996	.7692307696	.7692307692	.5917159769	2.100767	-.000000005472	1
1.80	.8333291655	.8333333341	.8333333333	.6944444457	2.893519	-.000000009920	2
1.90	.9090841649	.9090909105	.9090909091	.8264462836	4.098081	-.000000018867	2
2.00	.9999886177	1.0000000031	1.0000000000	1.0000000062	6.000000	-.000000037971	2
2.10	1.1110909118	1.1111111183	1.1111111111	1.2345679171	9.144948	-.000000081756	2
2.20	1.2499619024	1.2500000181	1.2500000000	1.5625000452	14.648438	-.000000191091	2
2.30	1.4284939401	1.4285714801	1.4285714286	2.0408164737	24.989591	-.000000494606	2
2.40	1.6664931766	1.6666668380	1.6666666667	2.7777783489	46.296315	-.000001458397	3
2.50	1.9995592550	2.0000007007	2.0000000000	4.0000028029	96.000135	-.000005110618	3
2.60	2.4986674434	2.5000038421	2.5000000000	6.2500192106	234.376441	-.000022778531	3
2.70	3.3281300231	3.3333663564	3.3333333333	11.1113312657	740.770095	-.000145726008	4
2.80	4.9691934602	5.0006270166	5.0000000000	25.0062705593	3751.881404	-.001737044955	7

Table 12.6.4

IMPROVED PREDICTOR-CORRECTOR METHOD

T	PREDICTED	CORRECTED	ACTUAL	DF	D3F	TRUNC ERROR	N
0.00			.3333333333	.1111111111	.074074		
.05			.3389830508	.1149095088	.079225		
.10	.3448275853	.3448275862	.3448275862	.1189060642	.084832	0.000000000000	1
.15	.3508771919	.3508771930	.3508771930	.1231148046	.090944	0.000000000000	1
.20	.3571428560	.3571428571	.3571428571	.1275510204	.097616	0.000000000000	1
.25	.3636363623	.3636363636	.3636363636	.1322314050	.104911	0.000000000000	1
.30	.3703703689	.3703703704	.3703703704	.1371742112	.112901	0.000000000000	1
.35	.3773584890	.3773584906	.3773584906	.1423994304	.121666	0.000000000000	1
.40	.3846153828	.3846153846	.3846153846	.1479289941	.131298	0.000000000000	1
.45	.3921568607	.3921568627	.3921568627	.1537870050	.141903	0.000000000000	1
.50	.3999999977	.4000000000	.4000000000	.1600000000	.153600	0.000000000000	1
.55	.4081632627	.4081632653	.4081632653	.1665972511	.166528	0.000000000000	1
.60	.4166666638	.4166666667	.4166666667	.1736111111	.180845	0.000000000000	1
.65	.4255319116	.4255319149	.4255319149	.1810774106	.196734	-.000000000001	1
.70	.4347826050	.4347826087	.4347826087	.1890359168	.214407	-.000000000001	1
.75	.4444444402	.4444444444	.4444444444	.1975308642	.234111	-.000000000001	1
.80	.4545454497	.4545454545	.4545454545	.2066115702	.256130	-.000000000001	1
.85	.4651162736	.4651162791	.4651162791	.2163331531	.280800	-.000000000001	1
.90	.4761904699	.4761904762	.4761904762	.2267573696	.308513	-.000000000001	1
.95	.4878048708	.4878048780	.4878048780	.2379535990	.339731	-.000000000002	1
1.00	.4999999916	.5000000000	.5000000000	.2500000000	.375000	-.000000000002	1
1.05	.5128205030	.5128205128	.5128205128	.2629848784	.414966	-.000000000002	1
1.10	.5263157781	.5263157895	.5263157895	.2770083102	.460402	-.000000000003	1
1.15	.5405405272	.5405405405	.5405405405	.2921840760	.512229	-.000000000004	1
1.20	.5555555400	.5555555556	.5555555556	.3086419753	.571559	-.000000000005	1
1.25	.5714285530	.5714285714	.5714285714	.3265306122	.639733	-.000000000006	1
1.30	.5882352723	.5882352941	.5882352941	.3460207612	.718382	-.000000000007	1
1.35	.6060605801	.6060606061	.6060606061	.3673094582	.809497	-.000000000009	1
1.40	.6249999690	.6250000000	.6250000000	.3906250000	.915527	-.000000000011	1
1.45	.6451612530	.6451612903	.6451612903	.4162330905	1.039500	-.000000000015	1
1.50	.6666666216	.6666666667	.6666666667	.4444444444	1.185185	-.000000000019	1
1.55	.6896551175	.6896551724	.6896551724	.4756242568	1.357311	-.000000000024	1
1.60	.7142856473	.7142857143	.7142857143	.5102040816	1.561849	-.000000000032	1
1.65	.7407406576	.7407407407	.7407407407	.5486968450	1.806409	-.000000000042	1
1.70	.7692306658	.7692307692	.7692307692	.5917159763	2.100767	-.000000000057	1
1.75	.7999998703	.8000000000	.8000000000	.6400000000	2.457600	-.000000000077	1
1.80	.8333331692	.8333333333	.8333333333	.6944444445	2.893519	-.000000000105	1
1.85	.8695650077	.8695652174	.8695652174	.7561436673	3.430519	-.000000000146	1
1.90	.9090906384	.9090909091	.9090909091	.8264462810	4.098081	-.000000000205	1
1.95	.9523805989	.9523809524	.9523809524	.9070294785	4.936215	-.000000000292	1
2.00	.9999995326	1.0000000000	1.0000000000	1.0000000000	6.000000	-.000000000424	1
2.05	1.0526309524	1.0526315790	1.0526315789	1.1080332411	7.366426	-.000000000627	1
2.10	1.1111102585	1.1111111112	1.1111111111	1.2345679014	9.144947	-.000000000946	1
2.15	1.1764694086	1.1764705883	1.1764705882	1.3840830452	11.494115	-.000000001459	1
2.20	1.2499983372	1.2500000001	1.2500000000	1.5625000004	14.648438	-.000000002307	1
2.25	1.3333309399	1.3333333336	1.3333333333	1.7777777784	18.962963	-.000000003750	1
2.30	1.4285679014	1.4285714290	1.4285714286	2.0408163278	24.989588	-.000000006292	2
2.35	1.5384561992	1.5384615392	1.5384615385	2.3668639077	33.612269	-.000000010945	2
2.40	1.6666583310	1.6666666681	1.6666666666	2.7777777827	46.296296	-.000000019840	2
2.45	1.8181683299	1.8181818211	1.8181818182	3.3057851346	65.569292	-.000000037734	2
2.50	1.9999772354	2.0000000062	2.0000000000	4.0000000249	96.000001	-.000000075942	2
2.55	2.2221818236	2.2222222365	2.2222222222	4.9382716685	146.319162	-.000000163513	2
2.60	2.4999238048	2.5000000362	2.5000000000	6.2500001808	234.375014	-.000000382182	2
2.65	2.8569878802	2.8571429602	2.8571428571	8.1632658951	399.833460	-.000000989212	2
2.70	3.3329863532	3.3333336760	3.3333333333	11.1111133956	740.741045	-.000002916795	3
2.75	3.9991185100	4.0000014015	4.0000000000	16.0000112118	1536.002153	-.000010221237	3
2.80	4.9973348869	5.0000076843	5.0000000000	25.0000768431	3750.023053	-.000045557063	4

EXAMPLE 4. Use an automatic digital computer to compute a table of values for f, given that $f' = -2xf$, $f(0) = 1$, and $f(h) = \exp(-h^2)$. Take $h = .5$, $.2$, and $.1$.

Solution: We present Tables 12.6.5–12.6.7, obtained by using the program of Example 3.

Table 12.6.5

IMPROVED PREDICTOR-CORRECTOR METHOD

T	PREDICTED	CORRECTED	ACTUAL	DF	D3F	TRUNC ERROR	N
0.00			1.0000000000	0.0000000000	0.000000		
.50			.7788007831	-.7788007831	3.894004		
1.00	.3834493801	.3679170446	.3678794412	-.7358340891	1.471668	-.000382917794	4
1.50	.1042862014	.1052917861	.1053992246	-.3158753584	-.947626	.000156937030	3
2.00	.0125572663	.0184568435	.0183156389	-.0738273740	-.738274	.000062507781	7
2.50	.0007030063	.0015529753	.0019304541	-.0077648764	-.147533	.000007400731	9

Table 12.6.6

IMPROVED PREDICTOR-CORRECTOR METHOD

T	PREDICTED	CORRECTED	ACTUAL	DF	D3F	TRUNC ERROR	N
0.00			1.0000000000	0.0000000000	0.000000		
.20			.9607894392	-.3843157757	2.244404		
.40	.8522587674	.8521437770	.8521437890	-.6817150216	3.653993	-.000000589399	2
.60	.6978474106	.6976763039	.6976763261	-.8372115647	3.817685	-.000000798523	2
.80	.5274396437	.5272923995	.5272924240	-.8436678391	2.902217	-.000000537408	2
1.00	.3679484146	.3678794289	.3678794412	-.7357588578	1.471518	-.000000046110	2
1.20	.2369129036	.2369277558	.2369277587	-.5686266139	.136470	.000000335798	2
1.40	.1407927044	.1408584262	.1408584209	-.3944035934	-.725703	.000000427212	2
1.60	.0772311115	.0773047414	.0773047404	-.2473751726	-1.048871	.000000281514	2
1.80	.0391113685	.0391639002	.0391638951	-.1409900407	-.981291	.000000068873	3
2.00	.0182919500	.0183156367	.0183156389	-.0732625468	-.732625	-.000000072893	3
2.20	.0079052136	.0079070639	.0079070541	-.0347910813	-.464809	-.000000111630	2
2.40	.0031597139	.0031511037	.0031511116	-.0151252980	-.257735	-.000000080901	3
2.60	.0011696512	.0011592484	.0011592292	-.0060280916	-.126831	-.000000038928	3
2.80	.0004016510	.0003936388	.0003936690	-.0022043774	-.055903	-.000000002409	3

Table 12.6.7

IMPROVED PREDICTOR-CORRECTOR METHOD

T	PREDICTED	CORRECTED	ACTUAL	DF	D3F	TRUNC ERROR	N
0.00			1.0000000000	0.0000000000	0.000000		
.10			.9900498337	-.1980099667	1.180139		
.20	.9607913865	.9607894391	.9607894392	-.3843157757	2.244404	-.000000002571	1
.30	.9139348133	.9139311852	.9139311853	-.5483587111	3.092743	-.000000004695	1
.40	.8521486113	.8521437889	.8521437890	-.6817150311	3.653993	-.000000006015	1
.50	.7788061765	.7788007829	.7788007831	-.7788007829	3.894004	-.000000006343	1
.60	.6976816336	.6976763259	.6976763261	-.8372115910	3.817685	-.000000005687	1
.70	.6126310263	.6126263940	.6126263942	-.8576769516	3.465015	-.000000004243	1
.80	.5272959405	.5272924238	.5272924240	-.8436678781	2.902218	-.000000002331	1
.90	.4448602242	.4448580661	.4448580662	-.8007445189	2.210055	-.000000000325	1
1.00	.3678802050	.3678794411	.3678794412	-.7357588821	1.471518	.000000001434	1
1.10	.2981967956	.2981972794	.2981972794	-.6560340147	.760999	.000000002699	1
1.20	.2369263046	.2369277587	.2369277587	-.5686266209	.136470	.000000003352	1
1.30	.1845174453	.1845195241	.1845195240	-.4797507626	-.364611	.000000003404	1
1.40	.1408560693	.1408584210	.1408584209	-.3944035789	-.725703	.000000002969	1
1.50	.1053969074	.1053992247	.1053992246	-.3161976741	-.948593	.000000002222	1
1.60	.0773026886	.0773047406	.0773047404	-.2473751698	-1.048871	.000000001353	1
1.70	.0555745672	.0555762127	.0555762126	-.1889591232	-1.050613	.000000000524	2
1.80	.0391627117	.0391638951	.0391638951	-.1409900225	-.981291	-.000000000149	1
1.90	.0270511113	.0270518469	.0270518469	-.1027970182	-.867607	-.000000000609	1
2.00	.0183152892	.0183156389	.0183156389	-.0732625555	-.732626	-.000000000849	1
2.10	.0121551273	.0121551783	.0121551783	-.0510517489	-.594242	-.000000000904	1
2.20	.0079072083	.0079070540	.0079070541	-.0347910377	-.464808	-.000000000822	1
2.30	.0050420347	.0050417602	.0050417603	-.0231920971	-.351592	-.000000000664	1
2.40	.0031514372	.0031511116	.0031511116	-.0151253355	-.257736	-.000000000476	1
2.50	.0019307812	.0019304541	.0019304541	-.0096522707	-.183393	-.000000000299	2
2.60	.0011595264	.0011592291	.0011592292	-.0060279915	-.126829	-.000000000149	2
2.70	.0006825795	.0006823281	.0006823281	-.0036845716	-.085335	-.000000000044	2
2.80	.0003938699	.0003936690	.0003936690	-.0022045464	-.055907	.000000000029	1

427

EXAMPLE 5.   Use an automatic digital computer to produce a table of values for f, given that $f' = -.5/f$, $f(0) = 6^{1/2}$, and $f(h) = (6 - h)^{1/2}$. Take $h = .5$ and $.2$.

Solution: We present Tables 12.6.8 and 12.6.9, obtained by using the program of Example 3.

Table 12.6.8

IMPROVED PREDICTOR—CORRECTOR METHOD

T	PREDICTED	CORRECTED	ACTUAL	DF	D3F	TRUNC ERROR	N
0.00			2.4494897428	-.2041241452	-.004253		
.50			2.3452078799	-.2132007164	-.005286		
1.00	2.2360687778	2.2360679775	2.2360679775	-.2236067978	-.006708	.000000001576	1
1.50	2.1213215737	2.1213203435	2.1213203436	-.2357022604	-.008730	.000000002938	1
2.00	2.0000019790	2.0000000000	2.0000000000	-.2500000000	-.011719	.000000005856	1
2.50	1.8708320623	1.8708286933	1.8708286934	-.2672612419	-.016363	.000000012677	1
3.00	1.7320569691	1.7320508073	1.7320508076	-.2886751346	-.024056	.000000030497	2
3.50	1.5811512144	1.5811388296	1.5811388301	-.3162277661	-.037947	.000000084360	2
4.00	1.4142419024	1.4142135616	1.4142135624	-.3535533908	-.066291	.000000283234	2
4.50	1.2248233029	1.2247448768	1.2247448714	-.4082482887	-.136083	.000001269145	2
5.00	1.0002951579	1.0000001967	1.0000000000	-.4999999017	-.375000	.000009217323	3

Table 12.6.9

IMPROVED PREDICTOR—CORRECTOR METHOD

T	PREDICTED	CORRECTED	ACTUAL	DF	D3F	TRUNC ERROR	N
0.00			2.4494897428	-.2041241452	-.004253		
.20			2.4083189158	-.2076136996	-.004629		
.40	2.3664319197	2.3664319132	2.3664319132	-.2112885637	-.005053	.000000000002	1
.60	2.3237900152	2.3237900077	2.3237900077	-.2151657415	-.005534	.000000000002	1
.80	2.2803508591	2.2803508502	2.2803508502	-.2192645048	-.006082	.000000000003	1
1.00	2.2360679880	2.2360679775	2.2360679775	-.2236067977	-.006708	.000000000004	1
1.20	2.1908902426	2.1908902300	2.1908902300	-.2282177323	-.007429	.000000000005	1
1.40	2.1447610740	2.1447610590	2.1447610590	-.2331262021	-.008263	.000000000006	1
1.60	2.0976177146	2.0976176963	2.0976176963	-.2383656473	-.009234	.000000000008	1
1.80	2.0493901755	2.0493901532	2.0493901532	-.2439750182	-.010373	.000000000011	1
2.00	2.0000000275	2.0000000000	2.0000000000	-.2500000000	-.011719	.000000000015	1
2.20	1.9493589032	1.9493588690	1.9493588690	-.2564945880	-.013322	.000000000020	1
2.40	1.8973666392	1.8973665961	1.8973665961	-.2635231383	-.015250	.000000000028	1
2.60	1.8439089465	1.8439088915	1.8439088915	-.2711630723	-.017593	.000000000040	1
2.80	1.7888544532	1.7888543820	1.7888543820	-.2795084972	-.020472	.000000000058	1
3.00	1.7320509011	1.7320508076	1.7320508076	-.2886751346	-.024056	.000000000087	1
3.20	1.6733201781	1.6733200531	1.6733200531	-.2988071523	-.028585	.000000000132	1
3.40	1.6124517203	1.6124515497	1.6124515497	-.3100868365	-.034403	.000000000207	1
3.60	1.5491935368	1.5491933385	1.5491933385	-.3227486122	-.042025	.000000000335	1
3.80	1.4832400393	1.4832396974	1.4832396974	-.3370999312	-.052237	.000000000565	1
4.00	1.4142140685	1.4142135624	1.4142135624	-.3535533906	-.066291	.000000000997	1
4.20	1.3416415645	1.3416407865	1.3416407865	-.3726779963	-.086268	.000000001858	1
4.40	1.2649123157	1.2649110640	1.2649110641	-.3952847075	-.115806	.000000003704	1
4.60	1.1832180873	1.1832159565	1.1832159566	-.4225771274	-.161700	.000000008018	1
4.80	1.0954490119	1.0954451149	1.0954451150	-.4564354647	-.237727	.000000019288	2
5.00	1.0000078325	.9999999997	1.0000000000	-.5000000002	-.375000	.000000053354	2

EXAMPLE 6.   Use an automatic digital computer to produce a table of values for f, given that $f' = 2x \exp(-f)$, $f(0) = 0$, and $f(h) = \log(1 + h^2)$. Take $h = .5$, $.2$, and $.1$.

Solution: We present Tables 12.6.10–12.6.12, obtained by using the program of Example 3.

Table 12.6.10

IMPROVED PREDICTOR-CORRECTOR METHOD

T	PREDICTED	CORRECTED	ACTUAL	DF	D3F	TRUNC ERROR	N
0.00			0.0000000000	0.0000000000	0.000000		
.50			.2231435513	.8000000000	-2.816000		
1.00	.6826666667	.6932092167	.6931471806	.9999379658	-1.000000	.000142807196	2
1.50	1.1814148509	1.1785998980	1.1786549963	.9231277845	-.131016	-.000134354298	3
2.00	1.6108780175	1.6095230547	1.6094379124	.7999318891	.063902	.000007875999	3
2.50	1.9811943678	1.9809076324	1.9810014689	.6897198902	.085362	.000011920978	3
3.00	2.3027996921	2.3027038857	2.3025850930	.5999287286	.071932	-.000003694480	2

Table 12.6.11

IMPROVED PREDICTOR-CORRECTOR METHOD

T	PREDICTED	CORRECTED	ACTUAL	DF	D3F	TRUNC ERROR	N
0.00			0.0000000000	0.0000000000	0.000000		
.20			.0392207132	.3846153846	-2.105143		
.40	.1482324382	.1484199934	.1484200051	.6896551805	-2.911149	.000002295464	2
.60	.3073197226	.3074847403	.3074846997	.8823529054	-2.518827	.000000838944	2
.80	.4946442823	.4946962260	.4946962418	.9756097716	-1.712105	-.000000529690	2
1.00	.6931630351	.6931472067	.6931471806	.9999999738	-1.000000	-.000000514039	1
1.20	.8920295488	.8919980076	.8919980393	.9836065886	-.515462	-.000000191818	2
1.40	1.0852152778	1.0851892986	1.0851892683	.9459459173	-.224567	-.000000025600	2
1.60	1.2697775287	1.2697605076	1.2697605449	.8988764380	-.062414	.000000023110	2
1.80	1.4445734364	1.4445633075	1.4445632692	.8490565713	.022670	.000000023529	2
2.00	1.6094435886	1.6094378691	1.6094379124	.8000000347	.064000	.000000018280	2
2.20	1.7647339882	1.7647308428	1.7647307968	.7534246229	.081295	.000000009509	1
2.40	1.9110245038	1.9110228397	1.9110228901	.7100592074	.085771	.000000007189	1
2.60	2.0489832484	2.0489823879	2.0489823342	.6701030568	.083683	.000000002352	1
2.80	2.1792872164	2.1792868188	2.1792868766	.6334841995	.078471	.000000003039	1
3.00	2.3025853225	2.3025851544	2.3025850930	.5999999632	.072000	-.000000000053	1
3.20	2.4194788040	2.4194787790	2.4194788445	.5693950551	.065260	.000000001730	1
3.40	2.5305172042	2.5305172303	2.5305171610	.5414012364	.058755	-.000000000818	1
3.60	2.6361959531	2.6361960240	2.6361960973	.5157593502	.052719	.000000001331	1
3.80	2.7369615539	2.7369616218	2.7369615446	.4922279413	.047242	-.000000001067	1
4.00	2.8332131789	2.8332132628	2.8332133441	.4705882736	.042337	.000000001215	1
4.20	2.9253098290	2.9253098944	2.9253098093	.4506437384	.037976	-.000000001152	1
4.40	3.0135720282	3.0135721023	3.0135721917	.4322200779	.034116	.000000001186	1
4.60	3.0982889026	3.0982889552	3.0982888619	.4151624161	.030706	-.000000001184	1
4.80	3.1797189516	3.1797190122	3.1797191097	.3993344815	.027695	.000000001184	1
5.00	3.2580966002	3.2580966395	3.2580965380	.3846153456	.025034	-.000000001198	1

Table 12.6.12

IMPROVED PREDICTOR-CORRECTOR METHOD

T	PREDICTED	CORRECTED	ACTUAL	DF	D3F	TRUNC ERROR	N
0.00			0.0000000000	0.0000000000	0.000000		
.10			.0099503309	.1980198020	−1.160826		
.20	.0392170185	.0392207131	.0392207132	.3846153846	−2.105143	.000000013793	1
.30	.0861716933	.0861776963	.0861776962	.5504587156	−2.696465	.000000019158	1
.40	.1484136347	.1484200052	.1484200051	.6896551723	−2.911148	.000000014927	2
.50	.2231383480	.2231435515	.2231435513	.7999999998	−2.816000	.000000006349	1
.60	.3074813385	.3074846999	.3074846997	.8823529411	−2.518828	−.000000000916	1
.70	.3987745305	.3987761201	.3987761200	.9395973153	−2.124579	−.000000004539	1
.80	.4946959699	.4946962419	.4946962418	.9756097561	−1.712105	−.000000005079	1
.90	.5933273696	.5933268453	.5933268453	.9944751381	−1.329569	−.000000004047	1
1.00	.6931480798	.6931471805	.6931471806	1.0000000000	−1.000000	−.000000002640	1
1.10	.7929935120	.7929925155	.7929925155	.9954751131	−.729674	−.000000001451	1
1.20	.8919989785	.8919980393	.8919980393	.9836065574	−.515462	−.000000000639	1
1.30	.9895420065	.9895411936	.9895411936	.9665427509	−.349960	−.000000000162	1
1.40	1.0851899363	1.0851892683	1.0851892683	.9459459460	−.224567	.000000000082	1
1.50	1.1786555271	1.1786549964	1.1786549963	.9230769231	−.131088	.000000000182	1
1.60	1.2697609570	1.2697605448	1.2697605449	.8988764045	−.062414	.000000000207	1
1.70	1.3584094726	1.3584091577	1.3584091576	.8740359897	−.012707	.000000000193	1
1.80	1.4445635070	1.4445632692	1.4445632692	.8490566038	.022670	.000000000165	1
1.90	1.5282280350	1.5282278570	1.5282278570	.8242950108	.047320	.000000000134	1
2.00	1.6094380446	1.6094379124	1.6094379124	.8000000000	.064000	.000000000106	1
2.10	1.6882491904	1.6882490929	1.6882490929	.7763401109	.074801	.000000000081	1
2.20	1.7647308682	1.7647307968	1.7647307968	.7534246576	.081295	.000000000063	1
2.30	1.8389611226	1.8389610707	1.8389610707	.7313195548	.084659	.000000000047	1
2.40	1.9110229273	1.9110228900	1.9110228901	.7100591716	.085771	.000000000036	1
2.50	1.9810014954	1.9810014689	1.9810014689	.6896551724	.085284	.000000000026	1
2.60	2.0489823526	2.0489823342	2.0489823342	.6701030928	.083683	.000000000020	1
2.70	2.1150499817	2.1150499692	2.1150499691	.6513872135	.081324	.000000000014	1
2.80	2.1792868848	2.1792868766	2.1792868766	.6334841629	.078471	.000000000012	1
2.90	2.2417729586	2.2417729536	2.2417729536	.6163655685	.075316	.000000000008	1
3.00	2.3025850956	2.3025850929	2.3025850930	.6000000000	.072000	.000000000007	1
3.10	2.3617969536	2.3617969527	2.3617969526	.5843543826	.068624	.000000000004	1
3.20	2.4194788442	2.4194788444	2.4194788445	.5693950178	.065260	.000000000004	0
3.30	2.4756977097	2.4756977108	2.4756977107	.5550883095	.061959	.000000000002	1
3.40	2.5305171594	2.5305171610	2.5305171610	.5414012739	.058755	.000000000002	1
3.50	2.5839975505	2.5839975525	2.5839975524	.5283018868	.055670	.000000000001	1
3.60	2.6361960590	2.6361960973	2.6361960973	.5157593124	.052719	.000000000001	1
3.70	2.6871669879	2.6871669902	2.6871669902	.5037440435	.049908	0.000000000000	1
3.80	2.7369615421	2.7369615445	2.7369615446	.4922279793	.047242	.000000000001	1
3.90	2.7856283334	2.7856283358	2.7856283357	.4811844540	.044719	0.000000000000	1
4.00	2.8332133416	2.8332133440	2.8332133441	.4705882353	.042337	.000000000001	1
4.10	2.8797600951	2.8797600974	2.8797600973	.4604154969	.040091	0.000000000000	1
4.20	2.9253098070	2.9253098092	2.9253098093	.4506437769	.037976	.000000000001	1
4.30	2.9699015115	2.9699015136	2.9699015135	.4412519240	.035987	0.000000000000	1
4.40	3.0135721896	3.0135721916	3.0135721917	.4322200393	.034116	0.000000000000	1
4.50	3.0563568936	3.0563568954	3.0563568954	.4235294117	.032358	0.000000000000	1
4.60	3.0982888600	3.0982888618	3.0982888619	.4151624549	.030706	0.000000000000	1
4.70	3.1393996218	3.1393996234	3.1393996234	.4071026418	.029154	−.000000000001	1
4.80	3.1797191080	3.1797191096	3.1797191097	.3993344426	.027695	0.000000000000	1
4.90	3.2192757435	3.2192757450	3.2192757449	.3918432627	.026323	−.000000000001	1
5.00	3.2580965366	3.2580965379	3.2580965380	.3846153846	.025034	0.000000000000	1

The method of this section is based on a quadrature formula which utilizes the second derivative of the given function. It is true that this complicates the calculations unless the second derivative is of a simple nature. This creates a difficulty for a computing procedure centered around paper and pencil or a desk calculator. However, this situation offers no difficulty to an automatic digital computer. It is merely a matter of setting up the subroutine FNS so that the machine performs as few computations as possible. Consider the following example.

EXAMPLE 7.   Prepare a table of values of f, given that $f' = f - f \cdot \tan$, $f(0) = 1$, and $f(h) = e^h \cos h$.

a. Take $h = .2$ and stop at 4.6.
b. Take $h = .1$ and stop at 2.9.
c. Take $h = .05$ and stop at 1.95.

Solution: We present an appropriate subroutine and the resulting tables (Tables 12.6.13–12.6.15).

```
SUBROUTINE FNS(X,F,DF,D3F)
TAN = SINF(X)/COSF(X)
SEC2 = 1. + TAN**2
DF = F - F*TAN
D2F = DF*(1. - TAN) - F*SEC2
D3F = D2F*(1. - TAN) - 2.*F*SEC2*TAN - 2.*DF*SEC2
RETURN
END
```

Table 12.6.13

IMPROVED PREDICTOR-CORRECTOR METHOD

T	PREDICTED	CORRECTED	ACTUAL	DF	D3F	TRUNC ERROR	N
0.00			1.0000000000	1.0000000000	-2.000000		
.20			1.1970560214	.9544007528	-2.879423		
.40	1.3740818409	1.3740615396	1.3740615389	.7931176385	-3.910011	-.000000023327	2
.60	1.5038763811	1.5038595412	1.5038595406	.4750138745	-5.065410	-.000000031727	2
.80	1.5505593283	1.5505492976	1.5505492968	-.0459560438	-6.294109	-.000000041175	2
1.00	1.4686928323	1.4686939394	1.4686939399	-.8186613470	-7.512098	-.000000051295	2
1.20	1.2030524962	1.2030701108	1.2030701127	-1.8914086263	-8.595098	-.000000061393	2
1.40	.6892102284	.6892507559	.6892507523	-3.3069449778	-9.370893	-.000000069151	2
1.60	-.1446969282	-.1446249625	-.1446261807	-5.0955037240	-9.612508	.000000119732	3
1.80	-1.3745840872	-1.3744749781	-1.3744925761	-7.2658343995	-9.033769	-.000000043446	2
2.00	-3.0750487726	-3.0748948703	-3.0749323206	-9.7936627372	-7.287746	-.000000277775	2
2.20	-5.3113740623	-5.3111646300	-5.3112305277	-12.6077650570	-3.970872	-.000000002332	2
2.40	-8.1285898840	-8.1283210170	-8.1284209884	-15.5739792196	1.365326	-.000000060164	2
2.60	-11.5371154495	-11.5367831182	-11.5369257005	-18.4772727680	9.192587	.000000030306	2
2.80	-15.4947165590	-15.4943226508	-15.4945135721	-21.0030165743	19.971257	.000000061910	2
3.00	-19.8847330614	-19.8842853565	-19.8845308441	-22.7187214956	34.099698	.000000170965	2
3.20	-24.4908787198	-24.4903948045	-24.4906967328	-23.0583470231	51.844885	.000000269132	2
3.40	-28.9693711386	-28.9688802670	-28.9692377681	-21.3119156132	73.251690	.000000424804	2
3.60	-32.8198232102	-32.8193700828	-32.8197747603	-16.6241028479	98.029275	.000000590180	2
3.80	-35.3571100071	-35.3567573472	-35.3571936185	-8.0063223608	125.414385	.000000797998	2
4.00	-35.6874606680	-35.6872924129	-35.6877324801	5.6322142522	154.013598	.000001019364	2
4.20	-32.6931687179	-32.6932919717	-32.6936954283	25.4281812577	181.629530	.000001255136	2
4.40	-25.0316744954	-25.0322205515	-25.0325292290	52.4756392246	205.080161	.000001489163	3
4.60	-11.1561558534	-11.1572801888	-11.1574173896	87.6981736438	220.025468	.000001549148	3

Table 12.6.14

IMPROVED PREDICTOR-CORRECTOR METHOD

T	PREDICTED	CORRECTED	ACTUAL	DF	D3F	TRUNC ERROR	N
0.00			1.0000000000	1.0000000000	-2.000000		
.10			1.0996496668	.9893166781	-2.419965		
.20	1.1970566805	1.1970560214	1.1970560214	.9544007528	-2.879423	-.000000000153	1
.30	1.2895700099	1.2895693740	1.2895693740	.8906588203	-3.376960	-.000000000182	1
.40	1.3740621321	1.3740615389	1.3740615389	.7931176381	-3.910011	-.000000000214	1
.50	1.4468895647	1.4468890366	1.4468890366	.6564499534	-4.474656	-.000000000248	1
.60	1.5038599775	1.5038595406	1.5038595406	.4750138743	-5.065410	-.000000000284	1
.70	1.5402033413	1.5402030254	1.5402030254	.2429079136	-5.674996	-.000000000321	1
.80	1.5505494579	1.5505492968	1.5505492968	-.0459560438	-6.294109	-.000000000360	1
.90	1.5289137803	1.5289138119	1.5289138119	-.3977594921	-6.911174	-.000000000400	1
1.00	1.4686936737	1.4686939399	1.4686939399	-.8186613473	-7.512098	-.000000000440	1
1.10	1.3626775096	1.3626780566	1.3626780566	-1.3146568148	-8.080026	-.000000000478	1
1.20	1.2030692350	1.2030701127	1.2030701127	-1.8914086292	-8.595098	-.000000000515	1
1.30	.9815312982	.9815325604	.9815325605	-2.5540482783	-9.034227	-.000000000549	1
1.40	.6892490481	.6892507522	.6892507523	-3.3069449600	-9.370893	-.000000000578	1
1.50	.3170199375	.3170221437	.3170221436	-4.1534402371	-9.574969	-.000000000576	2
1.60	-.1446289516	-.1446261787	-.1446261807	-5.0955465742	-9.612588	-.000000000223	2
1.70	-.7052913673	-.7052879690	-.7052879835	-6.1336088604	-9.446066	-.000000000659	2
1.80	-1.3744966394	-1.3744925496	-1.3744925761	-7.2659272871	-9.033884	-.000000000731	1
1.90	-2.1614847212	-2.1614798755	-2.1614799183	-8.4883422471	-8.330765	-.000000000514	1
2.00	-3.0749379207	-3.0749322606	-3.0749323206	-9.7937818268	-7.287835	-.000000000546	1
2.10	-4.1226655191	-4.1226589886	-4.1226590699	-11.1717732077	-5.852910	-.000000000438	1
2.20	-5.3112378723	-5.3112304236	-5.3112305277	-12.6079212393	-3.970921	-.000000000379	1
2.30	-6.6455668767	-6.6455584707	-6.6455586015	-14.0833581680	-1.584482	-.000000000239	1
2.40	-8.1284302180	-8.1284208289	-8.1284209884	-15.5741704606	1.365342	-.000000000106	1
2.50	-9.7599374487	-9.7599270661	-9.7599272581	-17.0508102039	4.938088	.000000000094	1
2.60	-11.5369368404	-11.5369254740	-11.5369257005	-18.4775007646	9.192700	.000000000308	1
2.70	-13.4523629855	-13.4523506687	-13.4523509331	-19.8116485061	14.186106	.000000000586	1
2.80	-15.4945264733	-15.4945132679	-15.4945135721	-21.0032749615	19.971503	.000000000894	1
2.90	-17.6463484933	-17.6463344943	-17.6463348411	-21.9944864975	26.596365	.000000001267	1

Table 12.6.15

IMPROVED PREDICTOR-CORRECTOR METHOD

T	PREDICTED	CORRECTED	ACTUAL	DF	D3F	TRUNC ERROR	N
0.00			1.0000000000	1.0000000000	-2.000000		
.05			1.0499572813	.9974156252	-2.204998		
.10	1.0996496876	1.0996496668	1.0996496668	.9893166781	-2.419965	-.000000000001	1
.15	1.1487881172	1.1487880966	1.1487880966	.9751657571	-2.644821	-.000000000001	1
.20	1.1970560417	1.1970560214	1.1970560214	.9544007528	-2.879423	-.000000000001	1
.25	1.2441081959	1.2441081760	1.2441081760	.9264352041	-3.123562	-.000000000001	1
.30	1.2895693933	1.2895693740	1.2895693740	.8906588203	-3.376960	-.000000000002	1
.35	1.3330333514	1.3330333328	1.3330333328	.8464381818	-3.639257	-.000000000002	1
.40	1.3740615565	1.3740615389	1.3740615389	.7931176381	-3.910011	-.000000000002	1
.45	1.4121821795	1.4121821630	1.4121821630	.7300204156	-4.188688	-.000000000002	1
.50	1.4468890518	1.4468890366	1.4468890366	.6564499534	-4.474656	-.000000000002	1
.55	1.4776407143	1.4776407007	1.4776407007	.5716914837	-4.767180	-.000000000002	1
.60	1.5038595525	1.5038595406	1.5038595406	.4750138743	-5.065410	-.000000000002	1
.65	1.5249310293	1.5249310194	1.5249310194	.3656717501	-5.368381	-.000000000003	1
.70	1.5402030330	1.5402030254	1.5402030254	.2429079136	-5.674996	-.000000000003	1
.75	1.5489853526	1.5489853476	1.5489853476	.1059560813	-5.984029	-.000000000003	1
.80	1.5505492990	1.5505492968	1.5505492968	-.0459560438	-6.294109	-.000000000003	1
.85	1.5441274886	1.5441274896	1.5441274896	-.2136033452	-6.603717	-.000000000003	1
.90	1.5289138074	1.5289138119	1.5289138119	-.3977594921	-6.911174	-.000000000003	1
.95	1.5040635748	1.5040635831	1.5040635831	-.5991927447	-7.214640	-.000000000003	1
1.00	1.4686939274	1.4686939399	1.4686939399	-.8186613473	-7.512098	-.000000000004	1
1.05	1.4218844443	1.4218844613	1.4218844613	-1.0569084891	-7.801355	-.000000000004	1
1.10	1.3626780346	1.3626780566	1.3626780566	-1.3146568148	-8.080026	-.000000000004	1
1.15	1.2900821121	1.2900821395	1.2900821395	-1.5926024649	-8.345533	-.000000000004	1
1.20	1.2030700795	1.2030701127	1.2030701127	-1.8914086292	-8.595098	-.000000000004	1
1.25	1.1005831475	1.1005831869	1.1005831869	-2.2116985960	-8.825730	-.000000000004	1
1.30	.9815325144	.9815325605	.9815325605	-2.5540482783	-9.034227	-.000000000004	1
1.35	.8448019330	.8448019862	.8448019862	-2.9189782052	-9.217164	-.000000000005	1
1.40	.6892506914	.6892507523	.6892507523	-3.3069449601	-9.370893	-.000000000005	1
1.45	.5137170363	.5137171052	.5137171052	-3.7183320563	-9.491533	-.000000000005	1
1.50	.3170220661	.3170221436	.3170221436	-4.1534402356	-9.574969	-.000000000005	1
1.55	.0979741246	.0979742112	.0979742111	-4.6124771831	-9.616851	-.000000000004	1
1.60	-.1446262769	-.1446261808	-.1446261807	-5.0955466480	-9.612589	-.000000000005	1
1.65	-.4119809782	-.4119808720	-.4119808719	-5.6026369665	-9.557350	-.000000000004	1
1.70	-.7052881003	-.7052879836	-.7052879835	-6.1336089872	-9.446066	-.000000000004	1
1.75	-1.0257353568	-1.0257352290	-1.0257352288	-6.6881833930	-9.273426	-.000000000005	1
1.80	-1.3744927157	-1.3744925763	-1.3744925761	-7.2659274282	-9.033885	-.000000000004	1
1.85	-1.7527043837	-1.7527042323	-1.7527042320	-7.8662410358	-8.721665	-.000000000004	1
1.90	-2.1614800826	-2.1614799187	-2.1614799183	-8.4883424168	-8.330765	-.000000000004	1
1.95	-2.6018855892	-2.6018854123	-2.6018854119	-9.1312530252	-7.854964	-.000000000004	1

It is clear from the examples that the predictor–corrector method of this section is an improvement on Milne's method. As we have pointed out, one of the features of this method is that it requires just one starting value in addition to the starting value supplied by the problem. To obtain the needed starting value, we must use a starting method; but a starting method can be improved by incorporating a continuing method into the starting method. Thus the thing to do is to construct a starting method which utilizes the improved continuing method of this section. The resulting starting method can be used to compute the starting value needed by our continuing method. We leave the details to the exercises (also, see Appendixes 1 and 2).

EXERCISES

1. Write a program for the predictor–corrector method of this section but without adding T_c to C. Use this program for the following, and compare the results with the examples of the text.

    a. Prepare a table of values for f between 0 and 2.8, given that $f' = f^2$, $f(0) = 1/3$, and $f(h) = 1/(3 - h)$. Take $h = .5, .2, .1,$ and $.05$.

    b. Prepare a table of values for f between 0 and 2.8, given that $f' = -2xf$, $f(0) = 1$, and $f(h) = \exp(-h^2)$. Take $h = .5, .2,$ and $.1$.

    c. Prepare a table of values for f between 0 and 5, given that $f' = -.5/f$, $f(0) = 6^{1/2}$, and $f(h) = (6 - h)^{1/2}$. Take $h = .5$ and $.2$.

    d. Prepare a table of values for f between 0 and 3, given that $f' = 2x \exp(-f)$, $f(0) = 0$, and $f(h) = \log(1 + h^2)$. Take $h = .5, .2,$ and $.1$.

2. Write a program for a starting method which incorporates the improved continuing method of this section. Use this starting method to compute the following.

    a. $f(.1)$, given that $f' = f^2$ and $f(0) = \tfrac{1}{3}$.

    b. $f(.1)$, given that $f' = -2xf$ and $f(0) = 1$.

    c. $f(.2)$, given that $f' = -.5/f$ and $f(0) = 6^{1/2}$.

    d. $f(.1)$, given that $f' = 2x \exp(-f)$ and $f(0) = 0$.

3. Use the starting method of Exercise 2 and the improved continuing method of this section to prepare a table of values for f between 2 and 3 which is accurate to six significant figures, given that $f' = x^2f + xf^2$ and $f(2) = -2$.

4. Prepare a table of values for f between 0 and 1 which is accurate to six significant figures, given that $f' = x^3f^3 - xf$ and $f(0) = 1$.

5. Prepare a table of values for f between 5 and 6 which is accurate to six significant figures, given that $f' = f/x - 2xf^2 + x^{-2}$ and $f(5) = 2$.

6. Write a program which will replace h by $h/2$ in case T_c exceeds $.00001$, and which will also compute the required starting value so that the computations can proceed. Try out your program on a problem of your own choice.

Chapter 13

The
Laplace Transform

13.1 Laplacian Functions; the Laplace Transform

In this chapter we shall develop a mathematical technique which is effective in solving linear differential equations with boundary conditions. We know that sometimes an operation on given objects can be effected by carrying out a simpler operation on objects associated with the given objects. For example, positive real numbers can be multiplied by first adding their logarithms and then taking the antilogarithm of the result. We want to do the same sort of thing to functions. To begin, we need a method of associating with each function of a given set some other function. The functions that we shall operate on are called *Laplacian* functions.

DEFINITION 13.1.1. We shall say that g is a *Laplacian* function iff

(i) $\{t \mid t > 0\} \subset \mathcal{D}_g$,

(ii) $\int_0^a g$ exists whenever $a > 0$,

(iii) there is a real number b such that $\lim_\infty e^{-bx} \cdot g = 0$.

We shall denote the set of all Laplacian functions by "L".

DEFINITION 13.1.2. $L = \{g \mid g \text{ is a Laplacian function}\}$.

Thus $g \in L$ iff g is a Laplacian function. For example, $x \in L$ since $\{t \mid t > 0\} \subset \mathcal{D}_x$, clearly $\int_0^a x$ exists whenever $a > 0$, and $\lim_\infty e^{-x} \cdot x = \lim_\infty - e^{-x} = 0$, by l'Hospital's Rule, and so here $b = 1$. On the other hand, $1/x \bar{\in} L$ since $\int_0^1 1/x$ does not exist.

It is easy to see that each constant function with domain R is Laplacian, that x^t is Laplacian if $t > -1$, that $\exp(ax)$ is Laplacian whenever $a \in R$, and that $x^t \cdot \exp(ax)$ is Laplacian whenever $a \in R$ provided $t > -1$.

We shall associate with each Laplacian function, say g, a function called its *Laplace transform* and denoted by "$\mathscr{L}g$". The Laplace transform of g is defined as follows.

DEFINITION 13.1.3. $\mathcal{L}g = \{(s, b) \mid b = \int_0^\infty e^{-sx} \cdot g\}$ provided $g \in L$.

Thus $s \in \mathcal{D}_{\mathcal{L}g}$ iff the improper integral $\int_0^\infty e^{-sx} \cdot g$ exists; moreover, if $s \in \mathcal{D}_{\mathcal{L}g}$, then $[\mathcal{L}g](s) = \int_0^\infty e^{-sx} \cdot g$.

EXAMPLE 1. Determine $\mathcal{L}1$.

Solution: Clearly, $\int_0^\infty e^{-sx} = 1/s$ iff $s > 0$; therefore

$$\mathcal{L}1 = 1/x \ \mathbf{R} \ \{s \mid s > 0\}.$$

EXAMPLE 2. Determine $\mathcal{L}e^{2x}$.

Solution: Now, $\int_0^\infty e^{-sx} \cdot e^{2x} = 1/(s - 2)$ iff $s > 2$; therefore the domain of $\mathcal{L}e^{-2x}$ is $\{s \mid s > 2\}$, so $\mathcal{L}e^{2x} = 1/(x - 2) \ \mathbf{R} \ \{s \mid s > 2\}$.

EXAMPLE 3. Determine $\mathcal{L}x^t$, given that $t > -1$.

Solution: The computations are simplified by using the gamma function. By Definition 11.5.1, $\int_0^\infty e^{-x} \cdot x^t = \Gamma(t + 1)$ whenever $t > -1$. Thus, if $t > -1$, then

$$\int_0^\infty e^{-sx} \cdot x^t = \frac{1}{s} \cdot \int_0^\infty (e^{-sx} \cdot x^t) \circ x/s \qquad \text{provided } s > 0$$

$$= s^{-t-1} \int_0^\infty e^{-x} \cdot x^t$$

$$= \Gamma(t + 1)/s^{t+1}.$$

Hence $\mathcal{L}x^t = \Gamma(t + 1)/x^{t+1} \ \mathbf{R} \ \{s \mid s > 0\}$ provided $t > -1$. In particular, if t is a nonnegative integer, then $\mathcal{L}x^t = t!/x^{t+1} \ \mathbf{R} \ \{s \mid s > 0\}$.

EXAMPLE 4. Determine $\mathcal{L}(x^t \cdot e^{ax})$, given that $t > -1$.

Solution: $\int_0^\infty e^{-sx} \cdot x^t \cdot e^{ax} = \int_0^\infty e^{-(s-a)x} \cdot x^t = \Gamma(t + 1)/(s - a)^{t+1}$ provided $s > a$. Thus, if $t > -1$, then

$$\mathcal{L}(x^t \cdot e^{ax}) = \Gamma(t + 1)/(x - a)^{t+1} \ \mathbf{R} \ \{s \mid s > a\}.$$

In particular, if t is a nonnegative integer, then

$$\mathcal{L}(x^t \cdot e^{ax}) = t!/(x - a)^{t+1} \ \mathbf{R} \ \{s \mid s > a\}.$$

We now consider some theorems.

THEOREM 13.1.1 $f + g \in L$ and $f \cdot g \in L$ whenever $f \in L$ and $g \in L$.

Proof: Consider Definition 13.1.1.

The following theorem, which we state without proof, assures us that the Laplace transform of a Laplacian function is not vacuous.

THEOREM 13.1.2. Let $g \in L$ and let b be a real number such that $\lim_{\infty} e^{-bx} \cdot g = 0$; then $\int_0^{\infty} e^{-sx} \cdot g$ exists whenever $s > b$.

Here is another result that we shall find useful.

THEOREM 13.1.3. Let $g \in L$ and let $a \in R$; then $\int_0^x e^{-ax} \cdot g \in L$.

To see the significance of this result, consider the differential equation $(\mathbf{D} - \mathbf{a})f = g$. Clearly, $f = e^{ax} \cdot \left(k + \int_0^x e^{-ax} \cdot g\right)$ is a complete solution. Since $e^{ax} \in L$ and $k \in L$, it follows from Theorems 13.1.1 and 13.1.3 that $f \in L$. In other words, if $g \in L$ and if $(\mathbf{D} - \mathbf{a})f = g$, then $f \in L$.

We shall find the following short table of Laplace transforms useful.

f	$\mathscr{L}f$
k	k/x R $\{s \mid s > 0\}$
x^t where $t > -1$	$\Gamma(t+1)/x^{t+1}$ R $\{s \mid s > 0\}$
$\exp(ax)$	$1/(x-a)$ R $\{s \mid s > a\}$
$x^t \cdot \exp(ax)$ where $t > -1$	$\Gamma(t+1)/(x-a)^{t+1}$ R $\{s \mid s > a\}$
$\sin ax$	$a/(x^2 + a^2)$ R $\{s \mid s > 0\}$
$\cos ax$	$x/(x^2 + a^2)$ R $\{s \mid s > 0\}$
$\sinh ax$	$a/(x^2 - a^2)$ R $\{s \mid s > a\}$
$\cosh ax$	$x/(x^2 - a^2)$ R $\{s \mid s > a\}$
$x \sin ax$	$2ax/(x^2 + a^2)^2$ R $\{s \mid s > 0\}$
$x \cos ax$	$(x^2 - a^2)/(x^2 + a^2)^2$ R $\{s \mid s > 0\}$
$e^{ax} \cdot \sin bx$	$b/[(x-a)^2 + b^2]$ R $\{s \mid s > a\}$
$e^{ax} \cdot \cos bx$	$(x-a)/[(x-a)^2 + b^2]$ R $\{s \mid s > a\}$

EXERCISES

1. Show that each of the following functions is Laplacian: x^2, $x^{1/2}$, $\exp(5x)$, $\exp(-3x)$, sin, cos $5x$, abs.

2. Show that none of the following functions is Laplacian: x^{-2}, tan, sec, Γ, $\exp \circ \exp$.

3. **a.** Prove that $f \in L$ if $\{s \mid s > 0\} \subset \mathscr{D}_f$ and if there is a real number K such that $|f(t)| < K$ whenever $t > 0$.
   b. Show that $J_0 \in L$ and $J_1 \in L$.

4. Use Definition 13.1.3 to verify each of the following statements.
   a. $\mathscr{L}x = x^{-2}$ R $\{s \mid s > 0\}$.
   b. $\mathscr{L}x^3 e^{-2x} = 6/(x+2)^4$ R $\{s \mid s > -2\}$.
   c. $\mathscr{L} \sin 5x = 5/(x^2 + 25)$ R $\{s \mid s > 0\}$.
   d. $\mathscr{L}x \sin 5x = 10x(x^2 + 25)^{-2}$ R $\{s \mid s > 0\}$.
   e. $\mathscr{L} \cosh = x(x^2 - 1)^{-2}$ R $\{s \mid s > 1\}$.
   f. $\mathscr{L}e^{4x} \cdot \sin(-2x) = -2/[(x-4)^2 + 4]$ R $\{s \mid s > 4\}$.

5. Prove Theorem 13.1.1.

6. Let $f \in L$ and $g \in L$. Does it follow that $f/g \in L$?

7. Let $f \in L$ and $g \in L$. Does it follow that $f \circ g \in L$?

8. Let $g \in L$ and let $k \in R$. Prove that $kg \in L$ and that $\mathscr{L}kg = k\mathscr{L}g$.

9. Let $f \in L$ and let $g \in L$. Prove that $\mathscr{L}(f + g) = \mathscr{L}f + \mathscr{L}g$.

13.2   Properties of the Laplace Transform

We now present certain useful properties of the Laplace transform.

THEOREM 13.2.1. $\mathscr{L}kg = k\mathscr{L}g$ whenever $k \in R$ and $g \in L$.

Proof: Let s be any member of the domain of $\mathscr{L}kg$; then $[\mathscr{L}kg](s) = \int_0^\infty e^{-sx} \cdot kg$
$= k \int_0^\infty e^{-sx} \cdot g = k[\mathscr{L}g](s)$. Thus $\mathscr{L}kg = k\mathscr{L}g$.

THEOREM 13.2.2. $\mathscr{L}(f + g) = \mathscr{L}f + \mathscr{L}g$ whenever $f \in L$ and $g \in L$.

Proof: By Theorem 13.1.1, $f + g \in L$. Let s be any member of the domain of $\mathscr{L}(f + g)$; then

$$[\mathscr{L}(f + g)](s) = \int_0^\infty e^{-sx} \cdot (f + g) = \int_0^\infty e^{-sx} \cdot f + \int_0^\infty e^{-sx} \cdot g$$

$$= [\mathscr{L}f](s) + [\mathscr{L}g](s).$$

Hence $\mathscr{L}(f + g) = \mathscr{L}f + \mathscr{L}g$.

COROLLARY 13.2.1. $\mathscr{L}(k_1 f + k_2 g) = k_1\mathscr{L}f + k_2\mathscr{L}g$ whenever $k_1 \in R$, $k_2 \in R$, $f \in \mathscr{L}$, and $g \in \mathscr{L}$.

This corollary, which asserts that $\mathscr{L}$ is a *linear* operator on L, can be extended as follows.

COROLLARY 13.2.2.   Let $n \in N$, let $f_1, f_2, \cdots, f_n$ be any Laplacian functions, and let $k_1, k_2, \cdots, k_n$ be any real numbers; then $\mathscr{L}(k_1 f_1 + k_2 f_2 + \cdots + k_n f_n) = k_1\mathscr{L}f_1 + k_2\mathscr{L}f_2 + \cdots + k_n\mathscr{L}f_n$.

Proof: Use mathematical induction.

THEOREM 13.2.3.   Suppose that $g \in L$, $g' \in L$, and $0 \in \mathscr{D}_{\mathscr{L}g}$; then $\mathscr{L}g' = x\mathscr{L}g - g(0)$.

Proof: First, we shall prove that $\mathscr{L}g$ and $\mathscr{L}g'$ have the *same* domain. Let $s \in \mathscr{D}_{\mathscr{L}g}$;
then

$$[\mathscr{L}g](s) = \int_0^\infty e^{-sx} \cdot g = \frac{e^{-sx}}{-s} \cdot g \Big]_0^\infty + \frac{1}{s} \int_0^\infty e^{-sx} \cdot g';$$

so $\int_0^\infty e^{-sx} \cdot g' = s[\mathcal{L}g](s) - g(0)$. This establishes that $s \in \mathcal{D}_{\mathcal{L}g'}$; thus $\mathcal{D}_{\mathcal{L}g} \subset \mathcal{D}_{\mathcal{L}g'}$. Next, suppose that $s \in \mathcal{D}_{\mathcal{L}g'}$; then, by the same argument, $s \in \mathcal{D}_{\mathcal{L}g}$. So $\mathcal{D}_{\mathcal{L}g'} \subset \mathcal{D}_{\mathcal{L}g}$; hence $\mathcal{L}g$ and $\mathcal{L}g'$ have the same domain. Finally, we point out that our argument has already disclosed that $[\mathcal{L}g'](s) = s[\mathcal{L}g](s) - g(0)$ whenever $s \in \mathcal{D}_{\mathcal{L}g}$. Thus $\mathcal{L}g' = x\mathcal{L}g - g(0)$.

COROLLARY 13.2.3.   Suppose that $g \in \mathcal{L}, g' \in \mathcal{L}, g^{(2)} \in \mathcal{L}$, and $0 \in \mathcal{D}_{\mathcal{L}g} \cap \mathcal{D}_{\mathcal{L}g'}$; then $\mathcal{L}g^{(2)} = x^2\mathcal{L}g - xg(0) - g'(0)$.

Proof: $\mathcal{L}g^{(2)} = x\mathcal{L}g' - g'(0)$ by Th. 13.2.3

$\qquad\qquad = x[-g(0) + x\mathcal{L}g] - g'(0)$ by Th. 13.2.3

$\qquad\qquad = x^2\mathcal{L}g - xg(0) - g'(0)$.

COROLLARY 13.2.4.   Suppose that $g^{(t)} \in L$ whenever $t = 0, \cdots, n$ and that $0 \in \mathcal{D}_{\mathcal{L}g^{(t)}}$ whenever $t = 0, \cdots, n - 1$; then

$$\mathcal{L}g^{(n)} = -g^{(n-1)}(0) - xg^{(n-2)}(0) - x^2g^{(n-3)}(0) - \cdots - x^{n-1}g(0) + x^n\mathcal{L}g.$$

Proof: Use mathematical induction.

The following two theorems help us apply Laplace transforms to differential equations.

THEOREM 13.2.4.   Let $n \in N$, suppose that $g^{(t)} \in L$ whenever $t = 0, \cdots, n - 1$, and suppose that f is a function such that $(\mathbf{D} - \mathbf{a})f = g$, where a is a complex number. Then $f^{(t)} \in L$ whenever $t = 0, \cdots, n$.

Proof: We shall treat the case in which a is real. Since $(\mathbf{D} - \mathbf{a})f = g$, it follows that $f = e^{ax} \cdot \left[k + \int_0^x e^{-ax} \cdot g\right]$. Now, $e^{ax} \in L$ whenever $a \in R$; therefore, in view of Theorem 13.1.1, we have only to show that $\left[\int_0^x e^{-ax} \cdot g\right]^{(t)} \in L$ whenever $t = 0, \cdots, n$. By Theorem 13.1.3, $\int_0^x e^{-ax} \cdot g \in L$. Now, $\left[\int_0^x e^{-ax} \cdot g\right]' = e^{-ax} \cdot g$; moreover, $e^{-ax} \in L$ and $g \in L$. Therefore, by Theorem 13.1.1, $e^{-ax} \cdot g \in L$. Notice that $[e^{-ax} \cdot g]^{(t)}$ is a linear combination of $e^{-ax}, g, g', \cdots, g^{(t)}$; therefore $[e^{-ax} \cdot g]^{(t)} \in L$ whenever t is a natural number less than n. Thus $\left[\int_0^x e^{-ax} \cdot g\right]^{(t)} \in L$ whenever $t \leq n$. So $f^{(t)} \in L$ whenever $t \leq n$. This establishes Theorem 13.2.4 if a is real. A similar argument will establish the theorem if a is complex.

THEOREM 13.2.5.   Let $g \in L$, let $\mathcal{P}$ be any polynomial operator of degree n, and let f be any function such that $\mathcal{P}f = g$. Then $f^{(t)} \in L$ whenever $t = 0, \cdots, n$.

Proof: We shall use mathematical induction on n. In view of Theorem 13.2.4, 1 has the property. Suppose that k is a natural number with the property; i.e., if $\mathcal{P}$ is a polynomial operator of degree k and $\mathcal{P}f = g$, where $g \in L$, then $f^{(t)} \in L$ for $t = 0, \cdots, k$. We shall prove that $k + 1$ also has the property. Let $\mathcal{Q}$ be any polynomial operator of degree $k + 1$; then $\mathcal{Q} = (\mathbf{D} - \mathbf{a})\mathcal{P}$, where $\mathcal{P}$ is a polynomial operator of degree k. Suppose that $(\mathbf{D} - \mathbf{a})\mathcal{P}f = g$, where $g \in L$. Let $\mathcal{P}f = h$; then $(\mathbf{D} - \mathbf{a})h = g$. Thus, by Theorem 13.2.4, $h \in L$ and $h' \in L$. Since k has the property, we see that $f, f', \cdots, f^{(k)}$ are Laplacian functions. Moreover, $\mathbf{D}\mathcal{P}f = h'$ and $\mathbf{D}\mathcal{P}f = \mathcal{P}\mathbf{D}f = \mathcal{P}f'$; so $\mathcal{P}f' = h'$. But $h' \in L$ and $\mathcal{P}$ has degree k; so $f^{(k+1)} \in L$. This proves that $k + 1$ has the property. By mathematical induction, we have established Theorem 13.2.5.

As we have observed, Laplace transforms can be used to solve linear differential equations with constant coefficients; we point out that this application of Laplace transforms is based largely on Theorem 13.2.5. We shall demonstrate this point in Section 13.5.

EXERCISES

1. Prove Corollary 13.2.4.
2. Complete the proof of Theorem 13.2.4.
3. a. Use the definition of the derivative to prove that $[\mathcal{L}f]' = -\mathcal{L}(xf)$.
   b. Use mathematical induction to prove that $\mathcal{L}[x^n f] = (-1)^n [\mathcal{L}f]^{(n)}$ whenever $n \in N$.
4. Use the results of Exercise 3 to carry out the following.
   a. Determine $\mathcal{L}x$, given that $\mathcal{L}1 = 1/x$ R $\{s \mid s > 0\}$.
   b. Determine $\mathcal{L}x^2$, given that $\mathcal{L}1 = 1/x$ R $\{s \mid s > 0\}$.
   c. Determine $\mathcal{L}x^n$, where $n \in N$, given that $\mathcal{L}1 = 1/x$ R $\{s \mid s > 0\}$.
   d. Determine $\mathcal{L}(x \sin ax)$, given that $\mathcal{L} \sin ax = a/(x^2 + a^2)$ R $\{s \mid s > 0\}$.
   e. Determine $\mathcal{L}(x^2 \sin ax)$, given that $\mathcal{L} \sin ax = a/(x^2 + a^2)$ R $\{s \mid s > 0\}$.
   f. Determine $\mathcal{L}(x \sinh ax)$.
   g. Determine $\mathcal{L}(x^2 \sinh ax)$.
   h. Determine $\mathcal{L}(x \cosh)$.
   i. Determine $\mathcal{L}(x^2 \cosh)$.
   j. Determine $\mathcal{L}(x^2 \cosh 3x)$.
   k. Determine $\mathcal{L}(xe^{ax} \cdot \sin bx)$.
   l. Determine $\mathcal{L}(x^2 e^{ax} \cdot \sin bx)$.
   m. Determine $\mathcal{L}(xe^{ax} \cdot \cos bx)$.
5. Use Theorem 13.2.3 to prove that $\mathcal{L}\left[\int_0^x f\right] = (\mathcal{L}f)/x$ if $f \in L$ and if $\int_0^x f \in L$.

13.3   The Convolution Operation

Let f and g be Laplacian functions and let h be the function defined as follows: $t \in \mathcal{D}_h$ iff $\int_0^t f(t - x) \cdot g$ exists; moreover, if $t \in \mathcal{D}_h$, then $h(t) = \int_0^t f(t - x) \cdot g$. The function h is said to be the *convolution* of f and g. We shall denote the convolution of f and g by "$f \diamond g$".

DEFINITION 13.3.1.   Let $f \in L$ and $g \in L$; then
$$f \diamond g = \left\{ (a, b) \mid b = \int_0^a f(a - x) \cdot g \right\}.$$

EXAMPLE 1.   Simplify $x \diamond x^2$.

Solution: Let $t \in R$; then $[x \diamond x^2](t) = \int_0^t (t - x)x^2 = t^4/12$. Thus $x \diamond x^2 = x^4/12$.

In connection with this example, we point out that $\mathscr{L}(x \diamond x^2) = 2x^{-5} \; R \; \{s \mid s > 0\}$ and that $\mathscr{L}x \cdot \mathscr{L}x^2 = (1/x^2) \cdot (2/x^3) \; R \; \{s \mid s > 0\} = 2x^{-5} \; R \; \{s \mid s > 0\}$.

EXAMPLE 2.   Simplify $\exp \diamond x^2$.

Solution: Let $t \in R$; then

$$[\exp \diamond x^2](t) = \int_0^t e^{t-x} \cdot x^2 = -x^2 e^{t-x}\Big]_0^t + 2\int_0^t x e^{t-x}$$

$$= -t^2 - \Big[2x\, e^{t-x}\Big]_0^t + 2\int_0^t e^{t-x}$$

$$= -t^2 - 2t - 2 + 2e^t.$$

Thus $\exp \diamond x^2 = -x^2 - 2x - 2 + 2\exp$.

In connection with Example 2, we point out that

$$\mathscr{L}(\exp \diamond x^2) = \frac{-2}{x^3} - \frac{2}{x^2} - \frac{2}{x} + \frac{2}{x-1} \; R \; \{s \mid s > 1\} = \frac{2}{x^3(x-1)} \; R \; \{s \mid s > 1\}$$

and that

$$\mathscr{L}\exp \cdot \mathscr{L}x^2 = \frac{1}{x-1} \cdot \frac{2}{x^3} \; R \; \{s \mid s > 1\} = \frac{2}{x^3(x-1)} \; R \; \{s \mid s > 1\}.$$

Before considering the significance of the remarks which follow Examples 1 and 2, let us establish two interesting properties of the convolution operation.

THEOREM 13.3.1.   Let $f \in L$ and let $g \in L$; then $f \diamond g = g \diamond f$.

Proof: We must prove that $f \diamond g$ and $g \diamond f$ have the same domain, say D, and that $[f \diamond g](t) = [g \diamond f](t)$ whenever $t \in D$. Let $t \in \mathscr{D}_{f \diamond g}$;

then $[f \diamond g](t) = \int_0^t f(t - x) \cdot g$

$$= -\int_t^0 [f(t - x) \cdot g] \circ (t - x) \qquad \text{by technique of integration}$$

$$= \int_0^t f \cdot g(t - x)$$

$$= [g \diamond f](t).$$

This proves that if $t \in \mathscr{D}_{f \diamond g}$, then $t \in \mathscr{D}_{g \diamond f}$ and $[f \diamond g](t) = [g \diamond f](t)$. Similarly, it is easy to prove that if $t \in \mathscr{D}_{g \diamond f}$, then $t \in \mathscr{D}_{f \diamond g}$ and $[g \diamond f](t) = [f \diamond g](t)$. This establishes Theorem 13.3.1.

THEOREM 13.3.2.   Let $f \in L$; then $f \diamond 1 = \int_0^x f$.

Proof: Let $t \in R$; then $[f \diamond 1](t) = [1 \diamond f](t) = \int_0^t f$. Thus $f \diamond 1 = \int_0^x f$.

We now introduce the basic property of the convolution operation.

THEOREM 13.3.3.   Let $f \in L$ and let $g \in L$; then $\mathcal{L}[f \diamond g] = \mathcal{L}f \cdot \mathcal{L}g$.

Proof: The proof of this theorem is difficult and perhaps should be presented at a more advanced level. However, it may be helpful to consider some of the ideas involved so that we can build up an intuitive feeling for the difficulties. In the following we do not

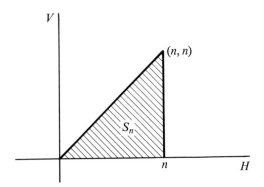

Figure 13.3.1

attempt to be rigorous; rather, we shall operate quite intuitively and freely. Let s be a member of the domain of $\mathcal{L}f$ and also of $\mathcal{L}g$, and let $h = f \diamond g$. Now, $[\mathcal{L}(f \diamond g)](s) = \int_0^\infty e^{-sx} \cdot (f \diamond g) = \lim \left(\int_0^n e^{-sx} \cdot (f \diamond g) \right)$. We shall utilize a double integral to evaluate $\int_0^n e^{-sx} \cdot (f \diamond g)$. We think of this because our integrand is a function whose values are given by definite integrals; thus Theorems 7.6.3 and 7.6.4 are applicable. Let $S_n = \{(a, b) | 0 \le a \le n \text{ and } 0 \le b \le a\}$ (see Figure 13.3.1) and let $_t F_2 = e^{-st} \cdot f(t - x) \cdot g$; then $F = e^{-sx} \cdot f(X - Y) \cdot g(Y)$. Thus, by Theorem 7.6.3, $\int_{S_n} F = \int_0^n h$, where $h(t) = \int_0^t e^{-st} \cdot f(t - x) \cdot g = e^{-st} \cdot [f \diamond g](t)$; so $\int_0^n e^{-sx} \cdot (f \diamond g) = \int_{S_n} F$. Notice that we can evaluate $\int_{S_n} F$ by applying Theorem 7.6.4. Now, $_t F_1 = e^{-sx} \cdot f(x - t) \cdot g(t)$; so $\int_{S_n} F = \int_0^n v$, where

$$v(t) = \int_t^n {}_t F_1 = \int_t^n e^{-sx} \cdot f(x - t) \cdot g(t)$$

$$= \int_0^{n-t} e^{-s(x+t)} \cdot f \cdot g(t) = e^{-st} \cdot g(t) \int_0^{n-t} e^{-sx} \cdot f$$

whenever $0 \le t \le n$. So far, so good! Our job is to determine the function v; i.e., we must compute $v(t)$ whenever $0 \le t \le n$. What is n? This is easy: n is a natural number.

Remember that we are after $\lim\left(\int_0^n e^{-sx} \cdot h\right)$; therefore we are free to ignore the first few terms of the sequence $\left(\int_0^n e^{-sx} \cdot h\right)$. Here, as elsewhere, *a few* terms means any finite number of terms, say $10^{(10^{10})}$ terms, or even more if we wish. Let us make good use of our freedom. By assumption, $\lim_{\infty} e^{-sx} \cdot g = 0$; thus $e^{-st} \cdot g(t)$ is small if t is large (remember, we are speaking intuitively). Moreover, $\left\{\int_0^{n-t} e^{-sx} \cdot f \mid n \geq t\right\}$ is bounded; indeed, $\left|\int_0^{n-t} e^{-sx} \cdot f\right| \leq \int_0^\infty e^{-sx} \cdot |f| = [\mathscr{L}|f|](s)$. We conclude that $v(t) \approx 0$ if t is sufficiently large. Also, $\int_0^\infty e^{-sx} \cdot f = [\mathscr{L}f](s)$; so $\int_0^{n-t} e^{-sx} \cdot f \approx [\mathscr{L}f](s)$ provided $n - t$ is large (e.g., n is large and t is small). Notice that $v(t)$ is the product of two terms $e^{-st} \cdot g(t)$ and $\int_0^{n-t} e^{-sx} \cdot f$. If t is large, then the first term dominates the expression; so $v(t) \approx 0$. If t is not large and is small compared to n, then the second term is approximated by $[\mathscr{L}f](s)$; so $v(t) \approx e^{-st} \cdot g(t) \cdot [\mathscr{L}f](s)$. We can have the best of both worlds! The idea is to choose n so large that $n - t$ is large *unless* t is large enough that $v(t) \approx 0$. In the latter case, $v(t) \approx e^{-st} \cdot g(t) \cdot [\mathscr{L}f](s)$ whenever $0 \leq t \leq n$. So, in any event $v \approx e^{-sx} \cdot g \cdot [\mathscr{L}f](s)$ provided that n is large; indeed, the approximation can be made as close as desired by taking n sufficiently large. We conclude that $\int_{S_n} F \approx [\mathscr{L}f](s)\int_0^n e^{-sx} \cdot g$ provided that n is large. Thus

$$\lim\left(\int_{S_n} F\right) = [\mathscr{L}f](s) \cdot \lim\left(\int_0^n (e^{-sx} \cdot g)\right)$$

$$= [\mathscr{L}f](s) \cdot \int_0^\infty (e^{-sx} \cdot g)$$

$$= [\mathscr{L}f](s) \cdot [\mathscr{L}g](s).$$

So $\mathscr{L}[f \diamond g] = \mathscr{L}f \cdot \mathscr{L}g$. This completes our proof.

We emphasize that this demonstration is presented at an intuitive level; a rigorous proof of this theorem must await a more advanced treatment.

EXAMPLE 3.   Determine $\mathscr{L}h$, given that $h(t) = \int_0^t x^2 \sin(t - x)$ whenever $t \in R$.

Solution: Clearly, $h = \sin \diamond x^2$. By Theorem 13.3.1,

$$\mathscr{L}[\sin \diamond x^2] = [\mathscr{L} \sin] \cdot [\mathscr{L}x^2]$$

$$= \frac{1}{x^2 + 1} \cdot \frac{2}{x^3} \quad R\ \{s \mid s > 0\}$$

$$= \frac{2}{x^3(x^2 + 1)} \quad R\ \{s \mid s > 0\}.$$

Thus $\mathscr{L}h = \dfrac{2}{x^3(x^2 + 1)} \quad R\ \{s \mid s > 0\}.$

Check: Note that $\int_0^t x^2 \sin(t-x) = t^2 + 2\cos t - 2$ whenever $t \in R$;   so $\sin \Diamond x^2$
$= x^2 + 2\cos - 2.$ Hence

$$\mathscr{L}[\sin \Diamond x^2] = \frac{2}{x^3} + \frac{2x}{x^2+1} - \frac{2}{x} \quad R\{s \mid s > 0\}$$

$$= \frac{2}{x^3(x^2+1)} \quad R\, s \mid s > 0\}.$$

We point out that Theorems 13.3.2 and 13.3.3 lead to the following result.

THEOREM 13.3.4.   Let $f \in \mathscr{L}$; then $\int_0^x f \in L$ and $\mathscr{L}\left[\int_0^x f\right] = (\mathscr{L}f)/x.$

Proof: The proof is immediate.

E X E R C I S E S

Simplify the following.

1. $x^2 \Diamond x.$

2. $x^2 \Diamond \exp.$

3. $x \Diamond x.$

4. $x \Diamond \sin.$

5. $\sin \Diamond x.$

6. $x^2 \Diamond \sin.$

7. $\sin \Diamond \sin.$

8. $\exp \Diamond \sin.$

9. Prove that $f \Diamond (g+h) = f \Diamond g + f \Diamond h$ whenever f, g, and h are Laplacian functions.

10. Prove that $(f+g) \Diamond h = f \Diamond h + g \Diamond h$ whenever f, g, and h are Laplacian functions.

11. Let $f \in L$, let $g \in L$, and let $0 \in \mathscr{D}_{f \cap g}$.
   a. Prove that $t \in \mathscr{D}_{f \Diamond g'}$ iff $t \in \mathscr{D}_{f' \Diamond g}$.
   b. Prove that $f \Diamond g' + g(0) \cdot f = f' \Diamond g + f(0) \cdot g.$
   c. Use part **b** to show that $x^2 \Diamond \cos = 2x \Diamond \sin.$
   d. Show that $\exp \Diamond x = \exp \Diamond 1 - x.$
   e. Show that $\sin^2 \Diamond \exp + \sin^2 = (\sin 2x) \Diamond \exp.$

12. Determine $\mathscr{L}h$, given that $h(t) = \int_0^t x \cos(t - x)$ whenever $t \in R.$

13. Determine $\mathscr{L}h$, given that $h(t) = \int_0^t (t - x)^3 \exp$ whenever $t \in R.$

14. Determine $\mathscr{L}h$, given that $h(t) = \int_0^t e^{t-x} \cdot \sin 3x$ whenever $t \in R.$

15. Prove that $\Diamond$ is associative.

16. Prove that there is no function, say φ, such that $f \Diamond \varphi = f$ whenever $f \in L.$

13.4   Properties of Continuous Functions and the Laplace Transform

Our purpose in this section is to establish that $\mathscr{L}f \neq \mathscr{L}g$ if

(i) $f \neq g$,

(ii) $f \in L$ and $g \in L$,

(iii) f and g are continuous,

(iv) $\mathcal{D}_f = \mathcal{D}_g = \{t \mid t > 0\}$.

We shall need certain information about continuous functions.

THEOREM 13.4.1. $\int_0^1 f > 0$ if

(i) f is continuous on $[0, 1]$,

(ii) $f(t) \geq 0$ whenever $t \in [0, 1]$,

(iii) there is a member of $[0, 1]$, say c, such that $f(c) > 0$.

Proof: Since $f(c) > 0$ and f is continuous on $[0, 1]$, there is a closed interval $\mathcal{I}$ such that $\mathcal{I} \subset [0, 1]$ and $f(t) > 0$ whenever $t \in \mathcal{I}$. But there is a member of $\mathcal{I}$, say s, such that the definite integral of f over $\mathcal{I}$ is $f(s)|\mathcal{I}|$. Since $f(s)|\mathcal{I}| > 0$, and since $f(t) \geq 0$ whenever $t \in [0, 1]$, it follows that $\int_0^1 f > 0$.

The following corollary is immediate.

COROLLARY 13.4.1. $f(t) = 0$ whenever $t \in [0, 1]$ if

(i) f is continuous on $[0, 1]$,

(ii) $f(t) \geq 0$ whenever $t \in [0, 1]$,

(iii) $\int_0^1 f = 0$.

We can now establish the following theorem.

THEOREM 13.4.2. $f(t) = 0$ whenever $t \in [0, 1]$ if

(i) f is continuous on $[0, 1]$,

(ii) $\int_0^1 x^n f = 0$ whenever $n \in N$.

Proof: This theorem is usually proved by applying the *Weierstrass approximation theorem* (which states that a function which is continuous on a closed interval can be approximated throughout the interval as closely as desired by a polynomial function). However, it is more convenient to use the polynomial function approximation to functions discussed in Section 11.3. In view of Theorem 11.3.2, corresponding to any positive real number h there is a polynomial function $\sum\limits_{k=1}^{n} b_k\varphi_k$ such that $\int_0^1\left[f-\sum\limits_{k=1}^{n} b_k\varphi_k\right]^2 < h.$ So

$$\int_0^1 f^2 \le \int_0^1\left[f^2+\left(\sum_{k=1}^{n} b_k\varphi_k\right)^2\right]$$

$$= \int_0^1\left[f^2+\left(\sum_{k=1}^{n} b_k\varphi_k\right)^2\right] + 2\int_0^1\left(f\cdot\sum_{k=1}^{n} b_k\varphi_k\right) \quad \text{since } \int_0^1\left(f\cdot\sum_{k=1}^{n} b_k\varphi_k\right) = 0, \text{ by (ii)}$$

$$= \int_0^1\left[f-\sum_{k=1}^{n} b_k\varphi_k\right]^2$$

$< h$ by assumption.

We conclude that $\int_0^1 f^2$ is less than each positive real number. But $\int_0^1 f^2$ is not negative; therefore $\int_0^1 f^2 = 0$. Hence, by Corollary 13.4.1, $f^2(t) = 0$ whenever $t \in [0, 1]$; so $f(t) = 0$ whenever $t \in [0, 1]$.

THEOREM 13.4.3. $f(t) = 0$ whenever $t \ge a$ if

(i) f is continuous on $\{t \mid t \ge a\}$,

(ii) $\int_a^t f = 0$ whenever $t > a$.

Proof: Suppose that there is a real number k such that $k \ge a$ and $f(k) \ne 0$. Since f is continuous on $\{t \mid t \ge a\}$, it follows that there is a closed interval, say $[k, b]$, such that $f(t)$ has the algebraic sign of $f(k)$ whenever $t \in [k, b]$. Hence, by the mean value theorem for definite integrals, $\int_k^b f \ne 0$. But $\int_k^b f = \int_a^b f - \int_a^k f = 0$, by assumption. This contradiction demonstrates that $f(t) = 0$ whenever $t \ge a$.

We are now ready to prove that distinct functions have distinct Laplace transforms provided that the functions are continuous, are Laplacian, and have domain $\{t \mid t > 0\}$.

THEOREM 13.4.4. $f = g$ if

(i) f and g are continuous,

(ii) $\mathscr{D}_f = \mathscr{D}_g = \{t \mid t > 0\}$,

(iii) f and g are Laplacian functions,

(iv) $\mathscr{L}f = \mathscr{L}g$.

Proof: By assumption, there is a real number a such that $\int_0^\infty e^{-sx} \cdot f = \int_0^\infty e^{-sx} \cdot g$ whenever $s \geq a$; therefore $\int_0^\infty e^{-(a+n)x} \cdot f = \int_0^\infty e^{-(a+n)x} \cdot g$ whenever $n \in N$. Thus

$$0 = \int_0^\infty e^{-(a+n)x} \cdot (f-g) = \int_0^\infty e^{-nx} \cdot [e^{-ax} \cdot (f-g)]$$

$$= [e^{-nx} \cdot v]_0^\infty + n \int_0^\infty e^{-nx} \cdot v \qquad \text{where } v = \int_0^x e^{-ax} \cdot (f-g)$$

$$= n \int_0^\infty e^{-nx} \cdot v$$

$$= n \int_1^0 [(e^{-nx} \cdot v) \circ (\log 1/x)] \cdot \frac{-1}{x}$$

$$= n \int_0^1 x^{n-1} \cdot v(\log 1/x).$$

Thus $\int_0^1 x^n v(\log 1/x) = 0$ whenever $n \in N$. Therefore, by Theorem 13.4.2, $v(\log 1/t) = 0$ whenever $t \in (0, 1)$; i.e., $\int_0^{\log 1/t} e^{-ax} \cdot (f-g) = 0$ whenever $t \in (0, 1)$. Thus, by Theorem 13.4.3, $[e^{-ax} \cdot (f-g)](s) = 0$ whenever $s > 0$. Since $0 \bar{\in} \mathscr{R}_{\exp}$, we conclude that $f(s) = g(s)$ whenever $s > 0$. This establishes Theorem 13.4.4.

Notice that Theorem 13.4.4 assures us that there is at most one function with domain $\{t \mid t > 0\}$, say f, such that $\mathscr{L}f = u$, where u is a given function. In short, if we know that f is a function with the property that $\mathscr{L}f = u$, and if we happen to observe that g is a function with Laplace transform u, then we can conclude that $f \mathrm{R} \{t \mid t > 0\} = g \mathrm{R}\{t \mid t > 0\}$; notice, however, that if $s < 0$, then we can have $f(s) \neq g(s)$. The point is that there are many functions with the same Laplace transform, but they all take the same values on $\{t \mid t > 0\}$. For example, x and abs have the same Laplace transform.

In Section 13.5 we shall be involved with the problem of finding a function f such that $\mathscr{L}f = g$, where g is given. For example, let us find f such that $\mathscr{L}f = 5/(x+3) \mathrm{R}\{t \mid t > -3\}$. This is easy. We know that $\mathscr{L}e^{-3x} = 1/(x+3) \mathrm{R}\{t \mid t > -3\}$; so $\mathscr{L}(5e^{-3x}) = 5/(x+3) \mathrm{R}$ $\{t \mid t > -3\}$. Of course, there are other functions with this Laplace transform.

EXAMPLE 1.   Find a function f such that

$$\mathscr{L}f = \frac{6}{x^3(x^2+4)} \mathrm{R} \{t \mid t > 0\}.$$

Solution: We shall use Theorem 13.3.3. Now,

$$\mathscr{L}f = \frac{6}{x^4} \cdot \frac{x}{x^2+4} \mathrm{R} \{t \mid t > 0\} = [\mathscr{L}x^3] \cdot [\mathscr{L}\cos 2x];$$

thus

$$f = x^3 \diamondsuit \cos 2x = \frac{3}{8}(2x^2 + \cos 2x - 1).$$

E X E R C I S E S

Find a function f such that:

1. $\mathscr{L}f = 6x^{-4}$ R $\{s\,|\,s>0\}$.

2. $\mathscr{L}f = \dfrac{2}{x(x^2+1)}$ R $\{s\,|\,s>0\}$.

3. $\mathscr{L}f = 5/x + 1/x^2$ R $\{s\,|\,s>0\}$.

4. $\mathscr{L}f = \dfrac{x^2-4}{x^2(x^2+4)^2}$ R $\{s\,|\,s>0\}$.

5. $\mathscr{L}f = \dfrac{1}{x+3}\cdot\dfrac{1}{x+4}$ R $\{s\,|\,s>-3\}$.

6. $\mathscr{L}f = \dfrac{1}{x^2(x+3)}$ R $\{s\,|\,s>-3\}$.

7. $\mathscr{L}f = \dfrac{x}{(x^2+1)(x-1)}$ R $\{s\,|\,s>1\}$.

8. $\mathscr{L}f = (x^2+4)^{-2}$ R $\{s\,|\,s>0\}$.

9. $\mathscr{L}f = \dfrac{x}{x^4-16}$ R $\{s\,|\,s>2\}$.

10. a. Use Theorem 13.4.4 to prove that

$$\int_0^1 (1-x)^a\cdot x^b = \frac{\Gamma(a+1)\Gamma(b+1)}{\Gamma(a+b+2)}$$

provided $a>-1$ and $b>-1$.

b. Prove that

$$\int_0^t (t-x)^a\cdot x^b = \frac{\Gamma(a+1)\Gamma(b+1)}{\Gamma(a+b+2)}t^{a+b+1}$$

provided $a>-1$, $b>-1$, and $t>0$.

13.5   Application to Differential Equations

Perhaps it is surprising that Laplace transforms can be used to solve certain differential equations. Consider the following example.

EXAMPLE 1.   Find f such that $f^{(2)}+2f'-3f=0$ R E, $f(0)=0$, and $f'(0)=4$.

Solution: Let f be such that $f^{(2)}+2f'-3f=0$ R E, $f(0)=0$, and $f'(0)=4$. Then $\mathscr{L}[f^{(2)}+2f'-3f]=\mathscr{L}[0\text{ R }E]=0$ R $\{s\,|\,s>0\}\cap E$. So, by Corollary 13.2.4, $\mathscr{L}f^{(2)}+2\mathscr{L}f'-3\mathscr{L}f=0$ R $\{s\,|\,s>0\}\cap E$. Hence, in view of Theorem 13.2.5 and Corollary 13.2.4,

$$-f'(0)-xf(0)+x^2\mathscr{L}f+2[-f(0)+x\mathscr{L}f]-3\mathscr{L}f=0 \text{ R } \{s\,|\,s>0\}\cap E;$$

so

$$[x^2+2x-3]\mathscr{L}f=f'(0)+xf(0)-2f(0) \text{ R } \{s\,|\,s>0\}\cap E$$

$$=4 \text{ R } \{s\,|\,s>0\}\cap E.$$

Thus

$$\mathcal{L}f = \frac{4}{(x+3)(x-1)} \text{ R } \{s \mid s > 0\} \cap E$$

$$= \frac{1}{x-1} - \frac{1}{x+3} \text{ R } \{s \mid s > 0\} \cap E.$$

But $\mathcal{L} \exp = \dfrac{1}{x-1} \text{ R } \{s \mid s > 1\}$ and $\mathcal{L} \exp(-3x) = \dfrac{1}{x+3} \text{ R } \{s \mid s > -3\}$; thus $f = \exp - \exp(-3x) \text{ R } \{s \mid s > 0\}$. It is a simple matter to verify that we can drop the restriction on our function; thus $\exp - \exp(-3x)$ is the required function.

Next, we try a slightly more complicated differential equation.

EXAMPLE 2.   Find f such that $f^{(2)} + 2f' - 3f = 2 \text{ R } E$, $f(0) = 0$, and $f'(0) = 4$.
Solution: As in Example 1, we see that $\mathcal{L}[f^{(2)} + 2f' - 3f] = \mathcal{L}[2 \text{ R } E]$; so $\mathcal{L}f^{(2)} + 2\mathcal{L}f' - 3\mathcal{L}f = \dfrac{2}{x} \text{ R } \{s \mid s > 0\} \cap E$. Therefore

$$-f'(0) - xf(0) + x^2 \mathcal{L}f + 2[-f(0) + x\mathcal{L}f] - 3\mathcal{L}f = \frac{2}{x} \text{ R } \{s \mid s > 0\} \cap E.$$

Thus $(x^2 + 2x - 3)\mathcal{L}f = \dfrac{2}{x} + 4 \text{ R } \{s \mid s > 0\} \cap E$; hence

$$\mathcal{L}f = \frac{2+4x}{x(x-1)(x+3)} \text{ R } \{s \mid s > 0\} \cap E = \frac{-2/3}{x} + \frac{3/2}{x-1} - \frac{5/6}{x+3} \text{ R } \{s \mid s > 0\} \cap E.$$

Therefore

$$f = -\frac{2}{3} + \frac{3}{2} \exp - \frac{5}{6} \exp(-3x) \text{ R } \{s \mid s > 0\};$$

again, it is clear that we can drop the restriction on our function; so

$$-\frac{2}{3} + \frac{3}{2} \exp - \frac{5}{6} \exp(-3x)$$

is the required function.

The technique illustrated in the preceding examples is based on Corollary 13.2.4 and the fact that $\mathcal{L}$ is a linear operator. In precisely the same way we can handle simultaneous differential equations. Consider a system of n linear differential equations with constant coefficients which involve n unknown functions $f_1, \cdots, f_n$. Applying our technique, we obtain a system of n equations in n unknown functions $\mathcal{L}f_1, \cdots, \mathcal{L}f_n$. If we can solve this system, we obtain $\mathcal{L}f_1, \cdots, \mathcal{L}f_n$, and so $f_1, \cdots, f_n$. The idea, then, is to eliminate the various derivatives of the unknown functions from the given system; this is achieved by applying Corollary 13.2.4.

EXAMPLE 3. Find f and g, given that $f^{(2)} - 3f' + 12g' = 3$ R E, $f' - g' + 2g = \exp(3x)$ R E, $f(0) = 0$, $f'(0) = 1$, and $g(0) = 0$.

Solution: Let f and g be functions which satisfy the given conditions. Applying our technique, we find that

$$x^2 \mathscr{L}f - xf(0) - f'(0) - 3x\mathscr{L}f + 3f(0) + 12x\mathscr{L}g - 12g(0) = 3/x \text{ R } E,$$

$$x\mathscr{L}f - f(0) - x\mathscr{L}g + g(0) + 2\mathscr{L}g = 1/(x-3) \text{ R } E.$$

We have reduced the given system to a system in the unknowns $\mathscr{L}f$ and $\mathscr{L}g$:

$$x(x-3)\mathscr{L}f + 12x\mathscr{L}g = 1 + 3/x \text{ R } E,$$

$$x\mathscr{L}f + (2-x)\mathscr{L}g = 1/(x-3) \text{ R } E.$$

Solving this system algebraically, we see that

$$\mathscr{L}f = \frac{3(x-2)}{x^2(x+1)(x+6)} + \frac{1}{x(x-3)} \quad \text{and} \quad \mathscr{L}g = \frac{3}{x(x+1)(x+6)}.$$

Using Theorem 13.3.3, we find that

$$g = 3 \diamond \frac{1}{5}(e^{-x} - e^{-6x}) = \frac{3}{5}\int_0^x (e^{-x} - e^{-6x}) = .5 + .1e^{-6x} - .6e^{-x},$$

$$f = g - 2 \diamond g + 1 \diamond e^{3x} = g - 2\int_0^x g + \int_0^x e^{3x}$$

$$= \frac{1}{30}e^{-6x} - \frac{6}{5}e^{-x} + \frac{1}{3}e^{3x} - x + \frac{5}{6}.$$

It remains to verify that these functions satisfy the given conditions; this is left as an exercise.

As another application, we shall show that we can sometimes use the Laplace transform to solve a linear differential equation with polynomial coefficients. We shall need the result contained in Exercise 3b, Section 13.2, which we now state: let $f \in L$ and let $n \in N$; then $\mathscr{L}(x^n f) = (-1)^n (\mathscr{L}f)^{(n)}$.

EXAMPLE 4 Find f, given that $xf^{(2)} - 2xf' + 2f = -2e^{2x}$, $f(0) = -1$, and $f'(0) = 1$.

Solution: Let f be any function which satisfies the given conditions. Then

$$\mathscr{L}[xf^{(2)}] - 2\mathscr{L}[xf'] + 2\mathscr{L}f = -2/(x-2),$$
$$-[\mathscr{L}f^{(2)}]' + 2(\mathscr{L}f')' + 2\mathscr{L}f = 2/(2-x),$$
$$-[x^2\mathscr{L}f - xf(0) - f'(0)]' + 2[x\mathscr{L}f - f(0)]' + 2\mathscr{L}f = 2/(2-x),$$
$$-[x^2\mathscr{L}f + x]' + 2[x\mathscr{L}f + 1]' + 2\mathscr{L}f = 2/(2-x),$$
$$-[2x\mathscr{L}f + x^2(\mathscr{L}f)' + 1] + 4\mathscr{L}f + 2x(\mathscr{L}f)' = 2/(2-x),$$
$$2(2-x)\mathscr{L}f + x(2-x)(\mathscr{L}f)' = (-4-x)/(2-x).$$

We have reduced the problem to that of solving the first-order differential equation

$$2g/x + g' = \frac{4 - x}{x(2 - x)^2}.$$

Here, x^2 is an integrating factor, and so we consider

$$2xg - \frac{x(4 - x)}{(2 - x)^2} + x^2g' = 0;$$

thus

$$x^2g - A\frac{x(4 - x)}{(2 - x)^2} = k$$

is a complete solution. But

$$A\frac{x(4 - x)}{(2 - x)^2} \equiv x^2/(2 - x);$$

hence there is a real number k such that $\mathscr{L}f = k/x^2 + 1/(2 - x)$. Therefore $f = kx - e^{2x}$; so $f' = k - 2e^{2x}$. Since $f'(0) = 1$, we see that $k = 3$. Hence $f = 3x - e^{2x}$. Checking, we verify that this function satisfies the given conditions.

E X E R C I S E S

Find f, given that:

1. $f^{(2)} - 3f' + 2f = 0$ R E, $f(0) = 1$, and $f'(0) = 1$.

2. $f^{(2)} - 3f' + 2f = 1$ R E, $f(0) = 1$, and $f'(0) = 1$.

3. $f^{(2)} - 3f' + 2f = x$ R E, $f(0) = 1$, and $f'(0) = 1$.

4. $f^{(3)} + 2f^{(2)} - f' - 2f = 0$ R E, $f(0) = 0$, $f'(0) = 0$, and $f^{(2)}(0) = 2$.

5. $f^{(3)} + 2f^{(2)} - f' - 2f = 3$ R E, $f(0) = 0$, $f'(0) = 0$, and $f^{(2)}(0) = 2$.

6. $f^{(3)} + 2f^{(2)} - f' - 2f = x$ R E, $f(0) = 0$, $f'(0) = 0$, and $f^{(2)}(0) = 2$.

7. Find f and g, given that $f' + 2g' - g = 2e^{2x} - e^x$, $g^{(2)} - 2g' - f' + f = 2$, $f(0) = 1$, $g(0) = 1$, and $g'(0) = 2$.
   (*Answer:* $f = 2 - e^x$, $g = e^{2x}$)

8. Find f and g, given that $f^{(2)} = g^{(3)}$, $f^{(2)} + 3f - 3g' = 0$, $f(0) = -2$, $f'(0) = 0$, $g(0) = 0$, $g'(0) = 0$, and $g^{(2)}(0) = 0$.
   (*Answer:* $f = 3x^2 - 2$, $g = x^3$)

9. Find f, g, and h, given that $3f' - g' - 2g = -5$, $6f' = h^{(2)}$, $4g - h^{(2)} = 4$, $f(0) = 0$, $g(0) = 1$, $h(0) = 0$, and $h'(0) = 0$.
   (*Answer:* $f = x^2$, $g = 3x + 1$, $h = 2x^3$)

10. Find f, given that $xf^{(2)} - xf' + 2f = 6x + 2$ exp, $f(0) = 1$, and $f'(0) = 1$.
   (*Answer:* $f = 3x^2 + \text{exp}$)

11. Find f such that $xf^{(2)} + f = x^2 + 2$, $f(0) = 2$, and $f'(0) = -2$.
   (*Answer:* $f = x^2 - 2x + 2$)

Appendixes

Appendix 1

An Accurate Starting Method

We now present a highly accurate starting method which is based on Theorem 12.3.1 and the predictor–corrector method of Section 12.6. The problem is to approximate $f(a + h)$, given $f(a)$ and f'. The computation is carried out in several stages. First, we approximate $f(a + .001h)$ by using Theorem 12.3.1. Next, we use our predictor–corrector method to obtain $f(a + .01h)$; here, the step size is $.001h$. Next, we apply our predictor–corrector method again to compute $f(a + .1h)$; here, the step size is $.01h$. Finally, we apply our continuing method to approximate $f(a + h)$; here, the step size is $.1h$. Notice that the accuracy of the final result depends largely upon the error introduced in the final stage where the step size is $.1h$. The importance of an accurate continuing method cannot be overemphasized. We obtain an accurate starting method only because we possess an accurate continuing method. In the following pages we present our program and the tables (Tables A1, A2, and A3) which it produced for the differential equation with boundary condition, $f' = (1 - \tan) \cdot f$ and $f(0) = 1$.

```
      40 READ 5, T, A1, H
         CALL FNS(T,A1,B1,D1)
       1 FORMAT(1H1,35X,24HIMPROVED STARTING METHOD//4X,1HT,6X,
         19HPREDICTED,5X,9HCORRECTED,7X,6HACTUAL,10X,2HDF,11X,3HD3F,6X,
         211HTRUNC ERROR,4X,1HN/)
         PRINT 1
       2 FORMAT(1H ,F5.3,29X,F14.10)
       3 FORMAT(1H ,F5.3,15X,2F14.10,42X,I4)
       4 FORMAT(1H ,F5.3,F15.10,3F14.10,F12.6,F16.12,I4)
       5 FORMAT(4F6.3)
         N = 0
         PRINT 2, T, A1
         H = .001*H
         QF = A1 + H*B1 + .5*H*H*D2F(T,A1) + H*H*H*D1/6.
       8 CF = A1 + 2.*H*DF(T,A1)/3. + H*H*D2F(T,A1)/6. + H*DF(T,QF)/3.
         IF (ABSF(CF - QF) - .00000000001)10,10,9
       9 QF = CF
         N = N+1
         GO TO 8
      10 T = T+H
         A2 = CF
         AF = F(T)
         RA2 = RNDOFF(A2,10)
         RAF = RNDOFF(AF,10)
         PRINT 3, T, RA2, RAF, N
         X1 = A1
         Y1 = B1
         Z1 = D1
         DO 15 I = 1,3
         DO 25 J = 1,9
         N = 0
         CALL FNS(T,A2,B2,D2)
         T = T + H

         A12HB2 = A1 + 2.*H*B2
         H3 = H*H*H
         H3D2 = H3*D2
      21 PA3 = A12HB2 + H3D2*.3333333333333
         QA = PA3
      17 CALL FNS(T,QA,B3,D3)
         CA3 = A12HB2 + H3*(D1 + 18.*D2 + D3)*.01666666666667
         IF (ABSF(CA3-QA) - .0000000005)19,19,18
      18 QA = CA3
         N = N + 1
         GO TO 17
      19 CALL FNS(T,CA3,B3,D3)
         CF = A1 + .2*H*(B1 + 8.*B2 + B3) + H3D2*.13333333333333
         CALL FNS(T,CF,B3,D3)
         CF = A1 + .2*H*(B1 + 8.*B2 + B3) + H3D2*.13333333333333
         TRUNC1 = (CF - CA3)*.190476
         CF = CF + TRUNC1
         CALL FNS(T,CF,B3,D3)
         A1 = A2
         A2 = CF
         B1 = B2
         B2 = B3
         D1 = D2
      25 D2 = D3
         RPA3 = RNDOFF(PA3,10)
         RCF = RNDOFF(CF,10)
         AF = F(T)
         RAF = RNDOFF(AF,10)
         RB2 = RNDOFF(B2,10)
         RD2 = RNDOFF(D2,6)
         RTRUNC = RNDOFF(TRUNC1,12)
         H = 10.*H
         A1 = X1
         B1 = Y1
         D1 = Z1
      15 PRINT 4, T, RPA3, RCF, RAF, RB2, RD2, RTRUNC, N
      20 PRINT 50
      50 FORMAT (1H1)
         IF (SENSE SWITCH 1)40,31
      31 CALL EXIT
         END
```

456

```
      FUNCTION RNDOFF(T,N)
      IF (T)100,200,300
100   RNDOFF = T - .5*.1**N
      GO TO 400
200   RNDOFF = T
      GO TO 400
300   RNDOFF = T + .5*.1**N
400   RETURN
      END

      FUNCTION F(X)
      F = COSF(X)*EXPF(X)
      RETURN
      END

      FUNCTION D2F(X,Y)
      TAN = SINF(X)/COSF(X)
      SEC2 = 1. + TAN**2
      DF = Y - Y*TAN
      D2F = DF*(1. - TAN) - Y*SEC2
      RETURN
      END

      FUNCTION DF(X,Y)
      DF = -Y*SINF(X)/COSF(X) + Y
      RETURN
      END

      SUBROUTINE FNS(X,F,DF,D3F)
      TAN = SINF(X)/COSF(X)
      SEC2 = 1. + TAN**2
      DF = F - F*TAN
      D2F = DF*(1. - TAN) - F*SEC2
      D3F = D2F*(1. - TAN) - 2.*F*TAN*SEC2 - 2.*DF*SEC2
      RETURN
      END
```

Table A1

IMPROVED STARTING METHOD

T	PREDICTED	CORRECTED	ACTUAL	DF	D3F	TRUNC ERROR	N
0.000			1.0000000000				
0.0005		1.0005000833	1.0005000000				2
.005	1.0049999586	1.0049999585	1.0049999582	.9999749169	-2.020050	-.000000000003	0
.050	1.0499572813	1.0499572813	1.0499572813	.9974156252	-2.204998	0.000000000000	0
.500	1.4468890518	1.4468890366	1.4468890366	.6564499534	-4.474656	-.000000000002	1

Table A2

IMPROVED STARTING METHOD

T	PREDICTED	CORRECTED	ACTUAL	DF	D3F	TRUNC ERROR	N
0.000			1.0000000000				
0.0002		1.0002000133	1.0002000000				1
.002	1.0019999974	1.0019999974	1.0019999973	.9999959947	-2.008008	0.000000000000	0
.020	1.0199973066	1.0199973066	1.0199973066	.9995946400	-2.080800	0.000000000000	0
.200	1.1970560216	1.1970560214	1.1970560214	.9544007528	-2.879423	0.000000000000	0

Table A3

IMPROVED STARTING METHOD

T	PREDICTED	CORRECTED	ACTUAL	DF	D3F	TRUNC ERROR	N
0.000			1.0000000000				
0.0001		1.0001000033	1.0001000000				1
.001	1.0009999997	1.0009999997	1.0009999997	.9999989993	-2.004002	0.000000000000	0
.010	1.0099996650	1.0099996650	1.0099996650	.9998993317	-2.040200	0.000000000000	0
.100	1.0996496668	1.0996496668	1.0996496668	.9893166781	-2.419965	0.000000000000	0

Appendix 2

A Self-Starting Continuing Method

In Section 12.6 we suggested that a self-starting continuing method is obtained by linking the continuing method of that section to an accurate starting method. In Appendix 1 we presented a highly accurate starting method; we now point out that the accuracy of that starting method depends upon the number of repetitions of a DO loop. Running through that DO loop an extra time improves the accuracy of the method considerably, provided that the original step size is less than .2, say, so that the truncation error of the predictor–corrector part of the starting method does not dominate the total error. Accordingly, we shall retain control over the number of repetitions of this DO loop by setting up a parameter N which represents the number of times through the loop. In this way we can improve the accuracy of our starting method by increasing N. Generally, $N = 2$ is quite suitable, although if the step size is small, say .02, $N = 1$ will give us eight- or nine-digit accuracy. Thus our choice of N is dictated by the required accuracy and the given step size.

It is convenient to set up our starting method as a subprogram, which we shall think of as a function called START. The arguments of this function are the given argument, the corresponding value of the unknown function, the step size, and the parameter N. The derivatives of the unknown function are loaded via FNS. The value of the function START is our approximation to the value of the unknown function which we need for our continuing method. In the following pages we present the subprogram for the function START and a program for our improved self-starting continuing method. Notice that we are using a more efficient form of the round-off function. Moreover, the subprogram that computes values of $f^{(2)}$ has been incorporated into FNS.

```
      FUNCTION RNDOFF(T,A)

      IF (T)100,200,300
100   RNDOFF = T - A
      RETURN
200   RNDOFF = T
      RETURN
300   RNDOFF = T + A
      RETURN
      END


      FUNCTION START(X,A1,H,N)

      CALL FNS(X,A1,B1,C1,D1)
      H = H*.1**N
      QF = A1 + H*B1 + .5*H*H*C1 + H*H*H*D1/6.
8     CALL FNS(X,QF,QB,QC,QD)
      CF = A1 + 2.*H*B1/3. + H*H*C1/6. + H*QB/3.
      IF (ABSF(CF - QF) - .00000000001)10,10,9
9     QF = CF
      GO TO 8
10    X = X + H
      A2 = CF
      X1 = A1
      Y1 = B1
      Z1 = D1
      DO 15 I = 1,N
      DO 25 J = 1,9
      CALL FNS(X,A2,B2,C2,D2)
      X = X + H
      A12HB2 = A1 + 2.*H*B2
      H3 = H*H*H
      H3D2 = H3*D2
21    PA3 = A12HB2 + H3D2*.3333333333333
      QA = PA3
17    CALL FNS(X,QA,B3,C3,D3)
      CA3 = A12HB2 + H3*(D1 + 18.*D2 + D3)*.01666666666667
      IF (ABSF(CA3-QA) - .0000000005)19,19,18
18    QA = CA3
      GO TO 17
19    CALL FNS(X,CA3,B3,C3,D3)
      CF = A1 + .2*H*(B1 + 8.*B2 + B3) + H3D2*.13333333333333
      CALL FNS(X,CF,B3,C3,D3)
      CF = A1 + .2*H*(B1 + 8.*B2 + B3) + H3D2*.13333333333333
      TRUNC1 = (CF - CA3)*.190476
      CF = CF + TRUNC1
      CALL FNS(X,CF,B3,C3,D3)
      A1 = A2
      A2 = CF
      B1 = B2
      B2 = B3
      D1 = D2
25    D2 = D3
      H = 10.*H
      A1 = X1
      B1 = Y1
15    D1 = Z1
      START = CF
      RETURN
      END
```

```
**    IMPROVED SELF-STARTING CONTINUING METHOD

*FANDK1504

    5 FORMAT(F5.2,F18.15,2F5.2,I1)
   40 READ 5, T, A1, H, FINAL, N
    1 FORMAT(1H1,40HIMPROVED SELF-STARTING CONTINUING METHOD//12X,5HCOMP
     1UTED, 9X,5HTRUNC/4X,1HT,9X,5HVALUE,10X,5HERROR/)
      PRINT 1
    2 FORMAT(1H0,F5.2,F16.10,F16.12)
    4 FORMAT(1H ,F5.2,F16.10,F16.12)
      K = 1
      L = 2
      H3 = H*H*H
      CALL FNS(T,A1,B1,C1,D1)
      RA1 = RNDOFF(A1,.00000000005)
      PRINT 4, T, RA1
      A2 = START(T,A1,H,N)
      CALL FNS(T,A2,B2,C2,D2)
      RA2 = RNDOFF(A2,.00000000005)
      PRINT 4, T, RA2
    6 T = T + H
      A12HB2 = A1 + 2.*H*B2
      H3D2 = H3*D2
      IF (T - FINAL)21,21,20
   21 PA3 = A12HB2 + H3D2*.3333333333333
      QA = PA3
   17 CALL FNS(T,QA,B3,C3,D3)
      CA3 = A12HB2 + H3*(D1 + 18.*D2 + D3)*.01666666666667
      IF (ABSF(CA3-QA) - .000000005)19,19,18
   18 QA = CA3
      GO TO 17
   19 CALL FNS(T,CA3,B3,C3,D3)
      CF = A1 + .2*H*(B1 + 8.*B2 + B3) + H3D2*.13333333333333
      CALL FNS(T,CF,B3,C3,D3)
      CF = A1 + .2*H*(B1 + 8.*B2 + B3) + H3D2*.13333333333333
      TRUNC1 = (CF - CA3)*.190476
      CF = CF + TRUNC1
      CALL FNS(T,CF,B3,C3,D3)
      A1 = A2
      A2 = CF
      B1 = B2
      B2 = B3
      D1 = D2
      D2 = D3
      RCF = RNDOFF(CF,.00000000005)
      RTRUNC = RNDOFF(TRUNC1,.00000000005)
      IF (L - 5)15,25,25
   25 L = 1
      IF (K - 9)10,70,70
   10 PRINT 2, T, RCF, RTRUNC
      K = K + 1
      GO TO 6
   70 PRINT 1
      K = 1
      L = 0
   15 PRINT 4, T, RCF, RTRUNC
      L = L + 1
      GO TO 6
   20 PRINT 50, N
   50 FORMAT(1H0,15X,5HN =I2//)
      IF (SENSE SWITCH 1)40,31
   31 CALL EXIT
      END
```

EXAMPLE 1.   Prepare a table of values of f, given that $f' = f - f \cdot \tan$ and $f(0) = 1$.

a. Take $h = .1$, $N = 1$, and stop at 2.5.
b. Take $h = .1$, $N = 2$, and stop at 2.5.
c. Take $h = .1$, $N = 3$, and stop at 2.5.
d. Take $h = .05$, $N = 1$, and stop at 2.5.
e. Take $h = .05$, $N = 2$, and stop at 2.5.
f. Take $h = .05$, $N = 3$, and stop at 2.5.
g. Take $h = .02$, $N = 1$, and stop at 2.5.
h. Take $h = .02$, $N = 2$, and stop at 2.5.

Solution: In the following pages we present an appropriate subroutine and the resulting tables (Tables 4–11).

```
SUBROUTINE FNS(X,F,DF,D2F,D3F)
TAN = SINF(X)/COSF(X)
SEC2 = 1. + TAN**2
DF = F - F*TAN
D2F = DF*(1. - TAN) - F*SEC2
D3F = D2F*(1. - TAN) - 2.*F*SEC2*TAN - 2.*DF*SEC2
RETURN
END
```

Table A4

IMPROVED SELF-STARTING CONTINUING METHOD

T	COMPUTED VALUE	TRUNC ERROR
0.00	1.0000000000	
.10	1.0996521639	
.20	1.1970563701	-.0000001981
.30	1.2895720101	.0000001321
.40	1.3740621799	-.0000001362
.50	1.4468918020	.0000000873
.60	1.5038603872	-.0000000719
.70	1.5402056719	.0000000279
.80	1.5505502165	-.0000000212
.90	1.5289166470	-.0000001100
1.00	1.4686947348	.0000000382
1.10	1.3626807444	-.0000000999
1.20	1.2030704868	.0000001520
1.30	.9815349476	-.0000002904
1.40	.6892502264	.0000005238
1.50	.3170241727	-.0000013852
1.60	-.1446381418	-.0000097228
1.70	-.7053675251	.0000047687
1.80	-1.3746386009	.0000074827
1.90	-2.1617156594	-.0000239546
2.00	-3.0752629702	.0000132688
2.10	-4.1231062502	-.0000088775
2.20	-5.3118033461	.0000063599
2.30	-6.0462781531	-.0000049130
2.40	-8.1292986104	.0000003620
2.50	-9.7609832933	-.0000031370

N = 1

Table A5

IMPROVED SELF-STARTING CONTINUING METHOD

T	COMPUTED VALUE	TRUNC ERROR
0.00	1.0000000000	
.10	1.0996496670	
.20	1.1970560214	-.000000000154
.30	1.2895693742	-.000000000181
.40	1.3740615389	-.000000000215
.50	1.4468890368	-.000000000247
.60	1.5038595406	-.000000000284
.70	1.5402030257	-.000000000321
.80	1.5505492969	-.000000000361
.90	1.5289138121	-.000000000400
1.00	1.4686939400	-.000000000439
1.10	1.3626780568	-.000000000479
1.20	1.2030701127	-.000000000514
1.30	.9815325606	-.000000000551
1.40	.6892507522	-.000000000574
1.50	.3170221439	-.000000000586
1.60	-.1446261796	-.000000000296
1.70	-.7052879750	-.000000000624
1.80	-1.3744925606	-.000000000675
1.90	-2.1614798932	-.000000000532
2.00	-3.0749322854	-.000000000536
2.10	-4.1226590222	-.000000000445
2.20	-5.3112304666	-.000000000374
2.30	-6.6455585248	-.000000000242
2.40	-8.1284208948	-.000000000103
2.50	-9.7599271454	.000000000092

N = 2

Table A6

IMPROVED SELF-STARTING CONTINUING METHOD

T	COMPUTED VALUE	TRUNC ERROR
0.00	1.0000000000	
.10	1.0996496668	
.20	1.1970560214	-.000000000153
.30	1.2895693740	-.000000000182
.40	1.3740615389	-.000000000214
.50	1.4468890366	-.000000000248
.60	1.5038595406	-.000000000284
.70	1.5402030254	-.000000000321
.80	1.5505492968	-.000000000360
.90	1.5289138119	-.000000000400
1.00	1.4686939399	-.000000000440
1.10	1.3626780566	-.000000000478
1.20	1.2030701127	-.000000000515
1.30	.9815325604	-.000000000549
1.40	.6892507522	-.000000000578
1.50	.3170221437	-.000000000576
1.60	-.1446261787	-.000000000223
1.70	-.7052879690	-.000000000659
1.80	-1.3744925496	-.000000000731
1.90	-2.1614798755	-.000000000514
2.00	-3.0749322606	-.000000000546
2.10	-4.1226589886	-.000000000438
2.20	-5.3112304236	-.000000000379
2.30	-6.6455584707	-.000000000239
2.40	-8.1284208289	-.000000000106
2.50	-9.7599270661	.000000000094

N = 3

Table A7

IMPROVED SELF-STARTING CONTINUING METHOD

T	COMPUTED VALUE	TRUNC ERROR
0.00	1.0000000000	
.05	1.0499575962	
.10	1.0996496899	-.000000001097
.15	1.1487884199	.000000001012
.20	1.1970560660	-.000000000935
.25	1.2441085083	.000000000857
.30	1.2895694385	-.000000000787
.35	1.3330336740	.000000000713
.40	1.3740616209	-.000000000648
.45	1.4121825125	.000000000576
.50	1.4468891334	-.000000000512
.55	1.4776410573	.000000000439
.60	1.5038596488	-.000000000374
.65	1.5249313813	.000000000298
.70	1.5402031409	-.000000000228
.75	1.5489857122	.000000000143
.80	1.5505494144	-.000000000064
.85	1.5441278536	-.000000000035
.90	1.5289139252	.000000000132
.95	1.5040639426	-.000000000257
1.00	1.4686940413	.000000000386
1.05	1.4218848117	-.000000000555
1.10	1.3626781365	.000000000743
1.15	1.2900824759	-.000000000996
1.20	1.2030701592	.000000001304
1.25	1.1005835052	-.000000001738
1.30	.9815325575	.000000002328
1.35	.8448022850	-.000000003234
1.40	.6892506752	.000000004692
1.45	.5137173946	-.000000007430
1.50	.3170219430	.000000013773
1.55	.0979745533	-.000000033623
1.60	-.1446284595	-.000000074538
1.65	-.4119880208	.000000087003
1.70	-.7052998599	.000000020983
1.75	-1.0257527667	-.000000008635
1.80	-1.3745158625	.000000005112
1.85	-1.7527341080	-.000000003511
1.90	-2.1615166032	.000000002598
1.95	-2.6019297130	-.000000002037
2.00	-3.0749845482	.000000001640
2.05	-3.5816280189	-.000000001369
2.10	-4.1227291199	.000000001153
2.15	-4.6990679931	-.000000000997
2.20	-5.3113207931	.000000000864
2.25	-5.9600467691	-.000000000764
2.30	-6.6456715593	.000000000675
2.35	-7.3684722834	-.000000000606
2.40	-8.1285591633	.000000000544
2.45	-8.9258586229	-.000000000491
2.50	-9.7600931767	.000000000448

N = 1

IMPROVED SELF-STARTING CONTINUING METHOD   IMPROVED SELF-STARTING CONTINUING METHOD

T	COMPUTED VALUE	TRUNC ERROR	T	COMPUTED VALUE	TRUNC ERROR
0.00	1.0000000000		0.00	1.0000000000	
.05	1.0499572813		.05	1.0499572813	
.10	1.0996496668	-.00000000001	.10	1.0996496668	-.00000000001
.15	1.1487880968	-.00000000001	.15	1.1487880965	-.00000000001
.20	1.1970560214	-.00000000001	.20	1.1970560214	-.00000000001
.25	1.2441081760	-.00000000001	.25	1.2441081760	-.00000000001
.30	1.2895693740	-.00000000002	.30	1.2895693740	-.00000000002
.35	1.3330333328	-.00000000002	.35	1.3330333328	-.00000000002
.40	1.3740615389	-.00000000002	.40	1.3740615389	-.00000000002
.45	1.4121821630	-.00000000002	.45	1.4121821630	-.00000000002
.50	1.4468890366	-.00000000002	.50	1.4468890366	-.00000000002
.55	1.4776407007	-.00000000002	.55	1.4776407007	-.00000000002
.60	1.5038595406	-.00000000002	.60	1.5038595406	-.00000000002
.65	1.5249310195	-.00000000003	.65	1.5249310194	-.00000000003
.70	1.5402030254	-.00000000003	.70	1.5402030254	-.00000000003
.75	1.5489853476	-.00000000003	.75	1.5489853476	-.00000000003
.80	1.5505492968	-.00000000003	.80	1.5505492968	-.00000000003
.85	1.5441274896	-.00000000003	.85	1.5441274896	-.00000000003
.90	1.5289138119	-.00000000003	.90	1.5289138119	-.00000000003
.95	1.5040635831	-.00000000003	.95	1.5040635831	-.00000000003
1.00	1.4686939399	-.00000000004	1.00	1.4686939399	-.00000000004
1.05	1.4218844613	-.00000000004	1.05	1.4218844613	-.00000000004
1.10	1.3626780566	-.00000000004	1.10	1.3626780566	-.00000000004
1.15	1.2900821395	-.00000000004	1.15	1.2900821395	-.00000000004
1.20	1.2030701127	-.00000000004	1.20	1.2030701127	-.00000000004
1.25	1.1005831869	-.00000000004	1.25	1.1005831869	-.00000000004
1.30	.9815325605	-.00000000004	1.30	.9815325605	-.00000000004
1.35	.8448019862	-.00000000005	1.35	.8448019862	-.00000000005
1.40	.6892507523	-.00000000005	1.40	.6892507523	-.00000000005
1.45	.5137171052	-.00000000005	1.45	.5137171052	-.00000000005
1.50	.3170221436	-.00000000004	1.50	.3170221436	-.00000000005
1.55	.0979742112	-.00000000005	1.55	.0979742112	-.00000000004
1.60	-.1446261808	-.00000000008	1.60	-.1446261808	-.00000000005
1.65	-.4119808723	0.00000000000	1.65	-.4119808720	-.00000000004
1.70	-.7052879841	-.00000000004	1.70	-.7052879830	-.00000000004
1.75	-1.0257352297	-.00000000005	1.75	-1.0257352290	-.00000000005
1.80	-1.3744925772	-.00000000005	1.80	-1.3744925763	-.00000000004
1.85	-1.7527042334	-.00000000005	1.85	-1.7527042323	-.00000000004
1.90	-2.1614799201	-.00000000004	1.90	-2.1614799187	-.00000000004
1.95	-2.6018854140	-.00000000004	1.95	-2.6018854123	-.00000000004
2.00	-3.0749323231	-.00000000004	2.00	-3.0749323212	-.00000000004
2.05	-3.5815670724	-.00000000004	2.05	-3.5815670701	-.00000000004
2.10	-4.1226590732	-.00000000003	2.10	-4.1226590706	-.00000000003
2.15	-4.6989880546	-.00000000003	2.15	-4.6989880516	-.00000000003
2.20	-5.3112305320	-.00000000002	2.20	-5.3112305286	-.00000000002
2.25	-5.9599453960	-.00000000002	2.25	-5.9599453928	-.00000000002
2.30	-6.6455586069	-.00000000001	2.30	-6.6455586027	-.00000000001
2.35	-7.3683469690	-.00000000001	2.35	-7.3683469643	-.00000000001
2.40	-8.1284209950	0.00000000000	2.40	-8.1284209898	0.00000000000
2.45	-8.9257068332	.00000000001	2.45	-8.9257068274	.00000000001
2.50	-9.7599272660	.00000000002	2.50	-9.7599272597	.00000000002

N = 2   N = 3

Table A10

IMPROVED SELF-STARTING CONTINUING METHOD

T	COMPUTED VALUE	TRUNC ERROR	T	COMPUTED VALUE	TRUNC ERROR
0.00	1.0000000000		1.26	1.0781335205	-.000000000055
.02	1.0199973268		1.28	1.0312113134	.000000000063
.04	1.0399782372	-.000000000030			
.06	1.0599258345	.000000000029	1.30	.9815325805	-.000000000071
.08	1.0798223987	-.000000000028	1.32	.9290252899	.000000000081
			1.34	.8736169446	-.000000000093
.10	1.0996496875	.000000000027	1.36	.8152342856	.000000000108
.12	1.1193886129	-.000000000026	1.38	.7538036682	-.000000000127
.14	1.1390195365	.000000000025			
.16	1.1585219515	-.000000000025	1.40	.6892507470	.000000000150
.18	1.1778747727	.000000000024	1.42	.6215008813	-.000000000182
			1.44	.5504787938	.000000000224
.20	1.1970560242	-.000000000023	1.46	.4761090164	-.000000000283
.22	1.2160431244	.000000000022	1.48	.3983155091	.000000000372
.24	1.2348125786	-.000000000022			
.26	1.2533402597	.000000000021	1.50	.3170221646	-.000000000515
.28	1.2716011057	-.000000000020	1.52	.2321523611	.000000000777
			1.54	.1436295666	.000000001363
.30	1.2895693959	.000000000019	1.56	.0513767602	.000000003217
.32	1.3072184535	-.000000000019	1.58	-.0446825958	.000000009662
.34	1.3245209179	.000000000018			
.36	1.3414484513	-.000000000017	1.60	-.1446253950	-.000000009758
.38	1.3579720076	.000000000016	1.62	-.2485290156	-.000000004619
			1.64	-.3564700880	.000000001706
.40	1.3740615442	-.000000000016	1.66	-.4685254626	-.000000000975
.42	1.3896852865	.000000000015	1.68	-.5847714415	.000000000656
.44	1.4048144442	.000000000014			
.46	1.4194134732	.000000000014	1.70	-.7052843036	-.000000000481
.48	1.4334497957	-.000000000013	1.72	-.8301397065	.000000000373
			1.74	-.9594130797	-.000000000300
.50	1.4468890595	.000000000012	1.76	-1.0931791151	.000000000249
.52	1.4596958616	-.000000000011	1.78	-1.2315120811	-.000000000211
.54	1.4718340060	.000000000011			
.56	1.4832662303	-.000000000010	1.80	-1.3744853678	.000000000182
.58	1.4939544619	.000000000009	1.82	-1.5221717437	-.000000000159
			1.84	-1.6746429395	.000000000140
.60	1.5038595476	-.000000000009	1.86	-1.8319698607	-.000000000125
.62	1.5129415091	.000000000008	1.88	-1.9942221984	.000000000112
.64	1.5211592754	-.000000000007			
.66	1.5284709372	.000000000006	1.90	-2.1614686060	-.000000000102
.68	1.5348334821	-.000000000005	1.92	-2.3337763309	.000000000093
			1.94	-2.5112113604	-.000000000085
.70	1.5402030490	.000000000005	1.96	-2.6938380686	.000000000078
.72	1.5445346654	-.000000000004	1.98	-2.8817193366	-.000000000072
.74	1.5477825022	.000000000003			
.76	1.5495996131	-.000000000002	2.00	-3.0749162102	.000000000067
.78	1.5508381900	.000000000001	2.02	-3.2734879973	-.000000000063
			2.04	-3.4774919337	.000000000058
.80	1.5505493044	0.000000000000	2.06	-3.6869812599	-.000000000055
.82	1.5489831639	-.000000000001	2.08	-3.9020148931	.000000000051
.84	1.5460888556	.000000000002			
.86	1.5418146034	-.000000000003	2.10	-4.1226374843	-.000000000048
.88	1.5361075139	.000000000004	2.12	-4.3488990955	.000000000046
			2.14	-4.5808452380	-.000000000043
.90	1.5289138354	-.000000000005	2.16	-4.8185185532	.000000000041
.92	1.5201787043	.000000000006	2.18	-5.0619588339	-.000000000039
.94	1.5098464082	.000000000008			
.96	1.4978601320	.000000000009	2.20	-5.3112027070	.000000000037
.98	1.4841622248	-.000000000011	2.22	-5.5562835383	-.000000000035
			2.24	-5.8272316166	.000000000033
1.00	1.4686939465	.000000000012	2.26	-6.0940731432	-.000000000032
1.02	1.4513957386	-.000000000014	2.28	-6.3668309154	.000000000030
1.04	1.4322069709	.000000000016			
1.06	1.4110662172	-.000000000018	2.30	-6.6455238019	-.000000000029
1.08	1.3879110013	.000000000020	2.32	-6.9301665254	-.000000000028
			2.34	-7.2207696239	-.000000000027
1.10	1.3626780789	-.000000000023	2.36	-7.5173391319	.000000000026
1.12	1.3353031816	.000000000025	2.38	-7.8198765280	-.000000000024
1.14	1.3057213064	-.000000000028			
1.16	1.2738664573	.000000000032	2.40	-8.1283784145	.000000000024
1.18	1.2396719432	-.000000000035	2.42	-8.4428364517	-.000000000023
			2.44	-8.7632370348	.000000000022
1.20	1.2030701157	.000000000039	2.46	-9.0895612161	-.000000000021
1.22	1.1639926777	-.000000000044	2.48	-9.4217843789	.000000000020
1.24	1.1223704156	.000000000049			
			2.50	-9.7598761471	-.000000000019

N = 1

Table A11

IMPROVED SELF-STARTING CONTINUING METHOD

T	COMPUTED VALUE	TRUNC ERROR	T	COMPUTED VALUE	TRUNC ERROR
0.00	1.0000000000		1.26	1.0781335000	0.000000000000
.02	1.0199973066		1.28	1.0312113129	0.000000000000
.04	1.0399782366	0.000000000000			
.06	1.0599258141	0.000000000000	1.30	.9815325605	0.000000000000
.08	1.0798223975	0.000000000000	1.32	.9290252910	0.000000000000
			1.34	.8736169250	0.000000000000
.10	1.0996496668	0.000000000000	1.36	.8152342885	0.000000000000
.12	1.1193886111	0.000000000000	1.38	.7538036490	0.000000000000
.14	1.1390195157	0.000000000000			
.16	1.1585219492	0.000000000000	1.40	.6892507523	0.000000000000
.18	1.1778747516	0.000000000000	1.42	.6215008622	0.000000000000
			1.44	.5504788019	0.000000000000
.20	1.1970560214	0.000000000000	1.46	.4761089970	0.000000000000
.22	1.2160431031	0.000000000000	1.48	.3983155211	0.000000000000
.24	1.2348125752	0.000000000000			
.26	1.2533402381	0.000000000000	1.50	.3170221436	0.000000000000
.28	1.2716011017	0.000000000000	1.52	.2321523793	0.000000000000
			1.54	.1436295405	0.000000000000
.30	1.2895693740	0.000000000000	1.56	.0513767912	0.000000000000
.32	1.3072184491	0.000000000000	1.58	-.0446827959	0.000000000000
.34	1.3245208958	0.000000000000			
.36	1.3414484464	0.000000000000	1.60	-.1446261807	0.000000000000
.38	1.3579719854	0.000000000000	1.62	-.2485302942	0.000000000000
			1.64	-.3564719743	0.000000000000
.40	1.3740615389	0.000000000000	1.66	-.4685278993	0.000000000000
.42	1.3896862640	0.000000000000	1.68	-.5847745192	0.000000000000
.44	1.4048144384	0.000000000000			
.46	1.4194134505	0.000000000000	1.70	-.7052879834	0.000000000000
.48	1.4334497896	0.000000000000	1.72	-.8301440668	0.000000000000
			1.74	-.9594180924	0.000000000000
.50	1.4468890366	0.000000000000	1.76	-1.0931848513	0.000000000000
.52	1.4596958552	0.000000000000	1.78	-1.2315185203	0.000000000000
.54	1.4718339830	0.000000000000			
.56	1.4832662236	0.000000000000	1.80	-1.3744925760	0.000000000000
.58	1.4939544386	0.000000000000	1.82	-1.5221797062	0.000000000000
			1.84	-1.6746517187	0.000000000000
.60	1.5038595406	0.000000000000	1.86	-1.8319794465	0.000000000000
.62	1.5129414857	0.000000000000	1.88	-1.9942326504	0.000000000000
.64	1.5211592682	0.000000000000			
.66	1.5284709137	0.000000000000	1.90	-2.1614799182	0.000000000000
.68	1.5348334747	0.000000000000	1.92	-2.3337885606	0.000000000000
			1.94	-2.5112245047	0.000000000000
.70	1.5402030254	0.000000000000	1.96	-2.6938521835	0.000000000000
.72	1.5445346579		1.98	-2.8817344219	0.000000000000
.74	1.5477024786	0.000000000000			
.76	1.5498996055	0.000000000000	2.00	-3.0749323204	0.000000000000
.78	1.5508381663	0.000000000000	2.02	-3.2735051347	0.000000000000
			2.04	-3.4775101518	0.000000000000
.80	1.5505492968	0.000000000000	2.06	-3.6870025632	0.000000000000
.82	1.5489831403	0.000000000000	2.08	-3.9020353341	0.000000000000
.84	1.5460888480	0.000000000000			
.86	1.5418145799	0.000000000000	2.10	-4.1226590695	0.000000000000
.88	1.5361075065	0.000000000000	2.12	-4.3489218760	0.000000000000
			2.14	-4.5808692232	0.000000000000
.90	1.5289138119	0.000000000000	2.16	-4.8185437934	0.000000000000
.92	1.5201786971	0.000000000000	2.18	-5.0619853391	0.000000000000
.94	1.5098463848	0.000000000000			
.96	1.4978601251	0.000000000000	2.20	-5.3112305272	0.000000000000
.98	1.4841622016	0.000000000000	2.22	-5.5663127849	0.000000000000
			2.24	-5.8272621392	0.000000000000
1.00	1.4686939399	0.000000000000	2.26	-6.0941050541	0.000000000000
1.02	1.4513957156	0.000000000000	2.28	-6.3668642637	0.000000000000
1.04	1.4322069648	0.000000000000			
1.06	1.4110661945	0.000000000000	2.30	-6.6455586010	0.000000000000
1.08	1.3879109958	0.000000000000	2.32	-6.9302028237	0.000000000000
			2.34	-7.2208074358	0.000000000000
1.10	1.3626780566	0.000000000000	2.36	-7.5173785051	0.000000000000
1.12	1.3353031768	0.000000000000	2.38	-7.8199174777	0.000000000000
1.14	1.3057212845	0.000000000000			
1.16	1.2738664533	0.000000000000	2.40	-8.1284209877	0.000000000000
1.18	1.2396719217	0.000000000000	2.42	-8.4428806641	0.000000000000
			2.44	-8.7632829327	0.000000000000
1.20	1.2030701127	0.000000000000	2.46	-9.0896088156	0.000000000000
1.22	1.1639926566	0.000000000000	2.48	-9.4218337255	0.000000000000
1.24	1.1223704138	0.000000000000	2.50	-9.7599272573	0.000000000000

$N = 2$

EXAMPLE 2.   Prepare a table of values of f, given that $f' = -1/\sin f$ and $f(0) = \pi/2$.

a. Take $h = .1$, $N = 2$, and stop at .9.
b. Take $h = .05$, $N = 2$, and stop at .95.
c. Take $h = .02$, $N = 2$, and stop at .98.
d. Take $h = .01$, $N = 1$, and stop at .99.

Solution: In the following pages we present an appropriate subroutine and the resulting tables (Tables A12–A15).

```
SUBROUTINE FNS(X,F,DF,D2F,D3F)

SF = SINF(F)
CF = COSF(F)
DF = -1./SF
D2F = CF*DF**3
D3F = DF**2*(3.*CF*D2F + DF)
RETURN
END
```

Table A12

IMPROVED SELF-STARTING CONTINUING METHOD

T	COMPUTED VALUE	TRUNC ERROR
0.00	1.5707963268	
.10	1.4706289056	
.20	1.3694384060	.000000004617
.30	1.2661036728	.000000008449
.40	1.1592794808	.000000019362
.50	1.0471975515	.000000052960
.60	.9272952195	.000000177627
.70	.7953988420	.000000797118
.80	.6435012932	.000005801240
.90	.4510375734	.000118920667

N = 2

Table A13

IMPROVED SELF-STARTING CONTINUING METHOD

T	COMPUTED VALUE	TRUNC ERROR
0.00	1.5707963268	
.05	1.5207754700	
.10	1.4706289056	.0000000000 30
.15	1.4202280540	.0000000000 35
.20	1.3694384060	.0000000000 46
.25	1.3181160717	.0000000000 64
.30	1.2661036728	.0000000000 95
.35	1.2132252231	.0000000000 147
.40	1.1592794807	.0000000000 236
.45	1.1040309877	.0000000000 396
.50	1.0471975512	.0000000000 698
.55	.9884320889	.0000000001 302
.60	.9272952180	.0000000002 596
.65	.8632118901	.0000000005 625
.70	.7953988302	.0000000013 545
.75	.7227342478	.000000037506
.80	.6435011091	.000000126063
.85	.5548110382	.000000565506
.90	.4510269202	.000004111755
.95	.3175075474	.000084209320

N = 2

Table A14

IMPROVED SELF-STARTING CONTINUING METHOD

T	COMPUTED VALUE	TRUNC ERROR
0.00	1.5707963268	
.02	1.5507949932	
.04	1.5307856524	0.00000000000
.06	1.5107602683	0.00000000000
.08	1.4907107468	0.00000000000
.10	1.4706289056	0.00000000000
.12	1.4505064444	0.00000000000
.14	1.4303349121	0.00000000000
.16	1.4101056738	0.00000000000
.18	1.3898098755	0.00000000000
.20	1.3694384060	0.00000000000
.22	1.3489818563	0.00000000000
.24	1.3284304758	0.00000000000
.26	1.3077741239	0.00000000000
.28	1.2870022176	0.00000000000
.30	1.2661036728	0.00000000000
.32	1.2450668395	0.00000000000
.34	1.2238794293	0.00000000000
.36	1.2025284334	0.00000000000
.38	1.1810000303	0.00000000000
.40	1.1592794807	.00000000000 1
.42	1.1373510067	.00000000000 1
.44	1.1151976534	.00000000000 1
.46	1.0928011283	.00000000000 1
.48	1.0701416144	.00000000000 1
.50	1.0471975512	.00000000000 2
.52	1.0239453761	.00000000000 2
.54	1.0003592174	.00000000000 3
.56	.9764105268	.00000000000 4
.58	.9520676361	.00000000000 5
.60	.9272952180	.00000000000 7
.62	.9020536236	.00000000000 9
.64	.8762980612	.00000000000 13
.66	.8499775659	.00000000000 18
.68	.8230336921	.00000000000 26
.70	.7953988302	.00000000000 38
.72	.7669940079	.00000000000 59
.74	.7377259685	.00000000000 92
.76	.7074832118	.00000000000 149
.78	.6761305096	.00000000000 251
.80	.6435011086	.000000000444
.82	.6093853080	.000000000828
.84	.5735131044	.000000001650
.86	.5355266543	.000000003574
.88	.4949341263	.000000008601
.90	.4510268117	.000000023803
.92	.4027158415	.000000079954
.94	.3481660235	.000000358432
.96	.2837941699	.000002604381
.98	.2003391625	.000053305809

N = 2

IMPROVED SELF-STARTING CONTINUING METHOD

T	COMPUTED VALUE	TRUNC ERROR	T	COMPUTED VALUE	TRUNC ERROR
0.00	1.5707963266		.50	1.0471975512	0.000000000000
.01	1.5607961601		.51	1.0356115365	0.000000000000
.02	1.5507949932	0.000000000000	.52	1.0239453761	0.000000000000
.03	1.5407918250	0.000000000000	.53	1.0121957615	0.000000000000
.04	1.5307856524	0.000000000000	.54	1.0003592174	0.000000000000
.05	1.5207754700	0.000000000000	.55	.9884320869	0.000000000000
.06	1.5107602683	0.000000000000	.56	.9764105268	0.000000000000
.07	1.5007390337	0.000000000000	.57	.9642904716	0.000000000000
.08	1.4907107468	0.000000000000	.58	.9520676361	0.000000000000
.09	1.4806743818	0.000000000000	.59	.9397374860	0.000000000000
.10	1.4706289056	0.000000000000	.60	.9272952180	0.000000000000
.11	1.4605732768	0.000000000000	.61	.9147357359	0.000000000000
.12	1.4505064444	0.000000000000	.62	.9020536236	0.000000000000
.13	1.4404273471	0.000000000000	.63	.8892431152	0.000000000000
.14	1.4303349121	0.000000000000	.64	.8762980612	0.000000000000
.15	1.4202280540	0.000000000000	.65	.8632118901	0.000000000000
.16	1.4101056738	0.000000000000	.66	.8499775659	0.000000000000
.17	1.3999666577	0.000000000000	.67	.8365875393	0.000000000000
.18	1.3898098755	0.000000000000	.68	.8230336921	0.000000000000
.19	1.3796341803	0.000000000000	.69	.8093072740	0.000000000000
.20	1.3694384060	0.000000000000	.70	.7953988302	0.000000000000
.21	1.3592213670	0.000000000000	.71	.7812981174	0.000000000000
.22	1.3489818563	0.000000000000	.72	.7669940079	.000000000001
.23	1.3387186439	0.000000000000	.73	.7524743762	.000000000001
.24	1.3284304758	0.000000000000	.74	.7377259065	.000000000001
.25	1.3181160717	0.000000000000	.75	.7227342478	.000000000001
.26	1.3077741239	0.000000000000	.76	.7074832118	.000000000001
.27	1.2974032953	0.000000000000	.77	.6919551751	.000000000002
.28	1.2870022176	0.000000000000	.78	.6761305096	.000000000003
.29	1.2765694890	0.000000000000	.79	.6599873294	.000000000003
.30	1.2661036728	0.000000000000	.80	.6435011088	.000000000005
.31	1.2556032944	0.000000000000	.81	.6266442116	.000000000006
.32	1.2450668395	0.000000000000	.82	.6093653080	.000000000009
.33	1.2344927516	0.000000000000	.83	.5916880424	.000000000013
.34	1.2238794293	0.000000000000	.84	.5735131044	.000000000016
.35	1.2132252231	0.000000000000	.85	.5548110330	.000000000027
.36	1.2025284334	0.000000000000	.86	.5355266543	.000000000042
.37	1.1917873061	0.000000000000	.87	.5155940062	.000000000065
.38	1.1810000303	0.000000000000	.88	.4949341263	.000000000106
.39	1.1701647341	0.000000000000	.89	.4734511573	.000000000176
.40	1.1592794807	0.000000000000	.90	.4510268118	.000000000314
.41	1.1483422646	0.000000000000	.91	.4275122649	.000000000566
.42	1.1373510067	0.000000000000	.92	.4027156410	.000000001169
.43	1.1263035499	0.000000000000	.93	.3763834823	.000000002531
.44	1.1121976534	0.000000000000	.94	.3481660212	.000000006091
.45	1.1040309877	0.000000000000	.95	.3175604292	.000000016851
.46	1.0928011283	0.000000000000	.96	.2837941091	.000000056591
.47	1.0815055488	0.000000000000	.97	.2455655188	.000000253658
.48	1.0701416144	0.000000000000	.98	.2003348834	.000001842514
.49	1.0587065739	0.000000000000	.99	.1415424858	.000037704230

K = 1

Tables

Table 1

THE GAMMA FUNCTION

T	.00	.01	.02	.03	.04	.05	.06	.07	.08	.09
-7.0		-.0202485	-.0103353	-.0070360	-.0053904	-.0044064	-.0037533	-.0032894	-.0029438	-.0026772
-6.9	-.0024660	-.0022951	-.0021545	-.0020374	-.0019387	-.0018549	-.0017832	-.0017216	-.0016685	-.0016225
-6.8	-.0015827	-.0015483	-.0015187	-.0014932	-.0014714	-.0014530	-.0014376	-.0014250	-.0014150	-.0014074
-6.7	-.0014020	-.0013987	-.0013974	-.0013981	-.0014009	-.0014048	-.0014109	-.0014186	-.0014280	-.0014392
-6.6	-.0014520	-.0014665	-.0014827	-.0015006	-.0015203	-.0015419	-.0015653	-.0015906	-.0016179	-.0016473
-6.5	-.0016789	-.0017127	-.0017489	-.0017877	-.0018290	-.0018732	-.0019204	-.0019708	-.0020245	-.0020819
-6.4	-.0021431	-.0022085	-.0022785	-.0023533	-.0024334	-.0025192	-.0026112	-.0027100	-.0028163	-.0029308
-6.3	-.0030542	-.0031877	-.0033322	-.0034889	-.0036594	-.0038454	-.0040487	-.0042717	-.0045171	-.0047881
-6.2	-.0050887	-.0054236	-.0057986	-.0062207	-.0066990	-.0072448	-.0078726	-.0086014	-.0094568	-.0104733
-6.1	-.0116996	-.0132056	-.0150966	-.0175380	-.0208052	-.0253942	-.0322972	-.0438288	-.0669334	-.1363334
-6.0		.1415367	.0721401	.0490410	.0375173	.0306245	.0260478	.0227953	.0203710	.0184993
-5.9	.0170151	.0158130	.0148231	.0139969	.0132997	.0127062	.0121974	.0117587	.0113790	.0110493
-5.8	.0107626	.0105133	.0102965	.0101087	.0099465	.0098075	.0096893	.0095902	.0095087	.0094434
-5.7	.0093932	.0093573	.0093348	.0093251	.0093277	.0093421	.0093681	.0094053	.0094536	.0095128
-5.6	.0095830	.0096640	.0097560	.0098591	.0099734	.0100992	.0102368	.0103865	.0105487	.0107239
-5.5	.0109127	.0111155	.0113331	.0115662	.0118156	.0120824	.0123675	.0126720	.0129973	.0133448
-5.4	.0137160	.0141126	.0145367	.0149904	.0154761	.0159966	.0165549	.0171544	.0177990	.0184931
-5.3	.0192417	.0200504	.0209259	.0218756	.0229081	.0240336	.0252639	.0266126	.0280963	.0297343
-5.2	.0315502	.0335723	.0358352	.0383819	.0412660	.0445554	.0483376	.0527268	.0578757	.0639921
-5.1	.0713673	.0804220	.0917874	.1064554	.1260793	.1536350	.1950748	.2642874	.4029393	.8193636
-5.0		-.8478047	-.4315978	-.2927749	-.2236030	-.1822155	-.1547239	-.1351762	-.1205963	-.1093311
-4.9	-.1003889	-.0931388	-.0871601	-.0821618	-.0779363	-.0743313	-.0712326	-.0685533	-.0622257	-.0641966
-4.8	-.0624234	-.0608718	-.0595140	-.0583271	-.0572920	-.0563929	-.0556166	-.0549520	-.0543896	-.0539217
-4.7	-.0535413	-.0532428	-.0530215	-.0528732	-.0527947	-.0527830	-.0528361	-.0529519	-.0531292	-.0533670
-4.6	-.0536646	-.0540217	-.0544384	-.0549150	-.0554521	-.0560507	-.0567120	-.0574375	-.0582291	-.0590889
-4.5	-.0600196	-.0610239	-.0621051	-.0632669	-.0645133	-.0658490	-.0672790	-.0688090	-.0704454	-.0721952
-4.4	-.0740662	-.0760671	-.0782076	-.0804986	-.0829521	-.0855819	-.0884030	-.0914328	-.0946905	-.0981982
-4.3	-.1019808	-.1060668	-.1104888	-.1152844	-.1204968	-.1261766	-.1323826	-.1391840	-.1466625	-.1549158
-4.2	-.1640611	-.1742400	-.1850263	-.1984364	-.2129324	-.2294602	-.2484551	-.2704886	-.2963234	-.3269995
-4.1	-.3639731	-.4093480	-.4662800	-.5397289	-.6379611	-.7788568	-.9831771	-1.3293659	-2.0227555	-4.1050118
-4.0		4.2305456	2.1483611	1.4550913	1.1090706	.9019667	.7643363	.6664185	.5933337	.5368158
-3.9	.4919058	.4554486	.4253412	.4001282	.3787704	.3605066	.3447659	.3311126	.3192080	.3087855
-3.8	.2996321	.2915760	.2844772	.2782201	.2727097	.2678661	.2636226	.2599229	.2567191	.2539710
-3.7	.2516440	.2497088	.2481406	.2469180	.2460234	.2454412	.2451593	.2451674	.2454570	.2460218
-3.6	.2468571	.2479597	.2495280	.2509615	.2528616	.2550306	.2574723	.2601917	.2631954	.2664911

Table 1 Γ (*Continued*)

T	.00	.01	.02	.03	.04	.05	.06	.07	.08	.09
-3.5	.2700882	.2739973	.2782309	.2828030	.2877294	.2930280	.2987187	.3048240	.3113688	.3183808
-3.4	.3258912	.3339344	.3425492	.3517787	.3616713	.3722811	.3836691	.3959039	.4090630	.4232342
-3.3	.4385174	.4550265	.4728921	.4922642	.5133166	.5362507	.5613023	.5887482	.6189159	.6521957
-3.2	.6890564	.7300657	.7759180	.8274713	.8857987	.9522600	1.0286040	1.1171180	1.2208525	1.3439680
-3.1	1.4922898	1.6742333	1.9024226	2.1966966	2.5901219	3.1422199	3.9720356	5.3573445	8.1314770	16.4610974
-3.0		-16.8798768	-8.5504771	-5.7767125	-4.3919197	-3.5627686	-3.0114850	-2.6190248	-2.3258679	-2.0989496
-2.9	-1.9184327	-1.7716951	-1.6503238	-1.5484959	-1.4620539	-1.3879503	-1.3239011	-1.2681611	-1.2193747	-1.1764728
-2.8	-1.1386021	-1.1050731	-1.0753234	-1.0488899	-1.0253884	-1.0044980	-.9859486	-.9695123	-.9549952	-.9422324
-2.7	-.9310828	-.9214256	-.9131572	-.9061890	-.9004450	-.8958603	-.8923799	-.8899575	-.8885544	-.8881389
-2.6	-.8886857	-.8901755	-.8925941	-.8959327	-.9001873	-.9053586	-.9114518	-.9184768	-.9264478	-.9353839
-2.5	-.9453087	-.9562507	-.9682436	-.9813263	-.9954360	-1.0109465	-1.0275924	-1.0455464	-1.0648812	-1.0856786
-2.4	-1.1080299	-1.1320277	-1.1578164	-1.1854944	-1.2152156	-1.2471418	-1.2814549	-1.3183600	-1.3580891	-1.4009052
-2.3	-1.4471074	-1.4970372	-1.5510860	-1.6097040	-1.6734120	-1.7428149	-1.8186195	-1.9016566	-1.9929091	-2.0935483
-2.2	-2.2049805	-2.3289096	-2.4674191	-2.6230839	-2.7991239	-2.9996191	-3.2296166	-3.4965793	-3.8090598	-4.1797403
-2.1	-4.6260983	-5.1733809	-5.8594615	-6.7438587	-7.9257731	-9.5837707	-12.0749884	-16.2327537	-24.5570607	-49.5479030
-2.0		50.4708315	25.4804216	17.1568362	13.0000824	10.5101675	8.5537659	7.6737426	6.7915344	6.1079435
-1.9	5.5634548	5.1201988	4.7529325	4.4441834	4.1814742	3.9555584	3.7598791	3.5888960	3.4386366	3.3058887
-1.8	3.1880859	3.0831540	2.9893990	2.9054250	2.8300721	2.7623695	2.7014993	2.6467685	2.5975870	2.5534498
-1.7	2.5139235	2.4786348	2.4472614	2.4195247	2.3951837	2.3740298	2.3558830	2.3405882	2.3280124	2.3180424
-1.6	2.3105829	2.3055544	2.3028928	2.3025471	2.3044795	2.3086644	2.3150876	2.3237462	2.3346485	2.3478136
-1.5	2.3632718	2.3810643	2.4012441	2.4238760	2.4490373	2.4768188	2.5073255	2.5406777	2.5770125	2.6164854
-1.4	2.6592719	2.7055700	2.7556029	2.8096216	2.8679088	2.9307833	2.9986045	3.0717788	3.1507667	3.2360910
-1.3	3.3283470	3.4282152	3.5364761	3.6540282	3.7819111	3.9213334	4.0737076	4.2406941	4.4242582	4.6267416
-1.2	4.8509571	5.1003121	5.3789737	5.6920920	6.0461076	6.4491811	6.9118074	7.4477139	8.0752068	8.8192521
-1.1	9.7148064	10.8123660	12.1876800	13.9597875	16.3270927	19.6467298	24.6329763	32.9524900	49.6052625	99.5912851
-1.0		-100.436955	-50.451235	-33.798967	-25.480161	-20.494827	-17.176306	-14.810323	-13.039746	-11.666172
-0.9	-10.570564	-9.677176	-8.935513	-8.310623	-7.777542	-7.317968	-6.918178	-6.567680	-6.258319	-5.983658
-0.8	-5.738555	-5.518846	-5.321130	-5.142602	-4.980927	-4.834147	-4.700609	-4.578910	-4.467850	-4.366399
-0.7	-4.273670	-4.188893	-4.111399	-4.040606	-3.976005	-3.917149	-3.863648	-3.815159	-3.771380	-3.732048
-0.6	-3.696933	-3.665832	-3.638571	-3.614999	-3.594988	-3.578430	-3.565235	-3.555332	-3.548666	-3.545199
-0.5	-3.544908	-3.547786	-3.553841	-3.563098	-3.575594	-3.591387	-3.610549	-3.633169	-3.659358	-3.689244
-0.4	-3.722981	-3.760742	-3.802732	-3.849182	-3.900356	-3.956557	-4.018130	-4.085466	-4.159012	-4.239279
-0.3	-4.326851	-4.422398	-4.526689	-4.640616	-4.765208	-4.901667	-5.051397	-5.216054	-5.397595	-5.598357
-0.2	-5.821149	-6.069371	-6.347189	-6.659748	-7.013485	-7.416558	-7.879460	-8.415917	-9.044232	-9.789370
-0.1	-10.686287	-11.785479	-13.162694	-14.936973	-17.306718	-20.629066	-25.618295	-33.941065	-50.597368	-100.587198

Table 1 Γ (*Continued*)

T	.00	.01	.02	.03	.04	.05	.06	.07	.08	.09
0.0		99.4325851	49.4422102	32.7849984	24.4609550	19.4700853	16.1457275	13.7736006	11.9965664	10.6162165
.1	9.5135077	8.6126864	7.8632515	7.2302419	6.6886862	6.2202729	5.8112692	5.4511742	5.1318212	4.8467634
.2	4.5908437	4.3598881	4.1504816	3.9598037	3.7855044	3.6250099	3.4784505	3.3426039	3.2168517	3.1001434
.3	2.9915690	2.8903361	2.7957514	2.7072062	2.6241633	2.5461470	2.4727348	2.4035500	2.3382557	2.2765495
.4	2.2181595	2.1628406	2.1103709	2.0605494	2.0131933	1.9681364	1.9252268	1.8843258	1.8453062	1.8080513
.5	1.7724539	1.7384151	1.7058438	1.6746559	1.6447734	1.6161243	1.5886414	1.5622627	1.5369303	1.5125902
.6	1.4891922	1.4666895	1.4450382	1.4241972	1.4041282	1.3847951	1.3661642	1.3482037	1.3308839	1.3141765
.7	1.2980553	1.2824953	1.2674730	1.2529663	1.2389541	1.2254167	1.2123354	1.1996924	1.1874709	1.1756551
.8	1.1642297	1.1531806	1.1424940	1.1321571	1.1221576	1.1124837	1.1031245	1.0940692	1.0853078	1.0768307
.9	1.0686287	1.0606931	1.0530156	1.0455881	1.0384031	1.0314533	1.0247318	1.0182319	1.0119474	1.0058720
1.0	1.0000000	.9943259	.9888442	.9835500	.9784382	.9735043	.9687436	.9641520	.9597253	.9554595
1.1	.9513508	.9473955	.9435902	.9399314	.9364161	.9330409	.9298031	.9266996	.9237278	.9208850
1.2	.9181687	.9155765	.9131059	.9107509	.9085211	.9064025	.9043971	.9025031	.9007185	.8990416
1.3	.8974707	.8960042	.8946405	.8933781	.8922155	.8911514	.8901845	.8893135	.8885371	.8878543
1.4	.8872638	.8867647	.8863558	.8860362	.8858051	.8855614	.8855043	.8856331	.8857470	.8859451
1.5	.8862269	.8865917	.8870388	.8875676	.8881777	.8888683	.8896392	.8904897	.8914196	.8924282
1.6	.8935153	.8946806	.8959237	.8972442	.8986420	.9001168	.9016684	.9032965	.9050010	.9067818
1.7	.9086387	.9105717	.9125806	.9146654	.9168260	.9190625	.9213749	.9237631	.9262273	.9287675
1.8	.9313838	.9340763	.9368451	.9396904	.9426124	.9456112	.9486870	.9518402	.9550709	.9583793
1.9	.9617658	.9652307	.9687743	.9723969	.9760989	.9798807	.9837425	.9876850	.9917084	.9958133
2.0	1.0000000	1.0042691	1.0086211	1.0130564	1.0175757	1.0221795	1.0268683	1.0316427	1.0365033	1.0414508
2.1	1.0464858	1.0516090	1.0568210	1.0621225	1.0675143	1.0729971	1.0785716	1.0842385	1.0899988	1.0958532
2.2	1.1018025	1.1078476	1.1139893	1.1202285	1.1265661	1.1330031	1.1395404	1.1461789	1.1529196	1.1597636
2.3	1.1667119	1.1737655	1.1809254	1.1881928	1.1955688	1.2030544	1.2106510	1.2183595	1.2261813	1.2341175
2.4	1.2421693	1.2503382	1.2586252	1.2670318	1.2755593	1.2842090	1.2929823	1.3018807	1.3109055	1.3200582
2.5	1.3293404	1.3387534	1.3482990	1.3579785	1.3677936	1.3777459	1.3878372	1.3980689	1.4084429	1.4189609
2.6	1.4296246	1.4404358	1.4513963	1.4625081	1.4737729	1.4851927	1.4967695	1.5085052	1.5204017	1.5324613
2.7	1.5446858	1.5570776	1.5696386	1.5823711	1.5952773	1.6083594	1.6216198	1.6350607	1.6486846	1.6624938
2.8	1.6764908	1.6906780	1.7050581	1.7196334	1.7344067	1.7493807	1.7645579	1.7799411	1.7955332	1.8113369
2.9	1.8273551	1.8435907	1.8600467	1.8767261	1.8936319	1.9107673	1.9281354	1.9457394	1.9635826	1.9816684
3.0	2.0000000	2.0185809	2.0374146	2.0565046	2.0758545	2.0954679	2.1153486	2.1355004	2.1559269	2.1766323
3.1	2.1976203	2.2188950	2.2404605	2.2623210	2.2844806	2.3069437	2.3297146	2.3527976	2.3761974	2.3999185
3.2	2.4239655	2.4443431	2.4730561	2.4981095	2.5235081	2.5492570	2.5753612	2.6018261	2.6286568	2.6558588
3.3	2.6834374	2.7113982	2.7397470	2.7684892	2.7976309	2.8271779	2.8571363	2.8875120	2.9183114	2.9499407
3.4	2.9812064	3.0133150	3.0458730	3.0788873	3.1123647	3.1465121	3.1807365	3.2156453	3.2510457	3.2869450

Table 1 Γ (Continued)

T	.00	.01	.02	.03	.04	.05	.06	.07	.08	.09
3.5	3.3233510	3.3602711	3.3977134	3.4356855	3.4741957	3.5132521	3.5528631	3.5930371	3.6337827	3.6751086
3.6	3.7170239	3.7595374	3.8026584	3.8463963	3.8907605	3.9357608	3.9814069	4.0277088	4.0746766	4.1223208
3.7	4.1706518	4.2196802	4.2694170	4.3198731	4.3710598	4.4229884	4.4756706	4.5291182	4.5833432	4.6383577
3.8	4.6941742	4.7508053	4.8082637	4.8665626	4.9257152	4.9857349	5.0466356	5.1084311	5.1711356	5.2347636
3.9	5.2993297	5.3648489	5.4313363	5.4988073	5.5672777	5.6367634	5.7072807	5.7788461	5.8514763	5.9251885
4.0	6.0000000	6.0759285	6.1529921	6.2312089	6.3105976	6.3911772	6.4729668	6.5559861	6.6402550	6.7257937
4.1	6.8126229	6.9007635	6.9902369	7.0810647	7.1732692	7.2668727	7.3618980	7.4583685	7.5563078	7.6557400
4.2	7.7566895	7.8591814	7.9632408	8.0688937	8.1761662	8.2850851	8.3956776	8.5079713	8.6219943	8.7377753
4.3	8.8553434	8.9747282	9.0959599	9.2190692	9.3440874	9.4710461	9.5999779	9.7309155	9.8638926	9.9989431
4.4	10.1361019	10.2754041	10.4168858	10.5605835	10.7065345	10.8547766	11.0053484	11.1582892	11.3136389	11.4714382
4.5	11.6317284	11.7945517	11.9599510	12.1279699	12.2986529	12.4720451	12.6481927	12.8271424	13.0089420	13.1936400
4.6	13.3812859	13.5719300	13.7656235	13.9624186	14.1623683	14.3655268	14.5719491	14.7816912	14.9948100	15.2113638
4.7	15.4314116	15.6550136	15.8822311	16.1131266	16.3477635	16.5862065	16.8285216	17.0747758	17.3250373	17.5793758
4.8	17.8378620	18.1005680	18.3675674	18.6389347	18.9147462	19.1950795	19.4800134	19.7696283	20.0640062	20.3632305
4.9	20.6673860	20.9765592	21.2908382	21.6103128	21.9350743	22.2652156	22.6008317	22.9420189	23.2888757	23.6415020
5.0	24.0000000	24.3644734	24.7350282	25.1117719	25.4948145	25.8842676	26.2802453	26.6828634	27.0922403	27.5084962
5.1	27.9317537	28.3621379	28.7997759	29.2447974	29.6973344	30.1575215	30.6254958	31.1013967	31.5853667	32.0775506
5.2	32.5780961	33.0871535	33.6048762	34.1314202	34.6669448	35.2116119	35.7655867	36.3290374	36.9021356	37.4850560
5.3	38.0779764	38.6810784	39.2945467	39.9185696	40.5533391	41.1990507	41.8559036	42.5241009	43.2038495	43.8953603
5.4	44.5984481	45.3145320	46.0426352	46.7833849	47.5370130	48.3037558	49.0838539	49.8775527	50.6851022	51.5067574
5.5	52.3427778	53.1934283	54.0589786	54.9397038	55.8358841	56.7478053	57.6757585	58.6200406	59.5809541	60.5588075
5.6	61.5539150	62.5665971	63.5971805	64.6459980	65.7133891	66.7996998	67.9052828	69.0304977	70.1757109	71.341962
5.7	72.5276345	73.7351141	74.9641310	76.2150888	77.4883990	78.7844811	80.1037628	81.4466804	82.8136783	84.2052100
5.8	85.6217375	87.0637322	88.5316746	90.0260546	91.5473718	93.0961354	94.6728650	96.2780899	97.9123504	99.5761970
5.9	101.270191	102.994906	104.750924	106.538842	108.359267	110.212817	112.100125	114.021834	115.978601	117.971095
6.0	120.000000	122.066012	124.169841	126.312213	128.493865	130.715552	132.978041	135.282118	137.628581	140.018245
6.1	142.451944	144.930525	147.454853	150.025811	152.644299	155.311236	158.027558	160.794221	163.612200	166.482488
6.2	169.406099	172.384070	175.417454	178.507328	181.654791	184.860962	188.126986	191.454027	194.843276	198.295946
6.3	201.813275	205.396526	209.046989	212.765976	216.554831	220.414921	224.347643	228.354422	232.436710	236.595992
6.4	240.833780	245.151618	249.551083	254.033780	258.601351	263.255469	267.997842	272.830213	277.754360	282.772098
6.5	287.885278	293.095790	298.405562	303.816562	309.330798	314.950319	320.677217	326.513626	332.461724	338.523734
6.6	344.701924	350.998610	357.416154	363.956969	370.623515	377.418304	384.343901	391.402922	398.598038	405.931976
6.7	413.407517	421.027502	428.794829	436.712459	444.783410	453.010766	461.397674	469.947346	478.663061	487.548166
6.8	496.606078	505.840284	515.254346	524.851899	534.636651	544.612392	554.782989	565.152388	575.724620	586.503800
6.9	597.494128	608.699892	620.125471	631.775334	643.654045	655.766263	668.116745	680.710349	693.552032	706.646860

Table 2

J_0

T	.00	.01	.02	.03	.04	.05	.06	.07	.08	.09
0.0	1.0000000	.9999750	.9999000	.9997750	.9996000	.9993751	.9991002	.9987754	.9984006	.9979760
.1	.9975016	.9969773	.9964032	.9957750	.9951060	.9943829	.9936104	.9927880	.9919164	.9909953
.2	.9900250	.9890054	.9879366	.9866187	.9856518	.9844359	.9831713	.9818579	.9804958	.9790853
.3	.9776262	.9761189	.9745634	.9729597	.9713081	.9696087	.9678615	.9660667	.9642245	.9623350
.4	.9603982	.9584145	.9563838	.9543065	.9521825	.9500121	.9477995	.9455528	.9432242	.9408698
.5	.9384698	.9360245	.9335339	.9309983	.9284179	.9257928	.9231233	.9204096	.9176518	.9148501
.6	.9120049	.9091162	.9061843	.9032094	.9001918	.8971316	.8940292	.8908846	.8876982	.8844702
.7	.8812009	.8778904	.8745391	.8711471	.8677147	.8642423	.8607300	.8571780	.8535868	.8499565
.8	.8462874	.8425797	.8388338	.8350500	.8312284	.8273695	.8234734	.8195405	.8155711	.8115654
.9	.8075238	.8034465	.7993339	.7951863	.7910039	.7867871	.7825361	.7782514	.7739332	.7695819
1.0	.7651977	.7607810	.7563321	.7518513	.7473390	.7427956	.7382214	.7336163	.7289813	.7243164
1.1	.7196220	.7148985	.7101461	.7053653	.7005564	.6957198	.6908557	.6859646	.6810469	.6761028
1.2	.6711327	.6661371	.6611163	.6560706	.6510004	.6459061	.6407880	.6356466	.6304822	.6252655
1.3	.6200860	.6148549	.6096023	.6043287	.5990343	.5937196	.5883850	.5830309	.5776576	.5722655
1.4	.5668551	.5614267	.5559807	.5505176	.5450376	.5395413	.5340289	.5285010	.5229579	.5174000
1.5	.5118277	.5062414	.5006415	.4950285	.4894026	.4837644	.4781143	.4724526	.4667797	.4610961
1.6	.4554022	.4496983	.4439850	.4382625	.4325313	.4267919	.4210446	.4152898	.4095280	.4037595
1.7	.3979864	.3922044	.3864185	.3806276	.3748321	.3690325	.3632292	.3574225	.3516128	.3458007
1.8	.3399864	.3341705	.3283532	.3225351	.3167166	.3108980	.3050797	.2992623	.2934460	.2876313
1.9	.2818186	.2760083	.2702008	.2643965	.2585959	.2527992	.2470071	.2412197	.2354376	.2296612
2.0	.2238908	.2181268	.2123697	.2066198	.2008776	.1951434	.1894177	.1837008	.1779931	.1722950
2.1	.1666070	.1609293	.1552625	.1496068	.1439626	.1383305	.1327106	.1271035	.1215095	.1159290
2.2	.1103623	.1048098	.0992720	.0937491	.0882416	.0827499	.0772742	.0718150	.0663726	.0609474
2.3	.0555398	.0501501	.0447787	.0394259	.0340921	.0287776	.0234828	.0182081	.0129538	.0077202
2.4	.0025077	-.0026834	-.0078527	-.0129999	-.0181247	-.0232267	-.0283057	-.0333611	-.0383929	-.0434005
2.5	-.0483838	-.0533423	-.0582758	-.0631839	-.0680064	-.0729229	-.0777531	-.0825567	-.0873334	-.0920829
2.6	-.0968050	-.1014992	-.1061654	-.1108031	-.1154123	-.1199924	-.1245434	-.1290648	-.1335565	-.1380181
2.7	-.1424494	-.1468500	-.1512198	-.1555585	-.1599658	-.1641414	-.1683852	-.1725967	-.1767759	-.1809224
2.8	-.1850360	-.1891165	-.1931636	-.1971771	-.2011568	-.2051024	-.2090137	-.2128905	-.2167325	-.2205396
2.9	-.2243115	-.2280481	-.2317491	-.2354142	-.2390434	-.2426364	-.2461931	-.2497151	-.2531964	-.2566427
3.0	-.2600520	-.2634239	-.2667583	-.2700551	-.2733140	-.2765350	-.2797178	-.2828623	-.2859683	-.2890357
3.1	-.2920643	-.2950541	-.2980048	-.3009162	-.3037084	-.3066211	-.3094142	-.3121675	-.3148811	-.3175547
3.2	-.3201882	-.3227815	-.3253345	-.3278471	-.3303193	-.3327508	-.3351416	-.3374917	-.3398009	-.3420691
3.3	-.3442963	-.3464823	-.3486272	-.3507308	-.3527931	-.3548140	-.3567934	-.3587314	-.3600277	-.3628825
3.4	-.3642956	-.3660670	-.3677967	-.3694845	-.3711306	-.3727349	-.3742972	-.3758177	-.3772963	-.3787330

Table 2 J_0 (*Continued*)

T	.00	.01	.02	.03	.04	.05	.06	.07	.08	.09
3.5	-.3801277	-.3814805	-.3827914	-.3840603	-.3852873	-.3864724	-.3876155	-.3887167	-.3897760	-.3907934
3.6	-.3917690	-.3927027	-.3935947	-.3944449	-.3952233	-.3960201	-.3967452	-.3974287	-.3980717	-.3986712
3.7	-.3992302	-.3997479	-.4002242	-.4006593	-.4010532	-.4014061	-.4017178	-.4019887	-.4022187	-.4024079
3.8	-.4025564	-.4026643	-.4027318	-.4027588	-.4027456	-.4026921	-.4025986	-.4024651	-.4022918	-.4020787
3.9	-.4018260	-.4015339	-.4012023	-.4008316	-.4004218	-.3999730	-.3994854	-.3989591	-.3983943	-.3977912
4.0	-.3971498	-.3964704	-.3957530	-.3949979	-.3942053	-.3933752	-.3925079	-.3916035	-.3906622	-.3896842
4.1	-.3886697	-.3876188	-.3865318	-.3854088	-.3842500	-.3830556	-.3818259	-.3805609	-.3792610	-.3779263
4.2	-.3765571	-.3751534	-.3737157	-.3722440	-.3707386	-.3691998	-.3676276	-.3660225	-.3643845	-.3627140
4.3	-.3610111	-.3592761	-.3575093	-.3557108	-.3538810	-.3520200	-.3501281	-.3482056	-.3462527	-.3442697
4.4	-.3422568	-.3402143	-.3381424	-.3360414	-.3339116	-.3317533	-.3295666	-.3273519	-.3251095	-.3228396
4.5	-.3205425	-.3182185	-.3158678	-.3134908	-.3110877	-.3086589	-.3062045	-.3037249	-.3012204	-.2986913
4.6	-.2961378	-.2935603	-.2905591	-.2883344	-.2856866	-.2830159	-.2803228	-.2776073	-.2748700	-.2721110
4.7	-.2693308	-.2665295	-.2637076	-.2608653	-.2580029	-.2551208	-.2522193	-.2492987	-.2463592	-.2434014
4.8	-.2404253	-.2374315	-.2344201	-.2313916	-.2283462	-.2252843	-.2222062	-.2191122	-.2160027	-.2128779
4.9	-.2097383	-.2065842	-.2034158	-.2002335	-.1970377	-.1938286	-.1906067	-.1873722	-.1841255	-.1808669
5.0	-.1775968	-.1743154	-.1710232	-.1677205	-.1644075	-.1610847	-.1577524	-.1544109	-.1510606	-.1477018
5.1	-.1443347	-.1409599	-.1375776	-.1341882	-.1307919	-.1273892	-.1239803	-.1205657	-.1171456	-.1137204
5.2	-.1102904	-.1068561	-.1034176	-.0999753	-.0965297	-.0930810	-.0896295	-.0861757	-.0827198	-.0792621
5.3	-.0758031	-.0723430	-.0688822	-.0654211	-.0619598	-.0584989	-.0550386	-.0515792	-.0481211	-.0446646
5.4	-.0412101	-.0377578	-.0343082	-.0308615	-.0274180	-.0239781	-.0205422	-.0171104	-.0136833	-.0102610
5.5	-.0068439	-.0034323	-.0000266	.0033730	.0067661	.0101524	.0135315	.0169033	.0202673	.0236233
5.6	.0269709	.0303098	.0336398	.0369605	.0402716	.0435728	.0468638	.0501444	.0534141	.0566727
5.7	.0599200	.0631556	.0663792	.0695906	.0727894	.0759753	.0791482	.0823076	.0854533	.0885851
5.8	.0917026	.0948055	.0978937	.1009668	.1040245	.1070666	.1100928	.1131028	.1160964	.1190734
5.9	.1220334	.1249761	.1279015	.1308091	.1336987	.1365701	.1394230	.1422573	.1450725	.1478686
6.0	.1506453	.1534022	.1561393	.1588562	.1615527	.1642286	.1668837	.1695178	.1721306	.1747218
6.1	.1772914	.1798391	.1823646	.1848678	.1873484	.1898062	.1922411	.1946529	.1970413	.1994061
6.2	.2017472	.2040644	.2063574	.2086262	.2108705	.2130901	.2152848	.2174546	.2195991	.2217183
6.3	.2238120	.2258800	.2279222	.2299383	.2319283	.2338920	.2358292	.2377398	.2396237	.2414807
6.4	.2433106	.2451134	.2468888	.2486369	.2503573	.2520501	.2537151	.2553522	.2569612	.2585420
6.5	.2600946	.2616188	.2631145	.2645817	.2660201	.2674298	.2688106	.2701625	.2714853	.2727789
6.6	.2740434	.2752785	.2764843	.2776606	.2788074	.2799246	.2810122	.2820700	.2830981	.2840964
6.7	.2850647	.2860032	.2869177	.2877901	.2886385	.2894568	.2902449	.2910029	.2917307	.2924283
6.8	.2930956	.2937327	.2943394	.2949159	.2954620	.2959779	.2964633	.2969185	.2973434	.2977379
6.9	.2981020	.2984359	.2987395	.2990127	.2992557	.2994685	.2996510	.2998033	.2999254	.3000174

Table 2 J_0 (*Continued*)

T	.00	.01	.02	.03	.04	.05	.06	.07	.08	.09
7.0	.3000793	.3001111	.3001128	.3000846	.3000264	.2999383	.2998204	.2996727	.2994953	.2992881
7.1	.2990514	.2987851	.2984893	.2981641	.2978096	.2974258	.2970128	.2965707	.2960996	.2955996
7.2	.2950707	.2945131	.2939268	.2933119	.2926686	.2919969	.2912970	.2905689	.2898128	.2890288
7.3	.2882169	.2873774	.2865103	.2856158	.2846939	.2837448	.2827687	.2817656	.2807358	.2796793
7.4	.2785962	.2774868	.2763512	.2751894	.2740018	.2727883	.2715492	.2702846	.2689947	.2676797
7.5	.2663397	.2649748	.2635853	.2621712	.2607329	.2592704	.2577839	.2562736	.2547397	.2531824
7.6	.2516018	.2499982	.2483717	.2467225	.2450508	.2433568	.2416407	.2399026	.2381429	.2363617
7.7	.2345591	.2327355	.2308910	.2290257	.2271400	.2252341	.2233081	.2213622	.2193967	.2174119
7.8	.2154078	.2133848	.2113430	.2092828	.2072042	.2051076	.2029932	.2008612	.1987118	.1965453
7.9	.1943618	.1921618	.1899452	.1877126	.1854639	.1831996	.1809198	.1786247	.1763147	.1739900
8.0	.1716508	.1692974	.1669299	.1645488	.1621542	.1597463	.1573255	.1548919	.1524459	.1499876
8.1	.1475175	.1450356	.1425423	.1400378	.1375223	.1349963	.1324598	.1299132	.1273568	.1247907
8.2	.1222153	.1196308	.1170375	.1144357	.1118256	.1092075	.1065816	.1039483	.1013077	.0986602
8.3	.0960061	.0933456	.0906789	.0880063	.0853282	.0826448	.0799563	.0772630	.0745652	.0718632
8.4	.0691572	.0664476	.0637345	.0610183	.0582992	.0555775	.0528534	.0501273	.0473994	.0446699
8.5	.0419393	.0392076	.0364752	.0337424	.0310094	.0282765	.0255440	.0228121	.0200812	.0173513
8.6	.0146230	.0118963	.0091717	.0064492	.0037293	.0010122	-.0017019	-.0044128	-.0071200	-.0098234
8.7	-.0125227	-.0152177	-.0179081	-.0205935	-.0232739	-.0259489	-.0286182	-.0312816	-.0339388	-.0365896
8.8	-.0392338	-.0418710	-.0445011	-.0471237	-.0497387	-.0523457	-.0549445	-.0575350	-.0601167	-.0626896
8.9	-.0652532	-.0678075	-.0703522	-.0728869	-.0754116	-.0779258	-.0804295	-.0829224	-.0854042	-.0878747
9.0	-.0903336	-.0927808	-.0952160	-.0976390	-.1000496	-.1024475	-.1048325	-.1072044	-.1095629	-.1119080
9.1	-.1142392	-.1165565	-.1188596	-.1211483	-.1234224	-.1256816	-.1279258	-.1301548	-.1323684	-.1345663
9.2	-.1367484	-.1389144	-.1410642	-.1431976	-.1453143	-.1474143	-.1494972	-.1515629	-.1536113	-.1556421
9.3	-.1576552	-.1596503	-.1616274	-.1635862	-.1655265	-.1674482	-.1693511	-.1712351	-.1730999	-.1749455
9.4	-.1767716	-.1785781	-.1803648	-.1821316	-.1838783	-.1856048	-.1873109	-.1889965	-.1906615	-.1923056
9.5	-.1939287	-.1955308	-.1971117	-.1986712	-.2002092	-.2017255	-.2032202	-.2046929	-.2061437	-.2075723
9.6	-.2089787	-.2103628	-.2117244	-.2130634	-.2143797	-.2156732	-.2169439	-.2181915	-.2194161	-.2206174
9.7	-.2217955	-.2229502	-.2240814	-.2251890	-.2262730	-.2273333	-.2283698	-.2293823	-.2303710	-.2313356
9.8	-.2322760	-.2331923	-.2340844	-.2349521	-.2357955	-.2366145	-.2374090	-.2381789	-.2389243	-.2396451
9.9	-.2403411	-.2410124	-.2416590	-.2422808	-.2428777	-.2434497	-.2439968	-.2445190	-.2450163	-.2454885
10.0	-.2459358	-.2463580	-.2467551	-.2471272	-.2474743	-.2477962	-.2480931	-.2483649	-.2486116	-.2488332
10.1	-.2490297	-.2492011	-.2493474	-.2494687	-.2495649	-.2496361	-.2496822	-.2497034	-.2496996	-.2496708
10.2	-.2496171	-.2495385	-.2494350	-.2493067	-.2491536	-.2489758	-.2487732	-.2485460	-.2482942	-.2480177
10.3	-.2477168	-.2473914	-.2470416	-.2466674	-.2462690	-.2458463	-.2453994	-.2449285	-.2444335	-.2439146
10.4	-.2433718	-.2428051	-.2422148	-.2416008	-.2409633	-.2403022	-.2396178	-.2389101	-.2381792	-.2374252

Table 2 J_0 (Continued)

T	.00	.01	.02	.03	.04	.05	.06	.07	.08	.09
10.5	-.2366482	-.2358483	-.2350255	-.2341800	-.2333120	-.2324214	-.2315085	-.2305732	-.2296158	-.2286364
10.6	-.2276350	-.2266119	-.2255670	-.2245006	-.2234127	-.2223036	-.2211732	-.2200218	-.2188495	-.2176565
10.7	-.2164427	-.2152085	-.2139539	-.2126791	-.2113843	-.2100695	-.2087349	-.2073807	-.2060071	-.2046141
10.8	-.2032020	-.2017708	-.2003208	-.1988522	-.1973650	-.1958594	-.1943357	-.1927939	-.1912343	-.1896570
10.9	-.1880622	-.1864501	-.1848208	-.1831745	-.1815115	-.1798318	-.1781356	-.1764232	-.1746947	-.1729504
11.0	-.1711903	-.1694147	-.1676238	-.1658178	-.1639968	-.1621611	-.1603109	-.1584463	-.1565675	-.1546748
11.1	-.1527683	-.1508483	-.1489149	-.1469684	-.1450089	-.1430367	-.1410520	-.1390549	-.1370458	-.1350247
11.2	-.1329919	-.1309477	-.1288922	-.1268256	-.1247483	-.1226602	-.1205618	-.1184532	-.1163346	-.1142063
11.3	-.1120685	-.1099213	-.1077650	-.1055999	-.1034261	-.1012439	-.0990535	-.0968552	-.0946491	-.0924354
11.4	-.0902145	-.0879865	-.0857517	-.0835102	-.0812623	-.0790083	-.0767484	-.0744828	-.0722117	-.0699353
11.5	-.0676539	-.0653678	-.0630771	-.0607821	-.0584830	-.0561801	-.0538735	-.0515636	-.0492505	-.0469344
11.6	-.0446157	-.0422945	-.0399711	-.0376456	-.0353184	-.0329897	-.0306597	-.0283286	-.0259967	-.0236642
11.7	-.0213313	-.0189982	-.0166653	-.0143327	-.0120006	-.0096694	-.0073391	-.0050101	-.0026825	-.0003567
11.8	.0019672	.0042889	.0066082	.0089249	.0112388	.0135496	.0158571	.0181610	.0204612	.0227574
11.9	.0250494	.0273370	.0296200	.0318980	.0341710	.0364386	.0387007	.0409570	.0432074	.0454516
12.0	.0476893	.0499204	.0521447	.0543619	.0565718	.0587743	.0609690	.0631559	.0653346	.0675049
12.1	.0696668	.0718199	.0739640	.0760989	.0782245	.0803406	.0824468	.0845431	.0866292	.0887050
12.2	.0907701	.0928245	.0948680	.0969003	.0989212	.1009306	.1029283	.1049140	.1068877	.1088491
12.3	.1107980	.1127342	.1146576	.1165679	.1184651	.1203489	.1222191	.1240756	.1259182	.1277467
12.4	.1295610	.1313609	.1331462	.1349167	.1366724	.1384129	.1401382	.1418482	.1435426	.1452212
12.5	.1468841	.1485309	.1501615	.1517758	.1533737	.1549550	.1565195	.1580671	.1595977	.1611111
12.6	.1626073	.1640860	.1655471	.1669905	.1684160	.1698236	.1712131	.1725845	.1739374	.1752719
12.7	.1765879	.1778851	.1791636	.1804231	.1816637	.1828851	.1840872	.1852700	.1864334	.1875772
12.8	.1887014	.1898058	.1908904	.1919550	.1929997	.1940242	.1950286	.1960127	.1969764	.1979197
12.9	.1988424	.1997446	.2006261	.2014869	.2023269	.2031460	.2039441	.2047213	.2054773	.2062123
13.0	.2069261	.2076187	.2082899	.2089399	.2095684	.2101755	.2107612	.2113253	.2118679	.2123888
13.1	.2128882	.2133659	.2138219	.2142562	.2146687	.2150594	.2154284	.2157755	.2161009	.2164043
13.2	.2166859	.2169457	.2171835	.2173995	.2175935	.2177657	.2179159	.2180443	.2181508	.2182354
13.3	.2182981	.2183389	.2183579	.2183551	.2183304	.2182839	.2182156	.2181256	.2180138	.2178803
13.4	.2177252	.2175484	.2173499	.2171299	.2168884	.2166254	.2163409	.2160349	.2157076	.2153590
13.5	.2149892	.2145981	.2141858	.2137525	.2132981	.2128227	.2123263	.2118092	.2112712	.2107125
13.6	.2101332	.2095332	.2089128	.2082720	.2076107	.2069293	.2062276	.2055059	.2047641	.2040024
13.7	.2032208	.2024195	.2015986	.2007581	.1998982	.1990189	.1981203	.1972026	.1962659	.1953102
13.8	.1943356	.1933424	.1923305	.1913002	.1902515	.1891845	.1880993	.1869962	.1858751	.1847363
13.9	.1835799	.1824059	.1812145	.1800059	.1787801	.1775373	.1762777	.1750014	.1737085	.1723991

Table 2 *J₀* (Continued)

T	.00	.01	.02	.03	.04	.05	.06	.07	.08	.09
14.0	.1710735	.1697317	.1683739	.1670002	.1656108	.1642058	.1627855	.1613498	.1598991	.1584334
14.1	.1569929	.1554577	.1539481	.1524242	.1508861	.1493340	.1477681	.1461885	.1445954	.1429890
14.2	.1413694	.1397368	.1380914	.1364334	.1347629	.1330800	.1313851	.1296782	.1279596	.1262293
14.3	.1244877	.1227348	.1209709	.1191961	.1174107	.1156147	.1138085	.1119921	.1101658	.1083297
14.4	.1064841	.1046292	.1027650	.1008919	.0990100	.0971195	.0952206	.0933135	.0913984	.0894754
14.5	.0875449	.0856069	.0836617	.0817095	.0797504	.0777848	.0758127	.0738344	.0718500	.0698599
14.6	.0678641	.0658629	.0638565	.0618450	.0598288	.0578079	.0557827	.0537533	.0517198	.0496826
14.7	.0476418	.0455977	.0435503	.0415000	.0394470	.0373914	.0353334	.0332733	.0312113	.0291476
14.8	.0270823	.0250157	.0229481	.0208795	.0188102	.0167404	.0146704	.0126003	.0105303	.0084606
14.9	.0063915	.0043232	.0022558	.0001896	-.0018753	-.0039386	-.0060002	-.0080597	-.0101171	-.0121721
15.0	-.0142245	-.0162741	-.0183207	-.0203641	-.0224042	-.0244406	-.0264732	-.0285019	-.0305263	-.0325464
15.1	-.0345619	-.0365725	-.0385782	-.0405787	-.0425738	-.0445634	-.0465472	-.0485250	-.0504967	-.0524620
15.2	-.0544208	-.0563729	-.0583180	-.0602560	-.0621868	-.0641100	-.0660256	-.0679333	-.0698380	-.0717245
15.3	-.0736075	-.0754820	-.0773477	-.0792045	-.0810521	-.0828904	-.0847192	-.0865384	-.0883477	-.0901471
15.4	-.0919362	-.0937150	-.0954833	-.0972409	-.0989876	-.1007233	-.1024478	-.1041610	-.1058626	-.1075525
15.5	-.1092307	-.1108968	-.1125507	-.1141923	-.1158215	-.1174380	-.1190418	-.1206326	-.1222103	-.1237748
15.6	-.1253260	-.1268636	-.1283875	-.1298977	-.1313938	-.1328759	-.1343438	-.1357973	-.1372363	-.1386606
15.7	-.1400702	-.1414649	-.1428446	-.1442091	-.1455583	-.1468921	-.1482104	-.1495130	-.1507998	-.1520708
15.8	-.1533257	-.1545646	-.1557872	-.1569934	-.1581832	-.1593565	-.1605130	-.1616528	-.1627757	-.1638816
15.9	-.1649705	-.1660422	-.1670966	-.1681336	-.1691532	-.1701552	-.1711396	-.1721063	-.1730551	-.1739861
16.0	-.1748991	-.1757940	-.1766708	-.1775294	-.1783697	-.1791917	-.1799952	-.1807802	-.1815467	-.1822945
16.1	-.1830237	-.1837341	-.1844257	-.1850984	-.1857523	-.1863871	-.1870029	-.1875996	-.1881773	-.1887357
16.2	-.1892749	-.1897949	-.1902956	-.1907770	-.1912390	-.1916815	-.1921047	-.1925084	-.1928926	-.1932572
16.3	-.1936024	-.1939279	-.1942339	-.1945203	-.1947870	-.1950342	-.1952616	-.1954694	-.1956576	-.1958260
16.4	-.1959748	-.1961039	-.1962134	-.1963031	-.1963732	-.1964235	-.1964543	-.1964653	-.1964567	-.1964285
16.5	-.1963807	-.1963133	-.1962262	-.1961196	-.1959935	-.1958479	-.1956827	-.1954981	-.1952941	-.1950707
16.6	-.1948279	-.1945657	-.1942843	-.1939836	-.1936637	-.1933247	-.1929665	-.1925892	-.1921930	-.1917777
16.7	-.1913435	-.1908905	-.1904186	-.1899280	-.1894187	-.1888908	-.1883442	-.1877792	-.1871958	-.1865940
16.8	-.1859739	-.1853355	-.1846791	-.1840045	-.1833120	-.1826015	-.1818732	-.1811272	-.1803635	-.1795822
16.9	-.1787834	-.1779672	-.1771337	-.1762830	-.1754152	-.1745303	-.1736286	-.1727100	-.1717747	-.1708227
17.0	-.1698543	-.1688694	-.1678682	-.1668508	-.1658174	-.1647680	-.1637027	-.1626217	-.1615250	-.1604129
17.1	-.1592853	-.1581425	-.1569846	-.1558116	-.1546238	-.1534212	-.1522039	-.1509721	-.1497260	-.1484656
17.2	-.1471911	-.1459027	-.1446004	-.1432844	-.1419548	-.1406118	-.1392556	-.1378862	-.1365038	-.1351086
17.3	-.1337006	-.1322802	-.1308473	-.1294021	-.1279449	-.1264757	-.1249947	-.1235021	-.1219979	-.1204825
17.4	-.1189559	-.1174182	-.1158697	-.1143105	-.1127408	-.1111607	-.1095704	-.1079700	-.1063598	-.1047399

Table 2 J_0 (*Continued*)

r	.00	.01	.02	.03	.04	.05	.06	.07	.08	.09
17.5	-.1031104	-.1014715	-.0998235	-.0981664	-.0965004	-.0948257	-.0931425	-.0914510	-.0897512	-.0880435
17.6	-.0863279	-.0846047	-.0828740	-.0811360	-.0793908	-.0776387	-.0758799	-.0741145	-.0723426	-.0705645
17.7	-.0687804	-.0669904	-.0651947	-.0633935	-.0615870	-.0597754	-.0579587	-.0561374	-.0543114	-.0524810
17.8	-.0506464	-.0488078	-.0469654	-.0451192	-.0432696	-.0414167	-.0395607	-.0377018	-.0358402	-.0339760
17.9	-.0321095	-.0302408	-.0283701	-.0264976	-.0246235	-.0227480	-.0208713	-.0189935	-.0171149	-.0152356
18.0	-.0133558	-.0114757	-.0095956	-.0077155	-.0058357	-.0039563	-.0020776	-.0001997	.0016771	.0035528
18.1	.0054270	.0072997	.0091706	.0110396	.0129064	.0147709	.0166330	.0184923	.0203487	.0222021
18.2	.0240523	.0258990	.0277422	.0295815	.0314169	.0332481	.0350750	.0368974	.0387152	.0405280
18.3	.0423358	.0441384	.0459356	.0477272	.0495131	.0512931	.0530669	.0548345	.0565956	.0583501
18.4	.0600979	.0618387	.0635723	.0652987	.0670175	.0687288	.0704323	.0721278	.0738151	.0754942
18.5	.0771648	.0788268	.0804800	.0821243	.0837595	.0853855	.0870020	.0886089	.0902061	.0917935
18.6	.0933708	.0949380	.0964948	.0980411	.0995768	.1011017	.1026157	.1041186	.1056103	.1070906
18.7	.1085595	.1100167	.1114621	.1128956	.1143171	.1157264	.1171234	.1185079	.1198798	.1212390
18.8	.1225853	.1239187	.1252390	.1265461	.1278398	.1291201	.1303868	.1316397	.1328789	.1341041
18.9	.1353152	.1365122	.1376949	.1388632	.1400170	.1411562	.1422807	.1433904	.1444851	.1455648
19.0	.1466294	.1476788	.1487129	.1497316	.1507347	.1517223	.1526942	.1536503	.1545905	.1555148
19.1	.1564231	.1573152	.1581912	.1590508	.1598942	.1607211	.1615315	.1623253	.1631025	.1638630
19.2	.1646067	.1653335	.1660435	.1667364	.1674124	.1680713	.1687130	.1693375	.1699448	.1705347
19.3	.1711073	.1716625	.1722003	.1727206	.1732233	.1737084	.1741760	.1746258	.1750580	.1754725
19.4	.1758692	.1762481	.1766092	.1769525	.1772779	.1775854	.1778749	.1781466	.1784003	.1786361
19.5	.1788538	.1790536	.1792354	.1793991	.1795449	.1796726	.1797823	.1798739	.1799475	.1800031
19.6	.1800407	.1800603	.1800618	.1800454	.1800109	.1799585	.1798881	.1797998	.1796935	.1795693
19.7	.1794274	.1792673	.1790895	.1788939	.1786806	.1784494	.1782006	.1779340	.1776498	.1773480
19.8	.1770286	.1766917	.1763373	.1759654	.1755761	.1751695	.1747456	.1743044	.1738459	.1733704
19.9	.1728777	.1723681	.1718414	.1712978	.1707374	.1701602	.1695663	.1689557	.1683285	.1676848
20.0	.1670247	.1663482	.1656554	.1649464	.1642212	.1634800	.1627228	.1619498	.1611609	.1603563
20.1	.1595361	.1587003	.1578491	.1569825	.1561007	.1552037	.1542916	.1533645	.1524226	.1514659
20.2	.1504946	.1495086	.1485082	.1474935	.1464645	.1454214	.1443643	.1432932	.1422083	.1411098
20.3	.1399977	.1388722	.1377333	.1365812	.1354160	.1342379	.1330469	.1318432	.1306269	.1293982
20.4	.1281571	.1269038	.1256384	.1243611	.1230720	.1217712	.1204589	.1191352	.1178002	.1164541
20.5	.1150970	.1137290	.1123504	.1109612	.1095615	.1081516	.1067316	.1053016	.1038618	.1024123
20.6	.1009532	.0994848	.0980071	.0965203	.0950246	.0935202	.0920071	.0904855	.0889557	.0874177
20.7	.0858747	.0843178	.0827563	.0811872	.0796108	.0780272	.0764366	.0748391	.0732348	.0716240
20.8	.0700069	.0683835	.0667540	.0651187	.0634776	.0618310	.0601790	.0585217	.0568595	.0551923
20.9	.0535204	.0518439	.0501631	.0484780	.0467889	.0450960	.0433993	.0416991	.0399956	.0382888

Table 2 J_0 (Continued)

T	.00	.01	.02	.03	.04	.05	.06	.07	.08	.09
21.0	.0365791	.0348665	.0331512	.0314334	.0297133	.0279911	.0262669	.0245408	.0228132	.0210841
21.1	.0193536	.0176221	.0158896	.0141564	.0124226	.0106883	.0089538	.0072192	.0054847	.0037505
21.2	.0020167	.0002836	-.0014488	-.0031802	-.0049105	-.0066394	-.0083669	-.0100928	-.0118168	-.0135388
21.3	-.0152587	-.0169762	-.0186913	-.0204036	-.0221131	-.0238196	-.0255230	-.0272229	-.0289194	-.0306122
21.4	-.0323011	-.0339860	-.0356667	-.0373431	-.0390149	-.0406821	-.0423444	-.0440018	-.0456539	-.0473007
21.5	-.0489420	-.0505777	-.0522076	-.0538314	-.0554492	-.0570606	-.0586656	-.0602640	-.0618556	-.0634403
21.6	-.0650179	-.0665883	-.0681513	-.0697068	-.0712545	-.0727945	-.0743264	-.0758502	-.0773658	-.0788729
21.7	-.0803714	-.0818612	-.0833421	-.0848140	-.0862767	-.0877302	-.0891742	-.0906086	-.0920333	-.0934482
21.8	-.0948530	-.0962478	-.0976323	-.0990063	-.1003699	-.1017228	-.1030649	-.1043961	-.1057162	-.1070252
21.9	-.1083229	-.1096091	-.1108838	-.1121469	-.1133981	-.1146375	-.1158648	-.1170800	-.1182829	-.1194734
22.0	-.1206515	-.1218169	-.1229697	-.1241096	-.1252366	-.1263506	-.1274514	-.1285390	-.1296133	-.1306741
22.1	-.1317214	-.1327550	-.1337749	-.1347809	-.1357731	-.1367512	-.1377151	-.1386649	-.1396004	-.1405215
22.2	-.1414282	-.1423203	-.1431977	-.1440605	-.1449085	-.1457416	-.1465597	-.1473628	-.1481509	-.1489238
22.3	-.1496814	-.1504237	-.1511507	-.1518622	-.1525582	-.1532387	-.1539035	-.1545527	-.1551861	-.1558037
22.4	-.1564055	-.1569913	-.1575612	-.1581151	-.1586529	-.1591747	-.1596803	-.1601697	-.1606428	-.1610997
22.5	-.1615403	-.1619646	-.1623724	-.1627639	-.1631389	-.1634974	-.1638394	-.1641649	-.1644738	-.1647662
22.6	-.1650419	-.1653010	-.1655435	-.1657694	-.1659785	-.1661710	-.1663467	-.1665058	-.1666481	-.1667738
22.7	-.1668827	-.1669748	-.1670502	-.1671089	-.1671509	-.1671761	-.1671846	-.1671764	-.1671515	-.1671098
22.8	-.1670515	-.1669765	-.1668849	-.1667766	-.1666517	-.1665101	-.1663520	-.1661773	-.1659861	-.1657784
22.9	-.1655542	-.1653135	-.1650564	-.1647829	-.1644931	-.1641870	-.1638645	-.1635258	-.1631710	-.1627999
23.0	-.1624128	-.1620096	-.1615903	-.1611551	-.1607040	-.1602370	-.1597541	-.1592555	-.1587412	-.1582113
23.1	-.1576658	-.1571047	-.1565282	-.1559363	-.1553290	-.1547065	-.1540688	-.1534159	-.1527480	-.1520651
23.2	-.1513673	-.1506547	-.1499273	-.1491852	-.1484286	-.1476574	-.1468718	-.1460719	-.1452576	-.1444293
23.3	-.1435868	-.1427303	-.1418600	-.1409758	-.1400779	-.1391664	-.1382414	-.1373029	-.1363511	-.1353861
23.4	-.1344080	-.1334168	-.1324128	-.1313663	-.1303063	-.1293241	-.1282695	-.1272024	-.1261232	-.1250317
23.5	-.1239282	-.1228128	-.1216856	-.1205467	-.1193963	-.1182343	-.1170611	-.1158767	-.1146811	-.1134747
23.6	-.1122573	-.1110293	-.1097907	-.1085417	-.1072823	-.1060127	-.1047331	-.1034435	-.1021441	-.1008351
23.7	-.0995165	-.0981886	-.0968514	-.0955051	-.0941498	-.0927856	-.0914128	-.0900313	-.0886415	-.0872434
23.8	-.0858371	-.0844229	-.0830008	-.0815710	-.0801337	-.0786889	-.0772369	-.0757778	-.0743117	-.0728388
23.9	-.0713592	-.0698732	-.0683807	-.0668820	-.0653773	-.0638667	-.0623503	-.0608283	-.0593009	-.0577681
24.0	-.0562303	-.0546874	-.0531398	-.0515874	-.0500306	-.0484694	-.0469040	-.0453345	-.0437612	-.0421842
24.1	-.0406036	-.0390195	-.0374323	-.0358420	-.0342487	-.0326527	-.0310540	-.0294530	-.0278496	-.0262441
24.2	-.0246367	-.0230274	-.0214166	-.0198042	-.0181905	-.0165757	-.0149599	-.0133433	-.0117260	-.0101082
24.3	-.0084900	-.0068717	-.0052533	-.0036351	-.0020171	-.0003997	.0012172	.0028332	.0044483	.0060623
24.4	.0076750	.0092863	.0108961	.0125040	.0141101	.0157141	.0173156	.0189152	.0205120	.0221062

Table 2 J_0 (*Continued*)

T	.00	.01	.02	.03	.04	.05	.06	.07	.08	.09
24.5	.0236974	.0252857	.0268708	.0284525	.0300307	.0316054	.0331762	.0347430	.0363057	.0378642
24.6	.0394183	.0409677	.0425125	.0440524	.0455872	.0471169	.0486412	.0501601	.0516733	.0531807
24.7	.0546823	.0561775	.0576669	.0591498	.0606261	.0620958	.0635587	.0650146	.0664635	.0679051
24.8	.0693393	.0707661	.0721851	.0735964	.0749998	.0763951	.0777822	.0791610	.0805313	.0818930
24.9	.0832460	.0845901	.0859252	.0872512	.0885679	.0898752	.0911731	.0924613	.0937397	.0950082
25.0	.0962668	.0975152	.0987534	.0999812	.1011985	.1024052	.1036012	.1047863	.1059606	.1071237
25.1	.1082757	.1094164	.1105457	.1116634	.1127696	.1138641	.1149467	.1160175	.1170762	.1181228
25.2	.1191571	.1201791	.1211887	.1221858	.1231703	.1241421	.1251011	.1260472	.1269803	.1279003
25.3	.1288072	.1297009	.1305812	.1314482	.1323016	.1331415	.1339678	.1347803	.1355790	.1363639
25.4	.1371348	.1378917	.1386345	.1393632	.1400777	.1407778	.1414636	.1421350	.1427920	.1434344
25.5	.1440622	.1446753	.1452738	.1458574	.1464263	.1469803	.1475194	.1480436	.1485527	.1490468
25.6	.1495258	.1499896	.1504383	.1508718	.1512900	.1516929	.1520805	.1524527	.1528096	.1531510
25.7	.1534770	.1537875	.1540825	.1543621	.1546260	.1548744	.1551072	.1553244	.1555261	.1557120
25.8	.1558824	.1560371	.1561761	.1562995	.1564071	.1564991	.1565755	.1566361	.1566811	.1567103
25.9	.1567239	.1567219	.1567041	.1566707	.1566216	.1565569	.1564766	.1563807	.1562691	.1561420
26.0	.1559993	.1558411	.1556673	.1554781	.1552734	.1550532	.1548177	.1545667	.1543004	.1540187
26.1	.1537218	.1534096	.1530822	.1527396	.1523819	.1520090	.1516211	.1512182	.1508004	.1503676
26.2	.1499200	.1494575	.1489803	.1484883	.1479817	.1474605	.1469248	.1463745	.1458099	.1452308
26.3	.1446375	.1440300	.1434082	.1427724	.1421225	.1414587	.1407810	.1400895	.1393842	.1386652
26.4	.1379327	.1371866	.1364271	.1356543	.1348682	.1340689	.1332565	.1324311	.1315928	.1307416
26.5	.1298776	.1290010	.1281119	.1272102	.1262962	.1253699	.1244315	.1234809	.1225183	.1215439
26.6	.1205577	.1195597	.1185503	.1175293	.1164970	.1154534	.1143986	.1133328	.1122561	.1111686
26.7	.1100704	.1089615	.1078422	.1067125	.1055726	.1044225	.1032625	.1020925	.1009128	.0997234
26.8	.0985245	.0973162	.0960986	.0948719	.0936361	.0923915	.0911380	.0898759	.0886053	.0873263
26.9	.0860391	.0847437	.0834404	.0821291	.0808102	.0794837	.0781497	.0768084	.0754599	.0741044
27.0	.0727419	.0713727	.0699969	.0686145	.0672259	.0658310	.0644300	.0630232	.0616105	.0601922
27.1	.0587684	.0573393	.0559049	.0544655	.0530212	.0515721	.0501184	.0486602	.0471977	.0457310
27.2	.0442603	.0427857	.0413073	.0398254	.0383400	.0368513	.0353596	.0338648	.0323671	.0308668
27.3	.0293640	.0278587	.0263513	.0248417	.0233302	.0218170	.0203021	.0187857	.0172680	.0157491
27.4	.0142293	.0127085	.0111870	.0096650	.0081426	.0066199	.0050970	.0035743	.0020517	.0005295
27.5	-.0009922	-.0025133	-.0040336	-.0055529	-.0070711	-.0085880	-.0101035	-.0116175	-.0131298	-.0146402
27.6	-.0161486	-.0176548	-.0191587	-.0206602	-.0221590	-.0236551	-.0251483	-.0266384	-.0281254	-.0296090
27.7	-.0310890	-.0325655	-.0340381	-.0355069	-.0369715	-.0384319	-.0398880	-.0413395	-.0427864	-.0442285
27.8	-.0456656	-.0470977	-.0485245	-.0499460	-.0513619	-.0527722	-.0541768	-.0555754	-.0569680	-.0583543
27.9	-.0597344	-.0611079	-.0624749	-.0638351	-.0651885	-.0665348	-.0678741	-.0692060	-.0705306	-.0718476

Table 2 J_0 (Continued)

T	.00	.01	.02	.03	.04	.05	.06	.07	.08	.09
28.0	-.0731570	-.0744586	-.0757523	-.0770380	-.0783155	-.0795847	-.0808455	-.0820977	-.0833414	-.0845762
28.1	-.0858021	-.0870191	-.0882269	-.0894254	-.0906146	-.0917943	-.0929644	-.0941248	-.0952754	-.0964160
28.2	-.0975466	-.0986670	-.0997772	-.1008770	-.1019663	-.1030451	-.1041131	-.1051704	-.1062168	-.1072522
28.3	-.1082765	-.1092896	-.1102915	-.1112819	-.1122609	-.1132283	-.1141841	-.1151281	-.1160602	-.1169804
28.4	-.1178886	-.1187847	-.1196686	-.1205403	-.1213995	-.1222464	-.1230807	-.1239024	-.1247114	-.1255077
28.5	-.1262911	-.1270617	-.1278193	-.1285638	-.1292952	-.1300134	-.1307184	-.1314101	-.1320884	-.1327532
28.6	-.1334046	-.1340423	-.1346665	-.1352769	-.1358737	-.1364566	-.1370257	-.1375809	-.1381221	-.1386494
28.7	-.1391625	-.1396616	-.1401466	-.1406174	-.1410739	-.1415162	-.1419442	-.1423579	-.1427572	-.1431420
28.8	-.1435124	-.1438684	-.1442098	-.1445367	-.1448490	-.1451468	-.1454299	-.1456984	-.1459522	-.1461914
28.9	-.1464158	-.1466256	-.1468206	-.1470008	-.1471663	-.1473170	-.1474530	-.1475741	-.1476805	-.1477720
29.0	-.1478488	-.1479107	-.1479578	-.1479901	-.1480077	-.1480104	-.1479983	-.1479714	-.1479297	-.1478733
29.1	-.1478020	-.1477161	-.1476154	-.1475000	-.1473698	-.1472250	-.1470655	-.1468913	-.1467026	-.1464992
29.2	-.1462813	-.1460487	-.1458017	-.1455402	-.1452642	-.1449738	-.1446690	-.1443498	-.1440163	-.1436686
29.3	-.1433065	-.1429303	-.1425399	-.1421354	-.1417168	-.1412842	-.1408377	-.1403771	-.1399028	-.1394145
29.4	-.1389125	-.1383968	-.1378675	-.1373245	-.1367680	-.1361980	-.1356145	-.1350177	-.1344077	-.1337843
29.5	-.1331479	-.1324983	-.1318357	-.1311601	-.1304717	-.1297704	-.1290564	-.1283297	-.1275905	-.1268387
29.6	-.1260746	-.1252980	-.1245092	-.1237083	-.1228952	-.1220701	-.1212331	-.1203842	-.1195236	-.1186514
29.7	-.1177675	-.1168722	-.1159655	-.1150475	-.1141184	-.1131781	-.1122268	-.1112647	-.1102917	-.1093080
29.8	-.1083137	-.1073089	-.1062938	-.1052683	-.1042327	-.1031870	-.1021313	-.1010658	-.0999905	-.0989056
29.9	-.0978112	-.0967073	-.0955941	-.0944718	-.0933404	-.0922000	-.0910508	-.0898929	-.0887264	-.0875514
30.0	-.0863680	-.0851764	-.0839766	-.0827689	-.0815533	-.0803300	-.0790990	-.0778605	-.0766147	-.0753616
30.1	-.0741014	-.0728342	-.0715601	-.0702793	-.0689919	-.0676981	-.0663979	-.0650914	-.0637790	-.0624605
30.2	-.0611363	-.0598064	-.0584709	-.0571301	-.0557839	-.0544327	-.0530764	-.0517153	-.0503495	-.0489791
30.3	-.0476042	-.0462250	-.0448417	-.0434543	-.0420631	-.0406681	-.0392695	-.0378674	-.0364620	-.0350535
30.4	-.0336418	-.0322273	-.0308101	-.0293902	-.0279678	-.0265431	-.0251162	-.0236873	-.0222565	-.0208239
30.5	-.0193897	-.0179541	-.0165171	-.0150790	-.0136398	-.0121997	-.0107588	-.0093174	-.0078755	-.0064332
30.6	-.0049909	-.0035485	-.0021062	-.0006641	.0007775	.0022186	.0036590	.0050986	.0065371	.0079746
30.7	.0094108	.0108456	.0122788	.0137103	.0151400	.0165677	.0179934	.0194167	.0208376	.0222560
30.8	.0236718	.0250846	.0264945	.0279013	.0293049	.0307051	.0321017	.0334947	.0348839	.0362691
30.9	.0376503	.0390273	.0403999	.0417680	.0431315	.0444903	.0458442	.0471930	.0485367	.0498752
31.0	.0512082	.0525356	.0538574	.0551733	.0564834	.0577873	.0590850	.0603764	.0616614	.0629398
31.1	.0642115	.0654763	.0667343	.0679851	.0692287	.0704650	.0716939	.0729152	.0741288	.0753347
31.2	.0765325	.0777224	.0789042	.0800776	.0812426	.0823992	.0835472	.0846864	.0858168	.0869363
31.3	.0880507	.0891540	.0902480	.0913326	.0924077	.0934732	.0945292	.0955752	.0966114	.0976377
31.4	.0986537	.0996597	.1006553	.1016406	.1026154	.1035796	.1045332	.1054759	.1064079	.1073289

Table 3

J_1

τ	.00	.01	.02	.03	.04	.05	.06	.07	.08	.09
0.0	0.0000000	.0049999	.0099995	.0149983	.0199960	.0249922	.0299865	.0349786	.0399680	.0449545
.1	.0499375	.0549169	.0598921	.0648628	.0698286	.0747893	.0797443	.0846933	.0896360	.0945720
.2	.0995008	.1044223	.1093358	.1142412	.1191381	.1240260	.1289046	.1337735	.1386325	.1434810
.3	.1483188	.1531455	.1579607	.1627641	.1675553	.1723340	.1770997	.1818522	.1865911	.1913160
.4	.1960266	.2007225	.2054034	.2100689	.2147188	.2193525	.2239699	.2285705	.2331540	.2377201
.5	.2422685	.2467987	.2513105	.2558035	.2602774	.2647318	.2691665	.2735811	.2779752	.2823486
.6	.2867010	.2910319	.2953412	.2996284	.3038932	.3081355	.3123547	.3165506	.3207230	.3248715
.7	.3289957	.3330955	.3371705	.3412203	.3452448	.3492436	.3532164	.3571629	.3610829	.3649760
.8	.3688420	.3726806	.3764916	.3802745	.3840292	.3877554	.3914529	.3951213	.3987603	.4023699
.9	.4059495	.4094991	.4130184	.4165071	.4199649	.4233917	.4267871	.4301509	.4334829	.4367829
1.0	.4400506	.4432858	.4464882	.4496577	.4527939	.4558968	.4589660	.4620014	.4650027	.4679698
1.1	.4709024	.4738003	.4766634	.4794913	.4822840	.4850413	.4877629	.4904486	.4930984	.4957119
1.2	.4982891	.5008297	.5033336	.5058006	.5082305	.5106233	.5129786	.5152965	.5175766	.5198189
1.3	.5220232	.5241895	.5263174	.5284070	.5304580	.5324703	.5344439	.5363785	.5382741	.5401305
1.4	.5419477	.5437255	.5454638	.5471625	.5488215	.5504407	.5520200	.5535593	.5550586	.5565177
1.5	.5579365	.5593150	.5606532	.5619508	.5632079	.5644245	.5656003	.5667354	.5678298	.5688833
1.6	.5698959	.5708676	.5717984	.5726881	.5735368	.5743443	.5751108	.5758362	.5765204	.5771634
1.7	.5777652	.5783259	.5788453	.5793235	.5797604	.5801562	.5805107	.5808241	.5810962	.5813272
1.8	.5815170	.5816656	.5817731	.5818396	.5818649	.5818493	.5817926	.5816951	.5815566	.5813772
1.9	.5811571	.5808962	.5805946	.5802523	.5798695	.5794463	.5789825	.5784784	.5779341	.5773495
2.0	.5767248	.5760601	.5753554	.5746109	.5738267	.5730028	.5721393	.5712364	.5702942	.5693127
2.1	.5682921	.5672326	.5661342	.5649970	.5638212	.5626069	.5613543	.5600635	.5587345	.5573677
2.2	.5559630	.5545208	.5530410	.5515239	.5499696	.5483784	.5467502	.5450854	.5433841	.5416464
2.3	.5398725	.5380627	.5362170	.5343358	.5324190	.5304671	.5284801	.5264582	.5244016	.5223106
2.4	.5201853	.5180259	.5158327	.5136058	.5113456	.5090521	.5067256	.5043663	.5019745	.4995503
2.5	.4970941	.4946060	.4920863	.4895351	.4869528	.4843396	.4816957	.4790214	.4763168	.4735824
2.6	.4708183	.4680247	.4652020	.4623503	.4594700	.4565613	.4536245	.4506598	.4476676	.4446480
2.7	.4416014	.4385280	.4354281	.4323020	.4291500	.4259723	.4227693	.4195412	.4162882	.4130109
2.8	.4097092	.4063837	.4030346	.3996622	.3962667	.3928485	.3894079	.3859452	.3824607	.3789547
2.9	.3754275	.3718794	.3683108	.3647218	.3611130	.3574845	.3538368	.3501700	.3464846	.3427808
3.0	.3390590	.3353194	.3315626	.3277886	.3239979	.3201909	.3163677	.3125289	.3086746	.3048052
3.1	.3009211	.2970226	.2931101	.2891837	.2852440	.2812912	.2773257	.2733478	.2693579	.2655563
3.2	.2613432	.2573192	.2532845	.2492394	.2451844	.2411197	.2370457	.2329627	.2288711	.2247712
3.3	.2206635	.2165481	.2124255	.2082960	.2041599	.2000177	.1958696	.1917161	.1875574	.1833938
3.4	.1792259	.1750538	.1708779	.1666987	.1625163	.1583313	.1541439	.1499545	.1457634	.1415709

Table 3 J_1 (Continued)

T	.00	.01	.02	.03	.04	.05	.06	.07	.08	.09
3.5	.1373775	.1331835	.1289892	.1247949	.1206010	.1164079	.1122159	.1080253	.1038365	.0996498
3.6	.0954655	.0912841	.0871059	.0829311	.0787602	.0745934	.0704412	.0662737	.0621215	.0579748
3.7	.0538340	.0496993	.0455712	.0414500	.0373369	.0332293	.0291307	.0250402	.0209582	.0168850
3.8	.0128210	.0087665	.0047218	.0006872	-.0033369	-.0073502	-.0113524	-.0153432	-.0192223	-.0232894
3.9	-.0272440	-.0311861	-.0351151	-.0390308	-.0429330	-.0468212	-.0506953	-.0545548	-.0583995	-.0622291
4.0	-.0660433	-.0698418	-.0736243	-.0773905	-.0811401	-.0848728	-.0885884	-.0922865	-.0959669	-.0996292
4.1	-.1032733	-.1068987	-.1105054	-.1140928	-.1176609	-.1212093	-.1247378	-.1282461	-.1317339	-.1352009
4.2	-.1386469	-.1420717	-.1454750	-.1488565	-.1522160	-.1555532	-.1588679	-.1621598	-.1654287	-.1686744
4.3	-.1718966	-.1750950	-.1782695	-.1814198	-.1845457	-.1876469	-.1907233	-.1937745	-.1968005	-.1998009
4.4	-.2027755	-.2057242	-.2086467	-.2115429	-.2144125	-.2172252	-.2200710	-.2228596	-.2256209	-.2283545
4.5	-.2310604	-.2337384	-.2363882	-.2390097	-.2416027	-.2441671	-.2467026	-.2492091	-.2516864	-.2541344
4.6	-.2565528	-.2589416	-.2613006	-.2636296	-.2659284	-.2681970	-.2704352	-.2726428	-.2748196	-.2769657
4.7	-.2790807	-.2811647	-.2832174	-.2852387	-.2872286	-.2891868	-.2911133	-.2930080	-.2948707	-.2967014
4.8	-.2984999	-.3002661	-.3019999	-.3037013	-.3053702	-.3070064	-.3086098	-.3101805	-.3117182	-.3132230
4.9	-.3146947	-.3161332	-.3177386	-.3189017	-.3202075	-.3215549	-.3228269	-.3240653	-.3252702	-.3264415
5.0	-.3275791	-.3286831	-.3297533	-.3307898	-.3317925	-.3327613	-.3336963	-.3345974	-.3354646	-.3362979
5.1	-.3370972	-.3378626	-.3385940	-.3392915	-.3399950	-.3405846	-.3411802	-.3417418	-.3422695	-.3427632
5.2	-.3432230	-.3436489	-.3440409	-.3443991	-.3447234	-.3450140	-.3452707	-.3454938	-.3456831	-.3458388
5.3	-.3459608	-.3460493	-.3461043	-.3461259	-.3461140	-.3460688	-.3459903	-.3458785	-.3457337	-.3455557
5.4	-.3453448	-.3451009	-.3448242	-.3445147	-.3441725	-.3437977	-.3433905	-.3429508	-.3424788	-.3419746
5.5	-.3414382	-.3408699	-.3402696	-.3396376	-.3389739	-.3382786	-.3375518	-.3367938	-.3360045	-.3351841
5.6	-.3343328	-.3334507	-.3325379	-.3315946	-.3306208	-.3296168	-.3285826	-.3275185	-.3264245	-.3253009
5.7	-.3241477	-.3229651	-.3217534	-.3205126	-.3192429	-.3179445	-.3166176	-.3152623	-.3138787	-.3124672
5.8	-.3110277	-.3095607	-.3080661	-.3065442	-.3049952	-.3034193	-.3018166	-.3001874	-.2985318	-.2968501
5.9	-.2951424	-.2934090	-.2916501	-.2898658	-.2880563	-.2862220	-.2843629	-.2824793	-.2805715	-.2786396
6.0	-.2766839	-.2747045	-.2727017	-.2706758	-.2686269	-.2665553	-.2644612	-.2623449	-.2602066	-.2580464
6.1	-.2558648	-.2536618	-.2514378	-.2491929	-.2469275	-.2446417	-.2423358	-.2400101	-.2376649	-.2353003
6.2	-.2329166	-.2305141	-.2280930	-.2256536	-.2231961	-.2207209	-.2182281	-.2157181	-.2131910	-.2106472
6.3	-.2080869	-.2055105	-.2029180	-.2003100	-.1976865	-.1950749	-.1923944	-.1897264	-.1870440	-.1843476
6.4	-.1816375	-.1789139	-.1761771	-.1733274	-.1706650	-.1678903	-.1651035	-.1623049	-.1594949	-.1566736
6.5	-.1538413	-.1509984	-.1481451	-.1452818	-.1424086	-.1395260	-.1366341	-.1337333	-.1308238	-.1279060
6.6	-.1249802	-.1220465	-.1191054	-.1161571	-.1132019	-.1102401	-.1072720	-.1042978	-.1013179	-.0983326
6.7	-.0953421	-.0923468	-.0893469	-.0863427	-.0833346	-.0803228	-.0773076	-.0742893	-.0712681	-.0682445
6.8	-.0652187	-.0621909	-.0591615	-.0561307	-.0530989	-.0500663	-.0470332	-.0440000	-.0409669	-.0379341
6.9	-.0349021	-.0318710	-.0288412	-.0258130	-.0227866	-.0197623	-.0167404	-.0137213	-.0107051	-.0076922

Table 3 J_1 (*Continued*)

T	.00	.01	.02	.03	.04	.05	.06	.07	.08	.09
7.0	-.0046828	-.0016773	.0013241	.0043211	.0073134	.0103007	.0132828	.0162594	.0192302	.0221949
7.1	.0251533	.0281050	.0310498	.0339875	.0369177	.0398402	.0427547	.0456609	.0485586	.0514476
7.2	.0543274	.0571980	.0600589	.0629100	.0657511	.0685817	.0714017	.0742109	.0770089	.0797955
7.3	.0825704	.0853335	.0880844	.0908230	.0935488	.0962619	.0989617	.1016482	.1043211	.1069802
7.4	.1096251	.1122557	.1148718	.1174730	.1200593	.1226303	.1251857	.1277255	.1302494	.1327571
7.5	.1352484	.1377232	.1401811	.1426220	.1450456	.1474518	.1498404	.1522110	.1545636	.1568979
7.6	.1592138	.1615109	.1637892	.1660484	.1682883	.1705088	.1727096	.1748906	.1770516	.1791923
7.7	.1813127	.1834125	.1854916	.1875497	.1895868	.1916026	.1935970	.1955697	.1975208	.1994499
7.8	.2013569	.2032417	.2051041	.2069439	.2087611	.2105554	.2123267	.2140749	.2157999	.2175014
7.9	.2191794	.2208337	.2224642	.2240708	.2256533	.2272116	.2287457	.2302553	.2317403	.2332007
8.0	.2346363	.2360471	.2374329	.2387936	.2401291	.2414393	.2427241	.2439835	.2452173	.2464254
8.1	.2476078	.2487643	.2498950	.2509996	.2520782	.2531307	.2541570	.2551569	.2561306	.2570778
8.2	.2579986	.2588928	.2597605	.2606016	.2614159	.2622036	.2629644	.2636985	.2644056	.2650859
8.3	.2657393	.2663657	.2669651	.2675375	.2680829	.2686012	.2690924	.2695566	.2699936	.2704035
8.4	.2707863	.2711419	.2714704	.2717718	.2720460	.2722931	.2725131	.2727059	.2728717	.2730104
8.5	.2731220	.2732065	.2732640	.2732946	.2732981	.2732747	.2732244	.2731472	.2730432	.2729124
8.6	.2727548	.2725706	.2723596	.2721221	.2718580	.2715674	.2712504	.2709069	.2705372	.2701412
8.7	.2697190	.2692707	.2687964	.2682961	.2677699	.2672179	.2666402	.2660368	.2654079	.2647535
8.8	.2640737	.2633687	.2626384	.2618831	.2611028	.2602976	.2594677	.2586131	.2577339	.2568303
8.9	.2559024	.2549502	.2539740	.2529738	.2519497	.2509019	.2498306	.2487357	.2476176	.2464762
9.0	.2453118	.2441244	.2429143	.2416816	.2404263	.2391487	.2378489	.2365270	.2351833	.2338178
9.1	.2324307	.2310222	.2295925	.2281416	.2266698	.2251772	.2236640	.2221304	.2205765	.2190026
9.2	.2174087	.2157950	.2141618	.2125092	.2108375	.2091467	.2074370	.2057087	.2039620	.2021970
9.3	.2004139	.1986130	.1967943	.1949582	.1931047	.1912342	.1893468	.1874427	.1855221	.1835852
9.4	.1816322	.1796634	.1776789	.1756789	.1736637	.1716335	.1695884	.1675288	.1654548	.1633666
9.5	.1612644	.1591486	.1570192	.1548765	.1527208	.1505523	.1483711	.1461775	.1439718	.1417542
9.6	.1395248	.1372840	.1350319	.1327688	.1304950	.1282106	.1259159	.1236111	.1212965	.1189722
9.7	.1166386	.1142959	.1119443	.1095840	.1072154	.1048385	.1024537	.1000612	.0976613	.0952542
9.8	.0928401	.0904193	.0879920	.0855585	.0831189	.0806737	.0782229	.0757669	.0733059	.0708401
9.9	.0683698	.0658953	.0634167	.0609343	.0584484	.0559592	.0534670	.0509720	.0484745	.0459746
10.0	.0434727	.0409691	.0384638	.0359573	.0334497	.0309412	.0284322	.0259229	.0234135	.0209043
10.1	.0183955	.0158874	.0133801	.0108741	.0083694	.0058663	.0033652	.0008662	-.0016305	-.0041246
10.2	-.0066157	-.0091038	-.0115886	-.0140698	-.0165472	-.0190205	-.0214895	-.0239540	-.0264137	-.0288844
10.3	-.0313178	-.0337618	-.0362001	-.0386324	-.0410586	-.0434783	-.0458914	-.0482976	-.0506967	-.0530885
10.4	-.0554728	-.0578492	-.0602176	-.0625779	-.0649296	-.0672727	-.0696068	-.0719318	-.0742475	-.0765537

Table 3 J_1 (Continued)

T	.00	.01	.02	.03	.04	.05	.06	.07	.08	.09
10.5	-.0788500	-.0811364	-.0834125	-.0856782	-.0879333	-.0901775	-.0924107	-.0946326	-.0968431	-.0990418
10.6	-.1012287	-.1034034	-.1055659	-.1077159	-.1098532	-.1119776	-.1140889	-.1161870	-.1182715	-.1203424
10.7	-.1223994	-.1244424	-.1264711	-.1284855	-.1304852	-.1324701	-.1344401	-.1363949	-.1383343	-.1402583
10.8	-.1421666	-.1440590	-.1459354	-.1477956	-.1496394	-.1514668	-.1532774	-.1550711	-.1568479	-.1586075
10.9	-.1603497	-.1620744	-.1637815	-.1654708	-.1671422	-.1687954	-.1704305	-.1720471	-.1736452	-.1752247
11.0	-.1767853	-.1783270	-.1798496	-.1813530	-.1828371	-.1843017	-.1857467	-.1871720	-.1885774	-.1899629
11.1	-.1913283	-.1926735	-.1939984	-.1953028	-.1965868	-.1978500	-.1990926	-.2003142	-.2015150	-.2026946
11.2	-.2038531	-.2049904	-.2061063	-.2072008	-.2082738	-.2093252	-.2103549	-.2113628	-.2123488	-.2133129
11.3	-.2142550	-.2151751	-.2160729	-.2169486	-.2178019	-.2186329	-.2194415	-.2202277	-.2209912	-.2217322
11.4	-.2224506	-.2231462	-.2238192	-.2244693	-.2250966	-.2257010	-.2262825	-.2268410	-.2273766	-.2278891
11.5	-.2283786	-.2288450	-.2292883	-.2297085	-.2301055	-.2304793	-.2308300	-.2311575	-.2314617	-.2317427
11.6	-.2320005	-.2322350	-.2324463	-.2326344	-.2327992	-.2329407	-.2330591	-.2331542	-.2332261	-.2332747
11.7	-.2333002	-.2333026	-.2332817	-.2332378	-.2331707	-.2330806	-.2329674	-.2328312	-.2326720	-.2324898
11.8	-.2322847	-.2320568	-.2318060	-.2315324	-.2312361	-.2309170	-.2305754	-.2302111	-.2298243	-.2294150
11.9	-.2289832	-.2285292	-.2280528	-.2275541	-.2270334	-.2264905	-.2259255	-.2253387	-.2247299	-.2240994
12.0	-.2234471	-.2227732	-.2220777	-.2213608	-.2206225	-.2198629	-.2190821	-.2182803	-.2174574	-.2166136
12.1	-.2157490	-.2148637	-.2139578	-.2130314	-.2120846	-.2111175	-.2101303	-.2091230	-.2080958	-.2070488
12.2	-.2059820	-.2048957	-.2037900	-.2026649	-.2015206	-.2003572	-.1991749	-.1979738	-.1967540	-.1955156
12.3	-.1942588	-.1929838	-.1916907	-.1903795	-.1890506	-.1877039	-.1863397	-.1849580	-.1835591	-.1821432
12.4	-.1807102	-.1792605	-.1777942	-.1763114	-.1748122	-.1732969	-.1717656	-.1702185	-.1686557	-.1670774
12.5	-.1654838	-.1638750	-.1622513	-.1606127	-.1589594	-.1572917	-.1556097	-.1539136	-.1522036	-.1504797
12.6	-.1487423	-.1469916	-.1452276	-.1434505	-.1416606	-.1398581	-.1380431	-.1362158	-.1343765	-.1325252
12.7	-.1306622	-.1287877	-.1269019	-.1250050	-.1230971	-.1211786	-.1192494	-.1173100	-.1153604	-.1134008
12.8	-.1114316	-.1094528	-.1074646	-.1054674	-.1034612	-.1014463	-.0994229	-.0973912	-.0953513	-.0933036
12.9	-.0912483	-.0891854	-.0871153	-.0850381	-.0829541	-.0808634	-.0787663	-.0766630	-.0745538	-.0724387
13.0	-.0703181	-.0681921	-.0660609	-.0639249	-.0617841	-.0596388	-.0574892	-.0553356	-.0531781	-.0510170
13.1	-.0488525	-.0466847	-.0445140	-.0423405	-.0401645	-.0379861	-.0358056	-.0336232	-.0314391	-.0292535
13.2	-.0270667	-.0248789	-.0226902	-.0205009	-.0183113	-.0161215	-.0139317	-.0117422	-.0095532	-.0073649
13.3	-.0051775	-.0029912	-.0008063	.0013771	.0035587	.0057383	.0079157	.0100907	.0122630	.0144326
13.4	.0165990	.0187622	.0209219	.0230780	.0252301	.0273781	.0295218	.0316610	.0337954	.0359249
13.5	.0380493	.0401683	.0422817	.0443894	.0464911	.0485866	.0506758	.0527583	.0548341	.0569029
13.6	.0589646	.0610188	.0630655	.0651044	.0671353	.0691581	.0711725	.0731784	.0751755	.0771637
13.7	.0791428	.0811125	.0830728	.0850233	.0869640	.0888946	.0908150	.0927250	.0946243	.0965129
13.8	.0983905	.1002570	.1021121	.1039558	.1057877	.1076079	.1094160	.1112119	.1129955	.1147665
13.9	.1165249	.1182704	.1200029	.1217222	.1234282	.1251207	.1267995	.1284645	.1301156	.1317525

Table 3 J_1 *(Continued)*

T	.00	.01	.02	.03	.04	.05	.06	.07	.08	.09
14.0	.1333752	.1349834	.1365770	.1381560	.1397201	.1412691	.1428030	.1443216	.1458248	.1473124
14.1	.1487844	.1502404	.1516805	.1531045	.1545122	.1559036	.1572785	.1586368	.1599783	.1613030
14.2	.1626107	.1639013	.1651747	.1664308	.1676695	.1688906	.1700940	.1712797	.1724475	.1735973
14.3	.1747291	.1758426	.1769380	.1780149	.1790734	.1801133	.1811346	.1821372	.1831209	.1840858
14.4	.1850317	.1859585	.1868661	.1877546	.1886237	.1894735	.1903038	.1911147	.1919059	.1926775
14.5	.1934295	.1941616	.1948740	.1955664	.1962389	.1968915	.1975240	.1981364	.1987287	.1993008
14.6	.1998527	.2003843	.2008956	.2013866	.2018572	.2023074	.2027371	.2031464	.2035352	.2039035
14.7	.2042513	.2045785	.2048851	.2051711	.2054365	.2056813	.2059054	.2061089	.2062918	.2064540
14.8	.2065956	.2067165	.2068167	.2068963	.2069553	.2069936	.2070113	.2070084	.2069849	.2069408
14.9	.2068762	.2067910	.2066853	.2065590	.2064124	.2062452	.2060577	.2058498	.2056215	.2053729
15.0	.2051040	.2048149	.2045057	.2041762	.2038267	.2034571	.2030675	.2026580	.2022286	.2017793
15.1	.2013102	.2008214	.2003130	.1997849	.1992373	.1986703	.1980838	.1974780	.1968530	.1962088
15.2	.1955454	.1948631	.1941618	.1934416	.1927027	.1919450	.1911688	.1903740	.1895608	.1887292
15.3	.1878794	.1870115	.1861255	.1852216	.1842998	.1833603	.1824032	.1814285	.1804363	.1794269
15.4	.1784003	.1773565	.1762958	.1752183	.1741239	.1730130	.1718855	.1707417	.1695816	.1684054
15.5	.1672132	.1660051	.1647812	.1635418	.1622868	.1610165	.1597310	.1584304	.1571149	.1557846
15.6	.1544396	.1530801	.1517062	.1503181	.1489160	.1474999	.1460700	.1446265	.1431695	.1416992
15.7	.1402157	.1387193	.1372099	.1356878	.1341533	.1326063	.1310471	.1294758	.1278927	.1262978
15.8	.1246913	.1230735	.1214444	.1198043	.1181532	.1164915	.1148192	.1131365	.1114436	.1097407
15.9	.1080279	.1063054	.1045735	.1028322	.1010818	.0993224	.0975542	.0957774	.0939922	.0921987
16.0	.0903972	.0885878	.0867707	.0849461	.0831142	.0812751	.0794291	.0775764	.0757170	.0738513
16.1	.0719794	.0701015	.0682178	.0663284	.0644336	.0625336	.0606285	.0587186	.0568040	.0548849
16.2	.0529615	.0510340	.0491027	.0471677	.0452291	.0432872	.0413423	.0393944	.0374437	.0354906
16.3	.0335351	.0315774	.0296179	.0276565	.0256936	.0237294	.0217640	.0197976	.0178305	.0158628
16.4	.0138947	.0119264	.0099581	.0079901	.0060224	.0040553	.0020891	.0001238	-.0018403	-.0038031
16.5	-.0057642	-.0077236	-.0096811	-.0116364	-.0135893	-.0155397	-.0174874	-.0194322	-.0213739	-.0233122
16.6	-.0252471	-.0271783	-.0291056	-.0310289	-.0329479	-.0348625	-.0367725	-.0386776	-.0405778	-.0424728
16.7	-.0443624	-.0462465	-.0481248	-.0499972	-.0518635	-.0537236	-.0555771	-.0574241	-.0592642	-.0610973
16.8	-.0629232	-.0647418	-.0665528	-.0683562	-.0701516	-.0719390	-.0737182	-.0754890	-.0772512	-.0790047
16.9	-.0807493	-.0824847	-.0842110	-.0859278	-.0876351	-.0893326	-.0910202	-.0926978	-.0943651	-.0960221
17.0	-.0976685	-.0993042	-.1009291	-.1025429	-.1041456	-.1057370	-.1073169	-.1088852	-.1104417	-.1119863
17.1	-.1135188	-.1150392	-.1165472	-.1180427	-.1195255	-.1209956	-.1224528	-.1238970	-.1253279	-.1267455
17.2	-.1281497	-.1295403	-.1309172	-.1322802	-.1336293	-.1349642	-.1362850	-.1375914	-.1388833	-.1401607
17.3	-.1414233	-.1426712	-.1439041	-.1451219	-.1463246	-.1475120	-.1486840	-.1498406	-.1509815	-.1521067
17.4	-.1532162	-.1543097	-.1553872	-.1564487	-.1574939	-.1585228	-.1595354	-.1605315	-.1615110	-.1624738

Table 3 J_1 (Continued)

T	.00	.01	.02	.03	.04	.05	.06	.07	.08	.09
17.5	-.1634200	-.1643493	-.1652617	-.1661571	-.1670354	-.1678966	-.1687405	-.1695672	-.1703765	-.1711684
17.6	-.1719427	-.1726995	-.1734387	-.1741601	-.1748638	-.1755497	-.1762176	-.1768677	-.1774997	-.1781137
17.7	-.1787096	-.1792874	-.1798469	-.1803883	-.1809113	-.1814160	-.1819024	-.1823704	-.1828199	-.1832509
17.8	-.1836635	-.1840575	-.1844329	-.1847898	-.1851280	-.1854476	-.1857486	-.1860308	-.1862944	-.1865392
17.9	-.1867654	-.1869728	-.1871614	-.1873313	-.1874824	-.1876147	-.1877283	-.1878231	-.1878991	-.1879564
18.0	-.1879949	-.1880146	-.1880156	-.1879979	-.1879614	-.1879062	-.1878323	-.1877397	-.1876285	-.1874987
18.1	-.1873502	-.1871831	-.1869975	-.1867933	-.1865706	-.1863295	-.1860699	-.1857919	-.1854956	-.1851809
18.2	-.1848479	-.1844967	-.1841273	-.1837398	-.1833341	-.1829104	-.1824688	-.1820091	-.1815316	-.1810362
18.3	-.1805231	-.1799922	-.1794437	-.1788776	-.1782940	-.1776930	-.1770745	-.1764388	-.1757858	-.1751156
18.4	-.1744283	-.1737241	-.1730029	-.1722648	-.1715100	-.1707385	-.1699503	-.1691457	-.1683247	-.1674873
18.5	-.1666336	-.1657639	-.1648780	-.1639762	-.1630586	-.1621252	-.1611761	-.1602115	-.1592314	-.1582360
18.6	-.1572254	-.1561996	-.1551588	-.1541031	-.1530325	-.1519474	-.1508476	-.1497334	-.1486049	-.1474621
18.7	-.1463053	-.1451345	-.1439499	-.1427515	-.1415396	-.1403142	-.1390754	-.1378235	-.1365584	-.1352805
18.8	-.1339897	-.1326863	-.1313703	-.1300419	-.1287013	-.1273486	-.1259838	-.1246073	-.1232190	-.1218192
18.9	-.1204080	-.1189855	-.1175520	-.1161074	-.1146521	-.1131861	-.1117096	-.1102227	-.1087256	-.1072185
19.0	-.1057014	-.1041747	-.1026383	-.1010925	-.0995375	-.0979733	-.0964002	-.0948183	-.0932278	-.0916289
19.1	-.0900216	-.0884062	-.0867828	-.0851517	-.0835128	-.0818666	-.0802130	-.0785523	-.0768846	-.0752101
19.2	-.0735290	-.0718414	-.0701476	-.0684476	-.0667417	-.0650301	-.0633128	-.0615901	-.0598622	-.0581292
19.3	-.0563913	-.0546486	-.0529015	-.0511499	-.0493942	-.0476344	-.0458709	-.0441036	-.0423329	-.0405588
19.4	-.0387816	-.0370015	-.0352186	-.0334331	-.0316452	-.0298551	-.0280629	-.0262688	-.0244730	-.0226757
19.5	-.0208771	-.0190773	-.0172765	-.0154749	-.0136727	-.0118701	-.0100672	-.0082642	-.0064613	-.0046587
19.6	-.0028566	-.0010551	.0007456	.0025454	.0043439	.0061411	.0079368	.0097307	.0115228	.0133128
19.7	.0151006	.0168860	.0186688	.0204488	.0222259	.0239998	.0257705	.0275377	.0293012	.0310610
19.8	.0328168	.0345684	.0363156	.0380584	.0397965	.0415298	.0432580	.0449810	.0466988	.0484109
19.9	.0501174	.0518181	.0535127	.0552011	.0568832	.0585587	.0602276	.0618897	.0635447	.0651926
20.0	.0668331	.0684662	.0700916	.0717092	.0733189	.0749204	.0765137	.0780985	.0796748	.0812423
20.1	.0828010	.0843506	.0858911	.0874222	.0889438	.0904558	.0919581	.0934504	.0949326	.0964047
20.2	.0978664	.0993176	.1007583	.1021881	.1036071	.1050150	.1064117	.1077972	.1091712	.1105336
20.3	.1118844	.1132233	.1145503	.1158652	.1171679	.1184583	.1197362	.1210015	.1222542	.1234941
20.4	.1247210	.1259349	.1271356	.1283231	.1294972	.1306578	.1318048	.1329381	.1340576	.1351631
20.5	.1362547	.1373321	.1383953	.1394442	.1404787	.1414986	.1425040	.1434946	.1444704	.1454314
20.6	.1463774	.1473083	.1482241	.1491247	.1500099	.1508798	.1517342	.1525730	.1533962	.1542037
20.7	.1549955	.1557714	.1565314	.1572754	.1580034	.1587152	.1594109	.1600904	.1607535	.1614003
20.8	.1620307	.1626447	.1632421	.1638229	.1643871	.1649345	.1654655	.1659796	.1664769	.1669573
20.9	.1674209	.1678675	.1682972	.1687099	.1691055	.1694841	.1698456	.1701900	.1705173	.1708274

Table 3 J₁ (*Continued*)

T	.00	.01	.02	.03	.04	.05	.06	.07	.08	.09
21.0	.1711203	.1713960	.1716544	.1718957	.1721196	.1723263	.1725157	.1726878	.1728426	.1729801
21.1	.1731003	.1732031	.1732886	.1733568	.1734076	.1734412	.1734574	.1734563	.1734579	.1734022
21.2	.1733790	.1732790	.1731915	.1730868	.1729649	.1728258	.1726695	.1724960	.1723054	.1720977
21.3	.1718730	.1716312	.1713724	.1710966	.1708039	.1704943	.1701678	.1698245	.1694644	.1690876
21.4	.1686941	.1682839	.1678572	.1674139	.1669541	.1664779	.1659852	.1654763	.1649511	.1644097
21.5	.1638521	.1632784	.1626887	.1620831	.1614616	.1608242	.1601711	.1595023	.1588180	.1581181
21.6	.1574027	.1566720	.1559260	.1551648	.1543884	.1535970	.1527906	.1519694	.1511334	.1502827
21.7	.1494174	.1485376	.1476434	.1467348	.1458121	.1448752	.1439243	.1429595	.1419808	.1409885
21.8	.1399825	.1389630	.1379301	.1368840	.1358246	.1347522	.1336669	.1325687	.1314578	.1303342
21.9	.1291982	.1280498	.1268892	.1257164	.1245316	.1233350	.1221266	.1209065	.1196749	.1184320
22.0	.1171778	.1159125	.1146362	.1133490	.1120511	.1107426	.1094237	.1080944	.1067550	.1054055
22.1	.1040461	.1026770	.1012982	.0999099	.0985123	.0971055	.0956897	.0942649	.0928314	.0913893
22.2	.0899387	.0884797	.0870126	.0855375	.0840545	.0825638	.0810655	.0795598	.0780469	.0765268
22.3	.0749998	.0734659	.0719255	.0703785	.0688253	.0672658	.0657003	.0641290	.0625520	.0609695
22.4	.0593815	.0577884	.0561902	.0545871	.0529793	.0513669	.0497501	.0481290	.0465039	.0448748
22.5	.0432420	.0416056	.0399658	.0383228	.0366766	.0350275	.0333756	.0317212	.0300643	.0284051
22.6	.0267439	.0250807	.0234157	.0217492	.0200812	.0184119	.0167415	.0150702	.0133982	.0117255
22.7	.0100524	.0083791	.0067056	.0050322	.0033591	.0016863	.0000141	-.0016574	-.0033279	-.0049974
22.8	-.0066657	-.0083325	-.0099978	-.0116614	-.0133231	-.0149827	-.0166401	-.0182951	-.0199476	-.0215974
22.9	-.0232443	-.0248881	-.0265288	-.0281660	-.0297998	-.0314299	-.0330561	-.0346783	-.0362964	-.0379101
23.0	-.0395193	-.0411239	-.0427237	-.0443186	-.0459083	-.0474927	-.0490718	-.0506452	-.0522129	-.0537747
23.1	-.0553305	-.0568801	-.0584233	-.0599601	-.0614902	-.0630134	-.0645298	-.0660391	-.0675411	-.0690357
23.2	-.0705228	-.0720022	-.0734738	-.0749374	-.0763929	-.0778402	-.0792791	-.0807094	-.0821311	-.0835440
23.3	-.0849479	-.0863427	-.0877284	-.0891046	-.0904714	-.0918286	-.0931761	-.0945136	-.0958412	-.0971586
23.4	-.0984658	-.0997626	-.1010489	-.1023245	-.1035894	-.1048434	-.1060864	-.1073183	-.1085390	-.1097483
23.5	-.1109461	-.1121324	-.1133070	-.1144697	-.1156206	-.1167594	-.1178861	-.1190005	-.1201026	-.1211922
23.6	-.1222693	-.1233337	-.1243854	-.1254242	-.1264500	-.1274628	-.1284624	-.1294488	-.1304219	-.1313815
23.7	-.1323277	-.1332602	-.1341790	-.1350840	-.1359752	-.1368525	-.1377157	-.1385648	-.1393997	-.1402203
23.8	-.1410266	-.1418185	-.1425959	-.1433588	-.1441070	-.1448406	-.1455593	-.1462633	-.1469523	-.1476264
23.9	-.1482855	-.1489295	-.1495583	-.1501720	-.1507705	-.1513536	-.1519214	-.1524738	-.1530107	-.1535322
24.0	-.1540381	-.1545284	-.1550031	-.1554621	-.1559054	-.1563330	-.1567448	-.1571408	-.1575209	-.1578852
24.1	-.1582335	-.1585659	-.1588823	-.1591828	-.1594672	-.1597356	-.1599880	-.1602243	-.1604445	-.1606486
24.2	-.1608365	-.1610084	-.1611641	-.1613036	-.1614270	-.1615342	-.1616253	-.1617002	-.1617589	-.1618015
24.3	-.1618278	-.1618381	-.1618321	-.1618101	-.1617718	-.1617175	-.1616470	-.1615604	-.1614577	-.1613390
24.4	-.1612042	-.1610534	-.1608865	-.1607037	-.1605049	-.1602902	-.1600595	-.1598130	-.1595506	-.1592724

Table 3 J_1 (*Continued*)

T	.00	.01	.02	.03	.04	.05	.06	.07	.08	.09
24.5	-.1589784	-.1586687	-.1583432	-.1580021	-.1576454	-.1572730	-.1568852	-.1564818	-.1560629	-.1556287
24.6	-.1551791	-.1547142	-.1542340	-.1537387	-.1532282	-.1527026	-.1521619	-.1516064	-.1510359	-.1504505
24.7	-.1498504	-.1492356	-.1486061	-.1479620	-.1473034	-.1466304	-.1459431	-.1452414	-.1445255	-.1437955
24.8	-.1430514	-.1422934	-.1415214	-.1407357	-.1399362	-.1391230	-.1382963	-.1374562	-.1366026	-.1357357
24.9	-.1348557	-.1339625	-.1330564	-.1321373	-.1312054	-.1302607	-.1293035	-.1283337	-.1273515	-.1263570
25.0	-.1253502	-.1243314	-.1233006	-.1222578	-.1212033	-.1201371	-.1190593	-.1179701	-.1168695	-.1157577
25.1	-.1146348	-.1135009	-.1123561	-.1112005	-.1100344	-.1088577	-.1076706	-.1064732	-.1052656	-.1040481
25.2	-.1028206	-.1015834	-.1003365	-.0990801	-.0978143	-.0965392	-.0952550	-.0939618	-.0926597	-.0913489
25.3	-.0900295	-.0887017	-.0873655	-.0860211	-.0846686	-.0833083	-.0819401	-.0805643	-.0791811	-.0777904
25.4	-.0763926	-.0749876	-.0735757	-.0721571	-.0707318	-.0693000	-.0678618	-.0664174	-.0649670	-.0635107
25.5	-.0620485	-.0605808	-.0591076	-.0576290	-.0561453	-.0546566	-.0531630	-.0516647	-.0501618	-.0486544
25.6	-.0471429	-.0456272	-.0441075	-.0425840	-.0410569	-.0395262	-.0379922	-.0364551	-.0349148	-.0333717
25.7	-.0318259	-.0302775	-.0287266	-.0271735	-.0256183	-.0240612	-.0225022	-.0209416	-.0193795	-.0178161
25.8	-.0162515	-.0146859	-.0131194	-.0115523	-.0099846	-.0084164	-.0068481	-.0052797	-.0037114	-.0021433
25.9	-.0005755	.0009916	.0025581	.0041237	.0056883	.0072517	.0088138	.0103744	.0119333	.0134905
26.0	.0150457	.0165989	.0181497	.0196982	.0212441	.0227873	.0243276	.0258649	.0273991	.0289299
26.1	.0304572	.0319809	.0335009	.0350169	.0365288	.0380365	.0395398	.0410387	.0425328	.0440221
26.2	.0455065	.0469857	.0484597	.0499283	.0513914	.0528487	.0543003	.0557458	.0571853	.0586185
26.3	.0600453	.0614655	.0628791	.0642858	.0656857	.0670784	.0684639	.0698420	.0712126	.0725757
26.4	.0739309	.0752783	.0766176	.0779488	.0792716	.0805861	.0818920	.0831893	.0844778	.0857573
26.5	.0870278	.0882891	.0895412	.0907838	.0920169	.0932404	.0944540	.0956578	.0968516	.0980353
26.6	.0992087	.1003718	.1015244	.1026665	.1037979	.1049185	.1060282	.1071269	.1082144	.1092908
26.7	.1103559	.1114095	.1124517	.1134822	.1145010	.1155080	.1165030	.1174861	.1184571	.1194159
26.8	.1203624	.1212965	.1222182	.1231273	.1240238	.1249076	.1257786	.1266367	.1274818	.1283139
26.9	.1291329	.1299386	.1307311	.1315103	.1322760	.1330283	.1337670	.1344920	.1352034	.1359010
27.0	.1365847	.1372546	.1379105	.1385524	.1391803	.1397940	.1403935	.1409788	.1415498	.1421065
27.1	.1426487	.1431765	.1436899	.1441887	.1446729	.1451425	.1455974	.1460376	.1464631	.1468738
27.2	.1472696	.1476507	.1480168	.1483681	.1487043	.1490257	.1493320	.1496233	.1499995	.1501607
27.3	.1504068	.1506378	.1508537	.1510544	.1512400	.1514104	.1515656	.1517056	.1518304	.1519401
27.4	.1520345	.1521137	.1521776	.1522264	.1522600	.1522783	.1522814	.1522693	.1522420	.1521996
27.5	.1521419	.1520691	.1519811	.1518779	.1517597	.1516263	.1514779	.1513143	.1511358	.1509421
27.6	.1507335	.1505100	.1502714	.1500180	.1497496	.1494665	.1491684	.1488556	.1485281	.1481858
27.7	.1478289	.1474573	.1470712	.1466705	.1462553	.1458256	.1453815	.1449231	.1444504	.1439634
27.8	.1434622	.1429469	.1424175	.1418741	.1413166	.1407453	.1401601	.1395612	.1389485	.1383222
27.9	.1376822	.1370288	.1363619	.1356817	.1349881	.1342813	.1335613	.1328283	.1320822	.1313233

Table 3 J_1 (Continued)

T	.00	.01	.02	.03	.04	.05	.06	.07	.08	.09
28.0	.1305515	.1297669	.1289697	.1281599	.1273375	.1265027	.1256556	.1247963	.1239248	.1230412
28.1	.1221457	.1212383	.1203191	.1193882	.1184457	.1174918	.1165264	.1155498	.1145619	.1135630
28.2	.1125531	.1115323	.1105007	.1094584	.1084056	.1073424	.1062688	.1051849	.1040910	.1029870
28.3	.1018732	.1007495	.0996162	.0984734	.0973211	.0961595	.0949888	.0938089	.0926201	.0914225
28.4	.0902161	.0890012	.0877778	.0865461	.0853062	.0840582	.0828022	.0815384	.0802669	.0789879
28.5	.0777014	.0764076	.0751066	.0737985	.0724836	.0711619	.0698335	.0684987	.0671574	.0658099
28.6	.0644564	.0630968	.0617315	.0603604	.0589838	.0576018	.0562145	.0548221	.0534247	.0520224
28.7	.0506155	.0492040	.0477880	.0463678	.0449434	.0435151	.0420829	.0406470	.0392075	.0377646
28.8	.0363185	.0348692	.0334170	.0319619	.0305041	.0290438	.0275811	.0261161	.0246491	.0231801
28.9	.0217093	.0202368	.0187628	.0172874	.0158109	.0143332	.0128547	.0113754	.0098954	.0084150
29.0	.0069342	.0054533	.0039723	.0024914	.0010108	-.0004694	-.0019490	-.0034280	-.0049060	-.0063831
29.1	-.0078591	-.0093337	-.0108069	-.0122786	-.0137485	-.0152165	-.0166825	-.0181463	-.0196078	-.0210669
29.2	-.0225233	-.0239770	-.0254278	-.0268756	-.0283202	-.0297615	-.0311993	-.0326335	-.0340639	-.0354905
29.3	-.0369130	-.0383314	-.0397454	-.0411550	-.0425600	-.0439603	-.0453557	-.0467461	-.0481314	-.0495113
29.4	-.0508859	-.0522549	-.0536183	-.0549758	-.0563273	-.0576728	-.0590121	-.0603450	-.0616715	-.0629913
29.5	-.0643044	-.0656106	-.0669098	-.0682019	-.0694868	-.0707643	-.0720343	-.0732966	-.0745513	-.0757980
29.6	-.0770368	-.0782674	-.0794898	-.0807039	-.0819095	-.0831065	-.0842948	-.0854742	-.0866448	-.0878063
29.7	-.0889586	-.0901017	-.0912354	-.0923596	-.0934742	-.0945791	-.0956741	-.0967593	-.0978344	-.0988994
29.8	-.0999541	-.1009985	-.1020325	-.1030559	-.1040687	-.1050708	-.1060620	-.1070423	-.1080116	-.1089698
29.9	-.1099168	-.1108525	-.1117768	-.1126896	-.1135909	-.1144805	-.1153584	-.1162245	-.1170787	-.1179209
30.0	-.1187511	-.1195691	-.1203749	-.1211684	-.1219495	-.1227182	-.1234744	-.1242180	-.1249490	-.1256672
30.1	-.1263727	-.1270653	-.1277450	-.1284116	-.1290653	-.1297058	-.1303332	-.1309473	-.1315482	-.1321357
30.2	-.1327098	-.1332705	-.1338177	-.1343514	-.1348714	-.1353778	-.1358705	-.1363495	-.1368148	-.1372661
30.3	-.1377037	-.1381273	-.1385370	-.1389328	-.1393145	-.1396822	-.1400358	-.1403753	-.1407007	-.1410119
30.4	-.1413090	-.1415918	-.1418604	-.1421147	-.1423547	-.1425805	-.1427920	-.1429891	-.1431719	-.1433403
30.5	-.1434943	-.1436339	-.1437592	-.1438701	-.1439666	-.1440486	-.1441162	-.1441695	-.1442083	-.1442327
30.6	-.1442426	-.1442382	-.1442194	-.1441861	-.1441385	-.1440765	-.1440001	-.1439094	-.1438043	-.1436849
30.7	-.1435512	-.1434032	-.1432409	-.1430644	-.1428736	-.1426686	-.1424495	-.1422161	-.1419687	-.1417071
30.8	-.1414315	-.1411419	-.1408382	-.1405206	-.1401891	-.1398436	-.1394843	-.1391112	-.1387243	-.1383237
30.9	-.1379094	-.1374814	-.1370399	-.1365848	-.1361162	-.1356342	-.1351388	-.1346300	-.1341080	-.1335727
31.0	-.1330243	-.1324628	-.1318882	-.1313006	-.1307001	-.1300868	-.1294606	-.1288217	-.1281702	-.1275060
31.1	-.1268294	-.1261403	-.1254388	-.1247250	-.1239990	-.1232608	-.1225106	-.1217483	-.1209742	-.1201882
31.2	-.1193904	-.1185810	-.1177600	-.1169275	-.1160836	-.1152284	-.1143619	-.1134843	-.1125956	-.1116960
31.3	-.1107855	-.1098642	-.1089323	-.1079897	-.1070368	-.1060733	-.1050996	-.1041158	-.1031218	-.1021178
31.4	-.1011040	-.1000804	-.0990471	-.0980043	-.0969520	-.0958903	-.0948194	-.0937394	-.0926504	-.0915524

Table 4

ARCCOS

T	.000	.001	.002	.003	.004	.005	.006	.007	.008	.009
-1.00	3.1415927	3.0968676	3.0783366	3.0641136	3.0521201	3.0415509	3.0319923	3.0232019	3.0150171	3.0073277
-.99	3.0000532	2.9931324	2.9865180	2.9801723	2.9740648	2.9681703	2.9624678	2.9569395	2.9515702	2.9463468
-.98	2.9412578	2.9362933	2.9314444	2.9267033	2.9220603	2.9175174	2.9130606	2.9086876	2.9043938	2.9001749
-.97	2.8960271	2.8919469	2.8879309	2.8839762	2.8800800	2.8762397	2.8724529	2.8687174	2.8650311	2.8613921
-.96	2.8577985	2.8542487	2.8507410	2.8472739	2.8438461	2.8404561	2.8371027	2.8337848	2.8305011	2.8272505
-.95	2.8240322	2.8208451	2.8176883	2.8145609	2.8114620	2.8083909	2.8053469	2.8023291	2.7993369	2.7963696
-.94	2.7934266	2.7905073	2.7876111	2.7847374	2.7818857	2.7790554	2.7762461	2.7734575	2.7706885	2.7679393
-.93	2.7652092	2.7624978	2.7598048	2.7571297	2.7544722	2.7518319	2.7492085	2.7466016	2.7440109	2.7414361
-.92	2.7388768	2.7363329	2.7338039	2.7312896	2.7287899	2.7263042	2.7238326	2.7213746	2.7189300	2.7164987
-.91	2.7140804	2.7116748	2.7092818	2.7069011	2.7045326	2.7021760	2.6998312	2.6974980	2.6951761	2.6928655
-.90	2.6905658	2.6882771	2.6859990	2.6837315	2.6814744	2.6792275	2.6769907	2.6747639	2.6725468	2.6703394
-.89	2.6681415	2.6659530	2.6637738	2.6616036	2.6594425	2.6572903	2.6551469	2.6530121	2.6508859	2.6487680
-.88	2.6466585	2.6445572	2.6424641	2.6403789	2.6383016	2.6362321	2.6341704	2.6321163	2.6300696	2.6280305
-.87	2.6259986	2.6239741	2.6219567	2.6199464	2.6179431	2.6159467	2.6139572	2.6119744	2.6099983	2.6080289
-.86	2.6060660	2.6041096	2.6021595	2.6002158	2.5982784	2.5963472	2.5944221	2.5925030	2.5905900	2.5886829
-.85	2.5867816	2.5848862	2.5829965	2.5811126	2.5792342	2.5773615	2.5754943	2.5736325	2.5717762	2.5699252
-.84	2.5680795	2.5662391	2.5644039	2.5625739	2.5607490	2.5589291	2.5571143	2.5553044	2.5534994	2.5516993
-.83	2.5499040	2.5481135	2.5463278	2.5445467	2.5427703	2.5409985	2.5392313	2.5374686	2.5357104	2.5339567
-.82	2.5322073	2.5304624	2.5287218	2.5269854	2.5252534	2.5235255	2.5218019	2.5200824	2.5183670	2.5166557
-.81	2.5149484	2.5132452	2.5115460	2.5098507	2.5081593	2.5064718	2.5047882	2.5031083	2.5014323	2.4997601
-.80	2.4980915	2.4964267	2.4947656	2.4931081	2.4914542	2.4898039	2.4881572	2.4865140	2.4848743	2.4832381
-.79	2.4816053	2.4799760	2.4783501	2.4767275	2.4751083	2.4734925	2.4718799	2.4702706	2.4686646	2.4670617
-.78	2.4654621	2.4638657	2.4622725	2.4606824	2.4590953	2.4575114	2.4559306	2.4543528	2.4527780	2.4512063
-.77	2.4496375	2.4480717	2.4465088	2.4449489	2.4433918	2.4418377	2.4402864	2.4387379	2.4371923	2.4356495
-.76	2.4341094	2.4325722	2.4310377	2.4295059	2.4279768	2.4264504	2.4249268	2.4234057	2.4218873	2.4203716
-.75	2.4188584	2.4173478	2.4158399	2.4143344	2.4128315	2.4113312	2.4098333	2.4083380	2.4068451	2.4053547
-.74	2.4038667	2.4023811	2.4008980	2.3994173	2.3979394	2.3964630	2.3949894	2.3935181	2.3920492	2.3905826
-.73	2.3891183	2.3876562	2.3861965	2.3847390	2.3832837	2.3818307	2.3803799	2.3789313	2.3774849	2.3760407
-.72	2.3745986	2.3731587	2.3717210	2.3702854	2.3688518	2.3674204	2.3659911	2.3645639	2.3631587	2.3617156
-.71	2.3602945	2.3588755	2.3574585	2.3560435	2.3546305	2.3532195	2.3518104	2.3504034	2.3489982	2.3475951
-.70	2.3461938	2.3447945	2.3433971	2.3420016	2.3406080	2.3392162	2.3378264	2.3364383	2.3350522	2.3336679
-.69	2.3322854	2.3309047	2.3295258	2.3281488	2.3267735	2.3254000	2.3240283	2.3226584	2.3212901	2.3199237
-.68	2.3185590	2.3171960	2.3158347	2.3144751	2.3131172	2.3117610	2.3104065	2.3090537	2.3077025	2.3063530
-.67	2.3050051	2.3036589	2.3023143	2.3009713	2.2996299	2.2982901	2.2969520	2.2956154	2.2942804	2.2929470
-.66	2.2916151	2.2902848	2.2889560	2.2876288	2.2863031	2.2849789	2.2836563	2.2823352	2.2810155	2.2796974

491

Table 4 Arccos (*Continued*)

T	.000	.001	.002	.003	.004	.005	.006	.007	.008	.009
-.65	2.2783808	2.2770656	2.2757519	2.2744397	2.2731289	2.2718196	2.2705117	2.2692053	2.2679003	2.2665967
-.64	2.2652946	2.2639938	2.2626945	2.2613966	2.2601000	2.2588048	2.2575111	2.2562186	2.2549276	2.2536379
-.63	2.2523495	2.2510625	2.2497769	2.2484925	2.2472095	2.2459279	2.2446475	2.2433684	2.2420907	2.2408142
-.62	2.2395390	2.2382651	2.2369925	2.2357212	2.2344511	2.2331823	2.2319147	2.2306484	2.2293834	2.2281195
-.61	2.2268569	2.2255955	2.2243354	2.2230764	2.2218187	2.2205622	2.2193069	2.2180527	2.2167998	2.2155480
-.60	2.2142974	2.2130480	2.2117998	2.2105527	2.2093068	2.2080620	2.2068163	2.2055758	2.2043345	2.2030943
-.59	2.2018552	2.2006172	2.1993803	2.1981446	2.1969099	2.1956764	2.1944439	2.1932126	2.1919823	2.1907531
-.58	2.1895250	2.1882980	2.1870720	2.1858471	2.1846233	2.1834005	2.1821787	2.1809980	2.1797384	2.1785198
-.57	2.1773022	2.1760856	2.1748701	2.1736556	2.1724421	2.1712296	2.1700181	2.1688076	2.1675981	2.1663896
-.56	2.1651821	2.1639756	2.1627701	2.1615655	2.1603619	2.1591593	2.1579576	2.1567769	2.1555572	2.1543584
-.55	2.1531606	2.1519637	2.1507677	2.1495727	2.1483786	2.1471854	2.1459932	2.1448019	2.1436115	2.1424220
-.54	2.1412334	2.1400458	2.1388590	2.1376731	2.1364882	2.1353041	2.1341209	2.1329386	2.1317571	2.1305766
-.53	2.1293969	2.1282181	2.1270401	2.1258630	2.1246868	2.1235114	2.1223369	2.1211632	2.1199904	2.1188184
-.52	2.1176473	2.1164770	2.1153075	2.1141388	2.1129710	2.1118040	2.1106378	2.1094724	2.1083078	2.1071441
-.51	2.1059811	2.1048190	2.1036576	2.1024970	2.1013373	2.1001783	2.0990201	2.0978627	2.0967060	2.0955502
-.50	2.0943951	2.0932408	2.0920872	2.0909345	2.0897624	2.0886312	2.0874806	2.0863309	2.0851819	2.0840336
-.49	2.0828861	2.0817393	2.0805932	2.0794479	2.0783033	2.0771595	2.0760164	2.0748740	2.0737323	2.0725913
-.48	2.0714510	2.0703115	2.0691727	2.0680345	2.0668971	2.0657604	2.0646243	2.0634890	2.0623543	2.0612204
-.47	2.0600871	2.0589545	2.0578226	2.0566914	2.0555608	2.0544309	2.0533017	2.0521732	2.0510453	2.0499181
-.46	2.0487915	2.0476656	2.0465404	2.0454158	2.0442918	2.0431685	2.0420459	2.0409239	2.0398025	2.0386818
-.45	2.0375617	2.0364422	2.0353234	2.0342051	2.0330876	2.0319706	2.0308542	2.0297385	2.0286234	2.0275089
-.44	2.0263950	2.0252817	2.0241690	2.0230570	2.0219455	2.0208346	2.0197243	2.0186146	2.0175055	2.0163970
-.43	2.0152891	2.0141818	2.0130750	2.0119688	2.0108632	2.0097582	2.0086538	2.0075499	2.0064466	2.0053438
-.42	2.0042416	2.0031400	2.0020390	2.0009385	1.9998385	1.9987391	1.9976403	1.9965420	1.9954442	1.9943470
-.41	1.9932504	1.9921543	1.9910587	1.9899636	1.9888691	1.9877752	1.9866817	1.9855888	1.9844964	1.9834045
-.40	1.9823132	1.9812223	1.9801320	1.9790422	1.9779529	1.9768642	1.9757759	1.9746882	1.9736009	1.9725142
-.39	1.9714279	1.9703422	1.9692569	1.9681722	1.9670879	1.9660041	1.9649209	1.9638381	1.9627558	1.9616740
-.38	1.9605926	1.9595118	1.9584314	1.9573515	1.9562721	1.9551931	1.9541146	1.9530366	1.9519591	1.9508820
-.37	1.9498053	1.9487292	1.9476535	1.9465782	1.9455035	1.9444291	1.9433553	1.9422818	1.9412088	1.9401363
-.36	1.9390642	1.9379926	1.9369214	1.9358506	1.9347803	1.9337104	1.9326409	1.9315719	1.9305033	1.9294352
-.35	1.9283674	1.9273001	1.9262332	1.9251668	1.9241007	1.9230351	1.9219699	1.9209051	1.9198407	1.9187768
-.34	1.9177132	1.9166501	1.9155873	1.9145250	1.9134631	1.9124010	1.9113404	1.9102797	1.9092194	1.9081594
-.33	1.9070999	1.9060408	1.9049820	1.9039236	1.9028656	1.9018061	1.9007508	1.8996940	1.8986376	1.8975815
-.32	1.8965258	1.8954705	1.8944156	1.8933610	1.8923068	1.8912530	1.8901995	1.8891464	1.8880937	1.8870414
-.31	1.8859894	1.8849277	1.8838864	1.8828355	1.8817850	1.8807346	1.8796849	1.8786354	1.8775862	1.8765374

Table 4 Arccos (Continued)

T	.000	.001	.002	.003	.004	.005	.006	.007	.008	.009
-.30	1.8754890	1.8744409	1.8733931	1.8723457	1.8712986	1.8702518	1.8692054	1.8681594	1.8671136	1.8660682
-.29	1.8650233	1.8639784	1.8629340	1.8618899	1.8608462	1.8598028	1.8587598	1.8577169	1.8566744	1.8556323
-.28	1.8545904	1.8535489	1.8525077	1.8514669	1.8504263	1.8493860	1.8483461	1.8473064	1.8462671	1.8452281
-.27	1.8441694	1.8431509	1.8421128	1.8410750	1.8400375	1.8390004	1.8379633	1.8369267	1.8358903	1.8348543
-.26	1.8338185	1.8327851	1.8317479	1.8307130	1.8296784	1.8286440	1.8276100	1.8265762	1.8255427	1.8245095
-.25	1.8234766	1.8224439	1.8214115	1.8203794	1.8193476	1.8183160	1.8172847	1.8162537	1.8152229	1.8141924
-.24	1.8131622	1.8121322	1.8111025	1.8100730	1.8090438	1.8080149	1.8069862	1.8059578	1.8049296	1.8039017
-.23	1.8028740	1.8018466	1.8008194	1.7997925	1.7987658	1.7977394	1.7967132	1.7956872	1.7946615	1.7936360
-.22	1.7926108	1.7915858	1.7905610	1.7895365	1.7885122	1.7874882	1.7864645	1.7854407	1.7844174	1.7833942
-.21	1.7823713	1.7813486	1.7803261	1.7793039	1.7782818	1.7772600	1.7762384	1.7752171	1.7741959	1.7731750
-.20	1.7721542	1.7711537	1.7701134	1.7690933	1.7680735	1.7670538	1.7660343	1.7650150	1.7639960	1.7629771
-.19	1.7619585	1.7609400	1.7599218	1.7589037	1.7578859	1.7568682	1.7558507	1.7548334	1.7538164	1.7527995
-.18	1.7517828	1.7507663	1.7497499	1.7487338	1.7477179	1.7467021	1.7456865	1.7446711	1.7436559	1.7426409
-.17	1.7416260	1.7406113	1.7395968	1.7385825	1.7375683	1.7365543	1.7355405	1.7345269	1.7335134	1.7325001
-.16	1.7314870	1.7304740	1.7294612	1.7284486	1.7274361	1.7264238	1.7254116	1.7243996	1.7233878	1.7223761
-.15	1.7213646	1.7203532	1.7193420	1.7183310	1.7173201	1.7163093	1.7152987	1.7142882	1.7132779	1.7122678
-.14	1.7112577	1.7102479	1.7092381	1.7082285	1.7072191	1.7062098	1.7052006	1.7041916	1.7031827	1.7021739
-.13	1.7011653	1.7001568	1.6991485	1.6981402	1.6971321	1.6961242	1.6951163	1.6941086	1.6931010	1.6920935
-.12	1.6910862	1.6900790	1.6890719	1.6880649	1.6870581	1.6860513	1.6850447	1.6840382	1.6830318	1.6820255
-.11	1.6810194	1.6800133	1.6790074	1.6780016	1.6769958	1.6759902	1.6749847	1.6739793	1.6729740	1.6719688
-.10	1.6709637	1.6699588	1.6689539	1.6679491	1.6669444	1.6659398	1.6649353	1.6639309	1.6629266	1.6619224
-.09	1.6609183	1.6599142	1.6589103	1.6579065	1.6569027	1.6558990	1.6548954	1.6538919	1.6528885	1.6518852
-.08	1.6508819	1.6498787	1.6488756	1.6478726	1.6468697	1.6458666	1.6448640	1.6438613	1.6428587	1.6418561
-.07	1.6408536	1.6398512	1.6388488	1.6378466	1.6368443	1.6358422	1.6348401	1.6338381	1.6328361	1.6318342
-.06	1.6308324	1.6298306	1.6288289	1.6278272	1.6268256	1.6258241	1.6248226	1.6238212	1.6228198	1.6218185
-.05	1.6208172	1.6198160	1.6188148	1.6178136	1.6168126	1.6158115	1.6148105	1.6138096	1.6128087	1.6118078
-.04	1.6108070	1.6098062	1.6088055	1.6078048	1.6068041	1.6058035	1.6048029	1.6038023	1.6028018	1.6018013
-.03	1.6008008	1.5998004	1.5988000	1.5977996	1.5967993	1.5957989	1.5947986	1.5937984	1.5927981	1.5917979
-.02	1.5907977	1.5897975	1.5887973	1.5877971	1.5867970	1.5857969	1.5847966	1.5837967	1.5827966	1.5817965
-.01	1.5807965	1.5797964	1.5787964	1.5777964	1.5767964	1.5757963	1.5747963	1.5737963	1.5727963	1.5717963
0.00	1.5707963	1.5697963	1.5687963	1.5677963	1.5667963	1.5657963	1.5647963	1.5637963	1.5627962	1.5617962
.01	1.5607962	1.5597961	1.5587960	1.5577960	1.5567959	1.5557958	1.5547956	1.5537955	1.5527954	1.5517952
.02	1.5507950	1.5497948	1.5487946	1.5477943	1.5467940	1.5457937	1.5447934	1.5437930	1.5427927	1.5417923
.03	1.5407918	1.5397914	1.5387909	1.5377903	1.5367898	1.5357892	1.5347885	1.5337879	1.5327872	1.5317864
.04	1.5307857	1.5297848	1.5287840	1.5277831	1.5267821	1.5257811	1.5247801	1.5237790	1.5227779	1.5217767

Table 4 Arccos (Continued)

T	.000	.001	.002	.003	.004	.005	.006	.007	.008	.009
.05	1.5207755	1.5197742	1.5187729	1.5177715	1.5167700	1.5157686	1.5147670	1.5137654	1.5127638	1.5117620
.06	1.5107603	1.5097584	1.5087565	1.5077546	1.5067526	1.5057505	1.5047483	1.5037461	1.5027438	1.5017415
.07	1.5007390	1.4997365	1.4987340	1.4977313	1.4967286	1.4957258	1.4947230	1.4937200	1.4927170	1.4917139
.08	1.4907107	1.4897075	1.4887042	1.4877007	1.4866972	1.4856936	1.4846900	1.4836862	1.4826824	1.4816784
.09	1.4806744	1.4796703	1.4786660	1.4776617	1.4766573	1.4756528	1.4746483	1.4736436	1.4726388	1.4716339
.10	1.4706289	1.4696238	1.4686186	1.4676133	1.4666079	1.4656024	1.4645968	1.4635911	1.4625853	1.4615793
.11	1.4605733	1.4595671	1.4585608	1.4575545	1.4565479	1.4555413	1.4545346	1.4535277	1.4525208	1.4515137
.12	1.4505064	1.4494991	1.4484916	1.4474841	1.4464763	1.4454685	1.4444605	1.4434524	1.4424442	1.4414358
.13	1.4404273	1.4394187	1.4384100	1.4374011	1.4363920	1.4353829	1.4343736	1.4333641	1.4323545	1.4313448
.14	1.4303349	1.4293249	1.4283147	1.4273044	1.4262940	1.4252834	1.4242726	1.4232617	1.4222506	1.4212394
.15	1.4202281	1.4192165	1.4182049	1.4171930	1.4161810	1.4151689	1.4141566	1.4131441	1.4121314	1.4111186
.16	1.4101057	1.4090925	1.4080792	1.4070658	1.4060521	1.4050383	1.4040243	1.4030102	1.4019958	1.4009813
.17	1.3999667	1.3989518	1.3979368	1.3969215	1.3959061	1.3948906	1.3938748	1.3928588	1.3918427	1.3908264
.18	1.3898099	1.3887932	1.3877763	1.3867592	1.3857419	1.3847245	1.3837068	1.3826889	1.3816709	1.3806526
.19	1.3796342	1.3786155	1.3775967	1.3765776	1.3755583	1.3745389	1.3735192	1.3724993	1.3714792	1.3704589
.20	1.3694384	1.3684177	1.3673967	1.3663756	1.3653542	1.3643326	1.3633108	1.3622888	1.3612665	1.3602441
.21	1.3592214	1.3581984	1.3571753	1.3561519	1.3551283	1.3541045	1.3530804	1.3520561	1.3510316	1.3500069
.22	1.3489819	1.3479566	1.3469311	1.3459054	1.3448795	1.3438533	1.3428269	1.3418002	1.3407732	1.3397461
.23	1.3387186	1.3376910	1.3366630	1.3356349	1.3346064	1.3335778	1.3325488	1.3315196	1.3304902	1.3294605
.24	1.3284305	1.3274002	1.3263697	1.3253390	1.3243079	1.3232766	1.3222451	1.3212132	1.3201811	1.3191487
.25	1.3181161	1.3170831	1.3160499	1.3150164	1.3139827	1.3129486	1.3119143	1.3108797	1.3098448	1.3088096
.26	1.3077741	1.3067384	1.3057023	1.3046660	1.3036293	1.3025924	1.3015552	1.3005177	1.2994798	1.2984417
.27	1.2974033	1.2963646	1.2953255	1.2942862	1.2932466	1.2922066	1.2911664	1.2901258	1.2890849	1.2880437
.28	1.2870022	1.2859604	1.2849182	1.2838758	1.2828330	1.2817899	1.2807465	1.2797027	1.2786586	1.2776142
.29	1.2765695	1.2755244	1.2744790	1.2734333	1.2723872	1.2713408	1.2702941	1.2692470	1.2681996	1.2671518
.30	1.2661037	1.2650552	1.2640064	1.2629573	1.2619078	1.2608579	1.2598077	1.2587571	1.2577062	1.2566549
.31	1.2556033	1.2545513	1.2534989	1.2524462	1.2513931	1.2503397	1.2492858	1.2482317	1.2471771	1.2461222
.32	1.2450668	1.2440112	1.2429551	1.2418986	1.2408418	1.2397846	1.2387270	1.2376690	1.2366107	1.2355519
.33	1.2344928	1.2334332	1.2323733	1.2313129	1.2302522	1.2291911	1.2281296	1.2270676	1.2260053	1.2249426
.34	1.2238794	1.2228159	1.2217519	1.2206875	1.2196227	1.2185575	1.2174919	1.2164259	1.2153594	1.2142925
.35	1.2132252	1.2121575	1.2110893	1.2100207	1.2089517	1.2078823	1.2068124	1.2057420	1.2046713	1.2036001
.36	1.2025284	1.2014563	1.2003838	1.1993108	1.1982374	1.1971635	1.1960892	1.1950144	1.1939392	1.1928635
.37	1.1917873	1.1907107	1.1896336	1.1885561	1.1874780	1.1863996	1.1853206	1.1842412	1.1831613	1.1820809
.38	1.1810000	1.1799187	1.1788369	1.1777546	1.1766718	1.1755885	1.1745047	1.1734205	1.1723357	1.1712505
.39	1.1701647	1.1690785	1.1679917	1.1669045	1.1658167	1.1647285	1.1636397	1.1625504	1.1614606	1.1603703

Table 4 Arccos (Continued)

T	.000	.001	.002	.003	.004	.005	.006	.007	.008	.009
.40	1.1592795	1.1581881	1.1570963	1.1560039	1.1549109	1.1538175	1.1527235	1.1516290	1.1505340	1.1494384
.41	1.1483423	1.1472456	1.1461484	1.1450507	1.1439524	1.1428535	1.1417541	1.1406542	1.1395537	1.1384526
.42	1.1373210	1.1362488	1.1351461	1.1340428	1.1329389	1.1318344	1.1307294	1.1296238	1.1285177	1.1274109
.43	1.1263035	1.1251956	1.1240871	1.1229780	1.1218683	1.1207581	1.1196472	1.1185357	1.1174236	1.1163109
.44	1.1151977	1.1140838	1.1129693	1.1118541	1.1107384	1.1096221	1.1085051	1.1073875	1.1062693	1.1051505
.45	1.1040310	1.1029109	1.1017902	1.1006688	1.0995468	1.0984241	1.0973008	1.0961769	1.0950523	1.0939270
.46	1.0928011	1.0916746	1.0905474	1.0894195	1.0882909	1.0871617	1.0860318	1.0849013	1.0837700	1.0826381
.47	1.0815055	1.0803723	1.0792383	1.0781037	1.0769683	1.0758323	1.0746956	1.0735581	1.0724200	1.0712812
.48	1.0701416	1.0690014	1.0678604	1.0667187	1.0655763	1.0644332	1.0632893	1.0621447	1.0609994	1.0598534
.49	1.0587066	1.0575590	1.0564108	1.0552618	1.0541120	1.0529615	1.0518102	1.0506582	1.0495054	1.0483519
.50	1.0471976	1.0460425	1.0448866	1.0437300	1.0425726	1.0414144	1.0402554	1.0390956	1.0379350	1.0367737
.51	1.0356115	1.0344486	1.0332848	1.0321203	1.0309549	1.0297887	1.0286217	1.0274538	1.0262852	1.0251157
.52	1.0239454	1.0227742	1.0216022	1.0204294	1.0192557	1.0180812	1.0169058	1.0157296	1.0145525	1.0133746
.53	1.0121958	1.0110161	1.0098355	1.0086541	1.0074718	1.0062886	1.0051045	1.0039195	1.0027337	1.0015469
.54	1.0003592	.9991706	.9979812	.9967908	.9955994	.9944072	.9932141	.9920200	.9908249	.9896290
.55	.9884321	.9872342	.9860355	.9848357	.9836350	.9824334	.9812307	.9800271	.9788226	.9776170
.56	.9764105	.9752030	.9739945	.9727850	.9715746	.9703631	.9691506	.9679371	.9667226	.9655070
.57	.9642905	.9630729	.9618543	.9606346	.9594139	.9581922	.9569694	.9557455	.9545206	.9532947
.58	.9520676	.9508395	.9496103	.9483801	.9471487	.9459163	.9446827	.9434481	.9422123	.9409755
.59	.9397375	.9384984	.9372582	.9360168	.9347743	.9335307	.9322859	.9310400	.9297929	.9285446
.60	.9272952	.9260446	.9247929	.9235399	.9222858	.9210305	.9197739	.9185162	.9172573	.9159971
.61	.9147357	.9134731	.9122093	.9109442	.9096779	.9084104	.9071415	.9058715	.9046001	.9033275
.62	.9020536	.9007784	.8995020	.8982242	.8969442	.8956648	.8943831	.8931001	.8918158	.8905301
.63	.8892431	.8879548	.8866651	.8853740	.8840816	.8827878	.8814926	.8801961	.8788981	.8775988
.64	.8762981	.8749959	.8736923	.8723873	.8710809	.8697730	.8684637	.8671530	.8658407	.8645271
.65	.8632119	.8618952	.8605771	.8592575	.8579363	.8566137	.8552895	.8539639	.8526366	.8513079
.66	.8499776	.8486457	.8473123	.8459773	.8446407	.8433025	.8419627	.8406214	.8392784	.8379338
.67	.8365875	.8352397	.8338901	.8325390	.8311862	.8298316	.8284754	.8271176	.8257580	.8243967
.68	.8230337	.8216690	.8203025	.8189343	.8175643	.8161926	.8148191	.8134439	.8120668	.8106879
.69	.8093073	.8079248	.8065405	.8051543	.8037663	.8023764	.8009847	.7995911	.7981956	.7967982
.70	.7953988	.7939976	.7925944	.7911893	.7897822	.7883732	.7869622	.7855492	.7841342	.7827172
.71	.7812981	.7798771	.7784539	.7770288	.7756015	.7741722	.7727408	.7713075	.7698717	.7684339
.72	.7669940	.7655520	.7641077	.7626613	.7612127	.7597619	.7583089	.7568537	.7553963	.7539364
.73	.7524744	.7510101	.7495434	.7480745	.7466032	.7451290	.7436537	.7421754	.7406946	.7392115
.74	.7377260	.7362380	.7347476	.7332547	.7317593	.7302615	.7287611	.7272582	.7257528	.7242448

Table 4 Arccos (*Continued*)

T	.000	.001	.002	.003	.004	.005	.006	.007	.008	.009
.75	.7227342	.7212211	.7197053	.7181869	.7166659	.7151422	.7136158	.7120868	.7105550	.7090205
.76	.7074832	.7059432	.7044004	.7028547	.7013063	.6997550	.6982008	.6966438	.6950839	.6935210
.77	.6919552	.6903864	.6888146	.6872399	.6856621	.6840812	.6824973	.6809103	.6793202	.6777269
.78	.6761305	.6745309	.6729281	.6713221	.6697128	.6681002	.6664843	.6648651	.6632426	.6616167
.79	.6599873	.6583546	.6567184	.6550787	.6534355	.6517887	.6501385	.6484846	.6468271	.6451659
.80	.6435011	.6418326	.6401603	.6384843	.6368045	.6351209	.6334334	.6317420	.6300467	.6283474
.81	.6266442	.6249370	.6232257	.6215103	.6197908	.6180671	.6163393	.6146072	.6128709	.6111303
.82	.6093853	.6076360	.6058822	.6041240	.6023613	.6005941	.5988223	.5970459	.5952649	.5934791
.83	.5916886	.5898934	.5880933	.5862883	.5844784	.5826635	.5808437	.5790187	.5771887	.5753535
.84	.5735131	.5716674	.5698165	.5679601	.5660984	.5642212	.5623584	.5604801	.5585961	.5567065
.85	.5548110	.5529098	.5510027	.5490896	.5471706	.5452455	.5433142	.5413768	.5394331	.5374831
.86	.5355267	.5335638	.5315943	.5296182	.5276355	.5256460	.5236496	.5216463	.5196360	.5176186
.87	.5155940	.5135622	.5115230	.5094764	.5074223	.5053605	.5032910	.5012138	.4991286	.4970354
.88	.4949341	.4928246	.4907068	.4885805	.4864458	.4843023	.4821501	.4799890	.4778189	.4756397
.89	.4734512	.4712533	.4690459	.4668288	.4646019	.4623651	.4601182	.4578611	.4555936	.4533156
.90	.4510268	.4487272	.4464165	.4440947	.4417614	.4394166	.4370600	.4346915	.4323108	.4299178
.91	.4275123	.4250939	.4226626	.4202181	.4177601	.4152884	.4128028	.4103030	.4077888	.4052598
.92	.4027158	.4001566	.3975818	.3949911	.3923842	.3897607	.3871204	.3844629	.3817879	.3790948
.93	.3763835	.3736534	.3709042	.3681354	.3653466	.3625373	.3597070	.3568553	.3539816	.3510853
.94	.3481660	.3452230	.3422558	.3392636	.3362458	.3332017	.3301306	.3270318	.3239044	.3207475
.95	.3175604	.3143421	.3110916	.3078079	.3044899	.3011365	.2977466	.2943187	.2908516	.2873439
.96	.2837941	.2802005	.2765615	.2728752	.2691397	.2653529	.2615126	.2576164	.2536617	.2496458
.97	.2455655	.2414177	.2371989	.2329051	.2285321	.2240753	.2195298	.2148893	.2101482	.2052994
.98	.2003348	.1952459	.1900224	.1846531	.1791248	.1734223	.1675278	.1614204	.1550747	.1484603
.99	.1415395	.1342649	.1265756	.1183907	.1095994	.1000417	.0894726	.0774790	.0632561	.0447251

Index of Mathematical Expressions

Index